# Table of Contents

# Stress

The bolts used for the connections of this steel framework are subjected to stress. In this chapter we will discuss how engineers design these connections and their fasteners.

# Stress

## CHAPTER OBJECTIVES

■ In this chapter we will review some of the important principles of statics and show how they are used to determine the internal resultant loadings in a body. Afterwards the concepts of normal and shear stress will be introduced, and specific applications of the analysis and design of members subjected to an axial load or direct shear will be discussed.

## 1    Introduction

*Mechanics of materials* is a branch of mechanics that studies the internal effects of stress and strain in a solid body that is subjected to an external loading. Stress is associated with the strength of the material from which the body is made, while strain is a measure of the deformation of the body. In addition to this, mechanics of materials includes the study of the body's stability when a body such as a column is subjected to compressive loading. A thorough understanding of the fundamentals of this subject is of vital importance because many of the formulas and rules of design cited in engineering codes are based upon the principles of this subject.

**Historical Development.**   The origin of mechanics of materials dates back to the beginning of the seventeenth century, when Galileo performed experiments to study the effects of loads on rods and beams made of various materials. However, at the beginning of the eighteenth century, experimental methods for testing materials were vastly improved, and at that time many experimental and theoretical studies in this subject were undertaken primarily in France, by such notables as Saint-Venant, Poisson, Lamé and Navier.

Over the years, after many of the fundamental problems of mechanics of materials had been solved, it became necessary to use advanced mathematical and computer techniques to solve more complex problems. As a result, this subject expanded into other areas of mechanics, such as the *theory of elasticity* and the *theory of plasticity*. Research in these fields is ongoing, in order to meet the demands for solving more advanced problems in engineering.

# 2   Equilibrium of a Deformable Body

Since statics has an important role in both the development and application of mechanics of materials, it is very important to have a good grasp of its fundamentals. For this reason we will review some of the main principles of statics that will be used throughout the text.

**External Loads.**   A body is subjected to only two types of external loads; namely, surface forces and body forces, Fig. 1.

**Surface Forces.**   *Surface forces* are caused by the direct contact of one body with the surface of another. In all cases these forces are distributed over the *area* of contact between the bodies. If this area is small in comparison with the total surface area of the body, then the surface force can be *idealized* as a single **concentrated force**, which is applied to a *point* on the body. For example, the force of the ground on the wheels of a bicycle can be considered as a concentrated force. If the surface loading is applied along a narrow strip of area, the loading can be *idealized* as a **linear distributed load**, $w(s)$. Here the loading is measured as having an intensity of force/length along the strip and is represented graphically by a series of arrows along the line $s$. *The resultant force $\mathbf{F}_R$ of w(s) is equivalent to the area under the distributed loading curve, and this resultant acts through the centroid C or geometric center of this area.* The loading along the length of a beam is a typical example of where this idealization is often applied.

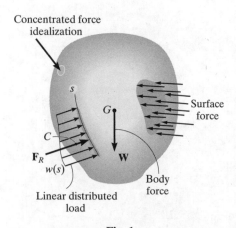

Concentrated force idealization

Surface force

Linear distributed load

Body force

**Fig. 1**

**Body Forces.** A *body force* is developed when one body exerts a force on another body without direct physical contact between the bodies. Examples include the effects caused by the earth's gravitation or its electromagnetic field. Although body forces affect each of the particles composing the body, these forces are normally represented by a single concentrated force acting on the body. In the case of gravitation, this force is called the *weight* of the body and acts through the body's center of gravity.

**Support Reactions.** The surface forces that develop at the supports or points of contact between bodies are called *reactions*. For two-dimensional problems, i.e., bodies subjected to coplanar force systems, the supports most commonly encountered are shown in Table 1. Note carefully the symbol used to represent each support and the type of reactions it exerts on its contacting member. As a general rule, *if the support prevents translation in a given direction, then a force must be developed on the member in that direction. Likewise, if rotation is prevented, a couple moment must be exerted on the member.* For example, the roller support only prevents translation perpendicular or normal to the surface. Hence, the roller exerts a normal force **F** on the member at its point of contact. Since the member can freely rotate about the roller, a couple moment cannot be developed on the member.

Many machine elements are pin connected in order to enable free rotation at their connections. These supports exert a force on a member, but no moment.

## TABLE 1

| Type of connection | Reaction | Type of connection | Reaction |
|---|---|---|---|
| Cable | One unknown: $F$ | External pin | Two unknowns: $F_x, F_y$ |
| Roller | One unknown: $F$ | Internal pin | Two unknowns: $F_x, F_y$ |
| Smooth support | One unknown: $F$ | Fixed support | Three unknowns: $F_x, F_y, M$ |

## Equations of Equilibrium.

Equilibrium of a body requires both a *balance of forces*, to prevent the body from translating or having accelerated motion along a straight or curved path, and a *balance of moments*, to prevent the body from rotating. These conditions can be expressed mathematically by two vector equations

$$\Sigma \mathbf{F} = \mathbf{0}$$
$$\Sigma \mathbf{M}_O = \mathbf{0}$$

(1)

Here, $\Sigma \mathbf{F}$ represents the sum of all the forces acting on the body, and $\Sigma \mathbf{M}_O$ is the sum of the moments of all the forces about any point $O$ either on or off the body. If an $x$, $y$, $z$ coordinate system is established with the origin at point $O$, the force and moment vectors can be resolved into components along each coordinate axis and the above two equations can be written in scalar form as six equations, namely,

$$\Sigma F_x = 0 \quad \Sigma F_y = 0 \quad \Sigma F_z = 0$$
$$\Sigma M_x = 0 \quad \Sigma M_y = 0 \quad \Sigma M_z = 0$$

(2)

Often in engineering practice the loading on a body can be represented as a system of *coplanar forces*. If this is the case, and the forces lie in the $x$–$y$ plane, then the conditions for equilibrium of the body can be specified with only three scalar equilibrium equations; that is,

$$\Sigma F_x = 0$$
$$\Sigma F_y = 0$$
$$\Sigma M_O = 0$$

(3)

In order to design the horizontal members of this building frame, it is first necessary to find the internal loadings at various points along their length.

Here all the moments are summed about point $O$ and so they will be directed along the $z$ axis.

Successful application of the equations of equilibrium requires complete specification of all the known and unknown forces that act *on* the body, and so *the best way to account for all these forces is to draw the body's free-body diagram.*

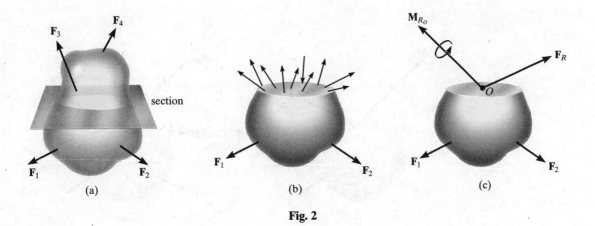

**Fig. 2**

## Internal Resultant Loadings.

In mechanics of materials, statics is primarily used to determine the resultant loadings that act within a body. For example, consider the body shown in Fig. 2*a*, which is held in equilibrium by the four external forces.* In order to obtain the internal loadings acting on a specific region within the body, it is necessary to pass an imaginary section or "cut" through the region where the internal loadings are to be determined. The two parts of the body are then separated, and a free-body diagram of one of the parts is drawn, Fig. 2*b*. Notice that there is actually a distribution of internal force acting on the "exposed" area of the section. These forces represent the effects of the material of the top part of the body acting on the adjacent material of the bottom part.

Although the exact distribution of this internal loading may be *unknown*, we can use the equations of equilibrium to relate the external forces on the bottom part of the body to the distribution's *resultant force and moment*, $\mathbf{F}_R$ and $\mathbf{M}_{R_O}$, *at any specific point O* on the sectioned area, Fig. 2*c*. It will be shown in later portions of the text that point $O$ is most often chosen at the *centroid* of the sectioned area, and so we will always choose this location for $O$, unless otherwise stated. Also, if a member is long and slender, as in the case of a rod or beam, the section to be considered is generally taken *perpendicular* to the longitudinal axis of the member. This section is referred to as the **cross section**.

*The body's weight is not shown, since it is assumed to be quite small, and therefore negligible compared with the other loads.

Fig. 2 (cont.)

The weight of this sign and the wind loadings acting on it will cause normal and shear forces and bending and torsional moments in the supporting column.

### Three Dimensions.

Later in this text we will show how to relate the resultant loadings, $\mathbf{F}_R$ and $\mathbf{M}_{R_O}$, to the *distribution of force* on the sectioned area, and thereby develop equations that can be used for analysis and design. To do this, however, the components of $\mathbf{F}_R$ and $\mathbf{M}_{R_O}$ acting both normal and perpendicular to the sectioned area must be considered, Fig. 2*d*. Four different types of resultant loadings can then be defined as follows:

### Normal force, N.

This force acts perpendicular to the area. It is developed whenever the external loads tend to push or pull on the two segments of the body.

### Shear force, V.

The shear force lies in the plane of the area, and it is developed when the external loads tend to cause the two segments of the body to slide over one another.

### Torsional moment or torque, T.

This effect is developed when the external loads tend to twist one segment of the body with respect to the other about an axis perpendicular to the area.

### Bending moment, M.

The bending moment is caused by the external loads that tend to bend the body about an axis lying within the plane of the area.

In this text, note that graphical representation of a moment or torque is shown in three dimensions as a vector with an associated curl. By the *right-hand rule*, the thumb gives the arrowhead sense of this vector and the fingers or curl indicate the tendency for rotation (twisting or bending).

8

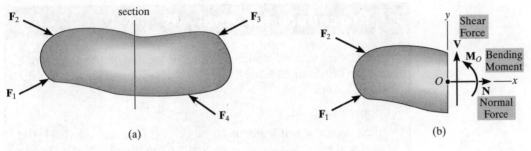

Fig. 3

## Coplanar Loadings.

If the body is subjected to a *coplanar system of forces*, Fig. 3a, then only normal-force, shear-force, and bending-moment components will exist at the section, Fig. 3b. If we use the $x, y, z$ coordinate axes, as shown on the left segment, then $\mathbf{N}$ can be obtained by applying $\Sigma F_x = 0$, and $\mathbf{V}$ can be obtained from $\Sigma F_y = 0$. Finally, the bending moment $\mathbf{M}_O$ can be determined by summing moments about point $O$ (the $z$ axis), $\Sigma M_O = 0$, in order to eliminate the moments caused by the unknowns $\mathbf{N}$ and $\mathbf{V}$.

## Important Points

- *Mechanics of materials* is a study of the relationship between the external loads applied to a body and the stress and strain caused by the internal loads within the body.

- External forces can be applied to a body as *distributed* or *concentrated surface loadings*, or as *body forces* that act throughout the volume of the body.

- Linear distributed loadings produce a *resultant force* having a *magnitude* equal to the *area* under the load diagram, and having a *location* that passes through the *centroid* of this area.

- A support produces a *force* in a particular direction on its attached member if it *prevents translation* of the member in that direction, and it produces a *couple moment* on the member if it *prevents rotation*.

- The equations of equilibrium $\Sigma \mathbf{F} = \mathbf{0}$ and $\Sigma \mathbf{M} = \mathbf{0}$ must be satisfied in order to prevent a body from translating with accelerated motion and from rotating.

- When applying the equations of equilibrium, it is important to first draw the free-body diagram for the body in order to account for all the terms in the equations.

- The method of sections is used to determine the internal resultant loadings acting on the surface of the sectioned body. In general, these resultants consist of a normal force, shear force, torsional moment, and bending moment.

## Procedure for Analysis

The resultant *internal* loadings at a point located on the section of a body can be obtained using the method of sections. This requires the following steps.

### Support Reactions.

• First decide which segment of the body is to be considered. If the segment has a support or connection to another body, then *before* the body is sectioned, it will be necessary to determine the reactions acting on the chosen segment. To do this draw the free-body diagram of the *entire body* and then apply the necessary equations of equilibrium to obtain these reactions.

### Free-Body Diagram.

• Keep all external distributed loadings, couple moments, torques, and forces in their *exact locations*, before passing an imaginary section through the body at the point where the resultant internal loadings are to be determined.

• Draw a free-body diagram of one of the "cut" segments and indicate the unknown resultants **N**, **V**, **M**, and **T** at the section. These resultants are normally placed at the point representing the geometric center or *centroid* of the sectioned area.

• If the member is subjected to a *coplanar* system of forces, only **N**, **V**, and **M** act at the centroid.

• Establish the $x$, $y$, $z$ coordinate axes with origin at the centroid and show the resultant internal loadings acting along the axes.

### Equations of Equilibrium.

• Moments should be summed at the section, about each of the coordinate axes where the resultants act. Doing this eliminates the unknown forces **N** and **V** and allows a direct solution for **M** (and **T**).

• If the solution of the equilibrium equations yields a negative value for a resultant, the *directional sense* of the resultant is *opposite* to that shown on the free-body diagram.

The following examples illustrate this procedure numerically and also provide a review of some of the important principles of statics.

## EXAMPLE | 1

Determine the resultant internal loadings acting on the cross section at $C$ of the cantilevered beam shown in Fig. 4a.

270 N/m

$A$           $B$

$C$

3 m       6 m

(a)

**Fig. 4**

### SOLUTION

**Support Reactions.** The support reactions at $A$ do not have to be determined if segment $CB$ is considered.

**Free-Body Diagram.** The free-body diagram of segment $CB$ is shown in Fig. 4b. It is important to keep the distributed loading on the segment until *after* the section is made. Only then should this loading be replaced by a single resultant force. Notice that the intensity of the distributed loading at $C$ is found by proportion, i.e., from Fig. 4a, $w/6 \text{ m} = (270 \text{ N/m})/9 \text{ m}$, $w = 180 \text{ N/m}$. The magnitude of the resultant of the distributed load is equal to the area under the loading curve (triangle) and acts through the centroid of this area. Thus, $F = \frac{1}{2}(180 \text{ N/m})(6 \text{ m}) = 540 \text{ N}$, which acts $\frac{1}{3}(6 \text{ m}) = 2 \text{ m}$ from $C$ as shown in Fig. 4b.

540 N

180 N/m

$\mathbf{M}_C$

$N_C \leftarrow$

$\mathbf{V}_C$   2 m      4 m

(b)

**Equations of Equilibrium.** Applying the equations of equilibrium we have

$\xrightarrow{+} \Sigma F_x = 0;$           $-N_C = 0$

                            $N_C = 0$          *Ans.*

$+\uparrow \Sigma F_y = 0;$         $V_C - 540 \text{ N} = 0$

                      $V_C = 540 \text{ N}$       *Ans.*

$\zeta + \Sigma M_C = 0;$      $-M_C - 540 \text{ N}(2 \text{ m}) = 0$

                   $M_C = -1080 \text{ N} \cdot \text{m}$     *Ans.*

**NOTE:** The negative sign indicates that $\mathbf{M}_C$ acts in the opposite direction to that shown on the free-body diagram. Try solving this problem using segment $AC$, by first obtaining the support reactions at $A$, which are given in Fig. 4c.

540 N

135 N

90 N/m                  180 N/m

$\mathbf{M}_C$

1215 N                $N_C$

$A$       $C$

3645 N·m

1 m    1.5 m $\mathbf{V}_C$

0.5 m

(c)

## EXAMPLE 2

(a)

(b)

(c)

**Fig. 5**

The 500-kg engine is suspended from the crane boom in Fig. 5a. Determine the resultant internal loadings acting on the cross section of the boom at point $E$.

### SOLUTION

**Support Reactions.** We will consider segment $AE$ of the boom, so we must first determine the pin reactions at $A$. Notice that member $CD$ is a two-force member. The free-body diagram of the boom is shown in Fig. 5b. Applying the equations of equilibrium,

$$\zeta + \Sigma M_A = 0; \qquad F_{CD}\left(\tfrac{3}{5}\right)(2 \text{ m}) - [500(9.81) \text{ N}](3 \text{ m}) = 0$$

$$F_{CD} = 12\ 262.5 \text{ N}$$

$$\xrightarrow{+} \Sigma F_x = 0; \qquad A_x - (12\ 262.5 \text{ N})\left(\tfrac{4}{5}\right) = 0$$

$$A_x = 9810 \text{ N}$$

$$+\uparrow \Sigma F_y = 0; \qquad -A_y + (12\ 262.5 \text{ N})\left(\tfrac{3}{5}\right) - 500(9.81) \text{ N} = 0$$

$$A_y = 2452.5 \text{ N}$$

**Free-Body Diagram.** The free-body diagram of segment $AE$ is shown in Fig. 5c.

**Equations of Equilibrium.**

$$\xrightarrow{+} \Sigma F_x = 0; \qquad N_E + 9810 \text{ N} = 0$$

$$N_E = -9810 \text{ N} = -9.81 \text{ kN} \qquad \textit{Ans.}$$

$$+\uparrow \Sigma F_y = 0; \qquad -V_E - 2452.5 \text{ N} = 0$$

$$V_E = -2452.5 \text{ N} = -2.45 \text{ kN} \qquad \textit{Ans.}$$

$$\zeta + \Sigma M_E = 0; \qquad M_E + (2452.5 \text{ N})(1 \text{ m}) = 0$$

$$M_E = -2452.5 \text{ N} \cdot \text{m} = -2.45 \text{ kN} \cdot \text{m} \qquad \textit{Ans.}$$

# EXAMPLE  3

Determine the resultant internal loadings acting on the cross section at $G$ of the beam shown in Fig. 6a. Each joint is pin connected.

(a)

(b)

**Fig. 6**

## SOLUTION

**Support Reactions.** Here we will consider segment $AG$. The free-body diagram of the *entire* structure is shown in Fig. 6b. Verify the calculated reactions at $E$ and $C$. In particular, note that $BC$ is a *two-force member* since only two forces act on it. For this reason the force at $C$ must act along $BC$, which is horizontal as shown.

Since $BA$ and $BD$ are also two-force members, the free-body diagram of joint $B$ is shown in Fig. 6c. Again, verify the magnitudes of forces $\mathbf{F}_{BA}$ and $\mathbf{F}_{BD}$.

(c)

**Free-Body Diagram.** Using the result for $\mathbf{F}_{BA}$, the free-body diagram of segment $AG$ is shown in Fig. 6d.

## Equations of Equilibrium.

(d)

$$\xrightarrow{+} \Sigma F_x = 0; \qquad 7750 \text{ lb}\left(\tfrac{4}{5}\right) + N_G = 0 \qquad N_G = -6200 \text{ lb} \qquad Ans.$$

$$+\uparrow \Sigma F_y = 0; \qquad -1500 \text{ lb} + 7750 \text{ lb}\left(\tfrac{3}{5}\right) - V_G = 0$$

$$V_G = 3150 \text{ lb} \qquad Ans.$$

$$\zeta + \Sigma M_G = 0; \quad M_G - (7750 \text{ lb})\left(\tfrac{3}{5}\right)(2 \text{ ft}) + 1500 \text{ lb}(2 \text{ ft}) = 0$$

$$M_G = 6300 \text{ lb} \cdot \text{ft} \qquad Ans.$$

13

## EXAMPLE 4

(a)

(b)

**Fig. 7**

Determine the resultant internal loadings acting on the cross section at $B$ of the pipe shown in Fig. 7a. End $A$ is subjected to a vertical force of 50 N, a horizontal force of 30 N, and a couple moment of 70 N·m. Neglect the pipe's mass.

### SOLUTION

The problem can be solved by considering segment $AB$, so we do not need to calculate the support reactions at $C$.

**Free-Body Diagram.** The $x$, $y$, $z$ axes are established at $B$ and the free-body diagram of segment $AB$ is shown in Fig. 7b. The resultant force and moment components at the section are assumed to act in the *positive coordinate directions* and to pass through the *centroid* of the cross-sectional area at $B$.

**Equations of Equilibrium.** Applying the six scalar equations of equilibrium, we have*

$\Sigma F_x = 0;$ $\qquad\qquad\qquad\qquad\qquad\qquad\qquad (F_B)_x = 0$ $\qquad$ *Ans.*

$\Sigma F_y = 0;$ $\qquad (F_B)_y + 30\text{ N} = 0 \qquad (F_B)_y = -30\text{ N}$ $\qquad$ *Ans.*

$\Sigma F_z = 0;$ $\qquad (F_B)_z - 50\text{ N} = 0 \qquad (F_B)_z = 50\text{ N}$ $\qquad$ *Ans.*

$\Sigma (M_B)_x = 0;$ $\qquad (M_B)_x + 70\text{ N} \cdot \text{m} - 50\text{ N} (0.5\text{ m}) = 0$

$$(M_B)_x = -45\text{ N} \cdot \text{m} \qquad\qquad Ans.$$

$\Sigma (M_B)_y = 0;$ $\qquad (M_B)_y + 50\text{ N} (1.25\text{ m}) = 0$

$$(M_B)_y = -62.5\text{ N} \cdot \text{m} \qquad\qquad Ans.$$

$\Sigma (M_B)_z = 0;$ $\qquad (M_B)_z + (30\text{ N})(1.25) = 0$ $\qquad$ *Ans.*

$$(M_B)_z = -37.5\text{ N} \cdot \text{m}$$

**NOTE:** What do the negative signs for $(F_B)_y$, $(M_B)_x$, $(M_B)_y$ and $(M_B)_z$ indicate? The normal force $N_B = |(F_B)_y| = 30\text{ N}$, whereas the shear force is $V_B = \sqrt{(0)^2 + (50)^2} = 50\text{ N}$. Also, the torsional moment is $T_B = |(M_B)_y| = 62.5\text{ N} \cdot \text{m}$ and the bending moment is $M_B = \sqrt{(45)^2 + (37.5)^2} = 58.6\text{ N} \cdot \text{m}$.

---

*The *magnitude* of each moment about an axis is equal to the magnitude of each force times the perpendicular distance from the axis to the line of action of the force. The *direction* of each moment is determined using the right-hand rule, with positive moments (thumb) directed along the positive coordinate axes.

It is suggested that you test yourself on the solutions to these examples, by covering them over and then trying to think about which equilibrium equations must be used and how they are applied in order to determine the unknowns. Then before solving any of the Problems, build your skills by first trying to solve the Preliminary Problems, which actually require little or no calculations, and then do some of the Fundamental Problems given on the following pages. The solutions and answers to all these problems are given at the end of the chapter. **Doing this throughout the text will help immensely in understanding how to apply the theory, and thereby develop your problem-solving skills.**

## PRELIMINARY PROBLEMS

**P1.** In each case, explain how to find the resultant internal loading acting on the cross section at point $A$. Draw all necessary free-body diagrams, and indicate the relevant equations of equilibrium. Do not calculate values. The lettered dimensions, angles, and loads are assumed to be known.

(a)

(b)

(c)

(d)

(e)

(f)

# FUNDAMENTAL PROBLEMS

**F1.** Determine the internal normal force, shear force, and bending moment at point C in the beam.

**F1**

**F2.** Determine the internal normal force, shear force, and bending moment at point C in the beam.

**F2**

**F3.** Determine the internal normal force, shear force, and bending moment at point C in the beam.

**F3**

**F4.** Determine the internal normal force, shear force, and bending moment at point C in the beam.

**F4**

**F5.** Determine the internal normal force, shear force, and bending moment at point C in the beam.

**F5**

**F6.** Determine the internal normal force, shear force, and bending moment at point C in the beam.

**F6**

# PROBLEMS

**1.** The shaft is supported by a smooth thrust bearing at $B$ and a journal bearing at $C$. Determine the resultant internal loadings acting on the cross section at $E$.

**Prob. 1**

**2.** Determine the resultant internal normal and shear force in the member at (a) section $a$–$a$ and (b) section $b$–$b$, each of which passes through point $A$. The 500-lb load is applied along the centroidal axis of the member.

**Prob. 2**

**3.** The beam $AB$ is fixed to the wall and has a uniform weight of 80 lb/ft. If the trolley supports a load of 1500 lb, determine the resultant internal loadings acting on the cross sections through points $C$ and $D$.

**Prob. 3**

**\*4.** The shaft is supported by a smooth thrust bearing at $A$ and a smooth journal bearing at $B$. Determine the resultant internal loadings acting on the cross section at $C$.

**Prob. 4**

**5.** Determine the resultant internal loadings in the beam at cross sections through points $D$ and $E$. Point $E$ is just to the right of the 3-kip load.

**Prob. 5**

**6.** Determine the normal force, shear force, and moment at a section through point $C$. Take $P = 8$ kN.

**7.** The cable will fail when subjected to a tension of 2 kN. Determine the largest vertical load $P$ the frame will support and calculate the internal normal force, shear force, and moment at the cross section through point $C$ for this loading.

**Probs. 6/7**

17

**\*8.** Determine the resultant internal loadings on the cross section through point $C$. Assume the reactions at the supports $A$ and $B$ are vertical.

**9.** Determine the resultant internal loadings on the cross section through point $D$. Assume the reactions at the supports $A$ and $B$ are vertical.

**Probs. 8/9**

**10.** The boom $DF$ of the jib crane and the column $DE$ have a uniform weight of 50 lb/ft. If the hoist and load weigh 300 lb, determine the resultant internal loadings in the crane on cross sections through points $A$, $B$, and $C$.

**Prob. 10**

**11.** The forearm and biceps support the 2-kg load at $A$. If $C$ can be assumed as a pin support, determine the resultant internal loadings acting on the cross section of the bone of the forearm at $E$. The biceps pulls on the bone along $BD$.

**Prob. 11**

**\*12.** The serving tray $T$ used on an airplane is supported on *each side* by an arm. The tray is pin connected to the arm at $A$, and at $B$ there is a smooth pin. (The pin can move within the slot in the arms to permit folding the tray against the front passenger seat when not in use.) Determine the resultant internal loadings acting on the cross section of the arm through point $C$ when the tray arm supports the loads shown.

**Prob. 12**

18

**13.** The blade of the hacksaw is subjected to a pretension force of $F = 100$ N. Determine the resultant internal loadings acting on section $a$–$a$ that passes through point $D$.

**14.** The blade of the hacksaw is subjected to a pretension force of $F = 100$ N. Determine the resultant internal loadings acting on section $b$–$b$ that passes through point $D$.

**Probs. 13/14**

**15.** A 150-lb bucket is suspended from a cable on the wooden frame. Determine the resultant internal loadings on the cross section at $D$.

***16.** A 150-lb bucket is suspended from a cable on the wooden frame. Determine the resultant internal loadings acting on the cross section at $E$.

**Probs. 15/16**

**17.** Determine resultant internal loadings acting on section $a$–$a$ and section $b$–$b$. Each section passes through the centerline at point $C$.

**Prob. 17**

**18.** The bolt shank is subjected to a tension of 80 lb. Determine the resultant internal loadings acting on the cross section at point $C$.

**Prob. 18**

**19.** Determine the resultant internal loadings acting on the cross section through point $C$. Assume the reactions at the supports $A$ and $B$ are vertical.

***20.** Determine the resultant internal loadings acting on the cross section through point $D$. Assume the reactions at the supports $A$ and $B$ are vertical.

**Probs. 19/20**

**21.** The forged steel clamp exerts a force of $F = 900$ N on the wooden block. Determine the resultant internal loadings acting on section $a$–$a$ passing through point $A$.

**Prob. 21**

**22.** The metal stud punch is subjected to a force of 120 N on the handle. Determine the magnitude of the reactive force at the pin $A$ and in the short link $BC$. Also, determine the internal resultant loadings acting on the cross section passing through the handle arm at $D$.

**23.** Solve Prob. 22 for the resultant internal loadings acting on the cross section passing through the handle arm at $E$ and at a cross section of the short link $BC$.

**Probs. 22/23**

**\*24.** Determine the resultant internal loadings acting on the cross section of the semicircular arch at $C$.

**Prob. 24**

**25.** Determine the resultant internal loadings acting on the cross section through point $B$ of the signpost. The post is fixed to the ground and a uniform pressure of 7 lb/ft² acts perpendicular to the face of the sign.

**Prob. 25**

20

**26.** The shaft is supported at its ends by two bearings $A$ and $B$ and is subjected to the forces applied to the pulleys fixed to the shaft. Determine the resultant internal loadings acting on the cross section located at point $C$. The 300-N forces act in the $-z$ direction and the 500-N forces act in the $+x$ direction. The journal bearings at $A$ and $B$ exert only $x$ and $z$ components of force on the shaft.

**Prob. 26**

**27.** The pipe assembly is subjected to a force of 600 N at $B$. Determine the resultant internal loadings acting on the cross section at $C$.

**Prob. 27**

**\*28.** The brace and drill bit is used to drill a hole at $O$. If the drill bit jams when the brace is subjected to the forces shown, determine the resultant internal loadings acting on the cross section of the drill bit at $A$.

**Prob. 28**

**29.** The curved rod $AD$ of radius $r$ has a weight per length of $w$. If it lies in the vertical plane, determine the resultant internal loadings acting on the cross section through point $B$. *Hint:* The distance from the centroid $C$ of segment $AB$ to point $O$ is $OC = [2r \sin (\theta/2)]/\theta$.

**Prob. 29**

**30.** A differential element taken from a curved bar is shown in the figure. Show that $dN/d\theta = V$, $dV/d\theta = -N$, $dM/d\theta = -T$, and $dT/d\theta = M$.

**Prob. 30**

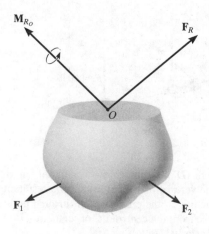

**Fig. 8**

# 3 Stress

It was stated in Section 2 that the force and moment acting at a specified point $O$ on the sectioned area of the body, Fig. 8, represents the resultant effects of the actual *distribution of loading* acting over the sectioned area, Fig. 9a. Obtaining this *distribution* is of primary importance in mechanics of materials. To solve this problem it is necessary to establish the concept of stress.

We begin by considering the sectioned area to be subdivided into small areas, such as $\Delta A$ shown in Fig. 9a. As we reduce $\Delta A$ to a smaller and smaller size, we must make two assumptions regarding the properties of the material. We will consider the material to be ***continuous***, that is, to consist of a *continuum* or uniform distribution of matter having no voids. Also, the material must be ***cohesive***, meaning that all portions of it are connected together, without having breaks, cracks, or separations. A typical finite yet very small force $\Delta F$, acting on $\Delta A$, is shown in Fig. 9a. This force, like all the others, will have a unique direction, but for further discussion we will replace it by its *three components*, namely, $\Delta F_x$, $\Delta F_y$, and $\Delta F_z$, which are taken tangent, tangent, and normal to the area, respectively. As $\Delta A$ approaches zero, so do $\Delta F$ and its components; however, the quotient of the force and area will, in general, approach a finite limit. This quotient is called *stress*, and as noted, it describes the *intensity of the internal force* acting on a *specific plane* (area) passing through a point.

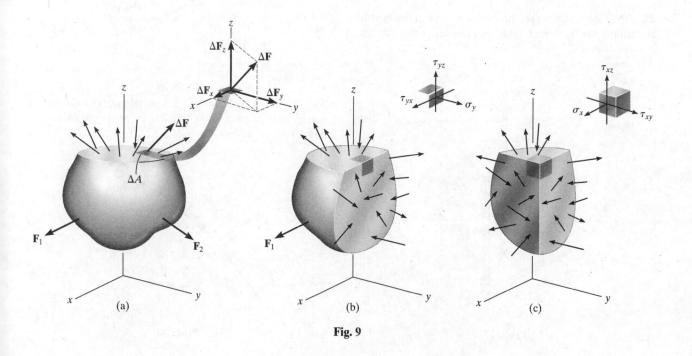

**Fig. 9**

## Normal Stress.
The *intensity* of the force acting normal to $\Delta A$ is defined as the **normal stress**, $\sigma$ (sigma). Since $\Delta \mathbf{F}_z$ is normal to the area then

$$\sigma_z = \lim_{\Delta A \to 0} \frac{\Delta F_z}{\Delta A} \qquad (4)$$

If the normal force or stress "pulls" on $\Delta A$ as shown in Fig. 9a, it is referred to as *tensile stress*, whereas if it "pushes" on $\Delta A$ it is called *compressive stress*.

## Shear Stress.
The intensity of force acting tangent to $\Delta A$ is called the **shear stress**, $\tau$ (tau). Here we have shear stress components,

$$\tau_{zx} = \lim_{\Delta A \to 0} \frac{\Delta F_x}{\Delta A}$$
$$\tau_{zy} = \lim_{\Delta A \to 0} \frac{\Delta F_y}{\Delta A} \qquad (5)$$

Note that in this subscript notation $z$ specifies the orientation of the area $\Delta A$, Fig. 10, and $x$ and $y$ indicate the axes along which each shear stress acts.

**Fig. 10**

## General State of Stress.
If the body is further sectioned by planes parallel to the $x$–$z$ plane, Fig. 9b, and the $y$–$z$ plane, Fig. 9c, we can then "cut out" a cubic volume element of material that represents the *state of stress* acting around the chosen point in the body. This state of stress is then characterized by three components acting on each face of the element, Fig. 11.

## Units.
Since stress represents a force per unit area, in the International Standard or SI system, the magnitudes of both normal and shear stress are specified in the basic units of newtons per square meter ($N/m^2$). This unit, called a pascal ($1\ Pa = 1\ N/m^2$) is rather small, and in engineering work prefixes such as kilo- ($10^3$), symbolized by k, mega- ($10^6$), symbolized by M, or giga- ($10^9$), symbolized by G, are used to represent larger, more realistic values of stress.* Likewise, in the Foot-Pound-Second system of units, engineers usually express stress in pounds per square inch (psi) or kilopounds per square inch (ksi), where 1 kilopound (kip) = 1000 lb.

**Fig. 11**

---

*Sometimes stress is expressed in units of $N/mm^2$, where $1\ mm = 10^{-3}\ m$. However, in the SI system, prefixes are not allowed in the denominator of a fraction and therefore it is better to use the equivalent $1\ N/mm^2 = 1\ MN/m^2 = 1\ MPa$.

## 4 Average Normal Stress in an Axially Loaded Bar

In this section we will determine the average stress distribution acting on the cross-sectional area of an axially loaded bar such as the one shown in Fig. 12a. This bar is **prismatic** since all cross sections are the same throughout its length. When the load $P$ is applied to the bar through the centroid of its cross-sectional area, then the bar will deform uniformly throughout the central region of its length, as shown in Fig. 12b, provided the material of the bar is both homogeneous and isotropic.

*Homogeneous material* has the same physical and mechanical properties throughout its volume, and *isotropic material* has these same properties in all directions. Many engineering materials may be approximated as being both homogeneous and isotropic as assumed here. Steel, for example, contains thousands of randomly oriented crystals in each cubic millimeter of its volume, and since most problems involving this material have a physical size that is very much larger than a single crystal, the above assumption regarding its material composition is quite realistic.

Note that anisotropic materials such as wood have different properties in different directions, and although this is the case, if the anisotropy is oriented along the bar's axis (as for instance in a typical wood rod), then the bar will also deform uniformly when subjected to the axial load $P$.

**Average Normal Stress Distribution.** If we pass a section through the bar, and separate it into two parts, then equilibrium requires the resultant normal force at the section to be $P$, Fig. 12c. Due to the *uniform* deformation of the material, it is necessary that the cross section be subjected to a *constant normal stress distribution*, Fig. 12d.

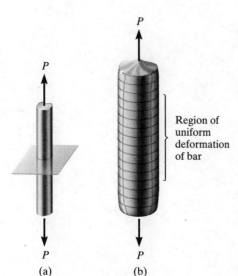

P

P

Region of uniform deformation of bar

P

P

(a)          (b)

P

Internal force

Cross-sectional area

External force

P

(c)

$z$

$P$

$\Delta F = \sigma \Delta A$

$\sigma$

$x$

$y$

$\Delta A$

$y$

$x$

$P$

(d)

**Fig. 12**

24

As a result, each small area $\Delta A$ on the cross section is subjected to a force $\Delta F = \sigma \, \Delta A$, and the *sum* of these forces acting over the entire cross-sectional area must be equivalent to the internal resultant force **P** at the section. If we let $\Delta A \to dA$ and therefore $\Delta F \to dF$, then, recognizing $\sigma$ is *constant*, we have

$$+\uparrow F_{Rz} = \Sigma F_z; \qquad \int dF = \int_A \sigma \, dA$$

$$P = \sigma A$$

$$\boxed{\sigma = \frac{P}{A}} \qquad (6)$$

Here

$\sigma$ = average normal stress at any point on the cross-sectional area

$P$ = *internal resultant normal force*, which acts through the *centroid* of the cross-sectional area. $P$ is determined using the method of sections and the equations of equilibrium

$A$ = cross-sectional area of the bar where $\sigma$ is determined

Since the internal load $P$ passes through the centroid of the cross-section, the uniform stress distribution will produce zero moments about the $x$ and $y$ axes passing through this point, Fig. 12d. To show this, we require the moment of $P$ about each axis to be equal to the moment of the stress distribution about the axes, namely,

$$(M_R)_x = \Sigma M_x; \qquad 0 = \int_A y \, dF = \int_A y\sigma \, dA = \sigma \int_A y \, dA$$

$$(M_R)_y = \Sigma M_y; \qquad 0 = -\int_A x \, dF = -\int_A x\sigma \, dA = -\sigma \int_A x \, dA$$

These equations are indeed satisfied, since by definition of the centroid, $\int y \, dA = 0$ and $\int x \, dA = 0$.

**Equilibrium.** It should be apparent that only a normal stress exists on any small volume element of material located at each point on the cross section of an axially loaded bar. If we consider vertical equilibrium of the element, Fig. 13, then apply the equation of force equilibrium,

$$\Sigma F_z = 0; \qquad \sigma(\Delta A) - \sigma'(\Delta A) = 0$$

$$\sigma = \sigma'$$

Fig. 13

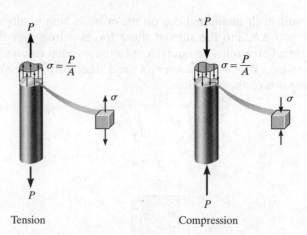

Tension                                     Compression

**Fig. 14**

In other words, the two normal stress components on the element must be equal in magnitude but opposite in direction. This is referred to as *uniaxial stress*.

The previous analysis applies to members subjected to either tension or compression, as shown in Fig. 14. As a graphical interpretation, the *magnitude* of the internal resultant force **P** is *equivalent* to the *volume* under the stress diagram; that is, $P = \sigma A$ (volume = height × base). Furthermore, as a consequence of the balance of moments, *this resultant passes through the centroid of this volume*.

Although we have developed this analysis for *prismatic* bars, this assumption can be relaxed somewhat to include bars that have a *slight taper*. For example, it can be shown, using the more exact analysis of the theory of elasticity, that for a tapered bar of rectangular cross section, for which the angle between two adjacent sides is 15°, the average normal stress, as calculated by $\sigma = P/A$, is only 2.2% *less* than its value found from the theory of elasticity.

### Maximum Average Normal Stress.

In our analysis both the internal force $P$ and the cross-sectional area $A$ were *constant* along the longitudinal axis of the bar, and as a result the normal stress $\sigma = P/A$ is also *constant* throughout the bar's length. Occasionally, however, the bar may be subjected to *several* external loads along its axis, or a change in its cross-sectional area may occur. As a result, the normal stress within the bar could be different from one section to the next, and, if the *maximum* average normal stress is to be determined, then it becomes important to find the location where the ratio $P/A$ is a *maximum*. To do this it is necessary to determine the internal force $P$ at various sections along the bar. Here it may be helpful to show this variation by drawing an *axial or normal force diagram*. Specifically, this diagram is a plot of the normal force $P$ versus its position $x$ along the bar's length. As a sign convention, $P$ will be positive if it causes tension in the member, and negative if it causes compression. Once the internal loading throughout the bar is known, the maximum ratio of $P/A$ can then be identified.

This steel tie rod is used as a hanger to suspend a portion of a staircase, and as a result it is subjected to tensile stress.

## Important Points

- When a body subjected to external loads is sectioned, there is a distribution of force acting over the sectioned area which holds each segment of the body in equilibrium. The intensity of this internal force at a point in the body is referred to as *stress*.

- Stress is the limiting value of force per unit area, as the area approaches zero. For this definition, the material is considered to be continuous and cohesive.

- The magnitude of the stress components at a point depends upon the type of loading acting on the body, and the orientation of the element at the point.

- When a prismatic bar is made from homogeneous and isotropic material, and is subjected to an axial force acting through the centroid of the cross-sectional area, then the center region of the bar will deform uniformly. As a result, the material will be subjected *only to normal stress*. This stress is uniform or *averaged* over the cross-sectional area.

## Procedure for Analysis

The equation $\sigma = P/A$ gives the *average* normal stress on the cross-sectional area of a member when the section is subjected to an internal resultant normal force **P**. For axially loaded members, application of this equation requires the following steps.

Internal Loading.

- Section the member *perpendicular* to its longitudinal axis at the point where the normal stress is to be determined and use the necessary free-body diagram and force equation of equilibrium to obtain the *internal axial force* **P** at the section.

Average Normal Stress.

- Determine the member's cross-sectional area at the section and calculate the average normal stress $\sigma = P/A$.

- It is suggested that $\sigma$ be shown acting on a small volume element of the material located at a point on the section where stress is calculated. To do this, first draw $\sigma$ on the face of the element coincident with the sectioned area $A$. Here $\sigma$ acts in the *same direction* as the internal force **P** since all the normal stresses on the cross section develop this resultant. The normal stress $\sigma$ on the other face of the element acts in the opposite direction.

# EXAMPLE 5

The bar in Fig. 15*a* has a constant width of 35 mm and a thickness of 10 mm. Determine the maximum average normal stress in the bar when it is subjected to the loading shown.

(a)

(b)

(c)

## SOLUTION

**Internal Loading.** By inspection, the internal axial forces in regions *AB*, *BC*, and *CD* are all constant yet have different magnitudes. Using the method of sections, these loadings are determined in Fig. 15*b*; and the normal force diagram, which represents these results graphically, is shown in Fig. 15*c*. The largest loading is in region *BC*, where $P_{BC} = 30$ kN. Since the cross-sectional area of the bar is *constant*, the largest average normal stress also occurs within this region of the bar.

**Average Normal Stress.** Applying Eq. 6, we have

$$\sigma_{BC} = \frac{P_{BC}}{A} = \frac{30(10^3) \text{ N}}{(0.035 \text{ m})(0.010 \text{ m})} = 85.7 \text{ MPa} \qquad Ans.$$

**NOTE:** The stress distribution acting on an arbitrary cross section of the bar within region *BC* is shown in Fig. 15*d*. Graphically the *volume* (or "block") represented by this distribution of stress is equivalent to the load of 30 kN; that is, 30 kN = (85.7 MPa)(35 mm)(10 mm).

(d)

**Fig. 15**

28

## EXAMPLE | 6

The 80-kg lamp is supported by two rods $AB$ and $BC$ as shown in Fig. 16a. If $AB$ has a diameter of 10 mm and $BC$ has a diameter of 8 mm, determine the average normal stress in each rod.

(a)

(b)

**Fig. 16**

### SOLUTION

**Internal Loading.** We must first determine the axial force in each rod. A free-body diagram of the lamp is shown in Fig. 16b. Applying the equations of force equilibrium,

$$\xrightarrow{+} \Sigma F_x = 0; \qquad F_{BC}\left(\tfrac{4}{5}\right) - F_{BA}\cos 60° = 0$$

$$+\uparrow \Sigma F_y = 0; \qquad F_{BC}\left(\tfrac{3}{5}\right) + F_{BA}\sin 60° - 784.8 \text{ N} = 0$$

$$F_{BC} = 395.2 \text{ N}, \qquad F_{BA} = 632.4 \text{ N}$$

By Newton's third law of action, equal but opposite reaction, these forces subject the rods to tension throughout their length.

**Average Normal Stress.** Applying Eq. 6,

$$\sigma_{BC} = \frac{F_{BC}}{A_{BC}} = \frac{395.2 \text{ N}}{\pi(0.004 \text{ m})^2} = 7.86 \text{ MPa} \qquad Ans.$$

$$\sigma_{BA} = \frac{F_{BA}}{A_{BA}} = \frac{632.4 \text{ N}}{\pi(0.005 \text{ m})^2} = 8.05 \text{ MPa} \qquad Ans.$$

(d)

(c)

**NOTE:** The average normal stress distribution acting over a cross section of rod $AB$ is shown in Fig. 16c, and at a point on this cross section, an element of material is stressed as shown in Fig. 16d.

# EXAMPLE | 7

The casting shown in Fig. 17a is made of steel having a specific weight of $\gamma_{st} = 490 \text{ lb/ft}^3$. Determine the average compressive stress acting at points $A$ and $B$.

**Fig. 17**

## SOLUTION

**Internal Loading.** A free-body diagram of the top segment of the casting where the section passes through points $A$ and $B$ is shown in Fig. 17b. The weight of this segment is determined from $W_{st} = \gamma_{st} V_{st}$. Thus the internal axial force $P$ at the section is

$$+\uparrow \Sigma F_z = 0; \qquad P - W_{st} = 0$$
$$P - (490 \text{ lb/ft}^3)(2.75 \text{ ft})\left[\pi(0.75 \text{ ft})^2\right] = 0$$
$$P = 2381 \text{ lb}$$

**Average Compressive Stress.** The cross-sectional area at the section is $A = \pi(0.75 \text{ ft})^2$, and so the average compressive stress becomes

$$\sigma = \frac{P}{A} = \frac{2381 \text{ lb}}{\pi(0.75 \text{ ft})^2} = 1347.5 \text{ lb/ft}^2$$

$$\sigma = 1347.5 \text{ lb/ft}^2 (1 \text{ ft}^2/144 \text{ in}^2) = 9.36 \text{ psi} \qquad Ans.$$

**NOTE:** The stress shown on the volume element of material in Fig. 17c is representative of the conditions at either point $A$ or $B$. Notice that this stress acts *upward* on the bottom or shaded face of the element since this face forms part of the bottom surface area of the section, and on this surface, the resultant internal force **P** is pushing upward.

## EXAMPLE 8

Member $AC$ shown in Fig. 18a is subjected to a vertical force of 3 kN. Determine the position $x$ of this force so that the average compressive stress at the smooth support $C$ is equal to the average tensile stress in the tie rod $AB$. The rod has a cross-sectional area of 400 mm² and the contact area at $C$ is 650 mm².

(a)                                          (b)

**Fig. 18**

### SOLUTION

**Internal Loading.** The forces at $A$ and $C$ can be related by considering the free-body diagram for member $AC$, Fig. 18b. There are three unknowns, namely, $F_{AB}$, $F_C$, and $x$. To solve this problem we will work in units of newtons and millimeters.

$$+\uparrow \Sigma F_y = 0; \qquad\qquad F_{AB} + F_C - 3000\text{ N} = 0 \qquad (1)$$

$$\zeta +\Sigma M_A = 0; \qquad -3000\text{ N}(x) + F_C(200\text{ mm}) = 0 \qquad (2)$$

**Average Normal Stress.** A necessary third equation can be written that requires the tensile stress in the bar $AB$ and the compressive stress at $C$ to be equivalent, i.e.,

$$\sigma = \frac{F_{AB}}{400\text{ mm}^2} = \frac{F_C}{650\text{ mm}^2}$$

$$F_C = 1.625 F_{AB}$$

Substituting this into Eq. 1, solving for $F_{AB}$, then solving for $F_C$, we obtain

$$F_{AB} = 1143\text{ N}$$
$$F_C = 1857\text{ N}$$

The position of the applied load is determined from Eq. 2,

$$x = 124\text{ mm} \qquad\qquad\qquad Ans.$$

**NOTE:** $0 < x < 200$ mm, as required.

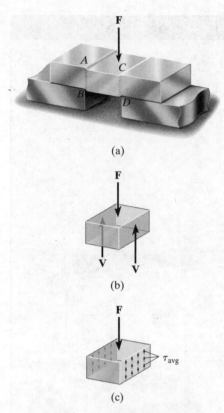

(a)

(b)

(c)

**Fig. 19**

The pin *A* used to connect the linkage of this tractor is subjected to *double shear* because shearing stresses occur on the surface of the pin at *B* and *C*. See Fig 1–21*c*.

# 5 Average Shear Stress

Shear stress has been defined in Section 3 as the stress component that acts *in the plane* of the sectioned area. To show how this stress can develop, consider the effect of applying a force **F** to the bar in Fig. 19*a*. If the supports are considered rigid, and **F** is large enough, it will cause the material of the bar to deform and fail along the planes identified by *AB* and *CD*. A free-body diagram of the unsupported center segment of the bar, Fig. 19*b*, indicates that the shear force $V = F/2$ must be applied at each section to hold the segment in equilibrium. The ***average shear stress*** distributed over each sectioned area that develops this shear force is defined by

$$\tau_{avg} = \frac{V}{A} \qquad (7)$$

Here

$\tau_{avg}$ = average shear stress at the section, which is assumed to be the *same* at each point located on the section

$V$ = internal resultant shear force on the section determined from the equations of equilibrium

$A$ = area at the section

The distribution of average shear stress acting over the sections is shown in Fig. 19*c*. Notice that $\tau_{avg}$ is in the *same direction* as **V**, since the shear stress must create associated forces all of which contribute to the internal resultant force **V** at the section.

The loading case discussed here is an example of ***simple or direct shear***, since the shear is caused by the *direct action* of the applied load **F**. This type of shear often occurs in various types of simple connections that use bolts, pins, welding material, etc. In all these cases, however, application of Eq. 7 is *only approximate*. A more precise investigation of the shear-stress distribution over the section often reveals that much larger shear stresses occur in the material than those predicted by this equation. Although this may be the case, application of Eq. 7 is generally acceptable for many problems in engineering design and analysis. For example, engineering codes allow its use when considering design sizes for fasteners such as bolts and for obtaining the bonding strength of glued joints subjected to shear loadings.

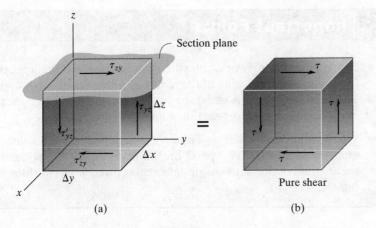

**Fig. 20**

## Shear Stress Equilibrium.
Fig. 20*a* shows a volume element of material taken at a point located on the surface of a sectioned area which is subjected to a shear stress $\tau_{zy}$. Force and moment equilibrium requires the shear stress acting on this face of the element to be accompanied by shear stress acting on three other faces. To show this we will first consider force equilibrium in the $y$ direction. Then

$$\overset{\overset{\text{force}}{\overbrace{\phantom{mmm}}}}{\underset{\text{stress area}}{\phantom{m}}}$$

$$\Sigma F_y = 0; \qquad \tau_{zy}(\Delta x \, \Delta y) - \tau'_{zy}\,\Delta x \, \Delta y = 0$$

$$\tau_{zy} = \tau'_{zy}$$

In a similar manner, force equilibrium in the $z$ direction yields $\tau_{yz} = \tau'_{yz}$. Finally, taking moments about the $x$ axis,

$$\overset{\text{moment}}{\overbrace{\phantom{mmmm}}}$$
$$\overset{\text{force} \qquad \text{arm}}{}$$
$$\overset{\text{stress area}}{}$$

$$\Sigma M_x = 0; \qquad -\tau_{zy}(\Delta x \, \Delta y)\,\Delta z + \tau_{yz}(\Delta x \, \Delta z)\,\Delta y = 0$$

$$\tau_{zy} = \tau_{yz}$$

so that

$$\tau_{zy} = \tau'_{zy} = \tau_{yz} = \tau'_{yz} = \tau$$

In other words, ***all four shear stresses must have equal magnitude and be directed either toward or away from each other at opposite edges of the element***, Fig. 20*b*. This is referred to as the *complementary property of shear*, and under the conditions shown in Fig. 20, the material is subjected to *pure shear*.

## Important Points

- If two parts are *thin or small* when joined together, the applied loads may cause shearing of the material with negligible bending. If this is the case, it is generally assumed that an *average shear stress* acts over the cross-sectional area.

- When shear stress $\tau$ acts on a plane, then equilibrium of a volume element of material at a point on the plane requires associated shear stress of the same magnitude act on three adjacent sides of the element.

## Procedure for Analysis

The equation $\tau_{avg} = V/A$ is used to determine the *average shear stress* in the material. Application requires the following steps.

### Internal Shear.

- Section the member at the point where the average shear stress is to be determined.

- Draw the necessary free-body diagram, and calculate the internal shear force $V$ acting at the section that is necessary to hold the part in equilibrium.

### Average Shear Stress.

- Determine the sectioned area $A$, and determine the average shear stress $\tau_{avg} = V/A$.

- It is suggested that $\tau_{avg}$ be shown on a small volume element of material located at a point on the section where it is determined. To do this, first draw $\tau_{avg}$ on the face of the element, coincident with the sectioned area $A$. This stress acts in the *same direction* as $V$. The shear stresses acting on the three adjacent planes can then be drawn in their appropriate directions following the scheme shown in Fig. 20.

## EXAMPLE | 9

Determine the average shear stress in the 20-mm-diameter pin at $A$ and the 30-mm-diameter pin at $B$ that support the beam in Fig. 21$a$.

(a)

### SOLUTION

**Internal Loadings.** The forces on the pins can be obtained by considering the equilibrium of the beam, Fig. 21$b$.

$$\zeta + \Sigma M_A = 0;$$

$$F_B\left(\frac{4}{5}\right)(6 \text{ m}) - 30 \text{ kN}(2 \text{ m}) = 0 \quad F_B = 12.5 \text{ kN}$$

$$\xrightarrow{+} \Sigma F_x = 0; \quad (12.5 \text{ kN})\left(\frac{3}{5}\right) - A_x = 0 \qquad A_x = 7.50 \text{ kN}$$

$$+\uparrow \Sigma F_y = 0; \quad A_y + (12.5 \text{ kN})\left(\frac{4}{5}\right) - 30 \text{ kN} = 0 \quad A_y = 20 \text{ kN}$$

(b)

Thus, the resultant force acting on pin $A$ is

$$F_A = \sqrt{A_x^2 + A_y^2} = \sqrt{(7.50 \text{ kN})^2 + (20 \text{ kN})^2} = 21.36 \text{ kN}$$

The pin at $A$ is supported by two fixed "leaves" and so the free-body diagram of the center segment of the pin shown in Fig. 21$c$ has *two* shearing surfaces between the beam and each leaf. The force of the beam (21.36 kN) acting on the pin is therefore supported by shear force on each of these surfaces. This case is called *double shear*. Thus,

$$V_A = \frac{F_A}{2} = \frac{21.36 \text{ kN}}{2} = 10.68 \text{ kN}$$

(c)

In Fig. 21$a$, note that pin $B$ is subjected to single shear, which occurs on the section between the cable and beam, Fig. 21$d$. For this pin segment,

$$V_B = F_B = 12.5 \text{ kN}$$

**Average Shear Stress.**

$$(\tau_A)_{\text{avg}} = \frac{V_A}{A_A} = \frac{10.68(10^3) \text{ N}}{\frac{\pi}{4}(0.02 \text{ m})^2} = 34.0 \text{ MPa} \qquad Ans.$$

$$(\tau_B)_{\text{avg}} = \frac{V_B}{A_B} = \frac{12.5(10^3) \text{ N}}{\frac{\pi}{4}(0.03 \text{ m})^2} = 17.7 \text{ MPa} \qquad Ans.$$

(d)

**Fig. 21**

# EXAMPLE | 10

If the wood joint in Fig. 22a has a width of 150 mm, determine the average shear stress developed along shear planes a–a and b–b. For each plane, represent the state of stress on an element of the material.

(a)                                                    (b)

**Fig. 22**

## SOLUTION

**Internal Loadings.** Referring to the free-body diagram of the member, Fig. 22b,

$$\xrightarrow{+} \Sigma F_x = 0; \qquad 6 \text{ kN} - F - F = 0 \qquad F = 3 \text{ kN}$$

Now consider the equilibrium of segments cut across shear planes a–a and b–b, shown in Figs. 22c and 22d.

$$\xrightarrow{+} \Sigma F_x = 0; \qquad V_a - 3 \text{ kN} = 0 \qquad V_a = 3 \text{ kN}$$

$$\xrightarrow{+} \Sigma F_x = 0; \qquad 3 \text{ kN} - V_b = 0 \qquad V_b = 3 \text{ kN}$$

**Average Shear Stress.**

$$(\tau_a)_{\text{avg}} = \frac{V_a}{A_a} = \frac{3(10^3) \text{ N}}{(0.1 \text{ m})(0.15 \text{ m})} = 200 \text{ kPa} \qquad \textit{Ans.}$$

$$(\tau_b)_{\text{avg}} = \frac{V_b}{A_b} = \frac{3(10^3) \text{ N}}{(0.125 \text{ m})(0.15 \text{ m})} = 160 \text{ kPa} \qquad \textit{Ans.}$$

The state of stress on elements located on sections a–a and b–b is shown in Figs. 22c and 22d, respectively.

$\tau_a = 200$ kPa     $V_a$

(c)

$\tau_b = 160$ kPa     $V_b$

(d)

## EXAMPLE | 11

The inclined member in Fig. 23a is subjected to a compressive force of 600 lb. Determine the average compressive stress along the smooth areas of contact defined by $AB$ and $BC$, and the average shear stress along the horizontal plane defined by $DB$.

(a)

**Fig. 23**

(b)

### SOLUTION

**Internal Loadings.** The free-body diagram of the inclined member is shown in Fig. 23b. The compressive forces acting on the areas of contact are

$$\xrightarrow{+} \Sigma F_x = 0; \qquad F_{AB} - 600 \text{ lb}\left(\tfrac{3}{5}\right) = 0 \qquad F_{AB} = 360 \text{ lb}$$
$$+\uparrow \Sigma F_y = 0; \qquad F_{BC} - 600 \text{ lb}\left(\tfrac{4}{5}\right) = 0 \qquad F_{BC} = 480 \text{ lb}$$

(c)

Also, from the free-body diagram of the top segment $ABD$ of the bottom member, Fig. 23c, the shear force acting on the sectioned horizontal plane $DB$ is

$$\xrightarrow{+} \Sigma F_x = 0; \qquad V - 360 \text{ lb} = 0 \qquad V = 360 \text{ lb}$$

**Average Stress.** The average compressive stresses along the horizontal and vertical planes of the inclined member are

$$\sigma_{AB} = \frac{F_{AB}}{A_{AB}} = \frac{360 \text{ lb}}{(1 \text{ in.})(1.5 \text{ in.})} = 240 \text{ psi} \qquad Ans.$$

$$\sigma_{BC} = \frac{F_{BC}}{A_{BC}} = \frac{480 \text{ lb}}{(2 \text{ in.})(1.5 \text{ in.})} = 160 \text{ psi} \qquad Ans.$$

(d)

These stress distributions are shown in Fig. 23d.

The average shear stress acting on the horizontal plane defined by $DB$ is

$$\tau_{avg} = \frac{360 \text{ lb}}{(3 \text{ in.})(1.5 \text{ in.})} = 80 \text{ psi} \qquad Ans.$$

This stress is shown uniformly distributed over the sectioned area in Fig. 23e.

(e)

## PRELIMINARY PROBLEMS

**P2.** In each case, determine the largest internal shear force resisted by the bolt. Include all necessary free-body diagrams.

(a)

(b)

**P2**

**P3.** Determine the largest internal normal force in the bar.

**P3**

**P4.** Determine the internal normal force at section $A$ if the rod is subjected to the external uniformly distributed loading along its length of 8 kN/m.

**P4**

**P5.** The lever is held to the fixed shaft using the pin $AB$. If the couple is applied to the lever, determine the shear force in the pin between the pin and the lever.

**P5**

**P6.** The single-V butt joint transmits the force of 5 kN from one plate to the other. Determine the resultant normal and shear force components that this force creates on the face of the weld, section $AB$.

**P6**

# FUNDAMENTAL PROBLEMS

**F7.** The uniform beam is supported by two rods $AB$ and $CD$ that have cross-sectional areas of 10 mm² and 15 mm², respectively. Determine the intensity $w$ of the distributed load so that the average normal stress in each rod does not exceed 300 kPa.

**F7**

**F8.** Determine the average normal stress developed on the cross section. Sketch the normal stress distribution over the cross section.

**F8**

**F9.** Determine the average normal stress developed on the cross section. Sketch the normal stress distribution over the cross section.

**F9**

**F10.** If the 600-kN force acts through the centroid of the cross section, determine the location $\bar{y}$ of the centroid and the average normal stress developed on the cross section. Also, sketch the normal stress distribution over the cross section.

**F10**

**F11.** Determine the average normal stress developed at points $A$, $B$, and $C$. The diameter of each segment is indicated in the figure.

**F11**

**F12.** Determine the average normal stress developed in rod $AB$ if the load has a mass of 50 kg. The diameter of rod $AB$ is 8 mm.

**F12**

## PROBLEMS

**31.** The supporting wheel on a scaffold is held in place on the leg using a 4-mm-diameter pin as shown. If the wheel is subjected to a normal force of 3 kN, determine the average shear stress developed in the pin. Neglect friction between the inner scaffold puller leg and the tube used on the wheel.

3 kN

**Prob. 31**

*32. The lever is held to the fixed shaft using a tapered pin AB, which has a mean diameter of 6 mm. If a couple is applied to the lever, determine the average shear stress in the pin between the pin and lever.

B  12 mm

A

250 mm ——— 250 mm

20 N                    20 N

**Prob. 32**

**33.** The bar has a cross-sectional area A and is subjected to the axial load P. Determine the average normal and average shear stresses acting over the shaded section, which is oriented at θ from the horizontal. Plot the variation of these stresses as a function of $\theta$ ($0 \leq \theta \leq 90°$).

P ←                                    → P

$\theta$

A

**Prob. 33**

**34.** The built-up shaft consists of a pipe AB and solid rod BC. The pipe has an inner diameter of 20 mm and outer diameter of 28 mm. The rod has a diameter of 12 mm. Determine the average normal stress at points D and E and represent the stress on a volume element located at each of these points.

4 kN  A                    B  6 kN                  C  → 8 kN

D                    6 kN  E

**Prob. 34**

**35.** If the turnbuckle is subjected to an axial force of P = 900 lb, determine the average normal stress developed in section a–a and in each of the bolt shanks at B and C. Each bolt shank has a diameter of 0.5 in.

*36. The average normal stresses developed in section a–a of the turnbuckle, and the bolts shanks at B and C, are not allowed to exceed 15 ksi and 45 ksi, respectively. Determine the maximum axial force **P** that can be applied to the turnbuckle. Each bolt shank has a diameter of 0.5 in.

a

A                                      ←1 in.→

                                        0.25 in.

P ←                                    → P

B                              C

a

**Probs. 35/36**

**37.** The plate has a width of 0.5 m. If the stress distri bution at the support varies as shown, determine the force **P** applied to the plate and the distance $d$ to where it is applied.

$$\sigma = (15x^{1/2}) \text{ MPa}$$

30 MPa

**Prob. 37**

**38.** The two members used in the construction of an aircraft fuselage are joined together using a 30° fish-mouth weld. Determine the average normal and average shear stress on the plane of each weld. Assume each inclined plane supports a horizontal force of 400 lb.

800 lb     800 lb

**Prob. 38**

**39.** If the block is subjected to the centrally applied force of 600 kN, determine the averege normal stress in the material. Show the stress acting on a differential volume element of the material.

**Prob. 39**

**\*40.** Determine the average normal stress in each of the 20-mm diameter bars of the truss. Set $P = 40$ kN.

**41.** If the average normal stress in each of the 20-mm diameter bars is not allowed to exceed 150 MPa, determine the maximum force **P** that can be applied to joint $C$.

**42.** Determine the average shear stress developed in pin $A$ of the truss. A horizontal force of $P = 40$ kN is applied to joint $C$. Each pin has a diameter of 25 mm and is subjected to double shear.

**Probs. 40/41/42**

**43.** The 150-kg bucket is suspended from end $E$ of the frame. Determine the average normal stress in the 6-mm diameter wire $CF$ and the 15-mm diameter short strut $BD$.

**\*44.** The 150-kg bucket is suspended from end $E$ of the frame. If the diameters of the pins at $A$ and $D$ are 6 mm and 10 mm, respectively, determine the average shear stress developed in these pins. Each pin is subjected to double shear.

**Probs. 43/44**

**45.** The pedestal has a triangular cross section as shown. If it is subjected to a compressive force of 500 lb, specify the *x* and *y* coordinates for the location of point $P(x, y)$, where the load must be applied on the cross section, so that the average normal stress is uniform. Compute the stress and sketch its distribution acting on the cross section at a location removed from the point of load application.

**Prob. 45**

**46.** The 20-kg chandelier is suspended from the wall and ceiling using rods *AB* and *BC*, which have diameters of 3 mm and 4 mm, respectively. Determine the angle $\theta$ so that the average normal stress in both rods is the same.

**47.** The chandelier is suspended from the wall and ceiling using rods *AB* and *BC*, which have diameters of 3 mm and 4 mm, respectively. If the average normal stress in both rods is not allowed to exceed 150 MPa, determine the largest mass of the chandelier that can be supported if $\theta = 45°$.

**Probs. 46/47**

**\*48.** The beam is supported by a pin at *A* and a short link *BC*. If $P = 15$ kN, determine the average shear stress developed in the pins at *A*, *B*, and *C*. All pins are in double shear as shown, and each has a diameter of 18 mm.

**Prob. 48**

**49.** The joint is subjected to the axial member force of 6 kip. Determine the average normal stress acting on sections *AB* and *BC*. Assume the member is smooth and is 1.5-in. thick.

**Prob. 49**

**50.** The driver of the sports car applies his rear brakes and causes the tires to slip. If the normal force on each rear tire is 400 lb and the coefficient of kinetic friction between the tires and the pavement is $\mu_k = 0.5$, determine the average shear stress developed by the friction force on the tires. Assume the rubber of the tires is flexible and each tire is filled with an air pressure of 32 psi.

**Prob. 50**

**51.** During the tension test, the wooden specimen is subjected to an average normal stress of 2 ksi. Determine the axial force **P** applied to the specimen. Also, find the average shear stress developed along section *a–a* of the specimen.

4 in.
2 in.
1 in.
4 in.

**Prob. 51**

***52.** If the joint is subjected to an axial force of $P = 9$ kN, determine the averege shear stress developed in each of the 6-mm diameter bolts between the plates and the members and along each of the four shaded shear planes.

**53.** The average shear stress in each of the 6-mm diameter bolts and along each of the four shaded shear planes is not allowed to exceed 80 MPa and 500 kPa, respectively. Determine the maximum axial force **P** that can be applied to the joint.

100 mm
100 mm

**Probs. 52/53**

**54.** When the hand is holding the 5-lb stone, the humerus $H$, assumed to be smooth, exerts normal forces $F_C$ and $F_A$ on the radius $C$ and ulna $A$, respectively, as shown. If the smallest cross-sectional area of the ligament at $B$ is 0.30 in², determine the greatest average tensile stress to which it is subjected.

75°
0.8 in.
2 in.
14 in.

**Prob. 54**

**55.** The 2-Mg concrete pipe has a center of mass at point $G$. If it is suspended from cables $AB$ and $AC$, determine the average normal stress developed in the cables. The diameters of $AB$ and $AC$ are 12 mm and 10 mm, respectively.

***56.** The 2-Mg concrete pipe has a center of mass at point $G$. If it is suspended from cables $AB$ and $AC$, determine the diameter of cable $AB$ so that the average normal stress developed in this cable is the same as in the 10-mm diameter cable $AC$.

30° 45°

**Probs. 55/56**

**57.** If the concrete pedestal has a specific weight of $\gamma$, determine the average normal stress developed in the pedestal as a function of $z$.

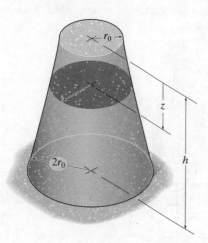

**Prob. 57**

**58.** The anchor bolt was pulled out of the concrete wall and the failure surface formed part of a frustum and cylinder. This indicates a shear failure occurred along the cylinder $BC$ and tension failure along the frustum $AB$. If the shear and normal stresses along these surfaces have the magnitudes shown, determine the force **P** that must have been applied to the bolt.

**Prob. 58**

**59.** The jib crane is pinned at $A$ and supports a chain hoist that can travel along the bottom flange of the beam, $1 \text{ ft} \le x \le 12 \text{ ft}$. If the hoist is rated to support a maximum of 1500 lb, determine the maximum average normal stress in the $\frac{3}{4}$-in. diameter tie rod $BC$ and the maximum average shear stress in the $\frac{5}{8}$-in. -diamater pin at $B$.

**Prob. 59**

**\*60.** If the shaft is subjected to an axial force of 5 kN, determine the bearing stress acting on the collar $A$.

**61.** If the 60-mm diameter shaft is subjected to an axial force of 5 kN, determine the average shear stress developed in the shear plane where the collar $A$ and shaft are connected.

**Probs. 60/61**

**62.** The crimping tool is used to crimp the end of the wire E. If a force of 20 lb is applied to the handles, determine the average shear stress in the pin at A. The pin is subjected to double shear and has a diameter of 0.2 in. Only a vertical force is exerted on the wire.

**63.** Solve Prob. 62 for pin B. The pin is subjected to double shear and has a diameter of 0.2 in.

**Probs. 62/63**

**\*64.** A vertical force of $P = 1500$ N is applied to the bell crank. Determine the average normal stress developed in the 10-mm diamater rod CD, and the average shear stress developed in the 6-mm diameter pin B that is subjected to double shear.

**65.** Determine the maximum vertical force **P** that can be applied to the bell crank so that the average normal stress developed in the 10-mm diameter rod CD, and the average shear strees developed in the 6-mm diameter double sheared pin B not exceed 175 MPa and 75 MPa respectively.

**Probs. 64/65**

**66.** Determine the largest load **P** that can be applied to the frame without causing either the average normal stress or the average shear stress at section a–a to exceed $\sigma = 150$ MPa and $\tau = 60$ MPa, respectively. Member CB has a square cross section of 25 mm on each side.

**Prob. 66**

**67.** The pedestal in the shape of a frustum of a cone is made of concrete having a specific weight of 150 lb/ft³. Determine the average normal stress acting in the pedestal at its base. *Hint:* The volume of a cone of radius r and height h is $V = \frac{1}{3}\pi r^2 h$.

**\*68.** The pedestal in the shape of a frustum of a cone is made of concrete having a specific weight of 150 lb/ft³. Determine the average normal stress acting in the pedestal at its midheight, $z = 4$ ft. *Hint:* The volume of a cone of radius r and height h is $V = \frac{1}{3}\pi r^2 h$.

**Probs. 67/68**

45

# 6 Allowable Stress Design

Cranes are often supported using bearing pads to give them stability. Care must be taken not to crush the supporting surface, due to the large bearing stress developed between the pad and the surface.

To ensure the safety of a structural member or mechanical element, it is necessary to restrict the applied load to one that is less than the load the member (or element) can fully support. There are many reasons for doing this. For example, the intended measurements of a structure or machine may not be exact, due to errors in fabrication or in the assembly of its component parts. Unknown vibrations, impact, or accidental loadings can occur that may not be accounted for in the design. Atmospheric corrosion, decay, or weathering tend to cause materials to deteriorate during service. And finally, some materials, such as wood, concrete, or fiber-reinforced composites, can show high variability in mechanical properties.

One method of specifying the allowable load for a member is to use a number called the factor of safety. The *factor of safety* (F.S.) is a ratio of the failure load $F_{fail}$ to the allowable load $F_{allow}$. Here $F_{fail}$ is found from experimental testing of the material, and the factor of safety is selected based on experience so that all the above mentioned uncertainties are accounted for when the member is used under similar conditions of loading and geometry. Stated mathematically,

$$\text{F.S.} = \frac{F_{fail}}{F_{allow}} \tag{8}$$

If the load applied to the member is *linearly related* to the stress developed within the member, as in the case of using $\sigma = P/A$ and $\tau_{avg} = V/A$, then we can also express the factor of safety as a ratio of the failure stress $\sigma_{fail}$ (or $\tau_{fail}$) to the *allowable stress* $\sigma_{allow}$ (or $\tau_{allow}$).[*] Here the area $A$ will cancel and so,

$$\text{F.S.} = \frac{\sigma_{fail}}{\sigma_{allow}} \tag{9}$$

or

$$\text{F.S.} = \frac{\tau_{fail}}{\tau_{allow}} \tag{10}$$

[*]In some cases, such as columns, the applied load is *not* linearly related to stress and therefore only Eq. 8 can be used to determine the factor of safety.

In any of these equations, the factor of safety must be *greater* than 1 in order to avoid the potential for failure. Specific values depend on the types of materials to be used and the intended purpose of the structure or machine. For example, the F.S. used in the design of aircraft or space-vehicle components may be close to 1 in order to reduce the weight of the vehicle. Or, in the case of a nuclear power plant, the factor of safety for some of its components may be as high as 3 due to uncertainties in loading or material behavior. In many cases, the factor of safety or the allowable stress for a specific case can be found in design codes and engineering handbooks. Once it is obtained, a design that is based on an allowable stress limit is called ***allowable stress design*** (ASD). This method is intended to ensure a balance between both public and environmental safety on the one hand and economic considerations on the other.

## Simple Connections.

By making simplifying assumptions regarding the behavior of the material, the equations $\sigma = P/A$ and $\tau_{avg} = V/A$ can often be used to analyze or design a simple connection or mechanical element. In particular, if a member is subjected to *normal force* at a section, its required area at the section is determined from

$$A = \frac{P}{\sigma_{allow}} \qquad (11)$$

On the other hand, if the section is subjected to an average *shear force*, then the required area at the section is

$$A = \frac{V}{\tau_{allow}} \qquad (12)$$

As discussed in Sec. 6, the allowable stress used in each of these equations is determined either by applying a factor of safety to the material's normal or shear failure stress or by finding these stresses directly from an appropriate design code.

Three examples of where the above equations apply are shown in Fig. 24.

$(\sigma_b)_{allow}$

Assumed uniform normal stress distribution

$$A = \frac{P}{(\sigma_b)_{allow}}$$

The area of the column base plate $B$ is determined from the allowable bearing stress for the concrete.

P

Assumed uniform shear stress
$\tau_{allow}$

$$l = \frac{P}{\tau_{allow}\pi d}$$

d

P

The embedded length $l$ of this rod in concrete can be determined using the allowable shear stress of the bonding glue.

The area of the bolt for this lap joint is determined from the shear stress which is largest between the plates.

$V = P$

Assumed uniform shear stress
$\tau_{allow}$

$$A = \frac{P}{\tau_{allow}}$$

P

**Fig. 24**

# 7 Limit State Design

We have stated in the previous section that a properly designed member must account for uncertainties resulting from the variability of both the material's properties and the loading that must be supported. Since uncertainty can be considered using statistics and probability theory, in structural engineering there has been an increasing trend to *separate* load uncertainty from material uncertainty.* This method of design is called **limit state design** (LSD), or more specifically, in the United States it is called **load and resistance factor design** (LRFD). We will now discuss how this method is applied.

**Load Factors.** Various types of loads $R$ can act on a structure or structural member, and each is multiplied by a **load factor** $\gamma$ (gamma) that accounts for its variability. The loads include *dead load*, which is the fixed weight of the structure, and *live loads,* which involve people or vehicles that move about. Other types of live loads include *wind*, *earthquake*, and *snow loads*. The dead load $D$ is multiplied by a small factor such as $\gamma_D = 1.4$, since it can be determined with greater certainty than, for example, the live load $L$ caused by people. It can have a load factor of $\gamma_L = 1.6$.

Building codes often require a structure to be designed to support various combinations of the loads, and when applied in combination, each type of load will have a unique load factor. For example, one load combination of dead $(D)$, live $(L)$, and snow $(S)$ loads is

$$R = 1.2D + 1.6L + 0.5S$$

The load factors for this combined loading reflect the *probability* that the total loading $R$ will occur for all the events stated. Here, however, the load factor $\gamma_S = 0.5$ is small because of the low probability that a maximum snow load will occur *simultaneously* with the maximum dead and live loads.

**Resistance Factors.** *Resistance factors* $\phi$ (phi) are determined from the probability of material failure as it relates to the material's quality and the consistency of its strength. These factors will differ for different types of materials. For example, concrete has smaller factors than steel because engineers have more confidence about the behavior of steel under load than they do about concrete. For example, a typical resistance factor $\phi = 0.9$ is used for a steel member in tension.

**Design Criteria.** Once the load and resistance factors $\gamma$ and $\phi$ have been specified using a code, then proper design of a structural member requires that its strength be greater than the load it supports. Thus, the LRFD criterion can be stated as

$$\phi P_n \geq \Sigma \gamma_i R_i \qquad (13)$$

Here $P_n$ is the **nominal strength** of the member, meaning the load, when applied to the member, causes it either to fail (ultimate load), or deform to a state where it is no longer serviceable or becomes unsuitable for its intended purpose. In summary then, the resistance factor $\phi$ reduces the nominal strength of the member and requires it to be equal to or greater than the applied load or combination of loads calculated using the load factors $\gamma$.

*ASD combines these uncertainties by using the factor of safety or defining the allowable stress.

## Important Point

- Design of a member for strength is based on selecting either an allowable stress or a factor of safety that will enable it to safely support its intended load (ASD), or using load and resistance factors to modify the strength of the material and the load, respectively (LRFD).

## Procedure for Analysis

When solving problems using the average normal and shear stress equations, a careful consideration should first be made as to choosing the section over which the critical stress is acting. Once this section is determined, the member must then be designed to have a sufficient area at the section to resist the stress that acts on it. This area is determined using the following steps.

Internal Loading.

- Section the member through the area and draw a free-body diagram of a segment of the member. The internal resultant force at the section is then determined using the equations of equilibrium.

Required Area.

- Provided either the allowable stress or the load and resistance factors are known or can be determined, then the required area needed to sustain the calculated load or factored load at the section is determined from $A = P/\sigma$ or $A = V/\tau$.

Appropriate factors of safety must be considered when designing cranes and cables used to transfer heavy loads.

## EXAMPLE | 12

The control arm is subjected to the loading shown in Fig. 25a. Determine to the nearest $\frac{1}{4}$ in. the required diameters of the steel pins at $A$ and $C$ if the allowable shear stress for the steel is $\tau_{\text{allow}} = 8$ ksi.

(a)

(b)

Fig. 25

3 kip

3 kip

Pin at $A$

(c)

6.082 kip

3.041 kip

3.041 kip

Pin at $C$

(d)

### SOLUTION

**Pin Forces.** A free-body diagram of the arm is shown in Fig. 25b. For equilibrium we have

$$\zeta + \Sigma M_C = 0; \quad F_{AB}(8 \text{ in.}) - 3 \text{ kip } (3 \text{ in.}) - 5 \text{ kip} \left(\tfrac{3}{5}\right)(5 \text{ in.}) = 0$$

$$F_{AB} = 3 \text{ kip}$$

$$\xrightarrow{+} \Sigma F_x = 0; \quad -3 \text{ kip} - C_x + 5 \text{ kip} \left(\tfrac{4}{5}\right) = 0 \qquad C_x = 1 \text{ kip}$$

$$+\uparrow \Sigma F_y = 0; \quad C_y - 3 \text{ kip} - 5 \text{ kip}\left(\tfrac{3}{5}\right) = 0 \qquad C_y = 6 \text{ kip}$$

The pin at $C$ resists the resultant force at $C$, which is

$$F_C = \sqrt{(1 \text{ kip})^2 + (6 \text{ kip})^2} = 6.083 \text{ kip}$$

**Pin A.** This pin is subjected to single shear, Fig. 25c, so that

$$A = \frac{V}{\tau_{\text{allow}}}; \qquad \pi\left(\frac{d_A}{2}\right)^2 = \frac{3 \text{ kip}}{8 \text{ kip/in}^2}; \qquad d_A = 0.691 \text{ in.}$$

Use $\qquad\qquad\qquad\qquad\qquad d_A = \tfrac{3}{4}$ in. $\qquad\qquad\qquad$ *Ans.*

**Pin C.** Since this pin is subjected to *double shear*, a shear force of 3.041 kip acts over its cross-sectional area *between* the arm and each supporting leaf for the pin, Fig. 25d. We have

$$A = \frac{V}{\tau_{\text{allow}}}; \qquad \pi\left(\frac{d_C}{2}\right)^2 = \frac{3.041 \text{ kip}}{8 \text{ kip/in}^2}; \qquad d_C = 0.696 \text{ in.}$$

Use $\qquad\qquad\qquad\qquad\qquad d_C = \tfrac{3}{4}$ in. $\qquad\qquad\qquad$ *Ans.*

## EXAMPLE | 13

The suspender rod is supported at its end by a fixed-connected circular disk as shown in Fig. 26a. If the rod passes through a 40-mm-diameter hole, determine the minimum required diameter of the rod and the minimum thickness of the disk needed to support the 20-kN load. The allowable normal stress for the rod is $\sigma_{allow} = 60$ MPa, and the allowable shear stress for the disk is $\tau_{allow} = 35$ MPa.

(a)                (b)

**Fig. 26**

## SOLUTION

**Diameter of Rod.** By inspection, the axial force in the rod is 20 kN. Thus the required cross-sectional area of the rod is

$$A = \frac{P}{\sigma_{allow}}; \qquad \frac{\pi}{4}d^2 = \frac{20(10^3) \text{ N}}{60(10^6) \text{ N/m}^2}$$

so that

$$d = 0.0206 \text{ m} = 20.6 \text{ mm} \qquad \qquad Ans.$$

**Thickness of Disk.** As shown on the free-body diagram in Fig. 26b, the material at the sectioned area of the disk must resist *shear stress* to prevent movement of the disk through the hole. If this shear stress is *assumed* to be uniformly distributed over the sectioned area, then, since $V = 20$ kN, we have

$$A = \frac{V}{\tau_{allow}}; \qquad 2\pi(0.02 \text{ m})(t) = \frac{20(10^3) \text{ N}}{35(10^6) \text{ N/m}^2}$$

$$t = 4.55(10^{-3})\text{m} = 4.55 \text{ mm} \qquad \qquad Ans.$$

## EXAMPLE 14

The shaft shown in Fig. 27*a* is supported by the collar at *C*, which is attached to the shaft and located on the right side of the bearing at *B*. Determine the largest value of *P* for the axial forces at *E* and *F* so that the bearing stress on the collar does not exceed an allowable stress of $(\sigma_b)_{\text{allow}} = 75$ MPa and the average normal stress in the shaft does not exceed an allowable stress of $(\sigma_t)_{\text{allow}} = 55$ MPa.

(a)                                         (b)

Axial
Force

(c)

**Fig. 27**

### SOLUTION

To solve the problem we will determine *P* for each possible failure condition. Then we will choose the *smallest* value. Why?

**Normal Stress.** Using the method of sections, the axial load within region *FE* of the shaft is 2*P*, whereas the *largest* axial force, 3*P*, occurs within region *EC*, Fig. 27*b*. The variation of the internal loading is clearly shown on the normal-force diagram, Fig. 27*c*. Since the cross-sectional area of the entire shaft is constant, region *EC* is subjected to the maximum average normal stress. Applying Eq. 11, we have

$$A = \frac{P}{\sigma_{\text{allow}}}; \qquad \pi(0.03 \text{ m})^2 = \frac{3P}{55(10^6)\text{N/m}^2}$$

$$P = 51.8 \text{ kN} \qquad\qquad\qquad Ans.$$

(d)

**Bearing Stress.** As shown on the free-body diagram in Fig. 27*d*, the collar at *C* must resist the load of 3*P*, which acts over a bearing area of $A_b = [\pi(0.04 \text{ m})^2 - \pi(0.03 \text{ m})^2] = 2.199(10^{-3})\text{m}^2$. Thus,

$$A = \frac{P}{\sigma_{\text{allow}}}; \qquad 2.199(10^{-3})\text{m}^2 = \frac{3P}{75(10^6)\text{N/m}^2}$$

$$P = 55.0 \text{ kN}$$

By comparison, the largest load that can be applied to the shaft is $P = 51.8$ kN, since any load larger than this will cause the allowable normal stress in the shaft to be exceeded.

**NOTE:** Here we have not considered a possible shear failure of the collar as in Example 13.

## EXAMPLE | 15

The 400-kg uniform bar $AB$ shown in Fig. 28a is supported by a steel rod $AC$ and a roller at $B$. If it supports a live distributed loading of 3 kN/m, determine the required diameter of the rod. The failure stress for the steel is $\sigma_{fail} = 345$ MPa. Use the LRFD method, where the resistance factor for tension is $\phi = 0.9$ and the load factors for the dead and live loads are $\gamma_D = 1.2$ and $\gamma_L = 1.6$, respectively.

(a)    (b)

**Fig. 28**

## SOLUTION

**Factored Loads.** Here the dead load is the bar's weight $D = 400(9.81)$ N $= 3.924$ kN. Therefore, the factored dead load is $1.2D = 4.709$ kN. The live load resultant is $L = (3 \text{ kN/m})(2 \text{ m}) = 6$ kN, so that the factored live load is $1.6L = 9.60$ kN.

From the free-body diagram of the bar, Fig. 28b, the factored load in the rod can now be determined.

$$\zeta + \Sigma M_B = 0; \quad 9.60 \text{ kN}(1 \text{ m}) + 4.709 \text{ kN}(1 \text{ m}) - F_{AC}(2 \text{ m}) = 0$$

$$F_{AC} = 7.154 \text{ kN}$$

**Area.** The nominal strength of the rod is determined from $P_n = \sigma_{fail} A$, and since the nominal strength is defined by the resistance factor $\phi = 0.9$, we require

$$\phi P_n \geq F_{AC}; \quad 0.9[345(10^6) \text{ N/m}^2] A_{AC} = 7.154(10^3) \text{ N}$$

$$A_{AC} = 23.04(10^{-6}) \text{ m}^2 = 23.04 \text{ mm}^2 = \frac{\pi}{4} d_{AC}^2$$

$$d_{AC} = 5.42 \text{ mm} \qquad \qquad Ans.$$

# FUNDAMENTAL PROBLEMS

**F13.** Rods *AC* and *BC* are used to suspend the 200-kg mass. If each rod is made of a material for which the average normal stress can not exceed 150 MPa, determine the minimum required diameter of each rod to the nearest mm.

**F13**

**F14.** The frame supports the loading shown. The pin at *A* has a diameter of 0.25 in. If it is subjected to double shear, determine the average shear stress in the pin.

**F14**

**F15.** Determine the maximum average shear stress developed in each 3/4-in.-diameter bolt.

**F15**

**F16.** If each of the three nails has a diameter of 4 mm and can withstand an average shear stress of 60 MPa, determine the maximum allowable force **P** that can be applied to the board.

**F16**

**F17.** The strut is glued to the horizontal member at surface *AB*. If the strut has a thickness of 25 mm and the glue can withstand an average shear stress of 600 kPa, determine the maximum force **P** that can be applied to the strut.

**F17**

**F18.** Determine the maximum average shear stress developed in the 30-mm-diameter pin.

**F18**

**F19.** If the eyebolt is made of a material having a yield stress of $\sigma_Y = 250$ MPa, determine the minimum required diameter $d$ of its shank. Apply a factor of safety F.S. = 1.5 against yielding.

**F19**

**F20.** If the bar assembly is made of a material having a yield stress of $\sigma_Y = 50$ ksi, determine the minimum required dimensions $h_1$ and $h_2$ to the nearest 1/8 in. Apply a factor of safety F.S. = 1.5 against yielding. Each bar has a thickness of 0.5 in.

**F20**

**F21.** Determine the maximum force **P** that can be applied to the rod if it is made of material having a yield stress of $\sigma_Y = 250$ MPa. Consider the possibility that failure occurs in the rod and at section $a$–$a$. Apply a factor of safety of F.S. = 2 against yielding.

**F21**

**F22.** The pin is made of a material having a failure shear stress of $\tau_{fail} = 100$ MPa. Determine the minimum required diameter of the pin to the nearest mm. Apply a factor of safety of F.S. = 2.5 against shear failure.

**F22**

**F23.** If the bolt head and the supporting bracket are made of the same material having a failure shear stress of $\tau_{fail} = 120$ MPa, determine the maximum allowable force **P** that can be applied to the bolt so that it does not pull through the plate. Apply a factor of safety of F.S. = 2.5 against shear failure.

**F23**

**F24.** Six nails are used to hold the hanger at $A$ against the column. Determine the minimum required diameter of each nail to the nearest 1/16 in. if it is made of material having $\tau_{fail} = 16$ ksi. Apply a factor of safety of F.S. = 2 against shear failure.

**F24**

55

# PROBLEMS

**69.** Member *B* is subjected to a compressive force of 800 lb. If *A* and *B* are both made of wood and are $\frac{3}{8}$ in. thick, determine to the nearest $\frac{1}{4}$ in. the smallest dimension *h* of the horizontal segment so that it does not fail in shear. The average shear stress for the segment is $\tau_{allow} = 300$ psi.

**Prob. 69**

**70.** The lever is attached to the shaft *A* using a key that has a width *d* and length of 25 mm. If the shaft is fixed and a vertical force of 200 N is applied perpendicular to the handle, determine the dimension *d* if the allowable shear stress for the key is $\tau_{allow} = 35$ MPa.

**Prob. 70**

**71.** The joint is fastened together using two bolts. Determine the required diameter of the bolts if the failure shear stress for the bolts is $\tau_{fail} = 350$ MPa. Use a factor of safety for shear of F.S. = 2.5.

**Prob. 71**

**\*72.** The truss is used to support the loading shown Determine the required cross-sectional area of member *BC* if the allowable normal strees is $\sigma_{allow} = 24$ ksi.

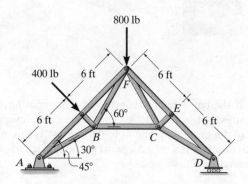

**Prob. 72**

**73.** The steel swivel bushing in the elevator control of an airplane is held in place using a nut and washer as shown in Fig. (*a*). Failure of the washer *A* can cause the push rod to separate as shown in Fig. (*b*). If the maximum average normal stress for the washer is $\sigma_{max} = 60$ ksi and the maximum average shear stress is $\tau_{max} = 21$ ksi, determine the force **F** that must be applied to the bushing that will cause this to happen. The washer is $\frac{1}{16}$ in. thick.

**Prob. 73**

**74.** Member $B$ is subjected to a compressive force of 600 lb. If $A$ and $B$ are both made of wood and are 1.5 in. thick, determine to the nearest $\frac{1}{8}$ in. the smallest dimension $a$ of the support so that the average shear stress along the blue line does not exceed $\tau_{allow} = 50$ psi. Neglect friction.

**Prob. 74**

**75.** The hangers support the joist uniformly, so that it is assumed the four nails on each hanger carry an equal portion of the load. If the joist is subjected to the loading shown, determine the average shear stress in each nail of the hanger at ends $A$ and $B$. Each nail has a diameter of 0.25 in. The hangers only support vertical loads.

**\*76.** The hangers support the joists uniformly, so that it is assumed the four nails on each hanger carry an equal portion of the load. Determine the smallest diameter of the nails at $A$ and at $B$ if the allowable stress for the nails is $\tau_{allow} = 4$ ksi. The hangers only support vertical loads.

**Probs. 75/76**

**77.** The tension member is fastened together using *two* bolts, one on each side of the member as shown. Each bolt has a diameter of 0.3 in. Determine the maximum load $P$ that can be applied to the member if the allowable shear stress for the bolts is $\tau_{allow} = 12$ ksi and the allowable average normal stress is $\sigma_{allow} = 20$ ksi.

**Prob. 77**

**78.** The 50-kg flowerpot is suspended from wires $AB$ and $BC$. If the wires have a normal failure stress of $\sigma_{fail} = 350$ MPa, determine the minimum diameter of each wire. Use a factor of safety of 2.5.

**79.** The 50-kg flowerpot is suspended from wires $AB$ and $BC$ which have diameters of 1.5 mm and 2 mm, respectively. If the wires have a normal failure stress of $\sigma_{fail} = 350$ MPa, determine the factor of safety of each wire.

**Probs. 78/79**

STRESS

**\*80.** The thrust bearing consists of a circular collar $A$ fixed to the shaft $B$. Determine the maximum axial force $P$ that can be applied to the shaft so that it does not cause the shear stress along a cylindrical surface $a$ or $b$ to exceed an allowable shear stress of $\tau_{allow} = 170$ MPa.

**82.** The steel pipe is supported on the circular base plate and concrete pedestal. If the thickness of the pipe is $t = 5$ mm and the base plate has a radius of 150 mm, determine the factors of safety against failure of the steel and concrete. The applied force is 500 kN, and the normal failure stresses for steel and concrete are $(\sigma_{fail})_{st} = 350$ MPa and $(\sigma_{fail})_{con} = 25$ MPa, respectively.

**Prob. 80**

**81.** The steel pipe is supported on the circular base plate and concrete pedestal. If the normal failure stress for the steel is $(\sigma_{fail})_{st} = 350$ MPa, determine the minimum thickness $t$ of the pipe if it supports the force of 500 kN. Use a factor of safety against failure of 1.5. Also, find the minimum radius $r$ of the base plate so that the minimum factor of safety against failure of the concrete due to bearing is 2.5. The failure bearing stress for concrete is $(\sigma_{fail})_{con} = 25$ MPa.

**Prob. 82**

**83.** The 60 mm $\times$ 60 mm oak post is supported on the pine block. If the allowable bearing stresses for these materials are $\sigma_{oak} = 43$ MPa and $\sigma_{pine} = 25$ MPa, determine the greatest load $P$ that can be supported. If a rigid bearing plate is used between these materials, determine its required area so that the maximum load $P$ can be supported. What is this load?

**Prob. 81**

**Prob. 83**

58

**\*84.** The frame is subjected to the load of 4 kN which acts on member *ABD* at *D*. Determine the required diameter of the pins at *D* and *C* if the allowable shear stress for the material is $\tau_{allow} = 40$ MPa. Pin *C* is subjected to double shear, whereas pin *D* is subjected to single shear.

**86.** The two aluminum rods support the vertical force of $P = 20$ kN. Determine their required diameters if the allowable tensile stress for the aluminum is $\sigma_{allow} = 150$ MPa.

**Prob. 84**

**Prob. 86**

**85.** The beam is made from southern pine and is supported by base plates resting on brick work. If the allowable bearing stresses for the materials are $(\sigma_{pine})_{allow} = 2.81$ ksi and $(\sigma_{brick})_{allow} = 6.70$ ksi, determine the required length of the base plates at *A* and *B* to the nearest $\frac{1}{4}$ inch in order to support the load shown. The plates are 3 in. wide.

**87.** The two aluminum rods *AB* and *AC* have diameters of 10 mm and 8 mm, respectively. Determine the largest vertical force **P** that can be supported. The allowable tensile stress for the aluminum is $\sigma_{allow} = 150$ MPa.

**Prob. 85**

**Prob. 87**

STRESS

*88. The compound wooden beam is connected together by a bolt at *B*. Assuming that the connections at *A*, *B*, *C*, and *D* exert only vertical forces on the beam, determine the required diameter of the bolt at *B* and the required outer diameter of its washers if the allowable tensile stress for the bolt is $(\sigma_t)_{allow} = 150$ MPa and the allowable bearing stress for the wood is $(\sigma_b)_{allow} = 28$ MPa. Assume that the hole in the washers has the same diameter as the bolt.

**Prob. 88**

89. Determine the required minimum thickness *t* of member *AB* and edge distance *b* of the frame if *P* = 9 kip and the factor of safety against failure is 2. The wood has a normal failure stress of $\sigma_{fail} = 6$ ksi, and shear failure stress of $\tau_{fail} = 1.5$ ksi.

**Prob. 89**

90. Determine the maximum allowable load **P** that can be safely supported by the frame if *t* = 1.25 in. and *b* = 3.5 in. The wood has a normal failure stress of $\sigma_{fail} = 6$ ksi, and shear failure stress of $\tau_{fail} = 1.5$ ksi. Use a factor of safety against failure of 2.

**Prob. 90**

91. If the allowable bearing stress for the material under the supports at *A* and *B* is $(\sigma_b)_{allow} = 1.5$ MPa determine the size of *square* bearing plates *A'* and *B'* required to support the load. Dimension the plates to the nearest mm. The reactions at the supports are vertical. Take *P* = 100 kN.

**Prob. 91**

*92. If the allowable bearing stress for the material under the supports at *A* and *B* is $(\sigma_b)_{allow} = 1.5$ MPa, determine the maximum load *P* that can be applied to the beam. The bearing plates *A'* and *B'* have square cross sections of 150 mm × 150 mm and 250 mm × 250 mm, respectively.

**Prob. 92**

60

**93.** The rods *AB* and *CD* are made of steel. Determine their smallest diameter so that they can support the dead loads shown. The beam is assumed to be pin connected at *A* and *C*. Use the LRFD method, where the resistance factor for steel in tension is $\phi = 0.9$, and the dead load factor is $\gamma_D = 1.4$. The failure stress is $\sigma_{\text{fail}} = 345\,\text{MPa}$.

**Prob. 93**

**94.** The aluminum bracket *A* is used to support the centrally applied load of 8 kip. If it has a constant thickness of 0.5 in., determine the smallest height *h* in order to prevent a shear failure. The failure shear stress is $\tau_{\text{fail}} = 23\,\text{ksi}$. Use a factor of safety for shear of F.S. = 2.5.

**Prob. 94**

**95.** The pin support *A* and roller support *B* of the bridge truss are supported on concrete abutments. If the bearing failure stress of the concrete is $(\sigma_{\text{fail}})_b = 4\,\text{ksi}$, determine the required minimum dimension of the square bearing plates at *C* and *D* to the nearest $\frac{1}{16}$ in. Apply a factor of safety of 2 against failure.

**Prob. 95**

***96.** The pin support *A* and roller support *B* of the bridge truss are supported on the concrete abutments. If the square bearing plates at *C* and *D* are 21 in. × 21 in., and the bearing failure stress for concrete is $(\sigma_{\text{fail}})_b = 4\,\text{ksi}$, determine the factor of safety against bearing failure for the concrete under each plate.

**Prob. 96**

# CHAPTER REVIEW

| | | |
|---|---|---|
| The internal loadings in a body consist of a normal force, shear force, bending moment, and torsional moment. They represent the resultants of both a normal and shear stress distribution that acts over the cross section. To obtain these resultants, use the method of sections and the equations of equilibrium. | $\Sigma F_x = 0$ <br> $\Sigma F_y = 0$ <br> $\Sigma F_z = 0$ <br> $\Sigma M_x = 0$ <br> $\Sigma M_y = 0$ <br> $\Sigma M_z = 0$ | |
| If a bar is made from homogeneous isotropic material and it is subjected to a series of external axial loads that pass through the centroid of the cross section, then a uniform normal stress distribution will act over the cross section. This average normal stress can be determined from $\sigma = P/A$, where $P$ is the internal axial load at the section. | $\sigma = \dfrac{P}{A}$ | |
| The average shear stress can be determined using $\tau_{\text{avg}} = V/A$, where $V$ is the shear force acting on the cross-sectional area $A$. This formula is often used to find the average shear stress in fasteners or in parts used for connections. | $\tau_{\text{avg}} = \dfrac{V}{A}$ | |
| The ASD method of design of any simple connection requires that the average stress along any cross section not exceed an allowable stress of $\sigma_{\text{allow}}$ or $\tau_{\text{allow}}$. These values are reported in codes and are considered safe on the basis of experiments or through experience. Sometimes a factor of safety is reported provided the ultimate stress is known. | $\text{F.S.} = \dfrac{\sigma_{\text{fail}}}{\sigma_{\text{allow}}} = \dfrac{\tau_{\text{fail}}}{\tau_{\text{allow}}}$ | |
| The LRFD method of design is used for the design of structural members. It modifies the load and the strength of the material separately, using load and resistance factors. | $\phi P_n \geq \Sigma \gamma_i R_i$ | |

# CONCEPTUAL PROBLEMS

**C1.** Here hurricane winds caused the failure of this highway sign. Assuming the wind creates a uniform pressure on the sign of 2 kPa, use reasonable dimensions for the sign and determine the resultant shear and moment at the two connections where the failure occurred.

**C3.** Here is an example of the single shear failure of a bolt. Using appropriate free-body diagrams, explain why the bolt failed along the section between the plates, and not along some intermediate section such as $a$–$a$.

C3

C1

**C4.** The vertical load on the hook is 1000 lb. Draw the appropriate free-body diagrams and determine the maximum average shear force on the pins at $A$, $B$, and $C$. Note that due to symmetry four wheels are used to support the loading on the railing.

**C2.** High-heel shoes can often do damage to soft wood or linoleum floors. Using reasonable dimensions for the heel of a regular shoe and a high-heel shoe, determine the bearing stress under each heel if the weight is transferred down only to the heel of one shoe.

C2

C4

# REVIEW PROBLEMS

**97.** The beam $AB$ is pin supported at $A$ and supported by a cable $BC$. A *separate* cable $CG$ is used to hold up the frame. If $AB$ weighs 120 lb/ft and the column $FC$ has a weight of 180 lb/ft, determine the resultant internal loadings acting on cross sections located at points $D$ and $E$. Neglect the thickness of both the beam and column in the calculation.

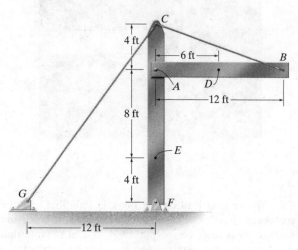

**Prob. 97**

**99.** To the nearest $\frac{1}{16}$ in., determine the required thickness of member $BC$ and the diameter of the pins at $A$ and $B$ if the allowable normal stress for member $BC$ is $\sigma_{allow} = 29$ ksi and the allowable shear stress for the pins is $\sigma_{allow} = 10$ ksi.

**Prob. 99**

**98.** The long bolt passes through the 30-mm-thick plate. If the force in the bolt shank is 8 kN, determine the average normal stress in the shank, the average shear stress along the cylindrical area of the plate defined by the section lines $a$–$a$, and the average shear stress in the bolt head along the cylindrical area defined by the section lines $b$–$b$.

**Prob. 98**

**\*100.** The circular punch $B$ exerts a force of 2 kN on the top of the plate $A$. Determine the average shear stress in the plate due to this loading.

**Prob. 100**

**101.** Determine the average punching shear stress the circular shaft creates in the metal plate through section $AC$ and $BD$. Also, what is the bearing stress developed on the surface of the plate under the shaft?

**Prob. 101**

**102.** The bearing pad consists of a 150 mm by 150 mm block of aluminum that supports a compressive load of 6 kN. Determine the average normal and shear stress acting on the plane through section $a$–$a$. Show the results on a differential volume element located on the plane.

**Prob. 102**

**103.** The yoke-and-rod connection is subjected to a tensile force of 5 kN. Determine the average normal stress in each rod and the average shear stress in the pin $A$ between the members.

**Prob. 103**

**\*104.** The cable has a specific weight $\gamma$ (weight/volume) and cross-sectional area $A$. If the sag $s$ is small, so that its length is approximately $L$ and its weight can be distributed uniformly along the horizontal axis, determine the average normal stress in the cable at its lowest point $C$.

**Prob. 104**

# Solutions and Answers for Preliminary Problems

**P1a**.

$$\zeta + \Sigma M_C = 0; \text{ get } T_B$$

$$\xrightarrow{+} \Sigma F_x = 0; \text{ get } N_A$$
$$+\uparrow \Sigma F_y = 0; \text{ get } V_A$$
$$\zeta + \Sigma M_A = 0; \text{ get } M_A$$

**P1b**.

$$\zeta + \Sigma M_B = 0; \text{ get } C_y$$

$$\xrightarrow{+} \Sigma F_x = 0; \text{ get } N_A$$
$$+\uparrow \Sigma F_y = 0; \text{ get } V_A$$
$$\zeta + \Sigma M_A = 0; \text{ get } M_A$$

**P1c**.

$$\zeta + \Sigma M_B = 0; \text{ get } C_y$$

$$\xrightarrow{+} \Sigma F_x = 0; \text{ get } N_A$$
$$+\uparrow \Sigma F_y = 0; \text{ get } V_A$$
$$\zeta + \Sigma M_A = 0; \text{ get } M_A$$

**P1d**.

$$+\nwarrow \Sigma F_y = 0; \text{ get } N_A$$
$$+\nearrow \Sigma F_x = 0; \text{ get } V_A$$
$$\zeta + \Sigma M_O = 0 \text{ or } \Sigma M_A = 0; \text{ get } M_A$$

**P1e**.

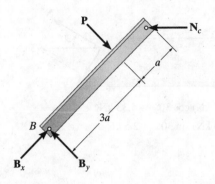

$\zeta + \Sigma M_B = 0$; get $N_C$

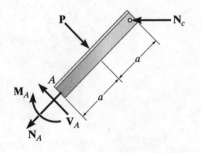

$+ \nearrow \Sigma F_x = 0$; get $N_A$
$+ \nwarrow \Sigma F_y = 0$; get $V_A$
$\zeta + \Sigma M_A = 0$; get $M_A$

**P1f**.

$+ \uparrow \Sigma F_y = 0$; get $C_y \, (= P)$
$\zeta + \Sigma M_B = 0$; get $D_x$

$+ \uparrow \Sigma F_y = 0$; get $N_A \, (= 0)$
$\xrightarrow{+} \Sigma F_x = 0$; get $V_A$
$\zeta + \Sigma M_A = 0$; get $M_A$

**P2a**.

$V_{\max} = 3$ kN

**P2b**.

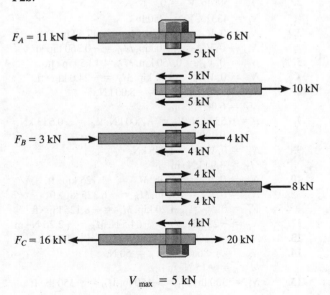

$V_{\max} = 5$ kN

**P3.**

$N_{max} = 10$ kN

**P6.**

$N = (5 \text{ kN}) \cos 30° = 4.33$ kN
$V = (5 \text{ kN}) \sin 30° = 2.5$ kN

**P4.**

$N_A = 24$ kN

**P5.**

$\Sigma M = 0; \ 20 \text{ N}(0.4 \text{ m}) - V(0.1 \text{ m}) = 0$
$V = 80$ N

# Selected Answers

**1.** $N_E = 0, V_E = -200$ lb, $M_E = -2.40$ kip·ft
**2.** $N_a = 500$ lb, $V_a = 0$,
$N_b = 433$ lb, $V_b = 250$ lb
**3.** $N_C = 0, V_C = 3.50$ kip, $M_C = -47.5$ kip·ft,
$N_D = 0, V_D = 0.240$ kip, $M_D = -0.360$ kip·ft
**5.** $N_D = 0, V_D = 0.750$ kip, $M_D = 13.5$ kip·ft,
$N_E = 0, V_E = -9.00$ kip, $M_E = -24.0$ kip·ft
**6.** $N_C = -30.0$ kN, $V_C = -8.00$ kN,
$M_C = 6.00$ kN·m
**7.** $P = 0.533$ kN, $N_C = -2.00$ kN, $V_C = -0.533$ kN,
$M_C = 0.400$ kN·m
**9.** $N_D = 0, V_D = -1.875$ kN,
$M_D = 3.94$ kN·m
**10.** $N_A = 0, V_A = 450$ lb, $M_A = -1.125$ kip·ft,
$N_B = 0, V_B = 850$ lb, $M_B = -6.325$ kip·ft,
$V_C = 0, N_C = -1.20$ kip, $M_C = -8.125$ kip·ft
**11.** $N_E = -22.5$ N, $V_E = -64.5$ N, $M_E = -2.26$ N·m
**13.** $N_{a-a} = -100$ N, $V_{a-a} = 0, M_{a-a} = -15$ N·m
**14.** $N_{b-b} = -86.6$ N, $V_{b-b} = 50$ N,
$M_{b-b} = -15$ N·m
**15.** $N_D = 300$ lb, $V_D = -150$ lb, $M_D = -150$ lb·ft

**17.** $N_{a-a} = -3.75$ kN, $V_{a-a} = 1.25$ kN,
$M_{a-a} = 3.75$ kN·m, $N_{b-b} = -1.77$ kN,
$V_{b-b} = 3.54$ kN·m, $M_{b-b} = 3.75$ kN·m
**18.** $N_C = -80$ lb, $V_C = 0, M_C = -480$ lb·in.
**19.** $N_C = 0, V_C = 4.50$ kip, $M_C = 31.5$ kip·ft
**21.** $N_{a-a} = 779$ N, $V_{a-a} = 450$ N, $M_{a-a} = 180$ N·m:
**22.** $F_{BC} = 1.39$ kN, $F_A = 1.49$ kN, $N_D = 120$ N,
$V_D = 0, M_D = 36.0$ N·m
**23.** $N_E = 0, V_E = 120$ N, $M_E = 48.0$ N·m,
Short link: $V = 0, N = 1.39$ kN, $M = 0$
**25.** $(V_B)_x = 105$ lb, $(V_B)_y = 0, (N_B)_z = 0$,
$(M_B)_x = 0, (M_B)_y = 788$ lb·ft,
$(T_B)_z = 52.5$ lb·ft
**26.** $(V_C)_x = -250$ N, $(N_C)_y = 0, (V_C)_z = -240$ N,
$(M_C)_x = -108$ N·m, $(T_C)_y = 0$,
$(M_C)_z = -138$ N·m
**27.** $(N_C)_x = 150$ N, $(V_C)_y = -260$ N,
$(V_C)_z = -520$ N, $(T_C)_x = -77.9$ N·m,
$(M_C)_y = 153$ N·m, $(M_C)_z = -99.0$ N·m
**29.** $N_B = -wr\theta \cos\theta, V_B = -wr\theta \sin\theta$,
$M_B = wr^2(\theta \cos\theta - \sin\theta)$

**31.** $\tau_{avg} = 119$ MPa

**33.** $\sigma_{avg} = \dfrac{P}{A}\sin^2\theta, \tau_{avg} = \dfrac{P}{2A}\sin 2\theta$

**34.** $\sigma_D = 13.3$ MPa (C), $\sigma_E = 70.7$ MPa (T)

**35.** $(\sigma_{a-a})_{avg} = 1.80$ ksi, $\sigma_b = 4.58$ ksi

**37.** $P = 40$ MN, $d = 2.40$ m

**38.** $\sigma = 66.7$ psi, $\tau = 115$ psi

**39.** $\sigma_{avg} = 5$ MPa

**41.** $P = 37.7$ kN

**42.** $(\tau_{avg})_A = 50.9$ MPa

**43.** $(\sigma_{avg})_{BD} = 23.6$ MPa, $(\sigma_{avg})_{CF} = 69.4$ MPa

**45.** $x = 4$ in., $y = 4$ in., $\sigma = 9.26$ psi

**46.** $\theta = 60.8°$

**47.** $m = 148$ kg

**49.** $\sigma_{AB} = 2.17$ ksi, $\sigma_{BC} = 0.819$ ksi

**50.** $\tau_{avg} = 16$ psi

**51.** $P = 4$ kip, $(\tau_{a-a})_{avg} = 250$ psi

**53.** $P = 9.05$ kN

**54.** $\sigma = 121$ psi

**55.** $\sigma_{AB} = 127$ MPa, $\sigma_{AC} = 129$ MPa

**57.** $\sigma_{avg} = \dfrac{\gamma}{3}\left[\dfrac{(z+h)^3 - h^3}{(z+h)^2}\right]$

**58.** $P = 68.3$ kN

**59.** $\sigma = 8.15$ ksi, $\tau = 5.87$ ksi

**61.** $\tau_{avg} = 1.77$ MPa

**62.** $(\tau_A)_{avg} = 3.71$ ksi

**63.** $(\tau_B)_{avg} = 1.59$ ksi

**65.** $P = 1.81$ kN

**66.** $P = 62.5$ kN

**67.** $\sigma = 5.86$ psi

**69.** Use $h = 2\dfrac{3}{4}$ in.

**70.** $d = 5.71$ mm

**71.** $d = 13.5$ mm

**73.** $F = 3.09$ kip

**74.** Use $a = 6\dfrac{1}{2}$ in.

**75.** For nails at $A$: $\tau_{avg} = 1.53$ ksi
For nails at $B$: $\tau_{avg} = 1.68$ ksi

**77.** $P = 3.26$ kip

**78.** $d_{AB} = 1.81$ mm, $d_{BC} = 2.00$ mm

**79.** $(\text{F.S.})_{AB} = 1.72, (\text{F.S.})_{BC} = 2.50$

**81.** $t = 3.47$ mm, $r = 126$ mm

**82.** $(\text{F.S.})_{st} = 2.14, (\text{F.S.})_{con} = 3.53$

**83.** $P = 90$ kN, $A = 6.19(10^{-3})$ m$^2$, $P_{max} = 155$ kN

**85.** Use $l_A = \dfrac{1}{2}$ in., $l_B = \dfrac{3}{4}$ in.

**86.** $d_{AB} = 15.5$ mm, $d_{AC} = 13.0$ mm

**87.** $P = 7.54$ kN

**89.** $t = 1$ in., $b = 3.46$ in.

**90.** $P = 9.09$ kip

**91.** $a_{A'} = 130$ mm, $a_{B'} = 300$ mm

**93.** $d_{AB} = 6.90$ mm, $d_{CD} = 6.20$ mm

**94.** $h = 1.74$ in.

**95.** Use $a_D = 19\dfrac{5}{8}$ in., $a_C = 21\dfrac{1}{16}$ in.

**97.** $N_D = -2.16$ kip, $V_D = 0$, $M_D = 2.16$ kip·ft,
$V_E = 0.540$ kip, $N_E = 4.32$ kip, $M_E = 2.16$ kip·ft

**98.** $\sigma_s = 208$ MPa, $(\tau_{avg})_a = 4.72$ MPa,
$(\tau_{avg})_b = 45.5$ MPa

**99.** Use $t = \dfrac{1}{4}$ in., $d_A = 1\dfrac{1}{8}$ in., $d_B = \dfrac{13}{16}$ in.

**101.** $\tau_{avg} = 25.5$ MPa, $\sigma_b = 4.72$ MPa

**102.** $\sigma_{a-a} = 200$ kPa, $\tau_{a-a} = 115$ kPa

**103.** $\sigma_{40} = 3.98$ MPa, $\sigma_{30} = 7.07$ MPa,
$\tau_{avg} = 5.09$ MPa

# Fundamental Problems Partial Solutions and Answers

**F1**   Entire beam:

$\zeta + \Sigma M_B = 0;$    $60 - 10(2) - A_y(2) = 0$    $A_y = 20$ kN

Left segment:

$\overset{+}{\to} \Sigma F_x = 0;$    $N_C = 0$    *Ans.*

$+\uparrow \Sigma F_y = 0;$    $20 - V_C = 0$    $V_C = 20$ kN    *Ans.*

$\zeta + \Sigma M_C = 0;$    $M_C + 60 - 20(1) = 0$    $M_C = -40$ kN$\cdot$m    *Ans.*

**F2**   Entire beam:

$\zeta + \Sigma M_A = 0;$    $B_y(3) - 100(1.5)(0.75) - 200(1.5)(2.25) = 0$
$B_y = 262.5$ N

Right segment:

$\overset{+}{\to} \Sigma F_x = 0;$    $N_C = 0$    *Ans.*

$+\uparrow \Sigma F_y = 0;$    $V_C + 262.5 - 200(1.5) = 0$    $V_C = 37.5$ N    *Ans.*

$\zeta + \Sigma M_C = 0;$    $262.5(1.5) - 200(1.5)(0.75) - M_C = 0$    $M_C = 169$ N$\cdot$m    *Ans.*

**F3**   Entire beam:

$\overset{+}{\to} \Sigma F_x = 0;$    $B_x = 0$

$\zeta + \Sigma M_A = 0;$    $20(2)(1) - B_y(4) = 0$    $B_y = 10$ kN

Right segment:

$\overset{+}{\to} \Sigma F_x = 0;$    $N_C = 0$    *Ans.*

$+\uparrow \Sigma F_y = 0;$    $V_C - 10 = 0$    $V_C = 10$ kN    *Ans.*

$\zeta + \Sigma M_C = 0;$    $-M_C - 10(2) = 0$    $M_C = -20$ kN$\cdot$m    *Ans.*

**F4**   Entire beam:

$\zeta + \Sigma M_B = 0;$    $\dfrac{1}{2}(10)(3)(2) + 10(3)(4.5) - A_y(6) = 0$    $A_y = 27.5$ kN

Left segment:

$\overset{+}{\to} \Sigma F_x = 0;$    $N_C = 0$    *Ans.*

$+\uparrow \Sigma F_y = 0;$    $27.5 - 10(3) - V_C = 0$    $V_C = -2.5$ kN    *Ans.*

$\zeta + \Sigma M_C = 0;$    $M_C + 10(3)(1.5) - 27.5(3) = 0$    $M_C = 37.5$ kN$\cdot$m    *Ans.*

**F5**   Entire beam:

$\overset{+}{\to} \Sigma F_x = 0;$    $A_x = 0$

$\zeta + \Sigma M_B = 0;$    $300(6)(3) - \dfrac{1}{2}(300)(3)(1) - A_y(6) = 0$    $A_y = 825$ lb

Left segment:

$\overset{+}{\to} \Sigma F_x = 0;$    $N_C = 0$    *Ans.*

$+\uparrow \Sigma F_y = 0;$    $825 - 300(3) - V_C = 0$    $V_C = -75$ lb    *Ans.*

$\zeta + \Sigma M_C = 0;$    $M_C + 300(3)(1.5) - 825(3) = 0$    $M_C = 1125$ lb$\cdot$ft    *Ans.*

**F6.**   Entire beam:

$\zeta + \Sigma M_A = 0;$    $F_{BD}\left(\dfrac{3}{5}\right)(4) - 5(6)(3) = 0$    $F_{BD} = 37.5$ kN

$\xrightarrow{+} \Sigma F_x = 0;$  $\qquad$ $37.5\left(\dfrac{4}{5}\right) - A_x = 0$ $\qquad\qquad$ $A_x = 30$ kN

$+\uparrow \Sigma F_y = 0;$  $\qquad$ $A_y + 37.5\left(\dfrac{3}{5}\right) - 5(6) = 0$ $\qquad$ $A_y = 7.5$ kN

Left segment:

$\xrightarrow{+} \Sigma F_x = 0;$  $\qquad$ $N_C - 30 = 0$ $\qquad\qquad$ $N_C = 30$ kN $\qquad$ *Ans.*

$+\uparrow \Sigma F_y = 0;$  $\qquad$ $7.5 - 5(2) - V_C = 0$ $\qquad$ $V_C = -2.5$ kN $\qquad$ *Ans.*

$\zeta + \Sigma M_C = 0;$  $\qquad$ $M_C + 5(2)(1) - 7.5(2) = 0$ $\qquad$ $M_C = 5$ kN·m $\qquad$ *Ans.*

$\sigma_C = \dfrac{N_C}{A_C} = \dfrac{2}{0.0625\pi} = 10.2$ ksi (T) $\qquad\qquad$ *Ans.*

**F7** Beam:

$\Sigma M_A = 0;\ T_{CD} = 2w$

$\Sigma F_y = 0;\ T_{AB} = w$

Rod *AB*:

$\sigma = \dfrac{P}{A};\ 300(10^3) = \dfrac{w}{10};$

$w = 3$ N/m

Rod *CD*:

$\sigma = \dfrac{P}{A};\ 300(10^3) = \dfrac{2w}{15};$

$w = 2.25$ N/m $\qquad\qquad$ *Ans.*

**F8** $A = \pi(0.1^2 - 0.08^2) = 3.6(10^{-3})\pi$ m$^2$

$\sigma_{\text{avg}} = \dfrac{P}{A} = \dfrac{300(10^3)}{3.6(10^{-3})\pi} = 26.5$ MPa $\qquad$ *Ans.*

**F9** $A = 3[4(1)] = 12$ in$^2$

$\sigma_{\text{avg}} = \dfrac{P}{A} = \dfrac{15}{12} = 1.25$ ksi $\qquad\qquad$ *Ans.*

**F10** Consider the cross section to be a rectangle and two triangles.

$\bar{y} = \dfrac{\Sigma\ \tilde{y}A}{\Sigma A} = \dfrac{0.15[(0.3)(0.12)] + (0.1)\left[\dfrac{1}{2}(0.16)(0.3)\right]}{0.3(0.12) + \dfrac{1}{2}(0.16)(0.3)}$

$= 0.13$ m $= 130$ mm $\qquad\qquad$ *Ans.*

$\sigma_{\text{avg}} = \dfrac{P}{A} = \dfrac{600(10^3)}{0.06} = 10$ MPa $\qquad$ *Ans.*

**F11**

$A_A = A_C = \dfrac{\pi}{4}(0.5^2) = 0.0625\pi$ in$^2$, $A_B = \dfrac{\pi}{4}(1^2) = 0.25\pi$ in$^2$

$\sigma_A = \dfrac{N_A}{A_A} = \dfrac{3}{0.0625\pi} = 15.3$ ksi (T) $\qquad$ *Ans.*

$\sigma_B = \dfrac{N_B}{A_B} = \dfrac{-6}{0.25\pi} = -7.64$ ksi $= 7.64$ ksi (C) $\qquad$ *Ans.*

**F12**

$F_{AD} = 50(9.81)$ N $= 490.5$ N

$+\uparrow \Sigma F_y = 0;$ $\qquad$ $F_{AC}\left(\dfrac{3}{5}\right) - 490.5 = 0$ $\qquad$ $F_{AC} = 817.5$ N

$\xrightarrow{+} \Sigma F_x = 0;$ $\qquad$ $817.5\left(\dfrac{4}{5}\right) - F_{AB} = 0$ $\qquad$ $F_{AB} = 654$ N

$A_{AB} = \dfrac{\pi}{4}(0.008^2) = 16(10^{-6})\pi$ m$^2$

$(\sigma_{AB})_{\text{avg}} = \dfrac{F_{AB}}{A_{AB}} = \dfrac{654}{16(10^{-6})\pi} = 13.0$ MPa $\qquad$ *Ans.*

**F13** Ring *C*:

$+\uparrow \Sigma F_y = 0;$ $\qquad$ $2F\cos 60° - 200(9.81) = 0$ $\quad F = 1962$ N

$(\sigma_{\text{allow}})_{\text{avg}} = \dfrac{F}{A};$ $\qquad$ $150(10^6) = \dfrac{1962}{\dfrac{\pi}{4}d^2}$

$d = 0.00408$ m $= 4.08$ mm

Use $d = 5$ mm $\qquad\qquad$ *Ans.*

**F14** Entire frame:

$\Sigma F_y = 0;\ A_y = 600$ lb

$\Sigma M_B = 0;\ A_x = 800$ lb

$F_A = \sqrt{(600)^2 + (800)^2} = 1000$ lb

$(\tau_A)_{\text{avg}} = \dfrac{F_A/2}{A} = \dfrac{1000/2}{\dfrac{\pi}{4}(0.25)^2} = 10.2$ ksi $\qquad$ *Ans.*

**F15** Double shear:

$\Sigma F_x = 0;$ $\quad$ $4V - 10 = 0$ $\quad V = 2.5$ kip

$A = \dfrac{\pi}{4}\left(\dfrac{3}{4}\right)^2 = 0.140625\pi$ in$^2$

$\tau_{\text{avg}} = \dfrac{V}{A} = \dfrac{2.5}{0.140625\pi} = 5.66$ ksi $\qquad$ *Ans.*

**F16** Single shear:

$\Sigma F_x = 0;$ $\qquad$ $P - 3V = 0$ $\qquad$ $V = \dfrac{P}{3}$

**71**

$$A = \frac{\pi}{4}(0.004^2) = 4(10^{-6})\pi \text{ m}^2$$

$$(\tau_{avg})_{allow} = \frac{V}{A}; \quad 60(10^6) = \frac{\frac{P}{3}}{4(10^{-6})\pi}$$

$$P = 2.262(10^3) \text{ N} = 2.26 \text{ kN} \qquad Ans.$$

**F17** $\xrightarrow{+} \Sigma F_x = 0; \quad V - P\cos 60° = 0 \qquad V = 0.5P$

$$A = \left(\frac{0.05}{\sin 60°}\right)(0.025) = 1.4434(10^{-3}) \text{ m}^2$$

$$(\tau_{avg})_{allow} = \frac{V}{A}; \quad 600(10^3) = \frac{0.5P}{1.4434(10^{-3})}$$

$$P = 1.732(10^3) \text{ N} = 1.73 \text{ kN} \qquad Ans.$$

**F18** The resultant force on the pin is
$$F = \sqrt{30^2 + 40^2} = 50 \text{ kN}.$$

Here we have double shear:

$$V = \frac{F}{2} = \frac{50}{2} = 25 \text{ kN}$$

$$A = \frac{\pi}{4}(0.03^2) = 0.225(10^{-3})\pi \text{ m}^2$$

$$\tau_{avg} = \frac{V}{A} = \frac{25(10^3)}{0.225(10^{-3})\pi} = 35.4 \text{ MPa} \qquad Ans.$$

**F19** $\xrightarrow{+} \Sigma F_x = 0; \quad 30 - N = 0 \qquad N = 30 \text{ kN}$

$$\sigma_{allow} = \frac{\sigma_Y}{F.S.} = \frac{250}{1.5} = 166.67 \text{ MPa}$$

$$\sigma_{allow} = \frac{N}{A}; \quad 166.67(10^6) = \frac{30(10^3)}{\frac{\pi}{4}d^2}$$

$$d = 15.14 \text{ mm}$$

Use $d = 16$ mm $\qquad Ans.$

**F20.**

$\xrightarrow{+} \Sigma F_x = 0; \quad N_{AB} - 30 = 0 \qquad N_{AB} = 30 \text{ kip}$

$\xrightarrow{+} \Sigma F_x = 0; \quad N_{BC} - 15 - 15 - 30 = 0 \qquad N_{BC} = 60 \text{ kip}$

$$\sigma_{allow} = \frac{\sigma_Y}{F.S.} = \frac{50}{1.5} = 33.33 \text{ ksi}$$

Segment $AB$:

$$\sigma_{allow} = \frac{N_{AB}}{A_{AB}}; \quad 33.33 = \frac{30}{h_1(0.5)}$$
$$h_1 = 1.8 \text{ in.}$$

Segment $BC$:

$$\sigma_{allow} = \frac{N_{BC}}{A_{BC}}; \quad 33.33 = \frac{60}{h_2(0.5)}$$
$$h_2 = 3.6 \text{ in.}$$

Use $h_1 = 1\frac{7}{8}$ in. and $h_2 = 3\frac{5}{8}$ in. $\qquad Ans.$

**F21** $\qquad N = P$

$$\sigma_{allow} = \frac{\sigma_Y}{F.S.} = \frac{250}{2} = 125 \text{ MPa}$$

$$A_r = \frac{\pi}{4}(0.04^2) = 1.2566(10^{-3}) \text{ m}^2$$

$$A_{a-a} = 2(0.06 - 0.03)(0.05) = 3(10^{-3}) \text{ m}^2$$

The rod will fail first.

$$\sigma_{allow} = \frac{N}{A_r}; \quad 125(10^6) = \frac{P}{1.2566(10^{-3})}$$

$$P = 157.08(10^3) \text{ N} = 157 \text{ kN} \qquad Ans.$$

**F22** $\xrightarrow{+} \Sigma F_x = 0; \quad 80 - 2V = 0 \qquad V = 40 \text{ kN}$

$$\tau_{allow} = \frac{\tau_{fail}}{F.S.} = \frac{100}{2.5} = 40 \text{ MPa}$$

$$\tau_{allow} = \frac{V}{A}; \quad 40(10^6) = \frac{40(10^3)}{\frac{\pi}{4}d^2}$$

$$d = 0.03568 \text{ m} = 35.68 \text{ mm}$$

Use $d = 36$ mm $\qquad Ans.$

**F23** $\qquad V = P$

$$\tau_{allow} = \frac{\tau_{fail}}{F.S.} = \frac{120}{2.5} = 48 \text{ MPa}$$

Area of shear plane for bolt head and plate:
$$A_b = \pi dt = \pi(0.04)(0.075) = 0.003\pi \text{ m}^2$$
$$A_p = \pi dt = \pi(0.08)(0.03) = 0.0024\pi \text{ m}^2$$

Since the area of shear plane for the plate is smaller,

$$\tau_{allow} = \frac{V}{A_p}; \quad 48(10^6) = \frac{P}{0.0024\pi}$$

$$P = 361.91(10^3) \text{ N} = 362 \text{ kN} \qquad Ans.$$

**F24**

$$\zeta + \Sigma M_B = 0; \quad \frac{1}{2}(300)(9)(6) - 6V(9) = 0 \qquad V = 150 \text{ lb}$$

$$\tau_{allow} = \frac{\tau_{fail}}{F.S.} = \frac{16}{2} = 8 \text{ ksi}$$

$$\tau_{allow} = \frac{V}{A}; \quad 8(10^3) = \frac{150}{\frac{\pi}{4}d^2}$$

$$d = 0.1545 \text{ in.}$$

Use $d = \frac{3}{16}$ in. $\qquad Ans.$

# Strain

From Chapter 2 of *Mechanics of Materials*, Ninth Edition. R. C. Hibbeler. Copyright © 2014 by Pearson Education, Inc. Published by Pearson Prentice Hall. All rights reserved.

This specimen exhibits noticeable strain before it fractured. Measurement of this strain is necessary so that the stress in the material can be determined in cases of complicated loadings.

# Strain

## 1 Deformation

Whenever a force is applied to a body, it will tend to change the body's shape and size. These changes are referred to as *deformation*, and they may be either highly visible or practically unnoticeable. For example, a rubber band will undergo a very large deformation when stretched, whereas only slight deformations of structural members occur when a building is occupied by people walking about. Deformation of a body can also occur when the temperature of the body is changed. A typical example is the thermal expansion or contraction of a roof caused by the weather.

In a general sense, the deformation of a body will not be uniform throughout its volume, and so the change in geometry of any line segment within the body may vary substantially along its length. Hence, to study deformational changes in a more uniform manner, we will consider line segments that are very short and located in the neighborhood of a point. Realize, however, that these changes will also depend on the orientation of the line segment at the point. For example, a line segment may elongate if it is oriented in one direction, whereas it may contract if it is oriented in another direction.

Note the before and after positions of three different line segments on this rubber membrane which is subjected to tension. The vertical line is lengthened, the horizontal line is shortened, and the inclined line changes its length and rotates.

## 2 Strain

In order to describe the deformation of a body by changes in length of line segments and the changes in the angles between them, we will develop the concept of strain. Strain is actually measured by experiments, and once the strain is obtained, it can then be shown how it can be related to the stress acting within the body.

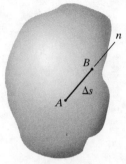

Undeformed body
(a)

**Normal Strain.** If we define the normal strain as the change in length of a line per unit length, then we will not have to specify the *actual length* of any particular line segment. Consider, for example, the line $AB$, which is contained within the undeformed body shown in Fig. 1a. This line lies along the $n$ axis and has an original length of $\Delta s$. After deformation, points $A$ and $B$ are displaced to $A'$ and $B'$, and the line becomes a curve having a length of $\Delta s'$, Fig. 1b. The change in length of the line is therefore $\Delta s' - \Delta s$. If we define the *average normal strain* using the symbol $\epsilon_{avg}$ (epsilon), then

$$\epsilon_{avg} = \frac{\Delta s' - \Delta s}{\Delta s} \qquad (1)$$

Deformed body
(b)

**Fig. 1**

As point $B$ is chosen closer and closer to point $A$, the length of the line will become shorter and shorter, such that $\Delta s \to 0$. Also, this causes $B'$ to approach $A'$, such that $\Delta s' \to 0$. Consequently, in the limit the normal strain at *point A* and in the direction of $n$ is

$$\epsilon = \lim_{B \to A \text{ along } n} \frac{\Delta s' - \Delta s}{\Delta s} \qquad (2)$$

Hence, when $\epsilon$ (or $\epsilon_{avg}$) is positive the initial line will elongate, whereas if $\epsilon$ is negative the line contracts.

Note that normal strain is a *dimensionless quantity*, since it is a ratio of two lengths. Although this is the case, it is sometimes stated in terms of a ratio of length units. If the SI system is used, then the basic unit for length is the meter (m). Ordinarily, for most engineering applications $\epsilon$ will be very small, so measurements of strain are in micrometers per meter ($\mu$m/m), where $1\ \mu$m $= 10^{-6}$ m. In the Foot-Pound-Second system, strain is often stated in units of inches per inch (in./in.). Sometimes for experimental work, strain is expressed as a percent (e.g., $0.001$ m/m $= 0.1\%$). As an example, a normal strain of $480(10^{-6})$ can be reported as $480(10^{-6})$ in./in., $480\ \mu$m/m, or $0.0480\%$. Also, one can state this answer as simply $480\ \mu$ ($480$ "micros").

**Shear Strain.** Deformations not only cause line segments to elongate or contract, but they also cause them to change direction. If we select two line segments that are originally perpendicular to one another, then the change in angle that occurs between them is referred to as *shear strain*. This angle is denoted by $\gamma$ (gamma) and is always measured in radians (rad), which are dimensionless. For example, consider the line segments $AB$ and $AC$ originating from the same point $A$ in a body, and directed along the perpendicular $n$ and $t$ axes, Fig. 2a. After deformation, the ends of both lines are displaced, and the lines themselves become curves, such that the angle between them at $A$ is $\theta'$, Fig. 2b. Hence the shear strain at point $A$ associated with the $n$ and $t$ axes becomes

$$\gamma_{nt} = \frac{\pi}{2} - \lim_{\substack{B \to A \text{ along } n \\ C \to A \text{ along } t}} \theta' \tag{3}$$

Notice that if $\theta'$ is smaller than $\pi/2$ the shear strain is positive, whereas if $\theta'$ is larger than $\pi/2$ the shear strain is negative.

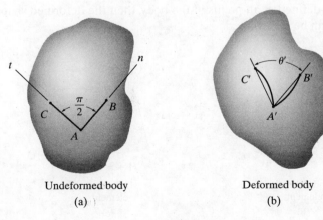

Undeformed body
(a)

Deformed body
(b)

**Fig. 2**

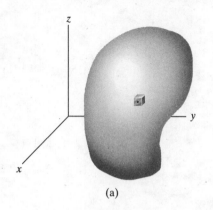

(a)

## Cartesian Strain Components.

Using the definitions of normal and shear strain, we will now show how these components can be used to describe the deformation of the body in Fig. 3a. To do so, imagine the body is subdivided into small elements such as the one shown in Figs. 2–3a and 3b. This element is rectangular, has undeformed dimensions $\Delta x$, $\Delta y$, and $\Delta z$, and is located in the neighborhood of a point in the body, Fig. 3a. If the element's dimensions are very small, then its deformed shape will be a parallelepiped, Fig. 3c, since very small line segments will remain approximately straight after the body is deformed. In order to achieve this deformed shape, we will first consider how the normal strain changes the lengths of the sides of the rectangular element, and then how the shear strain changes the angles of each side. For example, $\Delta x$ elongates $\epsilon_x \Delta x$, so its new length is $\Delta x + \epsilon_x \Delta x$. Therefore, the approximate lengths of the three sides of the parallelepiped are

$$(1 + \epsilon_x)\,\Delta x \qquad (1 + \epsilon_y)\,\Delta y \qquad (1 + \epsilon_z)\,\Delta z$$

And the approximate angles between these sides are

$$\frac{\pi}{2} - \gamma_{xy} \qquad \frac{\pi}{2} - \gamma_{yz} \qquad \frac{\pi}{2} - \gamma_{xz}$$

Notice that the **normal strains cause a change in volume** of the element, whereas the **shear strains cause a change in its shape**. Of course, both of these effects occur simultaneously during the deformation.

In summary, then, the *state of strain* at a point in a body requires specifying three normal strains, $\epsilon_x$, $\epsilon_y$, $\epsilon_z$, and three shear strains, $\gamma_{xy}$, $\gamma_{yz}$, $\gamma_{xz}$. These strains completely describe the deformation of a rectangular volume element of material located at the point and oriented so that its sides are originally parallel to the $x$, $y$, $z$ axes. Provided these strains are defined at all points in the body, then the deformed shape of the body can be determined.

Undeformed element

(b)

Deformed element

(c)

Fig. 3

**Small Strain Analysis.** Most engineering design involves applications for which only *small deformations* are allowed. In this text, therefore, we will assume that the deformations that take place within a body are almost infinitesimal. In particular, the *normal strains* occurring within the material are *very small* compared to 1, so that $\epsilon \ll 1$. This assumption has wide practical application in engineering, and it is often referred to as a *small strain analysis*. It can be used, for example, to approximate $\sin \theta = \theta$, $\cos \theta = 1$, and $\tan \theta = \theta$, provided $\theta$ is very small.

The rubber bearing support under this concrete bridge girder is subjected to both normal and shear strain. The normal strain is caused by the weight and bridge loads on the girder, and the shear strain is caused by the horizontal movement of the girder due to temperature changes.

## Important Points

- Loads will cause all material bodies to deform and, as a result, points in a body will undergo *displacements or changes in position*.

- *Normal strain* is a measure per unit length of the elongation or contraction of a small line segment in the body, whereas *shear strain* is a measure of the change in angle that occurs between two small line segments that are originally perpendicular to one another.

- The state of strain at a point is characterized by six strain components: three normal strains $\epsilon_x$, $\epsilon_y$, $\epsilon_z$ and three shear strains $\gamma_{xy}$, $\gamma_{yz}$, $\gamma_{xz}$. These components depend upon the original orientation of the line segments and their location in the body.

- Strain is the geometrical quantity that is measured using experimental techniques. Once obtained, the stress in the body can then be determined from material property relations.

- Most engineering materials undergo very small deformations, and so the normal strain $\epsilon \ll 1$. This assumption of "small strain analysis" allows the calculations for normal strain to be simplified, since first-order approximations can be made about their size.

## EXAMPLE 1

The slender rod shown in Fig. 4 is subjected to an increase of temperature along its axis, which creates a normal strain in the rod of $\epsilon_z = 40(10^{-3})z^{1/2}$, where $z$ is measured in meters. Determine (a) the displacement of the end $B$ of the rod due to the temperature increase, and (b) the average normal strain in the rod.

**Fig. 4**

### SOLUTION

**Part (a).**  Since the normal strain is reported at each point along the rod, a differential segment $dz$, located at position $z$, Fig. 4, has a deformed length that can be determined from Eq. 1; that is,

$$dz' = dz + \epsilon_z\,dz$$
$$dz' = \left[1 + 40(10^{-3})z^{1/2}\right]dz$$

The sum of these segments along the axis yields the *deformed length* of the rod, i.e.,

$$z' = \int_0^{0.2\ \text{m}} \left[1 + 40(10^{-3})z^{1/2}\right]dz$$
$$= \left[z + 40(10^{-3})\tfrac{2}{3}z^{3/2}\right]\Big|_0^{0.2\ \text{m}}$$
$$= 0.20239\ \text{m}$$

The displacement of the end of the rod is therefore

$$\Delta_B = 0.20239\ \text{m} - 0.2\ \text{m} = 0.00239\ \text{m} = 2.39\ \text{mm} \downarrow \quad Ans.$$

**Part (b).**  The average normal strain in the rod is determined from Eq. 1, which assumes that the rod or "line segment" has an original length of 200 mm and a change in length of 2.39 mm. Hence,

$$\epsilon_{\text{avg}} = \frac{\Delta s' - \Delta s}{\Delta s} = \frac{2.39\ \text{mm}}{200\ \text{mm}} = 0.0119\ \text{mm/mm} \quad Ans.$$

This strain is called a thermal strain, caused by temperature, *not* by any load.

## EXAMPLE | 2

When force **P** is applied to the rigid lever arm $ABC$ in Fig. 5a, the arm rotates counterclockwise about pin $A$ through an angle of 0.05°. Determine the normal strain developed in wire $BD$.

### SOLUTION I

**Geometry.** The orientation of the lever arm after it rotates about point $A$ is shown in Fig. 5b. From the geometry of this figure,

$$\alpha = \tan^{-1}\left(\frac{400 \text{ mm}}{300 \text{ mm}}\right) = 53.1301°$$

Then

$$\phi = 90° - \alpha + 0.05° = 90° - 53.1301° + 0.05° = 36.92°$$

For triangle $ABD$ the Pythagorean theorem gives

$$L_{AD} = \sqrt{(300 \text{ mm})^2 + (400 \text{ mm})^2} = 500 \text{ mm}$$

Using this result and applying the law of cosines to triangle $AB'D$,

$$L_{B'D} = \sqrt{L_{AD}^2 + L_{AB'}^2 - 2(L_{AD})(L_{AB'})\cos\phi}$$

$$= \sqrt{(500 \text{ mm})^2 + (400 \text{ mm})^2 - 2(500 \text{ mm})(400 \text{ mm})\cos 36.92°}$$

$$= 300.3491 \text{ mm}$$

**Normal Strain.**

$$\epsilon_{BD} = \frac{L_{B'D} - L_{BD}}{L_{BD}}$$

$$= \frac{300.3491 \text{ mm} - 300 \text{ mm}}{300 \text{ mm}} = 0.00116 \text{ mm/mm} \qquad Ans.$$

(a)

(b)

**Fig. 5**

### SOLUTION II

Since the strain is small, this same result can be obtained by approximating the elongation of wire $BD$ as $\Delta L_{BD}$, shown in Fig. 5b. Here,

$$\Delta L_{BD} = \theta L_{AB} = \left[\left(\frac{0.05°}{180°}\right)(\pi \text{ rad})\right](400 \text{ mm}) = 0.3491 \text{ mm}$$

Therefore,

$$\epsilon_{BD} = \frac{\Delta L_{BD}}{L_{BD}} = \frac{0.3491 \text{ mm}}{300 \text{ mm}} = 0.00116 \text{ mm/mm} \quad Ans.$$

## EXAMPLE 3

(a)

(b)

**Fig. 6**

The plate shown in Fig. 6a is fixed connected along AB and held in the horizontal guides at its top and bottom, AD and BC. If its right side CD is given a uniform horizontal displacement of 2 mm, determine (a) the average normal strain along the diagonal AC, and (b) the shear strain at E relative to the x, y axes.

### SOLUTION

**Part (a).** When the plate is deformed, the diagonal AC becomes AC', Fig. 6b. The lengths of diagonals AC and AC' can be found from the Pythagorean theorem. We have

$$AC = \sqrt{(0.150 \text{ m})^2 + (0.150 \text{ m})^2} = 0.21213 \text{ m}$$

$$AC' = \sqrt{(0.150 \text{ m})^2 + (0.152 \text{ m})^2} = 0.21355 \text{ m}$$

Therefore the average normal strain along the diagonal is

$$(\epsilon_{AC})_{\text{avg}} = \frac{AC' - AC}{AC} = \frac{0.21355 \text{ m} - 0.21213 \text{ m}}{0.21213 \text{ m}}$$

$$= 0.00669 \text{ mm/mm} \qquad \text{Ans.}$$

**Part (b).** To find the shear strain at E relative to the x and y axes, it is first necessary to find the angle $\theta'$ after deformation, Fig. 6b. We have

$$\tan\left(\frac{\theta'}{2}\right) = \frac{76 \text{ mm}}{75 \text{ mm}}$$

$$\theta' = 90.759° = \left(\frac{\pi}{180°}\right)(90.759°) = 1.58404 \text{ rad}$$

Applying Eq. 3, the shear strain at E is therefore

$$\gamma_{xy} = \frac{\pi}{2} - 1.58404 \text{ rad} = -0.0132 \text{ rad} \qquad \text{Ans.}$$

The *negative sign* indicates that the angle $\theta'$ is *greater than* 90°.

**NOTE:** If the x and y axes were horizontal and vertical at point E, then the 90° angle between these axes would not change due to the deformation, and so $\gamma_{xy} = 0$ at point E.

# PRELIMINARY PROBLEMS

**P1.** A loading causes the member to deform into the dashed shape. Explain how to determine the normal strains $\epsilon_{CD}$ and $\epsilon_{AB}$. The displacement $\Delta$ and the lettered dimensions are known.

(a)                                    **P1**

**P2.** A loading causes the member to deform into the dashed shape. Explain how to determine the normal strains $\epsilon_{CD}$ and $\epsilon_{AB}$. The displacement $\Delta$ and the lettered dimensions are known.

(b)

**P2**

**P3.** A loading causes the wires to elongate into the dashed shape. Explain how to determine the normal strain $\epsilon_{AB}$ in wire $AB$. The displacement $B$ and the distances between all lettered points are known.

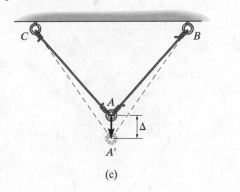

(c)                                    **P3**

**P4.** A loading causes the block to deform into the dashed shape. Explain how to determine the strains $\epsilon_{AB}$, $\epsilon_{AC}$, $\epsilon_{BC}$, $(\gamma_A)_{xy}$. The angles and distances between all lettered points are known.

(d)

**P4**

**P5.** A loading causes the block to deform into the dashed shape. Explain how to determine the strains $(\gamma_A)_{xy}$, $(\gamma_B)_{xy}$. The angles and distances between all lettered points are known.

(e)

**P5**

# FUNDAMENTAL PROBLEMS

**F1.** When force **P** is applied to the rigid arm *ABC,* point *B* displaces vertically downward through a distance of 0.2 mm. Determine the normal strain developed in wire *CD.*

**F1**

**F2.** If the applied force **P** causes the rigid arm *ABC* to rotate clockwise about pin *A* through an angle of 0.02°, determine the normal strain developed in wires *BD* and *CE.*

**F2**

**F3.** The rectangular plate is deformed into the shape of a parallelogram shown by the dashed line. Determine the average shear strain at corner *A* with respect to the *x* and *y* axes.

**F3**

**F4.** The triangular plate is deformed into the shape shown by the dashed line. Determine the normal strain developed along edge *BC* and the average shear strain at corner *A* with respect to the *x* and *y* axes.

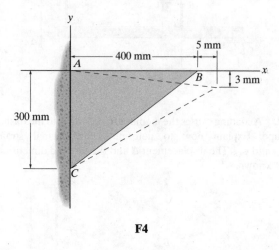

**F4**

**F5.** The square plate is deformed into the shape shown by the dashed line. Determine the average normal strain along diagonal *AC* and the shear strain of point *E* with respect to the *x* and *y* axes.

**F5**

# PROBLEMS

**1.** An air-filled rubber ball has a diameter of 6 in. If the air pressure within it is increased until the ball's diameter becomes 7 in., determine the average normal strain in the rubber.

**2.** A thin strip of rubber has an unstretched length of 15 in. If it is stretched around a pipe having an outer diameter of 5 in., determine the average normal strain in the strip.

**3.** The rigid beam is supported by a pin at $A$ and wires $BD$ and $CE$. If the load **P** on the beam causes the end $C$ to be displaced 10 mm downward, determine the normal strain developed in wires $CE$ and $BD$.

**Prob. 3**

**\*4.** The force applied at the handle of the rigid lever causes the lever to rotate clockwise about the pin $B$ through an angle of 2°. Determine the average normal strain developed in each wire. The wires are unstretched when the lever is in the horizontal position.

**Prob. 4**

**5.** The two wires are connected together at $A$. If the force **P** causes point $A$ to be displaced horizontally 2 mm, determine the normal strain developed in each wire.

**Prob. 5**

**6.** The rubber band of unstretched length $2r_0$ is forced down the frustum of the cone. Determine the average normal strain in the band as a function of $z$.

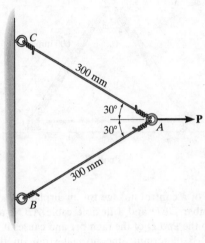

**Prob. 6**

**7.** The pin-connected rigid rods $AB$ and $BC$ are inclined at $\theta = 30°$ when they are unloaded. When the force **P** is applied $\theta$ becomes $30.2°$. Determine the average normal strain developed in wire $AC$.

**Prob. 7**

**\*8.** Part of a control linkage for an airplane consists of a rigid member $CBD$ and a flexible cable $AB$. If a force is applied to the end $D$ of the member and causes it to rotate by $\theta = 0.3°$, determine the normal strain in the cable. Originally the cable is unstretched.

**9.** Part of a control linkage for an airplane consists of a rigid member $CBD$ and a flexible cable $AB$. If a force is applied to the end $D$ of the member and causes a normal strain in the cable of $0.0035$ mm/mm, determine the displacement of point $D$. Originally the cable is unstretched.

**Probs. 8/9**

**10.** The corners of the square plate are given the displacements indicated. Determine the shear strain along the edges of the plate at $A$ and $B$.

**11.** The corners of the square plate are given the displacements indicated. Determine the average normal strains along side $AB$ and diagonals $AC$ and $DB$.

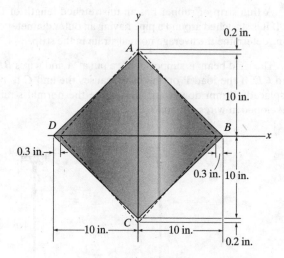

**Probs. 10/11**

**\*12.** The piece of rubber is originally rectangular. Determine the average shear strain $\gamma_{xy}$ at $A$ if the corners $B$ and $D$ are subjected to the displacements that cause the rubber to distort as shown by the dashed lines.

**13.** The piece of rubber is originally rectangular and subjected to the deformation shown by the dashed lines. Determine the average normal strain along the diagonal $DB$ and side $AD$.

**Probs. 12/13**

**14.** The force **P** applied at joint $D$ of the square frame causes the frame to sway and form the dashed rhombus. Determine the average normal strain developed in wire $AC$. Assume the three rods are rigid.

**15.** The force **P** applied at joint $D$ of the square frame causes the frame to sway and form the dashed rhombus. Determine the average normal strain developed in wire $AE$. Assume the three rods are rigid.

**17.** The plate is deformed uniformly into the shape shown by the dashed lines. If at $A$, $\gamma_{xy} = 0.0075$ rad., while $\epsilon_{AB} = \epsilon_{AF} = 0$, determine the average shear strain at point $G$ with respect to the $x'$ and $y'$ axes.

**Prob. 17**

**Probs. 14/15**

**18.** The piece of plastic is originally rectangular. Determine the shear strain $\gamma_{xy}$ at corners $A$ and $B$ if the plastic distorts as shown by the dashed lines.

**19.** The piece of plastic is originally rectangular. Determine the shear strain $\gamma_{xy}$ at corners $D$ and $C$ if the plastic distorts as shown by the dashed lines.

**\*16.** The triangular plate $ABC$ is deformed into the shape shown by the dashed lines. If at $A$, $\varepsilon_{AB} = 0.0075$, $\varepsilon_{AC} = 0.01$ and $\gamma_{xy} = 0.005$ rad, determine the average normal strain along edge $BC$.

**\*20.** The piece of plastic is originally rectangular. Determine the average normal strain that occurs along the diagonals $AC$ and $DB$.

**Prob. 16**

**Probs. 18/19/20**

**21.** The rectangular plate is deformed into the shape of a parallelogram shown by the dashed lines. Determine the average shear strain $\gamma_{xy}$ at corners $A$ and $B$.

**Prob. 21**

**22.** The triangular plate is fixed at its base, and its apex $A$ is given a horizontal displacement of 5 mm. Determine the shear strain, $\gamma_{xy}$, at $A$.

**23.** The triangular plate is fixed at its base, and its apex $A$ is given a horizontal displacement of 5 mm. Determine the average normal strain $\epsilon_x$ along the $x$ axis.

**\*24.** The triangular plate is fixed at its base, and its apex $A$ is given a horizontal displacement of 5 mm. Determine the average normal strain $\epsilon_{x'}$ along the $x'$ axis.

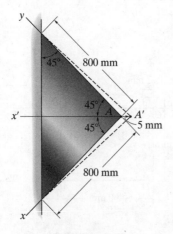

**Probs. 22/23/24**

**25.** The square rubber block is subjected to a shear strain of $\gamma_{xy} = 40(10^{-6})x + 20(10^{-6})y$, where $x$ and $y$ are in mm. This deformation is in the shape shown by the dashed lines, where all the lines parallel to the $y$ axis remain vertical after the deformation. Determine the normal strain along edge $BC$.

**Prob. 25**

**26.** The square plate is deformed into the shape shown by the dashed lines. If $DC$ has a normal strain $\epsilon_x = 0.004$, $DA$ has a normal strain $\epsilon_y = 0.005$ and at $D$, $\gamma_{xy} = 0.02$ rad, determine the average normal strain along diagonal $CA$.

**27.** The square plate is deformed into the shape shown by the dashed lines. If $DC$ has a normal strain $\epsilon_x = 0.004$, $DA$ has a normal strain $\epsilon_y = 0.005$ and at $D$, $\gamma_{xy} = 0.02$ rad, determine the shear strain at point $E$ with respect to the $x'$ and $y'$ axes.

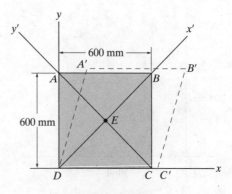

**Probs. 26/27**

88

**\*28.** The wire is subjected to a normal strain that is defined by $\epsilon = (x/L)e^{-(x/L)^2}$. If the wire has an initial length $L$, determine the increase in its length.

$\epsilon = (x/L)e^{-(x/L)^2}$

**Probs. 28**

**29.** The rectangular plate is deformed into the shape shown by the dashed lines. Determine the average normal strain along diagonal $AC$, and the average shear strain at corner $A$.

**30.** The rectangular plate is deformed into the shape shown by the dashed lines. Determine the average normal strain along diagonal $BD$, and the average shear strain at corner $B$.

**Probs. 29/30**

**31.** The nonuniform loading causes a normal strain in the shaft that can be expressed as $\epsilon_x = kx^2$, where $k$ is a constant. Determine the displacement of the end $B$. Also, what is the average normal strain in the rod?

**Prob. 31**

**\*32.** The rubber block is fixed along edge $AB$, and edge $CD$ is moved so that the vertical displacement of any point in the block is given by $v(x) = (v_0/b^3)x^3$. Determine the shear strain $\gamma_{xy}$ at points $(b/2, a/2)$ and $(b, a)$.

**Prob. 32**

**33.** The fiber $AB$ has a length $L$ and orientation $\theta$. If its ends $A$ and $B$ undergo very small displacements $u_A$ and $v_B$, respectively, determine the normal strain in the fiber when it is in position $A'B'$.

**Prob. 33**

**34.** If the normal strain is defined in reference to the final length, that is,

$$\epsilon_n' = \lim_{p \to p'} \left( \frac{\Delta s' - \Delta s}{\Delta s'} \right)$$

instead of in reference to the original length, Eq. 2, show that the difference in these strains is represented as a second-order term, namely, $\epsilon_n - \epsilon_n' = \epsilon_n \epsilon_n'$.

# Solutions and Answers for Preliminary Problems

**P1.**

$$\frac{\Delta'}{L} = \frac{\Delta}{3L}, \quad \Delta' = \frac{\Delta}{3}$$

$$\epsilon_{AB} = \frac{\Delta/3}{L/2} = \frac{2\Delta}{3L}$$

$$\epsilon_{CD} = \frac{\Delta}{L}$$

**P2.**

$$\frac{\Delta'}{2L} = \frac{\Delta}{L} \quad \Delta' = 2\Delta$$

$$\epsilon_{CD} = \frac{\Delta}{L}$$

$$\epsilon_{AB} = \frac{2\Delta}{L/2} = \frac{4\Delta}{L}$$

**P3.**

$$\epsilon_{AB} = \frac{L_{A'B} - L_{AB}}{L_{AB}}$$

**P4.**

$$\epsilon_{AB} = \frac{L_{AB'} - L_{AB}}{L_{AB}}, \quad \epsilon_{AC} = \frac{L_{AC'} - L_{AC}}{L_{AC}}$$

$$\epsilon_{BC} = \frac{L_{B'C'} - L_{BC}}{L_{BC}}, \quad (\gamma_A)_{xy} = \left(\frac{\pi}{2} - \theta\right) \text{rad}$$

**P5.**

$$(\gamma_A)_{xy} = \frac{\pi}{2} - \left(\frac{\pi}{2} + \theta_1\right)$$

$$= (-\theta_1) \text{ rad}$$

$$(\gamma_B)_{xy} = \frac{\pi}{2} - (\pi - \theta_2)$$

$$= \left(-\frac{\pi}{2} + \theta_2\right) \text{ rad}$$

# Selected Answers

1.    $\epsilon = 0.167$ in./in.
2.    $\epsilon = 0.0472$ in./in.
3.    $\epsilon_{CE} = 0.00250$ mm/mm, $\epsilon_{BD} = 0.00107$ mm/mm
5.    $\epsilon_{AC} = \epsilon_{AB} = 0.00578$ mm/mm
6.    $\epsilon_{avg} = \dfrac{\pi}{h}(z + h) - 1$
7.    $(\epsilon_{avg})_{AC} = 6.04(10^{-3})$ mm/mm
9.    $\Delta_D = 4.38$ mm
10.   $(\gamma_A)_{nt} = 0.0502$ rad, $(\gamma_B)_{nt} = -0.0502$ rad
11.   $\epsilon_{AB} = -0.00469$ in./in., $\epsilon_{AC} = 0.0200$ in./in., $\epsilon_{DB} = -0.0300$ in./in.
13.   $\epsilon_{DB} = -0.00680$ mm/mm, $\epsilon_{AD} = 0.0281(10^{-3})$ mm/mm
14.   $(\epsilon_{avg})_{AC} = 0.0258$ mm/mm
15.   $(\epsilon_{avg})_{AE} = 0.0207$ mm/mm
17.   $(\gamma_G)_{x'y'} = 4.50(10^{-3})$ rad

18.   $(\gamma_B)_{xy} = 11.6(10^{-3})$ rad, $(\gamma_A)_{xy} = 11.6(10^{-3})$ rad
19.   $(\gamma_C)_{xy} = 11.6(10^{-3})$ rad, $(\gamma_D)_{xy} = 11.6(10^{-3})$ rad
21.   $(\gamma_A)_{xy} = 0.0292$ rad, $(\gamma_B)_{xy} = 0.0292$ rad
22.   $\gamma_{xy} = 0.00880$ rad
23.   $\epsilon_x = 0.00443$ mm/mm
25.   $(\epsilon_{avg})_{BC} = 6.00(10^{-3})$ mm/mm
26.   $(\epsilon_{avg})_{CA} = -5.59(10^{-3})$ mm/mm
27.   $(\gamma_E)_{x'y'} = 0.996(10^{-3})$ rad
29.   $(\epsilon_{avg})_{AC} = 0.0168$ mm/mm, $(\gamma_A)_{xy} = 0.0116$ rad
30.   $(\epsilon_{avg})_{BD} = 1.60(10^{-3})$ mm/mm, $(\gamma_B)_{xy} = 0.0148$ rad
31.   $(\Delta x)_B = \dfrac{kL^3}{3}, (\epsilon_x)_{avg} = \dfrac{kL^2}{3}$
33.   $\epsilon_{AB} = \dfrac{v_B \sin\theta}{L} - \dfrac{u_A \cos\theta}{L}$

# Fundamental Problems Partial Solutions and Answers

**F1** $\dfrac{\delta_C}{600} = \dfrac{0.2}{400};$ $\qquad\qquad \delta_C = 0.3$ mm

$\qquad \epsilon_{CD} = \dfrac{\delta_C}{L_{CD}} = \dfrac{0.3}{300} = 0.001$ mm/mm $\qquad$ *Ans.*

**F2**

$\theta = \left(\dfrac{0.02°}{180°}\right)\pi$ rad $= 0.3491(10^{-3})$ rad

$\delta_B = \theta L_{AB} = 0.3491(10^{-3})(600) = 0.2094$ mm

$\delta_C = \theta L_{AC} = 0.3491(10^{-3})(1200) = 0.4189$ mm

$\epsilon_{BD} = \dfrac{\delta_B}{L_{BD}} = \dfrac{0.2094}{400} = 0.524(10^{-3})$ mm/mm $\qquad$ *Ans.*

$\epsilon_{CE} = \dfrac{\delta_C}{L_{CE}} = \dfrac{0.4189}{600} = 0.698(10^{-3})$ mm/mm $\qquad$ *Ans.*

**F3**

$\alpha = \dfrac{2}{400} = 0.005$ rad $\qquad \beta = \dfrac{4}{300} = 0.01333$ rad

$(\gamma_A)_{xy} = \dfrac{1}{2} - \theta$

$\qquad = \dfrac{\pi}{2} - \left(\dfrac{\pi}{2} - \alpha + \beta\right)$

$\qquad = \alpha - \beta$

$\qquad = 0.005 - 0.01333$

$\qquad = -0.00833$ rad $\qquad\qquad\qquad$ *Ans.*

**F4**

$L_{BC} = \sqrt{300^2 + 400^2} = 500$ mm

$L_{B'C} = \sqrt{(300 - 3)^2 + (400 + 5)^2} = 502.2290$ mm

$\alpha = \dfrac{3}{405} = 0.007407$ rad

$(\epsilon_{BC})_{\text{avg}} = \dfrac{L_{B'C} - L_{BC}}{L_{BC}} = \dfrac{502.2290 - 500}{500}$

$\qquad\qquad = 0.00446$ mm/mm $\qquad\qquad$ *Ans.*

$(\gamma_A)_{xy} = \dfrac{\pi}{2} - \theta = \dfrac{\pi}{2} - \left(\dfrac{\pi}{2} + \alpha\right) = -\alpha = -0.00741$ rad $\;$ *Ans.*

**F5**

$L_{AC} = \sqrt{L_{CD}^2 + L_{AD}^2} = \sqrt{300^2 + 300^2} = 424.2641$ mm

$L_{AC} = \sqrt{L_{C'D'}^2 + L_{A'D'}^2} = \sqrt{306^2 + 296^2} = 425.7370$ mm

$\dfrac{\theta}{2} = \tan^{-1}\left(\dfrac{L_{C'D'}}{L_{A'D'}}\right); \theta = 2\tan^{-1}\left(\dfrac{306}{296}\right) = 1.6040$ rad

$(\epsilon_{AC})_{\text{avg}} = \dfrac{L_{A'C'} - L_{AC}}{L_{AC}} = \dfrac{425.7370 - 424.2641}{424.2641}$

$\qquad\qquad = 0.00347$ mm/mm $\qquad\qquad$ *Ans.*

$(\gamma_E)_{xy} = \dfrac{\pi}{2} - \theta = \dfrac{\pi}{2} - 1.6040 = -0.0332$ rad $\qquad$ *Ans.*

# Mechanical Properties of Materials

From Chapter 3 of *Mechanics of Materials*, Ninth Edition. R. C. Hibbeler. Copyright © 2014 by Pearson Education, Inc. Published by Pearson Prentice Hall. All rights reserved.

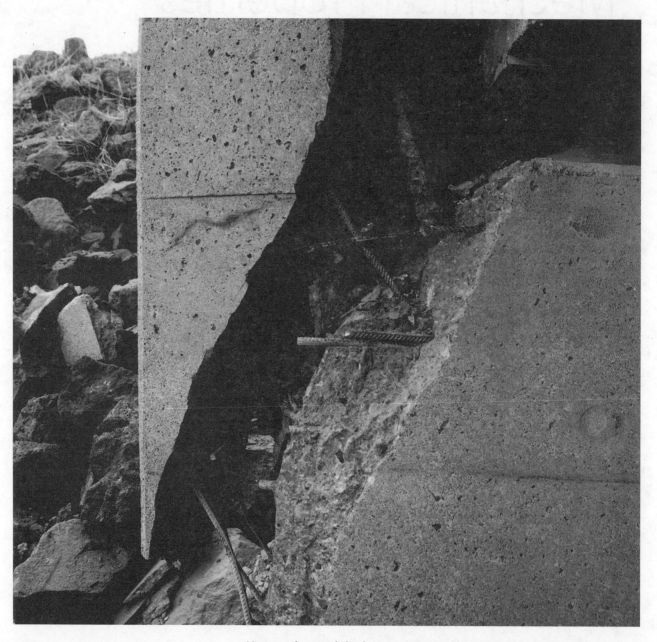

Horizontal ground displacements caused by an earthquake produced fracture of this concrete pier. The material properties of the steel and concrete must be determined so that engineers can properly design the pier to resist the loadings that caused this failure.

# Mechanical Properties of Materials

## CHAPTER OBJECTIVES

■ In this chapter we will show how stress can be related to strain by using experimental methods to determine the stress–strain diagram for a specific material. The behavior described by this diagram will then be discussed for materials that are commonly used in engineering. Also, mechanical properties and other tests that are related to the development of mechanics of materials will be discussed.

## 1    The Tension and Compression Test

The strength of a material depends on its ability to sustain a load without undue deformation or failure. This property is inherent in the material itself and must be determined by *experiment*. One of the most important tests to perform in this regard is the ***tension or compression test***. Although several important mechanical properties of a material can be determined from this test, it is used primarily to determine the relationship between the average normal stress and average normal strain in many engineering materials such as metals, ceramics, polymers, and composites.

$d_0 = 0.5$ in.

$L_0 = 2$ in.

**Fig. 1**

Typical steel specimen with attached strain gauge.

To perform a tension or compression test a specimen of the material is made into a "standard" shape and size. It has a constant circular cross section with enlarged ends, so that failure will not occur at the grips. Before testing, two small punch marks are placed along the specimen's uniform length. Measurements are taken of both the specimen's initial cross-sectional area, $A_0$, and the **gauge-length** distance $L_0$ between the punch marks. For example, when a metal specimen is used in a tension test it generally has an initial diameter of $d_0 = 0.5$ in. (13 mm) and a gauge length of $L_0 = 2$ in. (51 mm), Fig. 1. In order to apply an axial load with no bending of the specimen, the ends are usually seated into ball-and-socket joints. A testing machine like the one shown in Fig. 2 is then used to stretch the specimen at a very slow, constant rate until it fails. The machine is designed to read the load required to maintain this uniform stretching.

At frequent intervals during the test, data is recorded of the applied load $P$, as read on the dial of the machine or taken from a digital readout. Also, the elongation $\delta = L - L_0$ between the punch marks on the specimen may be measured using either a caliper or a mechanical or optical device called an **extensometer**. This value of $\delta$ (delta) is then used to calculate the average normal strain in the specimen. Sometimes, however, this measurement is not taken, since it is also possible to read the strain *directly* by using an **electrical-resistance strain gauge**, which looks like the one shown in Fig. 3. The operation of this gauge is based on the change in electrical resistance of a very thin wire or piece of metal foil under strain. Essentially the gauge is cemented to the specimen along its length. If the cement is very strong in comparison to the gauge, then the gauge is in effect an integral part of the specimen, so that when the specimen is strained in the direction of the gauge, the wire and specimen will experience the same strain. By measuring the electrical resistance of the wire, the gauge may be calibrated to read values of normal strain directly.

movable
upper
crosshead

tension
specimen

load
dial

motor
and load
controls

**Fig. 2**

Electrical–resistance
strain gauge

**Fig. 3**

# 2    The Stress–Strain Diagram

It is not feasible to prepare a test specimen to match the size, $A_0$ and $L_0$, of each structural member. Rather, the test results must be reported so they apply to a member of *any size*. To achieve this, the load and corresponding deformation data are used to calculate various values of the stress and corresponding strain in the specimen. A plot of the results produces a curve called the ***stress–strain diagram***. There are two ways in which it is normally described.

## Conventional Stress–Strain Diagram.    We can determine the *nominal* or *engineering stress* by dividing the applied load $P$ by the specimen's *original* cross-sectional area $A_0$. This calculation assumes that the stress is *constant* over the cross section and throughout the gauge length. We have

$$\sigma = \frac{P}{A_0} \tag{1}$$

Likewise, the *nominal* or *engineering strain* is found directly from the strain gauge reading, or by dividing the change in the specimen's gauge length, $\delta$, by the specimen's original gauge length $L_0$. Here the strain is assumed to be constant throughout the region between the gauge points. Thus,

$$\epsilon = \frac{\delta}{L_0} \tag{2}$$

If the corresponding values of $\sigma$ and $\epsilon$ are plotted so that the vertical axis is the stress and the horizontal axis is the strain, the resulting curve is called a ***conventional stress–strain diagram***. Realize, however, that two stress–strain diagrams for a particular material will be quite similar, but will never be exactly the same. This is because the results actually depend on variables such as the material's composition, microscopic imperfections, the way it is manufactured, the rate of loading, and the temperature during the time of the test.

We will now discuss the characteristics of the conventional stress–strain curve as it pertains to *steel*, a commonly used material for fabricating both structural members and mechanical elements. Using the method described above, the characteristic stress–strain diagram for a steel specimen is shown in Fig. 4. From this curve we can identify four different ways in which the material behaves, depending on the amount of strain induced in the material.

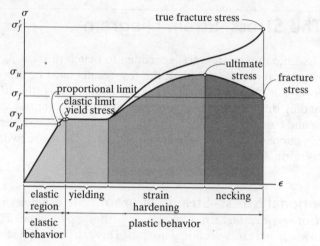

Conventional and true stress-strain diagrams
for ductile material (steel) (not to scale)

**Fig. 4**

**Elastic Behavior.** Elastic behavior of the material occurs when the strains in the specimen are within the light orange region shown in Fig. 4. Here the curve is actually a *straight line* throughout most of this region, so that the stress is *proportional* to the strain. The material in this region is said to be *linear elastic*. The upper stress limit to this linear relationship is called the **proportional limit**, $\sigma_{pl}$. If the stress slightly exceeds the proportional limit, the curve tends to bend and flatten out as shown. This continues until the stress reaches the **elastic limit**. Upon reaching this point, if the load is removed the specimen will still return back to its original shape. Normally for steel, however, the elastic limit is seldom determined, since it is very close to the proportional limit and therefore rather difficult to detect.

**Yielding.** A slight increase in stress above the elastic limit will result in a breakdown of the material and cause it to *deform permanently*. This behavior is called *yielding*, and it is indicated by the rectangular dark orange region of the curve. The stress that causes yielding is called the *yield stress* or *yield point*, $\sigma_Y$, and the deformation that occurs is called *plastic deformation*. Although not shown in Fig. 4, for low-carbon steels or those that are hot rolled, the yield point is often distinguished by two values. The *upper yield point* occurs first, followed by a sudden decrease in load-carrying capacity to a *lower yield point*. Notice that once the yield point is reached, then as shown in Fig. 4, the specimen will continue to elongate (strain) *without any increase in load*. When the material is in this state, it is often referred to as being *perfectly plastic*.

**Strain Hardening.** When yielding has ended, an increase in load can be supported by the specimen, resulting in a curve that rises continuously but becomes flatter until it reaches a maximum stress referred to as the *ultimate stress*, $\sigma_u$. The rise in the curve in this manner is called *strain hardening*, and it is identified in Fig. 4 as the region in light green.

**Necking.** Up to the ultimate stress, as the specimen elongates, its cross-sectional area will decrease. This decrease is fairly *uniform* over the specimen's entire gauge length; however, just after, at the ultimate stress, the cross-sectional area will begin to decrease in a *localized* region of the specimen. As a result, a constriction or "neck" tends to form in this region as the specimen elongates further, Fig. 5a. This region of the curve due to necking is indicated in dark green in Fig. 4. Here the stress–strain diagram tends to curve downward until the specimen breaks at the *fracture stress*, $\sigma_f$, Fig. 5b.

Typical necking pattern which has occurred on this steel specimen just before fracture.

**True Stress–Strain Diagram.** Instead of always using the *original* cross-sectional area and specimen length to calculate the (engineering) stress and strain, we could have used the *actual* cross-sectional area and specimen length at the *instant* the load is measured. The values of stress and strain found from these measurements are called *true stress* and *true strain*, and a plot of their values is called the *true stress–strain diagram*. When this diagram is plotted it has a form shown by the light-blue curve in Fig. 4. Note that the conventional and true $\sigma$–$\epsilon$ diagrams are practically coincident when the strain is small. The differences between the diagrams begin to appear in the strain-hardening range, where the magnitude of strain becomes more significant. In particular, there is a large divergence within the necking region. Here it can be seen from the conventional $\sigma$–$\epsilon$ diagram that the specimen *actually* supports a *decreasing load*, since $A_0$ is constant when calculating engineering stress, $\sigma = P/A_0$. However, from the true $\sigma$–$\epsilon$ diagram, the actual area $A$ within the necking region is always decreasing until fracture, $\sigma_f'$, and so the material actually sustains *increasing stress*, since $\sigma = P/A$.

This steel specimen clearly shows the necking that occurred just before the specimen failed. This resulted in the formation of a "cup-cone" shape at the fracture location, which is characteristic of ductile materials.

Necking

(a)

Failure of a
ductile material

(b)

**Fig. 5**

Although the true and conventional stress–strain diagrams are different, most engineering design is done so that the material supports a stress within the elastic range. This is because the deformation of the material is generally not severe and the material will restore itself when the load is removed. The true strain up to the elastic limit will remain small enough so that the error in using the engineering values of $\sigma$ and $\epsilon$ is very small (about 0.1%) compared with their true values. This is one of the primary reasons for using conventional stress–strain diagrams.

The above concepts can be summarized with reference to Fig. 6, which shows an actual conventional stress–strain diagram for a mild steel specimen. In order to enhance the details, the elastic region of the curve has been shown in light blue color using an exaggerated strain scale, also shown in light blue. Tracing the behavior, the proportional limit is reached at $\sigma_{pl} = 35$ ksi (241 MPa), where $\epsilon_{pl} = 0.0012$ in./in. This is followed by an upper yield point of $(\sigma_Y)_u = 38$ ksi (262 MPa), then suddenly a lower yield point of $(\sigma_Y)_l = 36$ ksi (248 MPa). The end of yielding occurs at a strain of $\epsilon_Y = 0.030$ in./in., which is 25 times greater than the strain at the proportional limit! Continuing, the specimen undergoes strain hardening until it reaches the ultimate stress of $\sigma_u = 63$ ksi (434 MPa), then it begins to neck down until a fracture occurs, $\sigma_f = 47$ ksi (324 MPa). By comparison, the strain at failure, $\epsilon_f = 0.380$ in./in., is 317 times greater than $\epsilon_{pl}$!

Stress-strain diagram for mild steel

**Fig. 6**

# 3 Stress–Strain Behavior of Ductile and Brittle Materials

Materials can be classified as either being ductile or brittle, depending on their stress–strain characteristics.

**Ductile Materials.** Any material that can be subjected to large strains before it fractures is called a ***ductile material***. Mild steel, as discussed previously, is a typical example. Engineers often choose ductile materials for design because these materials are capable of absorbing shock or energy, and if they become overloaded, they will usually exhibit large deformation before failing.

One way to specify the ductility of a material is to report its percent elongation or percent reduction in area at the time of fracture. The ***percent elongation*** is the specimen's fracture strain expressed as a percent. Thus, if the specimen's original gauge length is $L_0$ and its length at fracture is $L_f$, then

$$\text{Percent elongation} = \frac{L_f - L_0}{L_0}(100\%) \qquad (3)$$

As seen in Fig. 6, since $\epsilon_f = 0.380$, this value would be 38% for a mild steel specimen.

The ***percent reduction in area*** is another way to specify ductility. It is defined within the region of necking as follows:

$$\text{Percent reduction of area} = \frac{A_0 - A_f}{A_0}(100\%) \qquad (4)$$

Here $A_0$ is the specimen's original cross-sectional area and $A_f$ is the area of the neck at fracture. Mild steel has a typical value of 60%.

Besides steel, other metals such as brass, molybdenum, and zinc may also exhibit ductile stress–strain characteristics similar to steel, whereby they undergo elastic stress–strain behavior, yielding at constant stress, strain hardening, and finally necking until fracture. In most metals, however, constant yielding will *not occur* beyond the elastic range. One metal for which this is the case is aluminum. Actually, this metal often does not have a well-defined *yield point*, and consequently it is standard practice to define a ***yield strength*** using a graphical procedure called the ***offset method***. Normally for structural design a 0.2% strain (0.002 in./in.) is chosen, and from this point on the $\epsilon$ axis, a line parallel to the initial straight-line portion of the stress–strain diagram is drawn. The point where this line intersects the curve defines the yield strength. An example of the construction for determining the yield strength for an aluminum alloy is shown in Fig. 7. From the graph, the yield strength is $\sigma_{YS} = 51$ ksi (352 MPa). Apart from metals, 0.2% strain is used as the offset to determine the yield strength of many plastics.

Yield strength for an aluminum alloy

**Fig. 7**

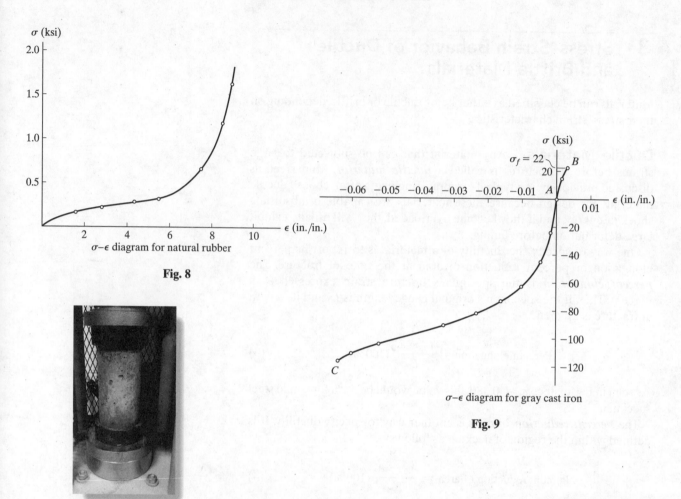

σ−ε diagram for natural rubber

**Fig. 8**

σ−ε diagram for gray cast iron

**Fig. 9**

Concrete used for structural purposes must be tested in compression to be sure it reaches its ultimate design stress after curing for 30 days.

Realize that the yield strength is not a physical property of the material, since it is a stress that causes a *specified* permanent strain in the material. In this text, however, we will assume that the yield strength, yield point, elastic limit, and proportional limit all *coincide* unless otherwise stated. An exception would be natural rubber, which in fact does not even have a proportional limit, since stress and strain are *not* linearly related. Instead, as shown in Fig. 8, this material, which is known as a polymer, exhibits *nonlinear elastic behavior*.

Wood is a material that is often moderately ductile, and as a result it is usually designed to respond only to elastic loadings. The strength characteristics of wood vary greatly from one species to another, and for each species they depend on the moisture content, age, and the size and arrangement of knots in the wood. Since wood is a fibrous material, its tensile or compressive characteristics will differ greatly when it is loaded either parallel or perpendicular to its grain. Specifically, wood splits easily when it is loaded in tension perpendicular to its grain, and consequently tensile loads are almost always intended to be applied parallel to the grain of wood members.

Tension failure of a brittle material

(a)

Compression causes material to bulge out

(b)

**Fig. 10**

$\sigma - \epsilon$ diagram for typical concrete mix

**Fig. 11**

## Brittle Materials.

Materials that exhibit little or no yielding before failure are referred to as ***brittle materials***. Gray cast iron is an example, having a stress–strain diagram in tension as shown by portion *AB* of the curve in Fig. 9. Here fracture at $\sigma_f = 22$ ksi (152 MPa) took place initially at an imperfection or microscopic crack and then spread rapidly across the specimen, causing complete fracture. Since the appearance of initial cracks in a specimen is quite random, brittle materials do not have a well-defined tensile fracture stress. Instead the *average* fracture stress from a set of observed tests is generally reported. A typical failed specimen is shown in Fig. 10*a*.

Compared with their behavior in tension, brittle materials, such as gray cast iron, exhibit a much higher resistance to axial compression, as evidenced by portion *AC* of the curve in Fig. 9. For this case any cracks or imperfections in the specimen tend to close up, and as the load increases the material will generally bulge or become barrel shaped as the strains become larger, Fig. 10*b*.

Like gray cast iron, concrete is classified as a brittle material, and it also has a low strength capacity in tension. The characteristics of its stress–strain diagram depend primarily on the mix of concrete (water, sand, gravel, and cement) and the time and temperature of curing. A typical example of a "complete" stress–strain diagram for concrete is given in Fig. 11. By inspection, its maximum compressive strength is about 12.5 times greater than its tensile strength, $(\sigma_c)_{max} = 5$ ksi (34.5 MPa) versus $(\sigma_t)_{max} = 0.40$ ksi (2.76 MPa). For this reason, concrete is almost always reinforced with steel bars or rods whenever it is designed to support tensile loads.

It can generally be stated that most materials exhibit both ductile and brittle behavior. For example, steel has brittle behavior when it contains a high carbon content, and it is ductile when the carbon content is reduced. Also, at low temperatures materials become harder and more brittle, whereas when the temperature rises they become softer and more ductile. This effect is shown in Fig. 12 for a methacrylate plastic.

Steel rapidly loses its strength when heated. For this reason engineers often require main structural members to be insulated in case of fire.

$\sigma - \epsilon$ diagrams for a methacrylate plastic

**Fig. 12**

## 4   Hooke's Law

As noted in the previous section, the stress–strain diagrams for most engineering materials exhibit a *linear relationship* between stress and strain within the elastic region. Consequently, an increase in stress causes a proportionate increase in strain. This fact was discovered by Robert Hooke in 1676 using springs and is known as *Hooke's law*. It may be expressed mathematically as

$$\sigma = E\epsilon \tag{5}$$

Here $E$ represents the constant of proportionality, which is called the **modulus of elasticity** or **Young's modulus**, named after Thomas Young, who published an account of it in 1807.

Equation 5 actually represents the equation of the *initial straight-lined portion* of the stress–strain diagram up to the proportional limit. Furthermore, the modulus of elasticity represents the *slope* of this line. Since strain is dimensionless, from Eq. 5, $E$ will have the same units as stress, such as psi, ksi, or pascals. As an example of its calculation, consider the stress–strain diagram for steel shown in Fig. 6. Here $\sigma_{pl} = 35$ ksi and $\epsilon_{pl} = 0.0012$ in./in., so that

$$E = \frac{\sigma_{pl}}{\epsilon_{pl}} = \frac{35 \text{ ksi}}{0.0012 \text{ in./in.}} = 29(10^3) \text{ ksi}$$

As shown in Fig. 13, the proportional limit for a particular type of steel alloy depends on its carbon content; however, most grades of steel, from the softest rolled steel to the hardest tool steel, have about the same modulus of

**Fig. 13**

elasticity, generally accepted to be $E_{st} = 29(10^3)$ ksi or 200 GPa. Values of $E$ for other commonly used engineering materials are often tabulated in engineering codes and reference books. It should be noted that the modulus of elasticity is a mechanical property that indicates the *stiffness* of a material. Materials that are very stiff, such as steel, have large values of $E$ [$E_{st} = 29(10^3)$ ksi or 200 GPa], whereas spongy materials such as vulcanized rubber may have low values [$E_r = 0.10$ ksi or 0.69 MPa].

The modulus of elasticity is one of the most important mechanical properties used in the development of equations presented in this text. It must always be remembered, though, that $E$ can be used only if a material has *linear elastic behavior*. Also, if the stress in the material is *greater* than the proportional limit, the stress–strain diagram ceases to be a straight line and so Eq. 5 is no longer valid.

## Strain Hardening.

If a specimen of ductile material, such as steel, is loaded into the *plastic region* and then unloaded, *elastic strain is recovered* as the material returns to its equilibrium state. The *plastic strain remains*, however, and as a result the material is subjected to a **permanent set**. For example, a wire when bent (plastically) will spring back a little (elastically) when the load is removed; however, it will not fully return to its original position. This behavior can be illustrated on the stress–strain diagram shown in Fig. 14*a*. Here the specimen is first loaded beyond its yield point $A$ to point $A'$. Since interatomic forces have to be overcome to elongate the specimen *elastically*, then these same forces pull the atoms back together when the load is removed, Fig. 14*a*. Consequently, the modulus of elasticity, $E$, is the same, and therefore the slope of line $O'A'$ is the same as line $OA$.

If the load is reapplied, the atoms in the material will again be displaced until yielding occurs at or near the stress $A'$, and the stress–strain diagram continues along the same path as before, Fig. 14*b*. It should be noted, however, that this new stress–strain diagram, defined by $O'A'B$, now has a *higher* yield point ($A'$), a consequence of strain-hardening. In other words, the material now has a *greater elastic region*; however, it has *less ductility*, a smaller plastic region, than when it was in its original state.

(a)

(b)

**Fig. 14**

This pin was made from a hardened steel alloy, that is, one having a high carbon content. It failed due to brittle fracture.

# 5 Strain Energy

As a material is deformed by an external load, the load will do external work, which in turn will be stored in the material as internal energy. This energy is related to the strains in the material, and so it is referred to as *strain energy*. To obtain this strain energy let us consider a volume element of material from a tension test specimen Fig. 15. It is subjected to the uniaxial stress $\sigma$. This stress develops a force $\Delta F = \sigma \Delta A = \sigma(\Delta x \, \Delta y)$ on the top and bottom faces of the element *after* the element of length $\Delta z$ undergoes a vertical displacement $\epsilon \, \Delta z$. By definition, *work* of $\Delta F$ is determined by the product of a force and the displacement in the direction of the force. Since the force is increased uniformly from zero to its final magnitude $\Delta F$ when the displacement $\epsilon \, \Delta z$ occurs, the work done on the element by the force is then equal to the *average* force magnitude ($\Delta F/2$) times the displacement $\epsilon \, \Delta z$. The conservation of energy requires this "external work" on the element to be equivalent to the "internal work" or strain energy stored in the element—assuming that no energy is lost in the form of heat. Consequently, the strain energy $\Delta U$ is $\Delta U = \left(\frac{1}{2}\Delta F\right) \epsilon \, \Delta z = \left(\frac{1}{2} \sigma \, \Delta x \, \Delta y\right) \epsilon \, \Delta z$. Since the volume of the element is $\Delta V = \Delta x \, \Delta y \, \Delta z$, then $\Delta U = \frac{1}{2} \sigma \epsilon \, \Delta V$.

For applications, it is often convenient to specify the strain energy per unit volume of material. This is called the *strain-energy density*, and it can be expressed as

$$u = \frac{\Delta U}{\Delta V} = \frac{1}{2} \sigma \epsilon \qquad (6)$$

Finally, if the material behavior is *linear elastic*, then Hooke's law applies, $\sigma = E\epsilon$, and therefore we can express the *elastic strain-energy density* in terms of the uniaxial stress $\sigma$ as

$$u = \frac{1}{2} \frac{\sigma^2}{E} \qquad (7)$$

**Modulus of Resilience.** In particular, when the stress $\sigma$ reaches the proportional limit, the strain-energy density, as calculated by Eq. 6 or 7, is referred to as the *modulus of resilience*, i.e.,

$$\boxed{u_r = \frac{1}{2} \sigma_{pl} \, \epsilon_{pl} = \frac{1}{2} \frac{\sigma_{pl}^2}{E}} \qquad (8)$$

From the elastic region of the stress–strain diagram, Fig. 16*a*, notice that $u_r$ is equivalent to the shaded *triangular area* under the diagram. Physically the modulus of resilience represents the largest amount of internal strain energy per unit volume the material can absorb without causing any permanent damage to the material. Certainly this becomes important when designing bumpers or shock absorbers.

**Fig. 15**

Modulus of resilience $u_r$

(a)

**Fig. 16**

**Modulus of Toughness.** Another important property of a material is the *modulus of toughness*, $u_t$. This quantity represents the *entire area* under the stress–strain diagram, Fig. 16b, and therefore it indicates the maximum amount of strain-energy the material can absorb just before it fractures. This property becomes important when designing members that may be accidentally overloaded. Note that alloying metals can also change their resilience and toughness. For example, by changing the percentage of carbon in steel, the resulting stress–strain diagrams in Fig. 17 show how the degrees of resilience (Fig. 16a) and toughness (Fig. 16b) can be changed.

Modulus of toughness $u_t$

(b)

**Fig. 16 (cont.)**

hard steel
(0.6% carbon)
highest strength

structural steel
(0.2% carbon)
toughest

soft steel
(0.1% carbon)
most ductile

**Fig. 17**

## Important Points

- A *conventional stress–strain diagram* is important in engineering since it provides a means for obtaining data about a material's tensile or compressive strength without regard for the material's physical size or shape.

- *Engineering stress and strain* are calculated using the *original* cross-sectional area and gauge length of the specimen.

- A *ductile material*, such as mild steel, has four distinct behaviors as it is loaded. They are *elastic behavior, yielding, strain hardening,* and *necking*.

- A material is *linear elastic* if the stress is proportional to the strain within the elastic region. This behavior is described by *Hooke's law*, $\sigma = E\epsilon$, where the *modulus of elasticity E* is the slope of the line.

- Important points on the stress–strain diagram are the *proportional limit, elastic limit, yield stress, ultimate stress*, and *fracture stress*.

- The *ductility* of a material can be specified by the specimen's *percent elongation* or the *percent reduction in area*.

- If a material does not have a distinct yield point, a *yield strength* can be specified using a graphical procedure such as the *offset method*.

- *Brittle materials*, such as gray cast iron, have very little or no yielding and so they can fracture suddenly.

- *Strain hardening* is used to establish a higher yield point for a material. This is done by straining the material beyond the elastic limit, then releasing the load. The modulus of elasticity remains the same; however, the material's ductility *decreases*.

- *Strain energy* is energy stored in a material due to its deformation. This energy per unit volume is called *strain-energy density*. If it is measured up to the proportional limit, it is referred to as the *modulus of resilience*, and if it is measured up to the point of fracture, it is called the *modulus of toughness*. It can be determined from the area under the $\sigma - \epsilon$ diagram.

This nylon specimen exhibits a high degree of toughness as noted by the large amount of necking that has occurred just before fracture.

## EXAMPLE 1

A tension test for a steel alloy results in the stress–strain diagram shown in Fig. 18. Calculate the modulus of elasticity and the yield strength based on a 0.2% offset. Identify on the graph the ultimate stress and the fracture stress.

**Fig. 18**

### SOLUTION

**Modulus of Elasticity.** We must calculate the *slope* of the initial straight-line portion of the graph. Using the magnified curve and scale shown in blue, this line extends from point $O$ to an estimated point $A$, which has coordinates of approximately (0.0016 in./in., 50 ksi). Therefore,

$$E = \frac{50 \text{ ksi}}{0.0016 \text{ in./in.}} = 31.2\,(10^3)\text{ ksi} \qquad Ans.$$

Note that the equation of line $OA$ is thus $\sigma = 31.2\,(10^3)\epsilon$.

**Yield Strength.** For a 0.2% offset, we begin at a strain of 0.2% or 0.0020 in./in. and graphically extend a (dashed) line parallel to $OA$ until it intersects the $\sigma-\epsilon$ curve at $A'$. The yield strength is approximately

$$\sigma_{YS} = 68 \text{ ksi} \qquad Ans.$$

**Ultimate Stress.** This is defined by the peak of the $\sigma-\epsilon$ graph, point $B$ in Fig. 18.

$$\sigma_u = 108 \text{ ksi} \qquad Ans.$$

**Fracture Stress.** When the specimen is strained to its maximum of $\epsilon_f = 0.23$ in./in., it fractures at point $C$. Thus,

$$\sigma_f = 90 \text{ ksi} \qquad Ans.$$

## EXAMPLE | 2

The stress–strain diagram for an aluminum alloy that is used for making aircraft parts is shown in Fig. 19. If a specimen of this material is stressed to 600 MPa, determine the permanent strain that remains in the specimen when the load is released. Also, find the modulus of resilience both before and after the load application.

**Fig. 19**

### SOLUTION

**Permanent Strain.** When the specimen is subjected to the load, it strain-hardens until point $B$ is reached on the $\sigma$–$\epsilon$ diagram. The strain at this point is approximately 0.023 mm/mm. When the load is released, the material behaves by following the straight line $BC$, which is parallel to line $OA$. Since both lines have the same slope, the strain at point $C$ can be determined analytically. The slope of line $OA$ is the modulus of elasticity, i.e.,

$$E = \frac{450 \text{ MPa}}{0.006 \text{ mm/mm}} = 75.0 \text{ GPa}$$

From triangle $CBD$, we require

$$E = \frac{BD}{CD}; \qquad 75.0(10^9) \text{ Pa} = \frac{600(10^6) \text{ Pa}}{CD}$$

$$CD = 0.008 \text{ mm/mm}$$

This strain represents the amount of *recovered elastic strain*. The permanent strain, $\epsilon_{OC}$, is thus

$$\epsilon_{OC} = 0.023 \text{ mm/mm} - 0.008 \text{ mm/mm}$$
$$= 0.0150 \text{ mm/mm} \qquad \qquad \textit{Ans.}$$

*Note:* If gauge marks on the specimen were originally 50 mm apart, then after the load is *released* these marks will be 50 mm + (0.0150)(50 mm) = 50.75 mm apart.

**Modulus of Resilience.** Applying Eq. 8, we have[*]

$$(u_r)_{\text{initial}} = \frac{1}{2} \sigma_{pl} \epsilon_{pl} = \frac{1}{2} (450 \text{ MPa})(0.006 \text{ mm/mm})$$

$$= 1.35 \text{ MJ/m}^3 \qquad \qquad \textit{Ans.}$$

$$(u_r)_{\text{final}} = \frac{1}{2} \sigma_{pl} \epsilon_{pl} = \frac{1}{2} (600 \text{ MPa})(0.008 \text{ mm/mm})$$

$$= 2.40 \text{ MJ/m}^3 \qquad \qquad \textit{Ans.}$$

**NOTE:** By comparison, the effect of strain-hardening the material has caused an increase in the modulus of resilience; however, note that the modulus of toughness for the material has decreased since the area under the original curve, $OABF$, is larger than the area under curve $CBF$.

[*]Work in the SI system of units is measured in joules, where 1 J = 1 N · m.

## EXAMPLE 3

(b)

(a)

**Fig. 20**

An aluminum rod, shown in Fig. 20a, has a circular cross section and is subjected to an axial load of 10 kN. If a portion of the stress–strain diagram is shown in Fig. 20b, determine the approximate elongation of the rod when the load is applied. Take $E_{al} = 70$ GPa.

### SOLUTION

For the analysis we will neglect the *localized deformations* at the point of load application and where the rod's cross-sectional area suddenly changes. (These effects will be discussed in Sections 1 and 7.) Throughout the midsection of each segment the normal stress and deformation are uniform.

In order to find the elongation of the rod, we must first obtain the strain. This is done by calculating the stress, then using the stress–strain diagram. The normal stress within each segment is

$$\sigma_{AB} = \frac{P}{A} = \frac{10(10^3)\ \text{N}}{\pi(0.01\ \text{m})^2} = 31.83\ \text{MPa}$$

$$\sigma_{BC} = \frac{P}{A} = \frac{10(10^3)\ \text{N}}{\pi(0.0075\ \text{m})^2} = 56.59\ \text{MPa}$$

From the stress–strain diagram, the material in segment $AB$ is strained *elastically* since $\sigma_{AB} < \sigma_Y = 40$ MPa. Using Hooke's law,

$$\epsilon_{AB} = \frac{\sigma_{AB}}{E_{al}} = \frac{31.83(10^6)\ \text{Pa}}{70(10^9)\ \text{Pa}} = 0.0004547\ \text{mm/mm}$$

The material within segment $BC$ is strained plastically, since $\sigma_{BC} > \sigma_Y = 40$ MPa. From the graph, for $\sigma_{BC} = 56.59$ MPa, $\epsilon_{BC} \approx 0.045$ mm/mm. The approximate elongation of the rod is therefore

$$\delta = \Sigma\epsilon L = 0.0004547(600\ \text{mm}) + 0.0450(400\ \text{mm})$$
$$= 18.3\ \text{mm} \qquad\qquad Ans.$$

# FUNDAMENTAL PROBLEMS

**F1.** Define a homogeneous material.

**F2.** Indicate the points on the stress–strain diagram which represent the proportional limit and the ultimate stress.

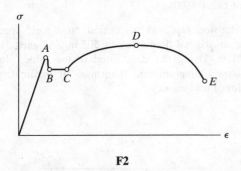

**F2**

**F3.** Define the modulus of elasticity $E$.

**F4.** At room temperature, mild steel is a ductile material. True or false?

**F5.** Engineering stress and strain are calculated using the *actual* cross-sectional area and length of the specimen. True or false?

**F6.** As the temperature increases the modulus of elasticity will increase. True or false?

**F7.** A 100-mm long rod has a diameter of 15 mm. If an axial tensile load of 100 kN is applied, determine its change in length. Assume linear-elastic behavior with $E = 200$ GPa.

**F8.** A bar has a length of 8 in. and cross-sectional area of 12 in². Determine the modulus of elasticity of the material if it is subjected to an axial tensile load of 10 kip and stretches 0.003 in. The material has linear-elastic behavior.

**F9.** A 10-mm-diameter rod has a modulus of elasticity of $E = 100$ GPa. If it is 4 m long and subjected to an axial tensile load of 6 kN, determine its elongation. Assume linear-elastic behavior.

**F10.** The material for the 50-mm-long specimen has the stress–strain diagram shown. If $P = 100$ kN, determine the elongation of the specimen.

**F11.** The material for the 50-mm-long specimen has the stress–strain diagram shown. If $P = 150$ kN is applied and then released, determine the permanent elongation of the specimen.

**F10/11**

**F12.** If the elongation of wire $BC$ is 0.2 mm after the force **P** is applied, determine the magnitude of **P**. The wire is A-36 steel and has a diameter of 3 mm.

**F12**

# PROBLEMS

**1.** A tension test was performed on a steel specimen having an original diameter of 0.503 in. and gauge length of 2.00 in. The data is listed in the table. Plot the stress–strain diagram and determine approximately the modulus of elasticity, the yield stress, the ultimate stress, and the rupture stress. Use a scale of 1 in. = 20 ksi and 1 in. = 0.05 in./in. Redraw the elastic region, using the same stress scale but a strain scale of 1 in. = 0.001 in./in.

| Load (kip) | Elongation (in.) |
|------------|------------------|
| 0          | 0                |
| 1.50       | 0.0005           |
| 4.60       | 0.0015           |
| 8.00       | 0.0025           |
| 11.00      | 0.0035           |
| 11.80      | 0.0050           |
| 11.80      | 0.0080           |
| 12.00      | 0.0200           |
| 16.60      | 0.0400           |
| 20.00      | 0.1000           |
| 21.50      | 0.2800           |
| 19.50      | 0.4000           |
| 18.50      | 0.4600           |

**Prob. 1**

**2.** Data taken from a stress–strain test for a ceramic are given in the table. The curve is linear between the origin and the first point. Plot the diagram, and determine the modulus of elasticity and the modulus of resilience.

**3.** Data taken from a stress–strain test for a ceramic are given in the table. The curve is linear between the origin and the first point. Plot the diagram, and determine approximately the modulus of toughness. The rupture stress is $\sigma_r = 53.4$ ksi.

| $\sigma$ (ksi) | $\epsilon$ (in./in.) |
|----------------|----------------------|
| 0              | 0                    |
| 33.2           | 0.0006               |
| 45.5           | 0.0010               |
| 49.4           | 0.0014               |
| 51.5           | 0.0018               |
| 53.4           | 0.0022               |

**Probs. 2/3**

**\*4.** A tension test was performed on a steel specimen having an original diameter of 0.503 in. and a gauge length of 2.00 in. The data is listed in the table. Plot the stress–strain diagram and determine approximately the modulus of elasticity, the ultimate stress, and the rupture stress. Use a scale of 1 in. = 15 ksi and 1 in. = 0.05 in./in. Redraw the linear-elastic region, using the same stress scale but a strain scale of 1 in. = 0.001 in.

**5.** A tension test was performed on a steel specimen having an original diameter of 0.503 in. and gauge length of 2.00 in. Using the data listed in the table, plot the stress–strain diagram and determine approximately the modulus of toughness.

| Load (kip) | Elongation (in.) |
|------------|------------------|
| 0          | 0                |
| 2.50       | 0.0009           |
| 6.50       | 0.0025           |
| 8.50       | 0.0040           |
| 9.20       | 0.0065           |
| 9.80       | 0.0098           |
| 12.0       | 0.0400           |
| 14.0       | 0.1200           |
| 14.5       | 0.2500           |
| 14.0       | 0.3500           |
| 13.2       | 0.4700           |

**Probs. 4/5**

**6.** A specimen is originally 1 ft long, has a diameter of 0.5 in., and is subjected to a force of 500 lb. When the force is increased from 500 lb to 1800 lb, the specimen elongates 0.009 in. Determine the modulus of elasticity for the material if it remains linear elastic.

**7.** A structural member in a nuclear reactor is made of a zirconium alloy. If an axial load of 4 kip is to be supported by the member, determine its required cross-sectional area. Use a factor of safety of 3 relative to yielding. What is the load on the member if it is 3 ft long and its elongation is 0.02 in.? $E_{zr} = 14(10^3)$ ksi, $\sigma_Y = 57.5$ ksi. The material has elastic behavior.

**\*8.** The strut is supported by a pin at $C$ and an A-36 steel guy wire $AB$. If the wire has a diameter of 0.2 in., determine how much it stretches when the distributed load acts on the strut.

**Prob. 8**

**9.** The $\sigma$–$\epsilon$ diagram for elastic fibers that make up human skin and muscle is shown. Determine the modulus of elasticity of the fibers and estimate their modulus of toughness and modulus of resilience.

**Prob. 9**

**10.** The stress–strain diagram for a metal alloy having an original diameter of 0.5 in. and a gauge length of 2 in. is given in the figure. Determine approximately the modulus of elasticity for the material, the load on the specimen that causes yielding, and the ultimate load the specimen will support.

**11.** The stress–strain diagram for a steel alloy having an original diameter of 0.5 in. and a gauge length of 2 in. is given in the figure. If the specimen is loaded until it is stressed to 90 ksi, determine the approximate amount of elastic recovery and the increase in the gauge length after it is unloaded.

**\*12.** The stress–strain diagram for a steel alloy having an original diameter of 0.5 in. and a gauge length of 2 in. is given in the figure. Determine approximately the modulus of resilience and the modulus of toughness for the material.

**Probs. 10/11/12**

**13.** A bar having a length of 5 in. and cross-sectional area of 0.7 in.$^2$ is subjected to an axial force of 8000 lb. If the bar stretches 0.002 in., determine the modulus of elasticity of the material. The material has linear-elastic behavior.

**Prob. 13**

**14.** The rigid pipe is supported by a pin at $A$ and an A-36 steel guy wire $BD$. If the wire has a diameter of 0.25 in., determine how much it stretches when a load of $P = 600$ lb acts on the pipe.

**15.** The rigid pipe is supported by a pin at $A$ and an A-36 guy wire $BD$. If the wire has a diameter of 0.25 in., determine the load $P$ if the end $C$ is displaced 0.15 in. downward.

**Probs. 14/15**

**17.** A tension test was performed on a magnesium alloy specimen having a diameter 0.5 in. and gauge length 2 in. The resulting stress–strain diagram is shown in the figure. Determine the approximate modulus of elasticity and the yield strength of the alloy using the 0.2% strain offset method.

**18.** A tension test was performed on a magnesium alloy specimen having a diameter 0.5 in. and gauge length of 2 in. The resulting stress–strain diagram is shown in the figure. If the specimen is stressed to 30 ksi and unloaded, determine the permanent elongation of the specimen.

**Probs. 17/18**

**19.** The stress–strain diagram for a bone is shown, and can be described by the equation $\epsilon = 0.45(10^{-6})\,\sigma + 0.36(10^{-12})\,\sigma^3$, where $\sigma$ is in kPa. Determine the yield strength assuming a 0.3% offset.

**\*20.** The stress–strain diagram for a bone is shown and can be described by the equation $\epsilon = 0.45(10^{-6})\,\sigma + 0.36(10^{-12})\,\sigma^3$, where $\sigma$ is in kPa. Determine the modulus of toughness and the amount of elongation of a 200-mm-long region just before it fractures if failure occurs at $\epsilon = 0.12$ mm/mm.

**\*16.** The wire has a diameter of 5 mm and is made from A-36 steel. If a 80-kg man is sitting on seat $C$, determine the elongation of wire $DE$.

**Prob. 16**

$\epsilon = 0.45(10^{-6})\sigma + 0.36(10^{-12})\sigma^3$

**Probs. 19/20**

**21.** The two bars are made of polystyrene, which has the stress–strain diagram shown. If the cross-sectional area of bar $AB$ is 1.5 in² and $BC$ is 4 in², determine the largest force $P$ that can be supported before any member ruptures. Assume that buckling does not occur.

**22.** The two bars are made of polystyrene, which has the stress–strain diagram shown. Determine the cross-sectional area of each bar so that the bars rupture simultaneously when the load $P = 3$ kip. Assume that buckling does not occur.

**\*24.** The wires $AB$ and $BC$ have original lengths of 2 ft and 3 ft, and diameters of $\frac{1}{8}$ in. and $\frac{3}{16}$ in., respectively. If these wires are made of a material that has the approximate stress–strain diagram shown, determine the elongations of the wires after the 1500-lb load is placed on the platform.

**Probs. 21/22**

**23.** The stress–strain diagram for many metal alloys can be described analytically using the Ramberg-Osgood three parameter equation $\epsilon = \sigma/E + k\sigma^n$, where $E$, $k$, and $n$ are determined from measurements taken from the diagram, Using the stress–strain diagram shown in the figure, take $E = 30(10^3)$ ksi and determine the other two parameters $k$ and $n$ and thereby obtain an analytical expression for the curve.

**Prob. 23**

**Prob. 24**

## 6  Poisson's Ratio

When a deformable body is subjected to an axial tensile force, not only does it elongate but it also contracts laterally. For example, if a rubber band is stretched, it can be noted that both the thickness and width of the band are decreased. Likewise, a compressive force acting on a body causes it to contract in the direction of the force and yet its sides expand laterally.

Consider a bar having an original radius $r$ and length $L$ and subjected to the tensile force $P$ in Fig. 21. This force elongates the bar by an amount $\delta$, and its radius contracts by an amount $\delta'$. Strains in the longitudinal or axial direction and in the lateral or radial direction are, respectively,

$$\epsilon_{\text{long}} = \frac{\delta}{L} \quad \text{and} \quad \epsilon_{\text{lat}} = \frac{\delta'}{r}$$

In the early 1800s, the French scientist S. D. Poisson realized that within the *elastic range* the *ratio* of these strains is a *constant*, since the deformations $\delta$ and $\delta'$ are proportional. This constant is referred to as **Poisson's ratio**, $\nu$ (nu), and it has a numerical value that is unique for a particular material that is both *homogeneous and isotropic*. Stated mathematically it is

$$\nu = -\frac{\epsilon_{\text{lat}}}{\epsilon_{\text{long}}} \tag{9}$$

The negative sign is included here since *longitudinal elongation* (positive strain) causes *lateral contraction* (negative strain), and vice versa. Notice that these strains are caused only by the axial or longitudinal force $P$; i.e., no force or stress acts in a lateral direction in order to strain the material in this direction.

Poisson's ratio is a *dimensionless* quantity, and for most nonporous solids it has a value that is generally between $\frac{1}{4}$ and $\frac{1}{3}$. Typical values of $\nu$ for common engineering materials are listed on the inside back cover. For an "ideal material" having no lateral deformation when it is stretched or compressed, Poisson's ratio will be 0. Furthermore, it will be shown in Sec. 10.6 that the *maximum* possible value for Poisson's ratio is 0.5. Therefore $0 \le \nu \le 0.5$.

When the rubber block is compressed (negative strain) its sides will expand (positive strain). The ratio of these strains remains constant.

**Fig. 21**

## EXAMPLE 4

A bar made of A-36 steel has the dimensions shown in Fig. 22. If an axial force of $P = 80$ kN is applied to the bar, determine the change in its length and the change in the dimensions of its cross section after applying the load. The material behaves elastically.

$P = 80$ kN

1.5 m

50 mm

$y$

$x$

$P = 80$ kN

100 mm

$z$

**Fig. 22**

## SOLUTION

The normal stress in the bar is

$$\sigma_z = \frac{P}{A} = \frac{80(10^3)\ \text{N}}{(0.1\ \text{m})(0.05\ \text{m})} = 16.0(10^6)\ \text{Pa}$$

A-36 steel $E_{st} = 200$ GPa, and so the strain in the $z$ direction is

$$\epsilon_z = \frac{\sigma_z}{E_{st}} = \frac{16.0(10^6)\ \text{Pa}}{200(10^9)\ \text{Pa}} = 80(10^{-6})\ \text{mm/mm}$$

The axial elongation of the bar is therefore

$$\delta_z = \epsilon_z L_z = [80(10^{-6})](1.5\ \text{m}) = 120\ \mu\text{m} \qquad Ans.$$

Using Eq. 9, where $\nu_{st} = 0.32$ as found from the inside back cover, the lateral contraction strains in *both* the $x$ and $y$ directions are

$$\epsilon_x = \epsilon_y = -\nu_{st}\,\epsilon_z = -0.32[80(10^{-6})] = -25.6\ \mu\text{m/m}$$

Thus the changes in the dimensions of the cross section are

$$\delta_x = \epsilon_x L_x = -[25.6(10^{-6})](0.1\ \text{m}) = -2.56\ \mu\text{m} \qquad Ans.$$

$$\delta_y = \epsilon_y L_y = -[25.6(10^{-6})](0.05\ \text{m}) = -1.28\ \mu\text{m} \qquad Ans.$$

(a)

(b)

**Fig. 23**

**Fig. 24**

# 7  The Shear Stress–Strain Diagram

When a small element of material is subjected to *pure shear*, equilibrium requires that equal shear stresses must be developed on four faces of the element. These stresses $\tau_{xy}$ must be directed toward or away from diagonally opposite corners of the element, as shown in Fig. 23*a*. Furthermore, if the material is *homogeneous* and *isotropic*, then this shear stress will distort the element uniformly, Fig. 23*b*. The shear strain $\gamma_{xy}$ measures the angular distortion of the element relative to the sides originally along the *x* and *y* axes.

The behavior of a material subjected to pure shear can be studied in a laboratory using specimens in the shape of thin tubes and subjecting them to a torsional loading. If measurements are made of the applied torque and the resulting angle of twist. The data can be used to determine the shear stress and shear strain, and a shear stress–strain diagram plotted. An example of such a diagram for a ductile material is shown in Fig. 24. Like the tension test, this material when subjected to shear will exhibit linear-elastic behavior and it will have a defined *proportional limit* $\tau_{pl}$. Also, strain hardening will occur until an *ultimate shear stress* $\tau_u$ is reached. And finally, the material will begin to lose its shear strength until it reaches a point where it fractures, $\tau_f$.

For most engineering materials, like the one just described, the elastic behavior is *linear*, and so Hooke's law for shear can be written as

$$\tau = G\gamma \tag{10}$$

Here *G* is called the **shear modulus of elasticity** or the **modulus of rigidity**. Its value represents the slope of the line on the $\tau$–$\gamma$ diagram, that is, $G = \tau_{pl}/\gamma_{pl}$. Typical values for common engineering materials are listed on the inside back cover. Notice that the units of measurement for *G* will be the *same* as those for $\tau$ (Pa or psi), since $\gamma$ is measured in radians, a dimensionless quantity.

The three material constants, *E*, $\nu$, and *G* are actually *related* by the equation

$$G = \frac{E}{2(1 + \nu)} \tag{11}$$

Provided *E* and *G* are known, the value of $\nu$ can then be determined from this equation rather than through experimental measurement. For example, in the case of A-36 steel, $E_{st} = 29(10^3)$ ksi and $G_{st} = 11(10^3)$ ksi, so that, from Eq. 11, $\nu_{st} = 0.32$.

# EXAMPLE 5

A specimen of titanium alloy is tested in torsion and the shear stress–strain diagram is shown in Fig. 25a. Determine the shear modulus $G$, the proportional limit, and the ultimate shear stress. Also, determine the maximum distance $d$ that the top of a block of this material, shown in Fig. 25b, could be displaced horizontally if the material behaves elastically when acted upon by a shear force $\mathbf{V}$. What is the magnitude of $\mathbf{V}$ necessary to cause this displacement?

(a)

## SOLUTION

**Shear Modulus.** This value represents the slope of the straight-line portion $OA$ of the $\tau$–$\gamma$ diagram. The coordinates of point $A$ are (0.008 rad, 52 ksi). Thus,

$$G = \frac{52 \text{ ksi}}{0.008 \text{ rad}} = 6500 \text{ ksi} \qquad Ans.$$

(b)

**Fig. 25**

The equation of line $OA$ is therefore $\tau = G\gamma = 6500\gamma$, which is Hooke's law for shear.

**Proportional Limit.** By inspection, the graph ceases to be linear at point $A$. Thus,

$$\tau_{pl} = 52 \text{ ksi} \qquad Ans.$$

**Ultimate Stress.** This value represents the maximum shear stress, point $B$. From the graph,

$$\tau_u = 73 \text{ ksi} \qquad Ans.$$

**Maximum Elastic Displacement and Shear Force.** Since the maximum elastic shear strain is 0.008 rad, a very small angle, the top of the block in Fig. 25b will be displaced horizontally:

$$\tan(0.008 \text{ rad}) \approx 0.008 \text{ rad} = \frac{d}{2 \text{ in.}}$$

$$d = 0.016 \text{ in.} \qquad Ans.$$

The corresponding *average* shear stress in the block is $\tau_{pl} = 52$ ksi. Thus, the shear force $V$ needed to cause the displacement is

$$\tau_{avg} = \frac{V}{A}; \qquad 52 \text{ ksi} = \frac{V}{(3 \text{ in.})(4 \text{ in.})}$$

$$V = 624 \text{ kip} \qquad Ans.$$

## EXAMPLE | 6

165 kN

$d_0$ — $L_0$

165 kN

**Fig. 26**

An aluminum specimen shown in Fig. 26 has a diameter of $d_0 = 25$ mm and a gauge length of $L_0 = 250$ mm. If a force of 165 kN elongates the gauge length 1.20 mm, determine the modulus of elasticity. Also, determine by how much the force causes the diameter of the specimen to contract. Take $G_{al} = 26$ GPa and $\sigma_Y = 440$ MPa.

### SOLUTION

**Modulus of Elasticity.** The average normal stress in the specimen is

$$\sigma = \frac{P}{A} = \frac{165(10^3) \text{ N}}{(\pi/4)(0.025 \text{ m})^2} = 336.1 \text{ MPa}$$

and the average normal strain is

$$\epsilon = \frac{\delta}{L} = \frac{1.20 \text{ mm}}{250 \text{ mm}} = 0.00480 \text{ mm/mm}$$

Since $\sigma < \sigma_Y = 440$ MPa, the material behaves elastically. The modulus of elasticity is therefore

$$E_{al} = \frac{\sigma}{\epsilon} = \frac{336.1(10^6) \text{ Pa}}{0.00480} = 70.0 \text{ GPa} \qquad Ans.$$

**Contraction of Diameter.** First we will determine Poisson's ratio for the material using Eq. 11.

$$G = \frac{E}{2(1 + \nu)}$$

$$26 \text{ GPa} = \frac{70.0 \text{ GPa}}{2(1 + \nu)}$$

$$\nu = 0.347$$

Since $\epsilon_{long} = 0.00480$ mm/mm, then by Eq. 9,

$$\nu = -\frac{\epsilon_{lat}}{\epsilon_{long}}$$

$$0.347 = -\frac{\epsilon_{lat}}{0.00480 \text{ mm/mm}}$$

$$\epsilon_{lat} = -0.00166 \text{ mm/mm}$$

The contraction of the diameter is therefore

$$\delta' = (0.00166)(25 \text{ mm})$$

$$= 0.0416 \text{ mm} \qquad Ans.$$

# *8 Failure of Materials Due to Creep and Fatigue

The mechanical properties of a material have up to this point been discussed only for a static or slowly applied load at constant temperature. In some cases, however, a member may have to be used in an environment for which loadings must be sustained over long periods of time at elevated temperatures, or in other cases, the loading may be repeated or cycled. We will not consider these effects in this text, although we will briefly mention how one determines a material's strength for these conditions, since they are given special treatment in design.

**Creep.** When a material has to support a load for a very long period of time, it may continue to deform until a sudden fracture occurs or its usefulness is impaired. This time-dependent permanent deformation is known as *creep*. Normally creep is considered when metals and ceramics are used for structural members or mechanical parts that are subjected to high temperatures. For some materials, however, such as polymers and composite materials—including wood or concrete—temperature is *not* an important factor, and yet creep can occur strictly from long-term load application. As a typical example, consider the fact that a rubber band will not return to its original shape after being released from a stretched position in which it was held for a very long period of time. In the general sense, therefore, both *stress and/or temperature* play a significant role in the *rate* of creep.

For practical purposes, when creep becomes important, a member is usually designed to resist a specified creep strain for a given period of time. An important mechanical property that is used in this regard is called the *creep strength*. This value represents the highest stress the material can withstand during a specified time without exceeding an allowable creep strain. The creep strength will vary with temperature, and for design, a given temperature, duration of loading, and allowable creep strain must all be specified. For example, a creep strain of 0.1% per year has been suggested for steel in bolts and piping.

Several methods exist for determining an allowable creep strength for a particular material. One of the simplest involves testing several specimens simultaneously at a constant temperature, but with each subjected to a *different axial stress*. By measuring the length of time needed to produce either an allowable strain or the fracture strain for each specimen, a curve of stress versus time can be established. Normally these tests are run to a maximum of 1000 hours. An example of the results for stainless steel at a temperature of 1200°F and prescribed creep strain of 1% is shown in Fig. 27. As noted, this material has a yield strength of 40 ksi (276 MPa) at room temperature (0.2% offset) and the creep strength at 1000 h is found to be approximately $\sigma_c = 20$ ksi (138 MPa).

The long-tem application of the cable loading on this pole has caused the pole to deform due to creep.

σ–t diagram for stainless steel
at 1200°F and creep strain at 1%

**Fig. 27**

For longer periods of time, extrapolations from the curves must be made. To do this usually requires a certain amount of experience with creep behavior, and some supplementary knowledge about the creep properties of the material. Once the material's creep strength has been determined, however, a factor of safety is applied to obtain an appropriate allowable stress for design.

**Fatigue.** When a metal is subjected to repeated *cycles* of stress or strain, it causes its structure to break down, ultimately leading to fracture. This behavior is called *fatigue*, and it is usually responsible for a large percentage of failures in connecting rods and crankshafts of engines; steam or gas turbine blades; connections or supports for bridges, railroad wheels, and axles; and other parts subjected to cyclic loading. In all these cases, fracture will occur at a stress that is *less* than the material's yield stress.

The nature of this failure apparently results from the fact that there are microscopic imperfections, usually on the surface of the member, where the localized stress becomes *much greater* than the average stress acting over the cross section. As this higher stress is cycled, it leads to the formation of minute cracks. Occurrence of these cracks causes a further increase of stress at their tips or boundaries, which in turn causes a further extension of the cracks into the material as the stress continues to be cycled. Eventually the cross-sectional area of the member is reduced to the point where the load can no longer be sustained, and as a result sudden fracture occurs. The material, even though known to be ductile, behaves as if it were *brittle*.

In order to specify a safe strength for a metallic material under repeated loading, it is necessary to determine a limit below which no evidence of failure can be detected after applying a load for a specified number of cycles. This limiting stress is called the *endurance* or *fatigue limit*. Using a testing machine for this purpose, a series of specimens are each subjected to a specified stress and cycled to failure. The results are plotted as a graph representing the stress $S$ (or $\sigma$) on the vertical axis and the number of cycles-to-failure $N$ on the horizontal axis. This graph is called an *S–N diagram* or *stress–cycle diagram*, and most often the values of $N$ are plotted on a logarithmic scale since they are generally quite large.

Examples of *S–N* diagrams for two common engineering metals are shown in Fig. 28. The endurance limit is usually identified as the stress for which the *S–N* graph becomes horizontal or asymptotic. As noted, it has a well-defined value of $(S_{el})_{st} = 27$ ksi (186 MPa) for steel. For aluminum, however, the endurance limit is not well defined, and so it is normally specified as the stress having a limit of 500 million cycles, $(S_{el})_{al} = 19$ ksi (131 MPa). Once a particular value is obtained, it is often assumed that for any stress below this value the fatigue life is infinite, and therefore the number of cycles to failure is no longer given consideration.

The design of members used for amusement park rides requires careful consideration of cyclic loadings that can cause fatigue.

Engineers must account for possible fatigue failure of the moving parts of this oil-pumping rig.

$S$–$N$ diagram for steel and aluminum alloys
($N$ axis has a logarithmic scale)

**Fig. 28**

## Important Points

- *Poisson's ratio*, $\nu$, is a ratio of the lateral strain of a homogeneous and isotropic material to its longitudinal strain. Generally these strains are of opposite signs, that is, if one is an elongation, the other will be a contraction.

- The *shear stress–strain diagram* is a plot of the shear stress versus the shear strain. If the material is homogeneous and isotropic, and is also linear elastic, the slope of the straight line within the elastic region is called the modulus of rigidity or the shear modulus, $G$.

- There is a mathematical relationship between $G$, $E$, and $\nu$.

- *Creep* is the time-dependent deformation of a material for which stress and/or temperature play an important role. Members are designed to resist the effects of creep based on their material creep strength, which is the largest initial stress a material can withstand during a specified time without exceeding a specified creep strain.

- *Fatigue* occurs in metals when the stress or strain is cycled. This phenomenon causes brittle fracture of the material. Members are designed to resist fatigue by ensuring that the stress in the member does not exceed its *endurance* or *fatigue limit*. This value is determined from an *S–N* diagram as the maximum stress the material can resist when subjected to a specified number of cycles of loading.

# FUNDAMENTAL PROBLEMS

**F13.** A 100-mm long rod has a diameter of 15 mm. If an axial tensile load of 10 kN is applied to it, determine the change in its diameter. $E = 70$ GPa, $\nu = 0.35$.

**F14.** A solid circular rod that is 600 mm long and 20 mm in diameter is subjected to an axial force of $P = 50$ kN. The elongation of the rod is $\delta = 1.40$ mm, and its diameter becomes $d' = 19.9837$ mm. Determine the modulus of elasticity and the modulus of rigidity of the material. Assume that the material does not yield.

**F16.** A 20-mm-wide block is bonded to rigid plates at its top and bottom. When the force **P** is applied the block deforms into the shape shown by the dashed line. If $a = 3$ mm and **P** is released, determine the permanent shear strain in the block.

**F14**

**F16**

**F15.** A 20-mm-wide block is firmly bonded to rigid plates at its top and bottom. When the force **P** is applied the block deforms into the shape shown by the dashed line. Determine the magnitude of **P**. The block's material has a modulus of rigidity of $G = 26$ GPa. Assume that the material does not yield and use small angle analysis.

**F15**

124

## PROBLEMS

**25.** The acrylic plastic rod is 200 mm long and 15 mm in diameter. If an axial load of 300 N is applied to it, determine the change in its length and the change in its diameter. $E_p = 2.70$ GPa, $\nu_p = 0.4$.

**27.** When the two forces are placed on the beam, the diameter of the A-36 steel rod $BC$ decreases from 40 mm to 39.99 mm. Determine the magnitude of each force **P**.

**\*28.** If $P = 150$ kN, determine the elastic elongation of rod $BC$ and the decrease in its diameter. Rod $BC$ is made of A-36 streel and has a diameter of 40 mm.

**Prob. 25**

**Probs. 27/28**

**26.** The thin-walled tube is subjected to an axial force of 40 kN. If the tube elongates 3 mm and its circumference decreases 0.09 mm, determine the modulus of elasticity, Poisson's ratio, and the shear modulus of the tube's material. The material behaves elastically.

**29.** The friction pad $A$ is used to support the member, which is subjected to an axial force of $P = 2$ kN. The pad is made from a material having a modulus of elasticity of $E = 4$ MPa and Poisson's ratio $\nu = 0.4$. If slipping does not occur, determine the normal and shear strains in the pad. The width is 50 mm. Assume that the material is linearly elastic. Also, neglect the effect of the moment acting on the pad.

**Prob. 26**

**Prob. 29**

**30.** The lap joint is connected together using a 1.25 in. diameter bolt. If the bolt is made from a material having a shear stress–strain diagram that is approximated as shown, determine the shear strain developed in the shear plane of the bolt when $P = 75$ kip.

**31.** The lap joint is connected together using a 1.25 in. diameter bolt. If the bolt is made from a material having a shear stress-strain diagram that is approximated as shown, determine the permanent shear strain in the shear plane of the bolt when the applied force $P = 150$ kip is removed.

**33.** The aluminum block has a rectangular cross section and is subjected to an axial compressive force of 8 kip. If the 1.5-in. side changed its length to 1.500132 in., determine Poisson's ratio and the new length of the 2-in. side. $E_{al} = 10(10^3)$ ksi.

**Prob. 33**

**Probs. 30/31**

**\*32.** A shear spring is made by bonding the rubber annulus to a rigid fixed ring and a plug. When an axial load $P$ is placed on the plug, show that the slope at point $y$ in the rubber is $dy/dr = -\tan \gamma = -\tan(P/(2\pi hGr))$. For small angles we can write $dy/dr = -P/(2\pi hGr)$. Integrate this expression and evaluate the constant of integration using the condition that $y = 0$ at $r = r_o$. From the result compute the deflection $y = \delta$ of the plug.

**34.** A shear spring is made from two blocks of rubber, each having a height $h$, width $b$, and thickness $a$. The blocks are bonded to three plates as shown. If the plates are rigid and the shear modulus of the rubber is $G$, determine the displacement of plate $A$ if a vertical load $\mathbf{P}$ is applied to this plate. Assume that the displacement is small so that $\delta = a \tan \gamma \approx a\gamma$.

**Prob. 32**

**Prob. 34**

# CHAPTER REVIEW

One of the most important tests for material strength is the tension test. The results, found from stretching a specimen of known size, are plotted as normal stress on the vertical axis and normal strain on the horizontal axis.

| | | |
|---|---|---|
| Many engineering materials exhibit initial linear elastic behavior, whereby stress is proportional to strain, defined by Hooke's law, $\sigma = E\epsilon$. Here $E$, called the modulus of elasticity, is the slope of this straight line on the stress–strain diagram. | $$\sigma = E\epsilon$$ |  ductile material |
| When the material is stressed beyond the yield point, permanent deformation will occur. In particular, steel has a region of yielding, whereby the material will exhibit an increase in strain with no increase in stress. The region of strain hardening causes further yielding of the material with a corresponding increase in stress. Finally, at the ultimate stress, a localized region on the specimen will begin to constrict, forming a neck. It is after this that the fracture occurs. | | 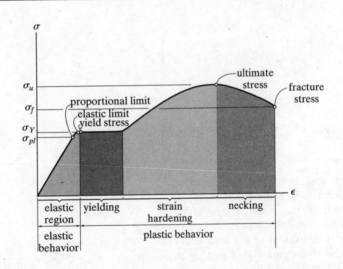 |
| Ductile materials, such as most metals, exhibit both elastic and plastic behavior. Wood is moderately ductile. Ductility is usually specified by the percent elongation to failure or by the percent reduction in the cross-sectional area. | $$\text{Percent elongation} = \frac{L_f - L_0}{L_0}\,(100\%)$$ $$\text{Percent reduction of area} = \frac{A_0 - A_f}{A_0}\,(100\%)$$ | |

| | | |
|---|---|---|
| Brittle materials exhibit little or no yielding before failure. Cast iron, concrete, and glass are typical examples. | | 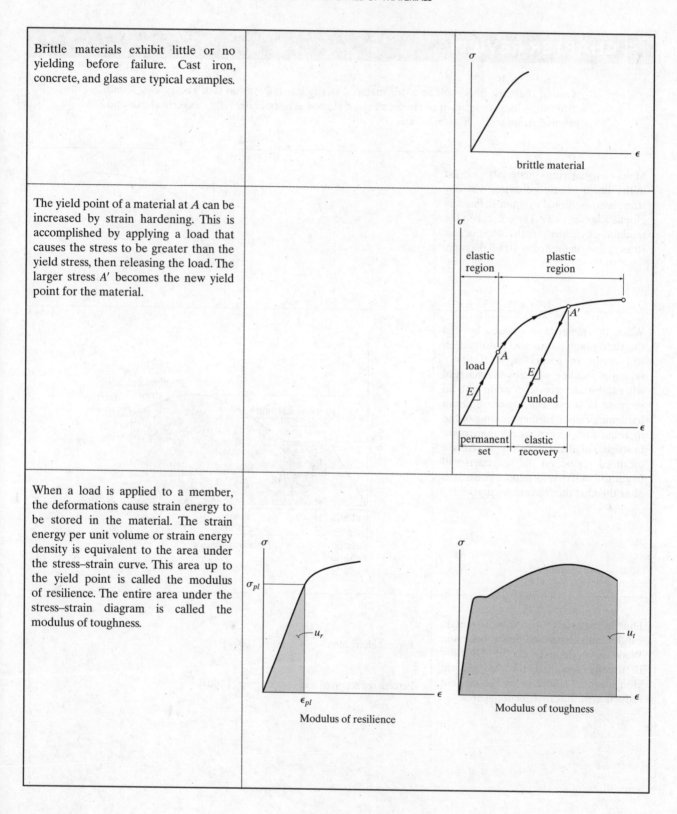brittle material |
| The yield point of a material at $A$ can be increased by strain hardening. This is accomplished by applying a load that causes the stress to be greater than the yield stress, then releasing the load. The larger stress $A'$ becomes the new yield point for the material. | | |
| When a load is applied to a member, the deformations cause strain energy to be stored in the material. The strain energy per unit volume or strain energy density is equivalent to the area under the stress–strain curve. This area up to the yield point is called the modulus of resilience. The entire area under the stress–strain diagram is called the modulus of toughness. | | |

| | | |
|---|---|---|
| Poisson's ratio $\nu$ is a dimensionless material property that relates the lateral strain to the longitudinal strain. Its range of values is $0 \le \nu \le 0.5$. | $$\nu = -\frac{\epsilon_{\text{lat}}}{\epsilon_{\text{long}}}$$ | |
| Shear stress versus shear strain diagrams can also be established for a material. Within the elastic region, $\tau = G\gamma$, where $G$ is the shear modulus, found from the slope of the line. The value of $\nu$ can be obtained from the relationship that exists between $G$, $E$ and $\nu$. | $$G = \frac{E}{2(1 + \nu)}$$ | |
| When materials are in service for long periods of time, considerations of creep become important. Creep is the time rate of deformation, which occurs at high stress and/or high temperature. Design requires that the stress in the material not exceed an allowable stress which is based on the material's creep strength.<br><br>Fatigue can occur when the material undergoes a large number of cycles of loading. This effect will cause microscopic cracks to form, leading to a brittle failure. To prevent fatigue, the stress in the material must not exceed a specified endurance or fatigue limit. | | |

# REVIEW PROBLEMS

**35.** The elastic portion of the tension stress–strain diagram for an aluminum alloy is shown in the figure. The specimen used for the test has a gauge length of 2 in. and a diameter of 0.5 in. When the applied load is 9 kip, the new diameter of the specimen is 0.49935 in. Compute the shear modulus $G_{al}$ for the aluminum.

**\*36.** The elastic portion of the tension stress–strain diagram for an aluminum alloy is shown in the figure. The specimen used for the test has a gauge length of 2 in. and a diameter of 0.5 in. If the applied load is 10 kip, determine the new diameter of the specimen. The shear modulus is $G_{al} = 3.8(10^3)$ ksi.

**Probs. 35/36**

**37.** The rigid beam rests in the horizontal position on two 2014-T6 aluminum cylinders having the *unloaded* lengths shown. If each cylinder has a diameter of 30 mm. determine the placement $x$ of the applied 80-kN load so that the beam remains horizontal. What is the new diameter of cylinder $A$ after the load is applied? $\nu_{al} = 0.35$.

**Prob. 37**

**38.** The wires each have a diameter of $\frac{1}{2}$ in., length of 2 ft, and are made from 304 stainless steel. If $P = 6$ kip, determine the angle of tilt of the rigid beam $AB$.

**39.** The wires each have a diameter of $\frac{1}{2}$ in., length of 2 ft, and are made from 304 stainless steel. Determine the magnitude of force **P** so that the rigid beam tilts 0.015°.

**Probs. 38/39**

**\*40.** The head $H$ is connected to the cylinder of a compressor using six steel bolts. If the clamping force in each bolt is 800 lb, determine the normal strain in the bolts. Each bolt has a diameter of $\frac{3}{16}$ in. If $\sigma_Y = 40$ ksi and $E_{st} = 29(10^3)$ ksi, what is the strain in each bolt when the nut is unscrewed so that the clamping force is released?

**Prob. 40**

**41.** The stress–strain diagram for polyethylene, which is used to sheath coaxial cables, is determined from testing a specimen that has a gauge length of 10 in. If a load $P$ on the specimen develops a strain of $\epsilon = 0.024$ in./in., determine the approximate length of the specimen, measured between the gauge points, when the load is removed. Assume the specimen recovers elastically.

**43.** The 8-mm-diameter bolt is made of an aluminum alloy. It fits through a magnesium sleeve that has an inner diameter of 12 mm and an outer diameter of 20 mm. If the original lengths of the bolt and sleeve are 80 mm and 50 mm, respectively, determine the strains in the sleeve and the bolt if the nut on the bolt is tightened so that the tension in the bolt is 8 kN. Assume the material at $A$ is rigid. $E_{al} = 70$ GPa, $E_{mg} = 45$ GPa.

**Prob. 41**

**Prob. 43**

**42.** The pipe with two rigid caps attached to its ends is subjected to an axial force $P$. If the pipe is made from a material having a modulus of elasticity $E$ and Poisson's ratio $\nu$, determine the change in volume of the material.

***44.** An acetal polymer block is fixed to the rigid plates at its top and bottom surfaces. If the top plate displaces 2 mm horizontally when it is subjected to a horizontal force $P = 2$ kN, determine the shear modulus of the polymer. The width of the block is 100 mm. Assume that the polymer is linearly elastic and use small angle analysis.

**Prob. 42**

**Prob. 44**

# Selected Answers

**1.** $(\sigma_{ult})_{approx} = 110$ ksi, $(\sigma_R)_{approx} = 93.1$ ksi, $(\sigma_Y)_{approx} = 55$ ksi, $E_{approx} = 32.0(10^3)$ ksi

**2.** $E = 55.3(10^3)$ ksi, $u_r = 9.96 \dfrac{in \cdot lb}{in^3}$

**3.** $(u_t)_{approx} = 85.0 \dfrac{in \cdot lb}{in^3}$

**5.** $u_t = 16.3 \dfrac{in \cdot kip}{in^3}$

**6.** $E = 8.83(10^3)$ ksi

**7.** $A = 0.209$ in$^2$, $P = 1.62$ kip

**9.** $E = 5.5$ psi, $u_t = 19.25$ psi, $u_r = 11$ psi

**10.** $E = 30.0(10^3)$ ksi, $P_Y = 11.8$ kip, $P_{ult} = 19.6$ kip

**11.** Elastic Recovery $= 0.003$ in./in., $\Delta L = 0.094$ in.

**13.** $E = 28.6(10^3)$ ksi

**14.** $\delta_{BD} = 0.0632$ in.

**15.** $P = 570$ lb

**17.** $E_{approx} = 6.50(10^3)$ ksi, $\sigma_{YS} = 25.9$ ksi

**18.** $\delta_P = 0.00637$ in.

**19.** $\sigma_{YS} = 2.03$ MPa

**21.** $P = 15.0$ kip

**22.** $A_{BC} = 0.8$ in$^2$, $A_{BA} = 0.2$ in$^2$

**23.** $n = 2.73$, $k = 4.23(10^{-6})$

**25.** $\delta = 0.126$ mm, $\Delta d = -0.00377$ mm

**26.** $E = 67.9$ GPa, $\nu = 0.344$, $G = 25.3$ GPa

**27.** $P = 157$ kN

**29.** $\epsilon = 0.08660$ mm/mm, $\gamma = 0.140$ rad

**30.** $\gamma = 3.06(10^{-3})$ rad

**31.** $\gamma_P = 0.0189$ rad

**33.** $\nu = 0.330$, $h' = 2.000176$ in.

**34.** $\delta = \dfrac{Pa}{2bhG}$

**35.** $G_{al} = 4.31(10^3)$ ksi

**37.** $x = 1.53$ m, $d'_A = 30.008$ mm

**38.** $\theta = 0.0139°$

**39.** $P = 6.48$ kip

**41.** $L = 10.17$ in.

**42.** $\delta V = \dfrac{PL}{E}(1 - 2\nu)$

**43.** $\epsilon_b = 0.00227$ mm/mm, $\epsilon_s = 0.000884$ mm/mm

# Fundamental Problems Partial Solutions and Answers

**F1** Material has uniform properties throughout. *Ans.*

**F2** Proportional limit is $A$. *Ans.*

Ultimate stress is $D$. *Ans.*

**F3** The initial slope of the $\sigma - \epsilon$ diagram. *Ans.*

**F4** True. *Ans.*

**F5** False. Use the *original* cross-sectional area and length. *Ans.*

**F6** False. It will normally decrease. *Ans.*

**F7** $\varepsilon = \dfrac{\sigma}{E} = \dfrac{P}{AE}$

$\delta = \epsilon L = \dfrac{PL}{AE} = \dfrac{100(10^3)(0.100)}{\dfrac{\pi}{4}(0.015)^2\,200(10^9)}$

$= 0.283$mm *Ans.*

**F8** $\epsilon = \dfrac{\sigma}{E} = \dfrac{P}{AE}$

$\delta = \epsilon L = \dfrac{PL}{AE};$

$0.003 = \dfrac{(10\,000)(8)}{12E}$

$E = 2.22(10^6)$ psi *Ans.*

**F9** $\epsilon = \dfrac{\sigma}{E} = \dfrac{P}{AE}$

$\delta = \epsilon L = \dfrac{PL}{AE} = \dfrac{6(10^3)4}{\dfrac{\pi}{4}(0.01)^2\,100(10^9)}$

$= 3.06$ mm *Ans.*

**F10** $\sigma = \dfrac{P}{A} = \dfrac{100(10^3)}{\dfrac{\pi}{4}(0.02)^2} = 318.31$ MPa

Since $\sigma < \sigma_Y = 450$ MPa, Hooke's Law is applicable.

$E = \dfrac{\sigma_Y}{\epsilon_Y} = \dfrac{450(10^6)}{0.00225} = 200$ GPa

$\epsilon = \dfrac{\sigma}{E} = \dfrac{318.31(10^6)}{200(10^9)} = 0.001592$ mm/mm

$\delta = \epsilon L = 0.001592(50) = 0.0796$ mm *Ans.*

**F11** $\sigma = \dfrac{P}{A} = \dfrac{150(10^3)}{\dfrac{\pi}{4}(0.02^2)} = 477.46$ MPa

Since $\sigma > \sigma_Y = 450$ MPa, Hooke's Law is not applicable. From the geometry of the stress-strain diagram,

$$\dfrac{\epsilon - 0.00225}{0.03 - 0.00225} = \dfrac{477.46 - 450}{500 - 450}$$

$\epsilon = 0.017493$

When the load is removed, the strain recovers along a line parallel to the original elastic line.

Here $E = \dfrac{\sigma_Y}{\epsilon_Y} = \dfrac{450(10^6)}{0.00225} = 200$ GPa.

The elastic recovery is

$\epsilon_r = \dfrac{\sigma}{E} = \dfrac{477.46(10^6)}{200(10^9)} = 0.002387$ mm/mm

$\epsilon_p = \epsilon - \epsilon_r = 0.017493 - 0.002387$

$\quad = 0.01511$ mm/mm

$\delta_p = \epsilon_p L = 0.01511(50) = 0.755$ mm    *Ans.*

**F12** $\epsilon_{BC} = \dfrac{\delta_{BC}}{L_{BC}} = \dfrac{0.2}{300} = 0.6667(10^{-3})$ mm/mm

$\sigma_{BC} = E\epsilon_{BC} = 200(10^9)[0.6667(10^{-3})]$

$\quad = 133.33$ MPa

Since $\sigma_{BC} < \sigma_Y = 250$ MPa, Hooke's Law is valid.

$\sigma_{BC} = \dfrac{F_{BC}}{A_{BC}};\quad 133.33(10^6) = \dfrac{F_{BC}}{\dfrac{\pi}{4}(0.003^2)}$

$\qquad\qquad F_{BC} = 942.48$ N

$\zeta + \Sigma M_A = 0;\quad 942.48(0.4) - P(0.6) = 0$

$\qquad\qquad P = 628.31$ N $= 628$ N    *Ans.*

**F13** $\sigma = \dfrac{P}{A} = \dfrac{10(10^3)}{\dfrac{\pi}{4}(0.015)^2} = 56.59$ MPa

$\epsilon_{long} = \dfrac{\sigma}{E} = \dfrac{56.59(10^6)}{70(10^9)} = 0.808(10^{-3})$

$\epsilon_{lat} = -\nu\epsilon_{long} = -0.35(0.808(10^{-3}))$

$\quad = -0.283(10^{-3})$

$\delta d = (-0.283(10^{-3}))(15 \text{ mm}) = -4.24(10^{-3})$ mm

    *Ans.*

**F14** $\sigma = \dfrac{P}{A} = \dfrac{50(10^3)}{\dfrac{\pi}{4}(0.02^2)} = 159.15$ MPa

$\epsilon_{long} = \dfrac{\delta}{L} = \dfrac{1.40}{600} = 0.002333$ mm/mm

$E = \dfrac{\sigma}{\epsilon_{long}} = \dfrac{159.15(10^6)}{0.002333} = 68.2$ GPa    *Ans.*

$\epsilon_{lat} = \dfrac{d' - d}{d} = \dfrac{19.9837 - 20}{20} = -0.815(10^{-3})$ mm/mm

$\nu = -\dfrac{\epsilon_{lat}}{\epsilon_{long}} = -\dfrac{-0.815(10^{-3})}{0.002333} = 0.3493$

$G = \dfrac{E}{2(1+\nu)} = \dfrac{68.21}{2(1+0.3493)} = 25.3$ GPa    *Ans.*

**F15** $\alpha = \dfrac{0.5}{150} = 0.003333$ rad

$\gamma = \dfrac{\pi}{2} - \theta = \dfrac{\pi}{2} - \left(\dfrac{\pi}{2} - \alpha\right)$

$\quad = \alpha = 0.003333$ rad

$\tau = G\gamma = [26(10^9)](0.003333) = 86.67$ MPa

$\tau = \dfrac{V}{A};\quad 86.67(10^6) = \dfrac{P}{0.15(0.02)}$

$P = 260$ kN    *Ans.*

**F16** $\alpha = \dfrac{3}{150} = 0.02$ rad

$\gamma = \dfrac{\pi}{2} - \theta = \dfrac{\pi}{2} - \left(\dfrac{\pi}{2} - \alpha\right) = \alpha = 0.02$ rad

When $P$ is removed, the shear strain recovers along a line parallel to the original elastic line.

$\gamma_r = \gamma_Y = 0.005$ rad

$\gamma_p = \gamma - \gamma_r = 0.02 - 0.005 = 0.015$ rad    *Ans.*

# Axial Load

From Chapter 4 of *Mechanics of Materials*, Ninth Edition. R. C. Hibbeler. Copyright © 2014 by Pearson Education, Inc. Published by Pearson Prentice Hall.

The string of drill pipe stacked on this oil rig will be subjected to extremely large axial deformations when it is placed in the hole.

# Axial Load

## CHAPTER OBJECTIVES

■ We now discuss how to determine the deformation of axially loaded members, and we will also develop a method for finding the support reactions when these reactions cannot be determined strictly from the equations of equilibrium. An analysis of the effects of thermal stress, stress concentrations, inelastic deformations, and residual stress will also be discussed.

## 1 Saint-Venant's Principle

Stress is a means of measuring the force distribution within a body and strain is a means of measuring a body's deformation. The mathematical relationship between stress and strain depends on the type of material from which the body is made. In particular, if the material behaves in a linear elastic manner, then Hooke's law applies, and there is a proportional relationship between stress and strain.

Load distorts lines located near load

Lines located away from the load and support remain straight

Load distorts lines located near support

(a)

**Fig. 1**

Using this idea, consider the manner in which a rectangular bar will deform elastically when the bar is subjected to a force **P** applied along its centroidal axis, Fig. 1*a*. Here the bar is fixed connected at one end, with the force applied through a hole at its other end. Due to the loading, the bar deforms as indicated by the once horizontal and vertical grid lines drawn on the bar. Notice how the *localized deformation* that occurs at each end tends to even out and become uniform throughout the midsection of the bar.

If the material remains elastic then the strains caused by this deformation are directly related to the stress in the bar. As a result, the stress will be distributed more uniformly throughout the cross-sectional area when the section is taken farther and farther from the point where any external load is applied. For example, consider a profile of the variation of the stress distribution acting at sections *a–a*, *b–b*, and *c–c*, each of which is shown in Fig. 1*b*. By comparison, the stress tends to reach a uniform value at section *c–c*, which is sufficiently removed from the end since the localized deformation caused by **P** *vanishes*. The minimum distance from the bar's end where this occurs can be determined using a mathematical analysis based on the theory of elasticity.

It has been found that this distance should at least be equal to the *largest dimension* of the loaded cross section. Hence, section *c–c* should be located at a distance at least equal to the width (not the thickness) of the bar.*

---

*When section *c–c* is so located, the theory of elasticity predicts the maximum stress to be $\sigma_{max} = 1.02\sigma_{avg}$.

$$\sigma_{avg} = \frac{P}{A}$$

section a–a      section b–b      section c–c      section c–c

(b)                          (c)

**Fig. 1 (cont.)**

In the same way, the stress distribution at the support will also even out and become uniform over the cross section located the same distance away from the support.

The fact that stress and deformation behave in this manner is referred to as *Saint-Venant's principle*, since it was first noticed by the French scientist Barré de Saint-Venant in 1855. Essentially it states that the *stress and strain produced at points in a body sufficiently removed from the region of load application will be the same as the stress and strain produced by any applied loadings that have the same statically equivalent resultant, and are applied to the body within the same region.* For example, if two symmetrically applied forces $P/2$ act on the bar, Fig. 1c, the stress distribution at section c–c will be uniform and therefore equivalent to $\sigma_{avg} = P/A$ as in Fig. 1c.

Notice how the lines on this rubber membrane distort after it is stretched. The localized distortions at the grips smooth out as stated by Saint-Venant's principle.

## 2  Elastic Deformation of an Axially Loaded Member

Using Hooke's law and the definitions of stress and strain, we will now develop an equation that can be used to determine the *elastic* displacement of a member subjected to axial loads. To generalize the development, consider the bar shown in Fig. 2a, which has a cross-sectional area that *gradually* varies along its length L. The bar is subjected to concentrated loads at its ends and a variable external load distributed along its length. This distributed load could, for example, represent the weight of the bar if it is in the vertical position, or friction forces acting on the bar's surface. Here we wish to find the ***relative displacement*** δ (delta) of one end of the bar with respect to the other end as caused by this loading. We will *neglect* the localized deformations that occur at points of concentrated loading and where the cross section suddenly changes. From Saint-Venant's principle, these effects occur within small regions of the bar's length and will therefore have only a slight effect on the final result. For the most part, the bar will deform uniformly, so the normal stress will be uniformly distributed over the cross section.

Using the method of sections, a differential element (or wafer) of length $dx$ and cross-sectional area $A(x)$ is isolated from the bar at the arbitrary position $x$. The free-body diagram of this element is shown in Fig. 2b. The resultant internal axial force will be a function of $x$ since the external distributed loading will cause it to vary along the length of the bar. This load, $P(x)$, will deform the element into the shape indicated by the dashed outline, and therefore the displacement of one end of the element with respect to the other end is $d\delta$. The stress and strain in the element are

$$\sigma = \frac{P(x)}{A(x)} \quad \text{and} \quad \epsilon = \frac{d\delta}{dx}$$

Provided the stress does not exceed the proportional limit, we can apply Hooke's law; i.e.,

$$\sigma = E(x)\epsilon$$

$$\frac{P(x)}{A(x)} = E(x)\left(\frac{d\delta}{dx}\right)$$

$$d\delta = \frac{P(x)dx}{A(x)E(x)}$$

(a)

(b)

**Fig. 2**

For the entire length $L$ of the bar, we must integrate this expression to find $\delta$. This yields

$$\delta = \int_0^L \frac{P(x)dx}{A(x)E(x)} \tag{1}$$

where
$\delta =$ displacement of one point on the bar relative to the other point
$L =$ original length of bar
$P(x) =$ internal axial force at the section, located a distance $x$ from one end
$A(x) =$ cross-sectional area of the bar expressed as a function of $x$
$E(x) =$ modulus of elasticity for the material expressed as a function of $x$.

## Constant Load and Cross-Sectional Area.

In many cases the bar will have a constant cross-sectional area $A$; and the material will be homogeneous, so $E$ is constant. Furthermore, if a constant external force is applied at each end, Fig. 3, then the internal force $P$ throughout the length of the bar is also constant. As a result, Eq. 1 can be integrated to yield

$$\delta = \frac{PL}{AE} \tag{2}$$

If the bar is subjected to several different axial forces along its length, or the cross-sectional area or modulus of elasticity changes abruptly from one region of the bar to the next, the above equation can be applied to each *segment* of the bar where these quantities remain *constant*. The displacement of one end of the bar with respect to the other is then found from the *algebraic addition* of the relative displacements of the ends of each segment. For this general case,

The vertical displacement of the rod at the top floor $B$ only depends upon the force in the rod along length $AB$. However, the displacement at the bottom floor $C$ depends upon the force in the rod along its entire length, $ABC$.

$$\delta = \sum \frac{PL}{AE} \tag{3}$$

**Fig. 3**

141

Positive sign convention for $P$ and $\delta$

**Fig. 4**

**Sign Convention.** In order to apply Eq. 3, we must develop a sign convention for the internal axial force and the displacement of one end of the bar with respect to the other end. To do so, we will consider both the force and displacement to be *positive* if they cause *tension and elongation*, respectively, Fig. 4; whereas a *negative* force and displacement will cause *compression* and *contraction*, respectively.

For example, consider the bar shown in Fig. 5a. The *internal axial forces* "$P$," are determined by the method of sections for each segment, Fig. 5b. They are $P_{AB} = +5$ kN, $P_{BC} = -3$ kN, $P_{CD} = -7$ kN. This variation in axial load is shown on the axial or *normal force diagram* for the bar, Fig. 5c. Since we now know how the *internal* force varies throughout the bar's length, the displacement of end $A$ relative to end $D$ is determined from

$$\delta_{A/D} = \sum \frac{PL}{AE} = \frac{(5 \text{ kN})L_{AB}}{AE} + \frac{(-3 \text{ kN})L_{BC}}{AE} + \frac{(-7 \text{ kN})L_{CD}}{AE}$$

If the other data are substituted and a positive answer is calculated, it means that end $A$ will move away from end $D$ (the bar elongates), whereas a negative result would indicate that end $A$ moves toward end $D$ (the bar shortens). The double subscript notation is used to indicate this relative displacement ($\delta_{A/D}$); however, if the displacement is to be determined relative to a *fixed point*, then only a single subscript will be used. For example, if $D$ is located at a *fixed* support, then the displacement will be denoted as simply $\delta_A$.

(a)

(b)

(c)

**Fig. 5**

## Important Points

- *Saint-Venant's principle* states that both the localized deformation and stress which occur within the regions of load application or at the supports tend to "even out" at a distance sufficiently removed from these regions.

- The displacement of one end of an axially loaded member relative to the other end is determined by relating the applied *internal* load to the stress using $\sigma = P/A$ and relating the displacement to the strain using $\epsilon = d\delta/dx$. Finally these two equations are combined using Hooke's law, $\sigma = E\epsilon$, which yields Eq. 1.

- Since Hooke's law has been used in the development of the displacement equation, it is important that no internal load causes yielding of the material, and that the material behaves in a linear elastic manner.

## Procedure for Analysis

The relative displacement between any two points $A$ and $B$ on an axially loaded member can be determined by applying Eq. 1 (or Eq. 2). Application requires the following steps.

Internal Force.

- Use the method of sections to determine the internal axial force $P$ within the member.

- If this force varies along the member's length due to an *external distributed loading*, a section should be made at the arbitrary location $x$ from one end of the member and the force represented as a function of $x$, i.e., $P(x)$.

- If several *constant external forces* act on the member, the internal force in each *segment* of the member, between any two external forces, must be determined.

- For any segment, an internal *tensile force* is *positive* and an internal *compressive force* is *negative*. For convenience, the results of the internal loading can be shown graphically by constructing the normal-force diagram.

Displacement.

- When the member's cross-sectional area *varies* along its length, the area must be expressed as a function of its position $x$, i.e., $A(x)$.

- If the cross-sectional area, the modulus of elasticity, or the internal loading *suddenly changes*, then Eq. 2 should be applied to each segment for which these quantities are constant.

- When substituting the data into Eqs. 1 through 3, be sure to account for the proper sign for the internal force **P**. Tensile loadings are positive and compressive loadings are negative. Also, use a consistent set of units. For any segment, if the result is a *positive* numerical quantity, it indicates *elongation*; if it is *negative*, it indicates a *contraction*.

## EXAMPLE | 1

The assembly shown in Fig. 6a consists of an aluminum tube AB having a cross-sectional area of 400 mm². A steel rod having a diameter of 10 mm is attached to a rigid collar and passes through the tube. If a tensile load of 80 kN is applied to the rod, determine the displacement of the end C of the rod. Take $E_{st}$ = 200 GPa, $E_{al}$ = 70 GPa.

Fig. 6

### SOLUTION

**Internal Force.** The free-body diagram of the tube and rod segments in Fig. 6b, shows that the rod is subjected to a tension of 80 kN and the tube is subjected to a compression of 80 kN.

**Displacement.** We will first determine the displacement of end C with respect to end B. Working in units of newtons and meters, we have

$$\delta_{C/B} = \frac{PL}{AE} = \frac{[+80(10^3) \text{ N}] (0.6 \text{ m})}{\pi (0.005 \text{ m})^2 [200 (10^9) \text{ N/m}^2]} = +0.003056 \text{ m} \rightarrow$$

The positive sign indicates that end C moves *to the right* relative to end B, since the bar elongates.

The displacement of end B with respect to the *fixed* end A is

$$\delta_B = \frac{PL}{AE} = \frac{[-80(10^3) \text{ N}](0.4 \text{ m})}{[400 \text{ mm}^2(10^{-6}) \text{ m}^2/\text{mm}^2][70(10^9) \text{ N/m}^2]}$$

$$= -0.001143 \text{ m} = 0.001143 \text{ m} \rightarrow$$

Here the negative sign indicates that the tube shortens, and so B moves to the *right* relative to A.

Since both displacements are to the right, the displacement of C relative to the fixed end A is therefore

$$(\overset{+}{\rightarrow}) \qquad \delta_C = \delta_B + \delta_{C/B} = 0.001143 \text{ m} + 0.003056 \text{ m}$$

$$= 0.00420 \text{ m} = 4.20 \text{ mm} \rightarrow \qquad \qquad Ans.$$

# EXAMPLE 2

Rigid beam $AB$ rests on the two short posts shown in Fig. 7a. $AC$ is made of steel and has a diameter of 20 mm, and $BD$ is made of aluminum and has a diameter of 40 mm. Determine the displacement of point $F$ on $AB$ if a vertical load of 90 kN is applied over this point. Take $E_{st} = 200$ GPa, $E_{al} = 70$ GPa.

(a)

## SOLUTION

**Internal Force.** The compressive forces acting at the top of each post are determined from the equilibrium of member $AB$, Fig. 7b. These forces are equal to the internal forces in each post, Fig. 7c.

**Displacement.** The displacement of the top of each post is

Post $AC$:

$$\delta_A = \frac{P_{AC}L_{AC}}{A_{AC}E_{st}} = \frac{[-60(10^3)\text{ N}](0.300\text{ m})}{\pi(0.010\text{ m})^2[200(10^9)\text{ N/m}^2]} = -286(10^{-6})\text{ m}$$

$$= 0.286\text{ mm} \downarrow$$

Post $BD$:

$$\delta_B = \frac{P_{BD}L_{BD}}{A_{BD}E_{al}} = \frac{[-30(10^3)\text{N}](0.300\text{ m})}{\pi(0.020\text{ m})^2[70(10^9)\text{ N/m}^2]} = -102(10^{-6})\text{ m}$$

$$= 0.102\text{ mm} \downarrow$$

(b)

(c)

A diagram showing the centerline displacements at $A$, $B$, and $F$ on the beam is shown in Fig. 7d. By proportion of the blue shaded triangle, the displacement of point $F$ is therefore

$$\delta_F = 0.102\text{ mm} + (0.184\text{ mm})\left(\frac{400\text{ mm}}{600\text{ mm}}\right) = 0.225\text{ mm} \downarrow \qquad Ans.$$

(d)

**Fig. 7**

# EXAMPLE | 3

(a)

(b)

**Fig. 8**

A member is made from a material that has a specific weight $\gamma$ and modulus of elasticity $E$. If it is in the form of a *cone* having the dimensions shown in Fig. 8a, determine how far its end is displaced due to gravity when it is suspended in the vertical position.

## SOLUTION

**Internal Force.** The internal axial force varies along the member since it is dependent on the weight $W(y)$ of a segment of the member below any section, Fig. 8b. Hence, to calculate the displacement, we must use Eq. 1. At the section located a distance $y$ from its free end, the radius $x$ of the cone as a function of $y$ is determined by proportion; i.e.,

$$\frac{x}{y} = \frac{r_0}{L}; \qquad x = \frac{r_0}{L} y$$

The volume of a cone having a base of radius $x$ and height $y$ is

$$V = \frac{1}{3}\pi y x^2 = \frac{\pi r_0^2}{3L^2} y^3$$

Since $W = \gamma V$, the internal force at the section becomes

$$+\uparrow \Sigma F_y = 0; \qquad P(y) = \frac{\gamma \pi r_0^2}{3L^2} y^3$$

**Displacement.** The area of the cross section is also a function of position $y$, Fig. 8b. We have

$$A(y) = \pi x^2 = \frac{\pi r_0^2}{L^2} y^2$$

Applying Eq. 1 between the limits of $y = 0$ and $y = L$ yields

$$\delta = \int_0^L \frac{P(y)\,dy}{A(y)\,E} = \int_0^L \frac{\left[ (\gamma \pi r_0^2 / 3L^2) y^3 \right] dy}{\left[ (\pi r_0^2 / L^2) y^2 \right] E}$$

$$= \frac{\gamma}{3E} \int_0^L y\,dy$$

$$= \frac{\gamma L^2}{6E}$$

*Ans.*

**NOTE:** As a partial check of this result, notice how the units of the terms, when canceled, give the displacement in units of length as expected.

# PRELIMINARY PROBLEMS

**P1.** In each case, determine the internal normal force between lettered points on the bar. Draw all necessary free-body diagrams.

(a)

(b)

**P1**

**P2.** Determine the internal normal force between lettered points on the cable and rod. Draw all necessary free-body diagrams.

**P2**

**P3.** The post weighs 8 kN/m. Determine the internal normal force in the post as a function of $x$.

**P3**

**P4.** The rod is subjected to an external axial force of 800 N and a uniform distributed load of 100 N/m along its length. Determine the internal normal force in the rod as a function of $x$.

**P4**

**P5.** The rigid beam supports the load of 60 kN. Determine the displacement at $B$. Take $E = 60$ GPa, and $A_{BC} = 2$ $(10^{-3})$ m$^2$.

**P5**

# FUNDAMENTAL PROBLEMS

**F1.** The 20-mm-diameter A-36 steel rod is subjected to the axial forces shown. Determine the displacement of end $C$ with respect to the fixed support at $A$.

**F1**

**F2.** Segments $AB$ and $CD$ of the assembly are solid circular rods, and segment $BC$ is a tube. If the assembly is made of 6061-T6 aluminum, determine the displacement of end $D$ with respect to end $A$.

Section $a$-$a$

**F2**

**F3.** The 30-mm-diameter A992 steel rod is subjected to the loading shown. Determine the displacement of end $C$.

**F3**

**F4.** If the 20-mm-diameter rod is made of A-36 steel and the stiffness of the spring is $k = 50$ MN/m, determine the displacement of end $A$ when the 60-kN force is applied.

**F4**

**F5.** The 20-mm-diameter 2014-T6 aluminum rod is subjected to the uniform distributed axial load. Determine the displacement of end $A$.

**F5**

**F6.** The 20-mm-diameter 2014-T6 aluminum rod is subjected to the triangular distributed axial load. Determine the displacement of end $A$.

**F6**

148

# PROBLEMS

**1.** The A992 steel rod is subjected to the loading shown. If the cross-sectional area of the rod is 60 mm², determine the displacement of $B$ and $A$. Neglect the size of the couplings at $B$, $C$, and $D$.

**3.** The composite shaft, consisting of aluminum, copper, and steel sections, is subjected to the loading shown. Determine the displacement of end $A$ with respect to end $D$ and the normal stress in each section. The cross-sectional area and modulus of elasticity for each section are shown in the figure. Neglect the size of the collars at $B$ and $C$.

**\*4.** Determine the displacement of $B$ with respect to $C$ of the composite shaft in Prob. 3.

| Aluminum | Copper | Steel |
|---|---|---|
| $E_{al} = 10(10^3)$ ksi | $E_{cu} = 18(10^3)$ ksi | $E_{st} = 29(10^3)$ ksi |
| $A_{AB} = 0.09$ in² | $A_{BC} = 0.12$ in² | $A_{CD} = 0.06$ in² |

**Probs. 3/4**

**Prob. 1**

**2.** The copper shaft is subjected to the axial loads shown. Determine the displacement of end $A$ with respect to end $D$ if the diameters of each segment are $d_{AB} = 0.75$ in., $d_{BC} = 1$ in., and $d_{CD} = 0.5$ in. Take $E_{cu} = 18(10^3)$ ksi.

**5.** The assembly consists of a steel rod $CB$ and an aluminum rod $BA$, each having a diameter of 12 mm. If the rod is subjected to the axial loadings at $A$ and at the coupling $B$, determine the displacement of the coupling $B$ and the end $A$. The unstretched length of each segment is shown in the figure. Neglect the size of the connections at $B$ and $C$, and assume that they are rigid. $E_{st} = 200$ GPa, $E_{al} = 70$ GPa.

**Prob. 2**

**Prob. 5**

149

**6.** The bar has a cross-sectional area of 3 in², and $E = 35\ (10^3)$ ksi. Determine the displacement of its end $A$ when it is subjected to the distributed loading.

**Prob. 6**

**9.** The assembly consists of two 10-mm diameter red brass C83400 copper rods $AB$ and $CD$, a 15-mm diameter 304 stainless steel rod $EF$, and a rigid bar $G$. If $P = 5$ kN, determine the horizontal displacement of end $F$ of rod $EF$.

**10.** The assembly consists of two 10-mm diameter red brass C83400 copper rods $AB$ and $CD$, a 15-mm diameter 304 stainless steel rod $EF$, and a rigid bar $G$. If the horizontal displacement of end $F$ of rod $EF$ is 0.45 mm, determine the magnitude of $P$.

**Probs. 9/10**

**7.** If $P_1 = 50$ kip and $P_2 = 150$ kip, determine the vertical displacement of end $A$ of the high strength precast concrete column.

**\*8.** If the vertical displacements of end $A$ of the high strength precast concrete column relative to $B$ and $B$ relative to $C$ are 0.08 in. and 0.1 in., respectively, determine the magnitudes of $\mathbf{P}_1$ and $\mathbf{P}_2$.

**11.** The load is supported by the four 304 stainless steel wires that are connected to the rigid members $AB$ and $DC$. Determine the vertical displacement of the 500-lb load if the members were originally horizontal when the load was applied. Each wire has a cross-sectional area of 0.025 in².

**\*12.** The load is supported by the four 304 stainless steel wires that are connected to the rigid members $AB$ and $DC$. Determine the angle of tilt of each member after the 500-lb load is applied. The members were originally horizontal, and each wire has a cross-sectional area of 0.025 in².

**Probs. 7/8**

**Probs. 11/12**

**13.** The rigid bar is supported by the pin-connected rod *CB* that has a cross-sectional area of 14 mm² and is made from 6061-T6 aluminum. Determine the vertical deflection of the bar at *D* when the distributed load is applied.

**Prob. 13**

**14.** The post is made of Douglas fir and has a diameter of 60 mm. If it is subjected to the load of 20 kN and the soil provides a frictional resistance that is uniformly distributed along its sides of $w = 4$ kN/m, determine the force **F** at its bottom needed for equilibrium. Also, what is the displacement of the top of the post *A* with respect to its bottom *B*? Neglect the weight of the post.

**15.** The post is made of Douglas fir and has a diameter of 60 mm. If it is subjected to the load of 20 kN and the soil provides a frictional resistance that is distributed along its length and varies linearly from $w = 0$ at $y = 0$ to $w = 3$ kN/m at $y = 2$ m, determine the force **F** at its bottom needed for equilibrium. Also, what is the displacement of the top of the post *A* with respect to its bottom *B*? Neglect the weight of the post.

**\*16.** The hanger consists of three 2014-T6 aluminum alloy rods, rigid beams *AC* and *BD*, and a spring. If the hook supports a load of $P = 60$ kN, determine the vertical displacement of *F*. Rods *AB* and *CD* each have a diameter of 10 mm, and rod *EF* has a diameter of 15 mm. The spring has a stiffness of $k = 100$ MN/m and is unstretched when $P = 0$.

**17.** The hanger consists of three 2014-T6 aluminum alloy rods, rigid beams *AC* and *BD*, and a spring. If the vertical displacement of end *F* is 5 mm, determine the magnitude of the load **P**. Rods *AB* and *CD* each have a diameter of 10 mm, and rod *EF* has a diameter of 15 mm. The spring has a stiffness of $k = 100$ MN/m and is unstretched when $P = 0$.

**Probs. 16/17**

**18.** Collar *A* can slide freely along the smooth vertical guide. If the supporting rod *AB* is made of 304 stainless steel and has a diameter of 0.75 in., determine the vertical displacement of the collar when $P = 10$ kip.

**19.** Collar *A* can slide freely along the smooth vertical guide. If the vertical displacement of the collar is 0.035 in. and the supporting 0.75 in. diameter rod *AB* is made of 304 stainless steel, determine the magnitude of **P**.

**Probs. 14/15**

**Probs. 18/19**

151

**\*20.** The A992 steel drill shaft of an oil well extends 12000 ft into the ground. Assuming that the pipe used to drill the well is suspended freely from the derrick at $A$, determine the maximum average normal stress in each pipe segment and the elongation of its end $D$ with respect to the fixed end at $A$. The shaft consists of three different sizes of pipe, $AB$, $BC$, and $CD$, each having the length, weight per unit length, and cross-sectional area indicated.

$A_{AB} = 2.50$ in.$^2$
$w_{AB} = 3.2$ lb/ft

5000 ft

$A_{BC} = 1.75$ in.$^2$
$w_{BC} = 2.8$ lb/ft

5000 ft

$A_{CD} = 1.25$ in.$^2$
$w_{CD} = 2.0$ lb/ft

2000 ft

**Prob. 20**

**21.** A spring-supported pipe hanger consists of two springs which are originally unstretched and have a stiffness of $k = 60$ kN/m, three 304 stainless steel rods, $AB$ and $CD$, which have a diameter of 5 mm, and $EF$, which has a diameter of 12 mm, and a rigid beam $GH$. If the pipe and the fluid it carries have a total weight of 4 kN, determine the displacement of the pipe when it is attached to the support.

**22.** A spring-supported pipe hanger consists of two springs, which are originally unstretched and have a stiffness of $k = 60$ kN/m, three 304 stainless steel rods, $AB$ and $CD$, which have a diameter of 5 mm, and $EF$, which has a diameter of 12 mm, and a rigid beam $GH$. If the pipe is displaced 82 mm when it is filled with fluid, determine the combined weight of the pipe and fluid.

0.75 m

0.75 m

0.25 m 0.25 m

**Probs. 21/22**

**23.** The rod has a slight taper and length $L$. It is suspended from the ceiling and supports a load $\mathbf{P}$ at its end. Show that the displacement of its end due to this load is $\delta = PL/(\pi E r_2 r_1)$. Neglect the weight of the material. The modulus of elasticity is $E$.

$r_2$

$L$

$r_1$

$\mathbf{P}$

**Prob. 23**

**\*24.** Determine the relative displacement of one end of the tapered plate with respect to the other end when it is subjected to an axial load $P$.

$P$

$d_2$

$t$

$h$

$d_1$

$P$

**Prob. 24**

**25.** Determine the elongation of the A-36 steel member when it is subjected to an axial force of 30 kN. The member is 10 mm thick. Use the result of Prob. 24.

20 mm

30 kN

75 mm

30 kN

0.5 m

**Prob. 25**

**26.** Determine the elongation of the tapered A992 steel shaft when it is subjected to an axial force of 18 kip. *Hint:* Use the result of Prob. 23.

$r_1 = 0.5$ in.  $r_2 = 2$ in.  $r_1 = 0.5$ in.

18 kip  ←4 in.→←—————20 in.—————→←4 in.→  18 kip

**Prob. 26**

**27.** The circular bar has a variable radius of $r = r_0 e^{ax}$ and is made of a material having a modulus of elasticity of $E$. Determine the displacement of end $A$ when it is subjected to the axial force $\mathbf{P}$.

$r = r_0 e^{ax}$

$A$ $\mathbf{P}$

**Prob. 27**

**\*28.** Bone material has a stress–strain diagram that can be defined by the relation $\sigma = E[\epsilon/(1 + kE\epsilon)]$, where $k$ and $E$ are constants. Determine the compression within the length $L$ of the bone, where it is assumed the cross-sectional area $A$ of the bone is constant.

**Prob. 28**

**29.** The weight of the kentledge exerts an axial force of $P = 1500$ kN on the 300-mm diameter high-strength concrete bore pile. If the distribution of the resisting skin friction developed from the interaction between the soil and the surface of the pile is approximated as shown, and the resisting bearing force $\mathbf{F}$ is required to be zero, determine the maximum intensity $p_0$ kN/m for equilibrium. Also, find the corresponding elastic shortening of the pile. Neglect the weight of the pile.

$P$

$p_0$

12 m

$F$

**Prob. 29**

**30.** The weight of the kentledge exerts an axial force of $P = 1500$ kN on the 300-mm diameter high-strength concrete bore pile. If the distribution of the resisting skin friction developed from the interaction between the soil and the surface of the pile is approximated as shown, determine the resisting bearing force $\mathbf{F}$ for equilibrium. Take $p_0 = 180$ kN/m. Also, find the corresponding elastic shortening of the pile. Neglect the weight of the pile.

$P$

$p_0$

12 m

$F$

**Prob. 30**

# 3 Principle of Superposition

The principle of superposition is often used to determine the stress or displacement at a point in a member when the member is subjected to a complicated loading. By subdividing the loading into components, the ***principle of superposition*** states that the resultant stress or displacement at the point can be determined by algebraically summing the stress or displacement caused by each load component applied separately to the member.

The following two conditions must be satisfied if the principle of superposition is to be applied.

1. ***The loading must be linearly related to the stress or displacement that is to be determined***. For example, the equations $\sigma = P/A$ and $\delta = PL/AE$ involve a linear relationship between $P$ and $\sigma$ or $\delta$.

2. ***The loading must not significantly change the original geometry or configuration of the member***. If significant changes do occur, the direction and location of the applied forces and their moment arms will change. For example, consider the slender rod shown in Fig. 9*a*, which is subjected to the load **P**. In Fig. 9*b*, **P** is replaced by two of its components, $\mathbf{P} = \mathbf{P}_1 + \mathbf{P}_2$. If **P** causes the rod to deflect a large amount, as shown, the moment of the load about its support, $Pd$, will not equal the sum of the moments of its component loads, $Pd \neq P_1 d_1 + P_2 d_2$, because $d_1 \neq d_2 \neq d$.

This principle will be used throughout this text whenever we assume Hooke's law applies and also, the bodies that are considered will be such that the loading will produce deformations that are so small that the change in position and direction of the loading will be insignificant and can be neglected.

(a)                                    (b)

**Fig. 9**

# 4 Statically Indeterminate Axially Loaded Member

Consider the bar shown in Fig. 10a which is fixed supported at both of its ends. From the free-body diagram, Fig. 10b, equilibrium requires

$$+\uparrow \Sigma F = 0; \qquad F_B + F_A - P = 0$$

(a)

This type of problem is called **statically indeterminate**, since the equilibrium equation(s) are not sufficient to determine the two reactions on the bar.

In order to establish an additional equation needed for solution, it is necessary to consider how points on the bar displace. Specifically, an equation that specifies the conditions for displacement is referred to as a **compatibility** or **kinematic condition**. In this case, a suitable compatibility condition would require the displacement of one end of the bar with respect to the other end to be equal to zero, since the end supports are fixed. Hence, the compatibility condition becomes

$$\delta_{A/B} = 0$$

This equation can be expressed in terms of the applied loads by using a **load–displacement relationship,** which depends on the material behavior. For example, if linear-elastic behavior occurs, $\delta = PL/AE$ can be used. Realizing that the internal force in segment $AC$ is $+F_A$, and in segment $CB$ the internal force is $-F_B$, Fig. 10c, the above equation can be written as

(b)     (c)

**Fig. 10**

$$\frac{F_A L_{AC}}{AE} - \frac{F_B L_{CB}}{AE} = 0$$

Since $AE$ is constant, then $F_A = F_B(L_{CB}/L_{AC})$, so that using the equilibrium equation, the equations for the reactions become

$$F_A = P\left(\frac{L_{CB}}{L}\right) \quad \text{and} \quad F_B = P\left(\frac{L_{AC}}{L}\right)$$

Since both of these results are positive, the direction of the reactions is shown correctly on the free-body diagram.

## Important Points

- The *principle of superposition* is sometimes used to simplify stress and displacement problems having complicated loadings. This is done by subdividing the loading into components, then algebraically adding the results.

- Superposition requires that the loading be linearly related to the stress or displacement, and the loading does not significantly change the original geometry of the member.

- A problem is *statically indeterminate* if the equations of equilibrium are not sufficient to determine all the reactions on a member.

- *Compatibility conditions* specify the displacement constraints that occur at the supports or other points on a member.

## Procedure for Analysis

The support reactions for statically indeterminate problems are determined by satisfying equilibrium, compatibility, and force-displacement requirements for the member.

### Equilibrium.

- Draw a free-body diagram of the member in order to identify all the forces that act on it.
- The problem can be classified as statically indeterminate if the number of unknown reactions on the free-body diagram is greater than the number of available equations of equilibrium.
- Write the equations of equilibrium for the member.

### Compatibility.

- Consider drawing a displacement diagram in order to investigate the way the member will elongate or contract when subjected to the external loads.
- Express the compatibility conditions in terms of the displacements caused by the loading.

### Load-Displacement.

- Use a load–displacement relation, such as $\delta = PL/AE$, to relate the unknown displacements to the reactions.
- Solve the equations for the reactions. If any of the results has a negative numerical value, it indicates that this force acts in the opposite sense of direction to that indicated on the free-body diagram.

Most concrete columns are reinforced with steel rods; and since these two materials work together in supporting the applied load, the forces in each material become statically indeterminate.

# EXAMPLE 4

The steel rod shown in Fig. 11a has a diameter of 10 mm. It is fixed to the wall at $A$, and before it is loaded, there is a gap of 0.2 mm between the wall at $B'$ and the rod. Determine the reactions at $A$ and $B'$ if the rod is subjected to an axial force of $P = 20$ kN as shown. Neglect the size of the collar at $C$. Take $E_{st} = 200$ GPa.

(a)

## SOLUTION

**Equilibrium.** As shown on the free-body diagram, Fig. 11b, we will *assume* that force $P$ is large enough to cause the rod's end $B$ to contact the wall at $B'$. The problem is statically indeterminate since there are two unknowns and only one equation of equilibrium.

(b)

$$\xrightarrow{+} \Sigma F_x = 0; \qquad -F_A - F_B + 20(10^3)\ \text{N} = 0 \qquad (1)$$

**Compatibility.** The force $P$ causes point $B$ to move to $B'$, with no further displacement. Therefore the compatibility condition for the rod is

$$\delta_{B/A} = 0.0002\ \text{m}$$

(c)

**Fig. 11**

**Load-Displacement.** This displacement can be expressed in terms of the unknown reactions using the load–displacement relationship, Eq. 2, applied to segments $AC$ and $CB$, Fig. 11c. Working in units of newtons and meters, we have

$$\delta_{B/A} = 0.0002\ \text{m} = \frac{F_A L_{AC}}{AE} - \frac{F_B L_{CB}}{AE}$$

$$0.0002\ \text{m} = \frac{F_A (0.4\ \text{m})}{\pi (0.005\ \text{m})^2 \left[200(10^9)\ \text{N/m}^2\right]}$$

$$- \frac{F_B (0.8\ \text{m})}{\pi (0.005\ \text{m})^2 \left[200(10^9)\ \text{N/m}^2\right]}$$

or

$$F_A (0.4\ \text{m}) - F_B (0.8\ \text{m}) = 3141.59\ \text{N} \cdot \text{m} \qquad (2)$$

Solving Eqs. 1 and 2 yields

$$F_A = 16.0\ \text{kN} \quad F_B = 4.05\ \text{kN} \qquad \textit{Ans.}$$

Since the answer for $F_B$ is *positive*, indeed end $B$ contacts the wall at $B'$ as originally assumed.

**NOTE:** If $F_B$ were a negative quantity, the problem would be statically determinate, so that $F_B = 0$ and $F_A = 20$ kN.

EXAMPLE | 5

(a)

(b)

(c)

**Fig. 12**

The aluminum post shown in Fig. 12$a$ is reinforced with a brass core. If this assembly supports an axial compressive load of $P = 9$ kip, applied to the rigid cap, determine the average normal stress in the aluminum and the brass. Take $E_{al} = 10(10^3)$ ksi and $E_{br} = 15(10^3)$ ksi.

SOLUTION

**Equilibrium.** The free-body diagram of the post is shown in Fig. 12$b$. Here the resultant axial force at the base is represented by the unknown components carried by the aluminum, $\mathbf{F}_{al}$, and brass, $\mathbf{F}_{br}$. The problem is statically indeterminate. Why?

Vertical force equilibrium requires

$$+\uparrow \Sigma F_y = 0; \qquad -9 \text{ kip} + F_{al} + F_{br} = 0 \qquad (1)$$

**Compatibility.** The rigid cap at the top of the post causes both the aluminum and brass to displace the same amount. Therefore,

$$\delta_{al} = \delta_{br}$$

**Load-Displacement.** Using the load–displacement relationships,

$$\frac{F_{al}L}{A_{al}E_{al}} = \frac{F_{br}L}{A_{br}E_{br}}$$

$$F_{al} = F_{br}\left(\frac{A_{al}}{A_{br}}\right)\left(\frac{E_{al}}{E_{br}}\right)$$

$$F_{al} = F_{br}\left[\frac{\pi[(2 \text{ in.})^2 - (1 \text{ in.})^2]}{\pi(1 \text{ in.})^2}\right]\left[\frac{10(10^3) \text{ ksi}}{15(10^3) \text{ ksi}}\right]$$

$$F_{al} = 2F_{br} \qquad (2)$$

Solving Eqs. 1 and 2 simultaneously yields

$$F_{al} = 6 \text{ kip} \qquad F_{br} = 3 \text{ kip}$$

Since the results are positive, indeed the stress will be compressive. The average normal stress in the aluminum and brass is therefore

$$\sigma_{al} = \frac{6 \text{ kip}}{\pi[(2 \text{ in.})^2 - (1 \text{ in.})^2]} = 0.637 \text{ ksi} \qquad Ans.$$

$$\sigma_{br} = \frac{3 \text{ kip}}{\pi(1 \text{ in.})^2} = 0.955 \text{ ksi} \qquad Ans.$$

**NOTE:** Using these results, the stress distributions are shown in Fig. 12$c$.

## EXAMPLE 6

The three A992 steel bars shown in Fig. 13a are pin connected to a *rigid* member. If the applied load on the member is 15 kN, determine the force developed in each bar. Bars *AB* and *EF* each have a cross-sectional area of 50 mm$^2$, and bar *CD* has a cross-sectional area of 30 mm$^2$.

(a)

### SOLUTION

**Equilibrium.** The free-body diagram of the rigid member is shown in Fig. 13b. This problem is statically indeterminate since there are three unknowns and only two available equilibrium equations.

$$+\uparrow \Sigma F_y = 0; \qquad F_A + F_C + F_E - 15 \text{ kN} = 0 \qquad (1)$$

$$\zeta + \Sigma M_C = 0; \quad -F_A(0.4 \text{ m}) + 15 \text{ kN}(0.2 \text{ m}) + F_E(0.4 \text{ m}) = 0 \qquad (2)$$

**Compatibility.** The applied load will cause the horizontal line *ACE* shown in Fig. 13c to move to the inclined line *A'C'E'*. The displacements of points *A*, *C*, and *E* can be related by similar triangles. Thus the compatibility equation that relates these displacements is

(b)

$$\frac{\delta_A - \delta_E}{0.8 \text{ m}} = \frac{\delta_C - \delta_E}{0.4 \text{ m}}$$

$$\delta_C = \frac{1}{2}\delta_A + \frac{1}{2}\delta_E$$

**Load-Displacement.** Using the load–displacement relationship, Eq. 2, we have

$$\frac{F_C L}{(30 \text{ mm}^2)E_{st}} = \frac{1}{2}\left[\frac{F_A L}{(50 \text{ mm}^2)E_{st}}\right] + \frac{1}{2}\left[\frac{F_E L}{(50 \text{ mm}^2)E_{st}}\right]$$

$$F_C = 0.3F_A + 0.3F_E \qquad (3)$$

(c)

**Fig. 13**

Solving Eqs. 1–3 simultaneously yields

$$F_A = 9.52 \text{ kN} \qquad\qquad Ans.$$

$$F_C = 3.46 \text{ kN} \qquad\qquad Ans.$$

$$F_E = 2.02 \text{ kN} \qquad\qquad Ans.$$

EXAMPLE 7

(a)

The bolt shown in Fig. 14a is made of 2014-T6 aluminum alloy and is tightened so it compresses a cylindrical tube made of Am 1004-T61 magnesium alloy. The tube has an outer radius of $\frac{1}{2}$ in., and it is assumed that both the inner radius of the tube and the radius of the bolt are $\frac{1}{4}$ in. The washers at the top and bottom of the tube are considered to be rigid and have a negligible thickness. Initially the nut is hand tightened snugly; then, using a wrench, the nut is further tightened one-half turn. If the bolt has 20 threads per inch, determine the stress in the bolt.

## SOLUTION

**Equilibrium.** The free-body diagram of a section of the bolt and the tube, Fig. 14b, is considered in order to relate the force in the bolt $F_b$ to that in the tube, $F_t$. Equilibrium requires

$$+\uparrow \Sigma F_y = 0; \qquad\qquad F_b - F_t = 0 \qquad\qquad (1)$$

F_t

F_b

(b)

**Compatibility.** When the nut is tightened on the bolt, the tube will shorten $\delta_t$, and the bolt will *elongate* $\delta_b$, Fig. 14c. Since the nut undergoes one-half turn, it advances a distance of $(\frac{1}{2})(\frac{1}{20}$ in.$) = 0.025$ in. along the bolt. Thus, the compatibility of these displacements requires

$$(+\uparrow) \qquad\qquad \delta_t = 0.025 \text{ in.} - \delta_b$$

**Load-Displacement.** Taking the moduli of elasticity and applying the load-displacement relationship, Eq. 2, yields

$$\frac{F_t (3 \text{ in.})}{\pi[(0.5 \text{ in.})^2 - (0.25 \text{ in.})^2][6.48(10^3) \text{ ksi}]} =$$

$$0.025 \text{ in.} - \frac{F_b (3 \text{ in.})}{\pi(0.25 \text{ in.})^2 [10.6(10^3) \text{ ksi}]}$$

$$0.78595 F_t = 25 - 1.4414 F_b \qquad\qquad (2)$$

Final position

$\delta_b$

$\delta_t$    0.025 in.

Initial position

(c)

Solving Eqs. 1 and 2 simultaneously, we get

$$F_b = F_t = 11.22 \text{ kip}$$

The stresses in the bolt and tube are therefore

$$\sigma_b = \frac{F_b}{A_b} = \frac{11.22 \text{ kip}}{\pi(0.25 \text{ in.})^2} = 57.2 \text{ ksi} \qquad\qquad Ans.$$

$$\sigma_t = \frac{F_t}{A_t} = \frac{11.22 \text{ kip}}{\pi[(0.5 \text{ in.})^2 - (0.25 \text{ in.})^2]} = 19.1 \text{ ksi}$$

These stresses are less than the reported yield stress for each material, $(\sigma_Y)_{al} = 60$ ksi and $(\sigma_Y)_{mg} = 22$ ksi (see the inside back cover), and therefore this "elastic" analysis is valid.

**Fig. 14**

# 5 The Force Method of Analysis for Axially Loaded Members

It is also possible to solve statically indeterminate problems by writing the compatibility equation using the principle of superposition. This method of solution is often referred to as the *flexibility or force method of analysis*. To show how it is applied, consider again the bar in Fig. 15*a*. If we choose the support at *B* as "redundant" and *temporarily* remove its effect on the bar, then the bar will become statically determinate as in Fig. 15*b*. By using the principle of superposition, we must add back the unknown redundant load $\mathbf{F}_B$, as shown in Fig. 15*c*.

If load **P** causes *B* to be displaced *downward* by an amount $\delta_P$, the reaction $\mathbf{F}_B$ must displace end *B* of the bar *upward* by an amount $\delta_B$, such that no displacement occurs at *B* when the two loadings are superimposed. Thus,

$$(+\downarrow) \qquad\qquad 0 = \delta_P - \delta_B$$

This equation represents the compatibility equation for displacements at point *B*, for which we have assumed that displacements are positive downward.

Applying the load–displacement relationship to each case, we have $\delta_P = PL_{AC}/AE$ and $\delta_B = F_B L/AE$. Consequently,

$$0 = \frac{PL_{AC}}{AE} - \frac{F_B L}{AE}$$

$$F_B = P\left(\frac{L_{AC}}{L}\right)$$

From the free-body diagram of the bar, Fig. 15*d*, the reaction at *A* can now be determined from the equation of equilibrium,

$$+\uparrow \Sigma F_y = 0; \qquad P\left(\frac{L_{AC}}{L}\right) + F_A - P = 0$$

Since $L_{CB} = L - L_{AC}$, then

$$F_A = P\left(\frac{L_{CB}}{L}\right)$$

These results are the same as those obtained in Sec. 4, except that here we have applied the condition of compatibility to obtain one reaction *and then* the equilibrium condition to obtain the other.

No displacement at *B*

(a)

‖

Displacement at *B* when redundant force at *B* is removed

(b)

+

Displacement at *B* when only the redundant force at *B* is applied

(c)

(d)

Fig. 15

161

## Procedure for Analysis

The force method of analysis requires the following steps.

Compatibility.

- Choose one of the supports as redundant and write the equation of compatibility. To do this, the known displacement at the redundant support, which is usually zero, is equated to the displacement at the support caused *only* by the external loads acting on the member *plus* (vectorially) the displacement at this support caused *only* by the redundant reaction acting on the member.

- Express the external load and redundant displacements in terms of the loadings by using a load–displacement relationship, such as $\delta = PL/AE$.

- Once established, the compatibility equation can then be solved for the magnitude of the redundant force.

Equilibrium.

- Draw a free-body diagram and write the appropriate equations of equilibrium for the member using the calculated result for the redundant. Solve these equations for any other reactions.

## EXAMPLE | 8

(a)

(b)

(c)

Fig. 16

The A-36 steel rod shown in Fig. 16a has a diameter of 10 mm. It is fixed to the wall at $A$, and before it is loaded there is a gap between the wall at $B'$ and the rod of 0.2 mm. Determine the reactions at $A$ and $B'$. Neglect the size of the collar at $C$. Take $E_{st} = 200$ GPa.

### SOLUTION

**Compatibility.** Here we will consider the support at $B'$ as redundant. Using the principle of superposition, Fig. 16b, we have

$$(\overset{+}{\rightarrow}) \qquad 0.0002 \text{ m} = \delta_P - \delta_B \qquad (1)$$

**Load-Displacement.** The deflections $\delta_P$ and $\delta_B$ are determined from Eq. 2.

$$\delta_P = \frac{PL_{AC}}{AE} = \frac{[20(10^3) \text{ N}](0.4 \text{ m})}{\pi(0.005 \text{ m})^2 [200(10^9) \text{ N/m}^2]} = 0.5093(10^{-3}) \text{ m}$$

$$\delta_B = \frac{F_B L_{AB}}{AE} = \frac{F_B (1.20 \text{ m})}{\pi(0.005 \text{ m})^2 [200(10^9) \text{ N/m}^2]} = 76.3944(10^{-9})F_B$$

Substituting into Eq. 1, we get

$$0.0002 \text{ m} = 0.5093(10^{-3}) \text{ m} - 76.3944(10^{-9})F_B$$

$$F_B = 4.05(10^3) \text{ N} = 4.05 \text{ kN} \qquad \qquad Ans.$$

**Equilibrium.** From the free-body diagram, Fig. 16c,

$$\overset{+}{\rightarrow} \Sigma F_x = 0; \quad -F_A + 20 \text{ kN} - 4.05 \text{ kN} = 0 \quad F_A = 16.0 \text{ kN} \quad Ans.$$

## PROBLEMS

**31.** The concrete column is reinforced using four steel reinforcing rods, each having a diameter of 18 mm. Determine the stress in the concrete and the steel if the column is subjected to an axial load of 800 kN. $E_{st} = 200$ GPa, $E_c = 25$ GPa.

**\*32.** The column is constructed from high-strength concrete and four A-36 steel reinforcing rods. If it is subjected to an axial force of 800 kN, determine the required diameter of each rod so that one-fourth of the load is carried by the steel and three-fourths by the concrete. $E_{st} = 200$ GPa, $E_c = 25$ GPa.

**Probs. 31/32**

**33.** The steel pipe is filled with concrete and subjected to a compressive force of 80 kN. Determine the average normal stress in the concrete and the steel due to this loading. The pipe has an outer diameter of 80 mm and an inner diameter of 70 mm. $E_{st} = 200$ GPa, $E_c = 24$ GPa.

**Prob. 33**

**34.** If column $AB$ is made from high strength pre-cast concrete and reinforced with four $\frac{3}{4}$ in. diameter A-36 steel rods, determine the average normal stress developed in the concrete and in each rod. Set $P = 75$ kip.

**35.** If column $AB$ is made from high strength pre-cast concrete and reinforced with four $\frac{3}{4}$ in. diameter A-36 steel rods, determine the maximum allowable floor loadings **P**. The allowable normal stress for the high strength concrete and the steel are $(\sigma_{allow})_{con} = 2.5$ ksi and $(\sigma_{allow})_{st} = 24$ ksi, respectively.

**Probs. 34/35**

**\*36.** Determine the support reactions at the rigid supports $A$ and $C$. The material has a modulus of elasticity of $E$.

**37.** If the supports at $A$ and $C$ are flexible and have a stiffness $k$, determine the support reactions at $A$ and $C$. The material has a modulus of elasticity of $E$.

**Probs. 36/37**

**38.** The load of 2800 lb is to be supported by the two essentially vertical A-36 steel wires. If originally wire $AB$ is 60 in. long and wire $AC$ is 40 in. long, determine the force developed in each wire after the load is suspended. Each wire has a cross-sectional area of 0.02 in². 

**39.** The load of 2800 lb is to be supported by the two essentially vertical A-36 steel wires. If originally wire $AB$ is 60 in. long and wire $AC$ is 40 in. long, determine the cross-sectional area of $AB$ if the load is to be shared equally between both wires. Wire $AC$ has a cross-sectional area of 0.02 in².

**Probs. 38/39**

**\*40.** The rigid member is held in the position shown by three A-36 steel tie rods. Each rod has an unstretched length of 0.75 m and a cross-sectional area of 125 mm². Determine the forces in the rods if a turnbuckle on rod $EF$ undergoes one full turn. The lead of the screw is 1.5 mm. Neglect the size of the turnbuckle and assume that it is rigid. *Note:* The lead would cause the rod, when *unloaded*, to shorten 1.5 mm when the turnbuckle is rotated one revolution.

**Prob. 40**

**41.** The 2014-T6 aluminum rod $AC$ is reinforced with the firmly bonded A992 steel tube $BC$. If the assembly fits snugly between the rigid supports so that there is no gap at $C$, determine the support reactions when the axial force of 400 kN is applied. The assembly is attached at $D$.

**42.** The 2014-T6 aluminum rod $AC$ is reinforced with the firmly bonded A992 steel tube $BC$. When no load is applied to the assembly, the gap between end $C$ and the rigid support is 0.5 mm. Determine the support reactions when the axial force of 400 kN is applied.

**Probs. 41/42**

**43.** The assembly consists of two red brass C83400 copper rods $AB$ and $CD$ of diameter 30 mm, a stainless 304 steel alloy rod $EF$ of diameter 40 mm, and a rigid cap $G$. If the supports at $A$, $C$ and $F$ are rigid, determine the average normal stress developed in rods $AB$, $CD$ and $EF$.

**Prob. 43**

**\*44.** The assembly consists of two red brass C83400 copper rods $AB$ and $CD$ having a diameter of 30 mm, a 304 stainless steel rod $EF$ having a diameter of 40 mm, and a rigid member $G$. If the supports at $A$, $C$ and $F$ each have a stiffness of $k = 200$ MN/m, determine the average normal stress developed in the rods when the load is applied.

**Prob. 44**

**45.** The bolt has a diameter of 20 mm and passes through a tube that has an inner diameter of 50 mm and an outer diameter of 60 mm. If the bolt and tube are made of A-36 steel, determine the normal stress in the tube and bolt when a force of 40 kN is applied to the bolt. Assume the end caps are rigid.

**Prob. 45**

**46.** If the gap between $C$ and the rigid wall at $D$ is initially 0.15 mm, determine the support reactions at $A$ and $D$ when the force $\mathbf{P} = 200$ kN is applied. The assembly is made of A-36 steel.

**Prob. 46**

**47.** The support consists of a solid red brass C83400 copper post surrounded by a 304 stainless steel tube. Before the load is applied the gap between these two parts is 1 mm. Given the dimensions shown, determine the greatest axial load that can be applied to the rigid cap $A$ without causing yielding of any one of the materials.

**Prob. 47**

**\*48.** The specimen represents a filament-reinforced matrix system made from plastic (matrix) and glass (fiber). If there are $n$ fibers, each having a cross-sectional area of $A_f$ and modulus of $E_f$, embedded in a matrix having a cross-sectional area of $A_m$ and modulus of $E_m$, determine the stress in the matrix and each fiber when the force $P$ is imposed on the specimen.

**Prob. 48**

**49.** The tapered member is fixed connected at its ends $A$ and $B$ and is subjected to a load $P = 7$ kip at $x = 30$ in. Determine the reactions at the supports. The material is 2 in. thick and is made from 2014-T6 aluminum.

**50.** The tapered member is fixed connected at its ends $A$ and $B$ and is subjected to a load **P**. Determine the greatest possible magnitude for **P** without exceeding an average normal stress of $\sigma_{allow} = 4$ ksi anywhere in the member, and determine the location $x$ at which **P** would need to be applied. The member is 2 in. thick.

**Probs. 49/50**

**51.** The rigid bar supports the uniform distributed load of 6 kip/ft. Determine the force in each cable if each cable has a cross-sectional area of 0.05 in², and $E = 31(10^3)$ ksi.

**\*52.** The rigid bar is originally horizontal and is supported by two cables each having a cross-sectional area of 0.05 in², and $E = 31(10^3)$ ksi. Determine the slight rotation of the bar when the uniform load is supplied.

**Probs. 51/52**

**53.** Each of the three A-36 steel wires has the same diameter. Determine the force in each wire needed to support the 200-kg load.

**54.** The 200-kg load is suspended from three A-36 steel wires each having a diameter of 4 mm. If wire $BD$ has a length of 800.25 mm before the load is applied, determine the average normal stress developed in each wire.

**Probs. 53/54**

**55.** The three suspender bars are made of A992 steel and have equal cross-sectional areas of 450 mm². Determine the average normal stress in each bar if the rigid beam is subjected to the loading shown.

**Prob. 55**

**\*56.** The rigid bar supports the 800-lb load. Determine the normal stress in each A-36 steel cable if each cable has a cross-sectional area of 0.04 in².

**57.** The rigid bar is originally horizontal and is supported by two A-36 steel cables each having a cross-sectional area of 0.04 in². Determine the rotation of the bar when the 800-lb load is applied.

**Probs. 56/57**

**58.** Two identical rods *AB* and *CD* each have a length *L* and diameter *d*, and are used to support the rigid beam, which is pinned at *F*. If a vertical force **P** is applied at the end of the beam, determine the normal stress developed in each rod. The rods are made of material that has a modulus of elasticity of *E*.

**59.** Two identical rods *AB* and *CD* each have a length *L* and diameter *d*, and are used to support the rigid beam, which is pinned at *F*. If a vertical force **P** is applied at the end of the beam, determine the angle of rotation of the beam. The rods are made of material that has a modulus of elasticity of *E*.

**Probs. 58/59**

**\*60.** The assembly consists of two posts *AD* and *CF* made of A-36 steel and having a cross-sectional area of 1000 mm², and a 2014-T6 aluminum post *BE* having a cross-sectional area of 1500 mm² If a central load of 400 kN is applied to the rigid cap, determine the normal stress in each post. There is a small gap of 0.1 mm between the post *BE* and the rigid member *ABC*.

**Prob. 60**

**61.** The three suspender bars are made of the same material and have equal cross-sectional areas *A*. Determine the average normal stress in each bar if the rigid beam *ACE* is subjected to the force **P**.

**Prob. 61**

**62.** If the 2-in. diameter supporting rods are made from A992 steel, determine the average normal stress developed in each rod when $P = 100$ kip.

**63.** If the supporting rods of equal diameter are made from A992 steel, determine the required diameter to the nearest $\frac{1}{8}$ in. of each rod when $P = 100$ kip. The allowable normal stress of the steel is $\sigma_{allow} = 24$ ksi.

**Probs. 62/63**

**\*64.** The center post $B$ of the assembly has an original length of 124.7 mm, whereas posts $A$ and $C$ have a length of 125 mm. If the caps on the top and bottom can be considered rigid, determine the average normal stress in each post. The posts are made of aluminum and have a cross-sectional area of 400 mm². $E_{al} = 70$ GPa.

**Prob. 64**

**65.** Initially the A-36 bolt shank fits snugly against the rigid caps $E$ and $F$ on the 6061-T6 aluminum sleeve. If the thread of the bolt shank has a lead of 1 mm, and the nut is tightened $\frac{3}{4}$ of a turn, determine the average normal stress developed in the bolt shank and the sleeve. The diameter of bolt shank is $d = 60$ mm.

**66.** Initially the A-36 bolt shank fits snugly against the rigid caps $E$ and $F$ on the 6061-T6 aluminum sleeve. If the thread of the bolt shank has a lead of 1 mm, and the nut is tightened $\frac{3}{4}$ of a turn, determine the required diameter $d$ of the shank and the force developed in the shank and sleeve so that the normal stress developed in the shank is four times that of the sleeve.

**Probs. 65/66**

**67.** The assembly consists of a 6061-T6-aluminum member and a C83400-red-brass member that rest on the rigid plates. Determine the distance $d$ where the vertical load **P** should be placed on the plates so that the plates remain horizontal when the materials deform. Each member has a width of 8 in. and they are not bonded together.

**Prob. 67**

# 6  Thermal Stress

A change in temperature can cause a body to change its dimensions. Generally, if the temperature increases, the body will expand, whereas if the temperature decreases, it will contract[*]. Ordinarily this expansion or contraction is *linearly* related to the temperature increase or decrease that occurs. If this is the case, and the material is homogeneous and isotropic, it has been found from experiment that the displacement of a member having a length $L$ can be calculated using the formula

Most traffic bridges are designed with expansion joints to accommodate the thermal movement of the deck and thus avoid any thermal stress.

$$\delta_T = \alpha \,\Delta T L \qquad (4)$$

where

$\alpha =$ a property of the material, referred to as the ***linear coefficient of thermal expansion***. The units measure strain per degree of temperature. They are $1/°F$ (Fahrenheit) in the FPS system, and $1/°C$ (Celsius) or $1/K$ (Kelvin) in the SI system. Typical values are given on the inside back cover

$\Delta T =$ the algebraic change in temperature of the member

$L =$ the original length of the member

$\delta_T =$ the algebraic change in the length of the member

Long extensions of ducts and pipes that carry fluids are subjected to variations in climate that will cause them to expand and contract. Expansion joints, such as the one shown, are used to mitigate thermal stress in the material.

The change in length of a *statically determinate* member can easily be calculated using Eq. 4, since the member is free to expand or contract when it undergoes a temperature change. However, in a *statically indeterminate* member, these thermal displacements will be constrained by the supports, thereby producing ***thermal stresses*** that must be considered in design. Determining these thermal stresses is possible using the methods outlined in the previous sections. The following examples illustrate some applications.

[*]There are some materials, like Invar, an iron-nickel alloy, and scandium trifluoride, that behave in the opposite way, but we will not consider these here.

# EXAMPLE 9

0.5 in.

0.5 in.

2 ft

(a)

$F$

$F$

(b)

$\delta_T$

$\delta_F$

(c)

**Fig. 17**

The A-36 steel bar shown in Fig. 17a is constrained to just fit between two fixed supports when $T_1 = 60°F$. If the temperature is raised to $T_2 = 120°F$, determine the average normal thermal stress developed in the bar.

## SOLUTION

**Equilibrium.** The free-body diagram of the bar is shown in Fig. 17b. Since there is no external load, the force at $A$ is equal but opposite to the force at $B$; that is,

$$+\uparrow \Sigma F_y = 0; \qquad F_A = F_B = F$$

The problem is statically indeterminate since this force cannot be determined from equilibrium.

**Compatibility.** Since $\delta_{A/B} = 0$, the thermal displacement $\delta_T$ at $A$ that occurs, Fig. 17c, is counteracted by the force **F** that is required to push the bar $\delta_F$ back to its original position. The compatibility condition at $A$ becomes

$$(+\uparrow) \qquad \delta_{A/B} = 0 = \delta_T - \delta_F$$

**Load-Displacement.** Applying the thermal and load–displacement relationships, we have

$$0 = \alpha \Delta T L - \frac{FL}{AE}$$

Thus, from the data on the inside back cover,

$$
\begin{aligned}
F &= \alpha \Delta T A E \\
&= [6.60(10^{-6})/°F](120°F - 60°F)(0.5 \text{ in.})^2 [29(10^3) \text{ kip/in}^2] \\
&= 2.871 \text{ kip}
\end{aligned}
$$

Since **F** also represents the internal axial force within the bar, the average normal compressive stress is thus

$$\sigma = \frac{F}{A} = \frac{2.871 \text{ kip}}{(0.5 \text{ in.})^2} = 11.5 \text{ ksi} \qquad Ans.$$

**NOTE:** From the magnitude of **F**, it should be apparent that changes in temperature can cause large reaction forces in statically indeterminate members.

## EXAMPLE | 10

The rigid beam shown in Fig. 18a is fixed to the top of the three posts made of A992 steel and 2014-T6 aluminum. The posts each have a length of 250 mm when no load is applied to the beam, and the temperature is $T_1 = 20°C$. Determine the force supported by each post if the bar is subjected to a uniform distributed load of 150 kN/m and the temperature is raised to $T_2 = 80°C$.

(a)

### SOLUTION

**Equilibrium.** The free-body diagram of the beam is shown in Fig. 18b. Moment equilibrium about the beam's center requires the forces in the steel posts to be equal. Summing forces on the free-body diagram, we have

$$+\uparrow \Sigma F_y = 0; \quad 2F_{st} + F_{al} - 90(10^3) \text{ N} = 0 \quad (1)$$

**Compatibility.** Due to load, geometry, and material symmetry, the top of each post is displaced by an equal amount. Hence,

$$(+\downarrow) \qquad\qquad \delta_{st} = \delta_{al} \qquad\qquad (2)$$

The final position of the top of each post is equal to its displacement caused by the temperature increase, plus its displacement caused by the internal axial compressive force, Fig. 18c. Thus, for the steel and aluminum post, we have

$$(+\downarrow) \qquad\qquad \delta_{st} = -(\delta_{st})_T + (\delta_{st})_F$$
$$(+\downarrow) \qquad\qquad \delta_{al} = -(\delta_{al})_T + (\delta_{al})_F$$

Applying Eq. 2 gives

$$-(\delta_{st})_T + (\delta_{st})_F = -(\delta_{al})_T + (\delta_{al})_F$$

**Load-Displacement.** Using Eqs. 2 and 4 and the material properties on the inside back cover, we get

(c)

**Fig. 18**

$$-[12(10^{-6})/°C](80°C - 20°C)(0.250 \text{ m}) + \frac{F_{st}(0.250 \text{ m})}{\pi(0.020 \text{ m})^2 [200(10^9) \text{ N/m}^2]}$$

$$= -[23(10^{-6})/°C](80°C - 20°C)(0.250 \text{ m}) + \frac{F_{al}(0.250 \text{ m})}{\pi(0.030 \text{ m})^2 [73.1(10^9) \text{ N/m}^2]}$$

$$F_{st} = 1.216 F_{al} - 165.9(10^3) \qquad (3)$$

To be *consistent*, all numerical data has been expressed in terms of newtons, meters, and degrees Celsius. Solving Eqs. 1 and 3 simultaneously yields

$$F_{st} = -16.4 \text{ kN} \quad F_{al} = 123 \text{ kN} \qquad\qquad Ans.$$

The negative value for $F_{st}$ indicates that this force acts opposite to that shown in Fig. 18b. In other words, the steel posts are in tension and the aluminum post is in compression.

# EXAMPLE | 11

(a)

(b)

(c)

**Fig. 19**

A 2014-T6 aluminum tube having a cross-sectional area of 600 mm² is used as a sleeve for an A-36 steel bolt having a cross-sectional area of 400 mm², Fig. 19a. When the temperature is $T_1 = 15°C$, the nut holds the assembly in a snug position such that the axial force in the bolt is negligible. If the temperature increases to $T_2 = 80°C$, determine the force in the bolt and sleeve.

## SOLUTION

**Equilibrium.** The free-body diagram of a top segment of the assembly is shown in Fig. 19b. The forces $F_b$ and $F_s$ are produced since the sleeve has a higher coefficient of thermal expansion than the bolt, and therefore the sleeve will expand more when the temperature is increased. It is required that

$$+\uparrow \Sigma F_y = 0; \qquad\qquad F_s = F_b \qquad\qquad (1)$$

**Compatibility.** The temperature increase causes the sleeve and bolt to expand $(\delta_s)_T$ and $(\delta_b)_T$, Fig. 19c. However, the redundant forces $F_b$ and $F_s$ elongate the bolt and shorten the sleeve. Consequently, the end of the assembly reaches a final position, which is not the same as its initial position. Hence, the compatibility condition becomes

$$(+\downarrow) \qquad \delta = (\delta_b)_T + (\delta_b)_F = (\delta_s)_T - (\delta_s)_F$$

**Load-Displacement.** Applying Eqs. 2 and 4, we have

$$[12(10^{-6})/°C](80°C - 15°C)(0.150\text{ m}) +$$

$$\frac{F_b(0.150\text{ m})}{(400\text{ mm}^2)(10^{-6}\text{ m}^2/\text{mm}^2)[200(10^9)\text{ N/m}^2]}$$

$$= [23(10^{-6})/°C](80°C - 15°C)(0.150\text{ m})$$

$$- \frac{F_s(0.150\text{ m})}{(600\text{ mm}^2)(10^{-6}\text{ m}^2/\text{mm}^2)[73.1(10^9)\text{ N/m}^2]}$$

Using Eq. 1 and solving gives

$$F_s = F_b = 20.3\text{ kN} \qquad\qquad Ans.$$

**NOTE:** Since linear elastic material behavior was assumed in this analysis, the average normal stresses should be checked to make sure that they do not exceed the proportional limits for the material.

# PROBLEMS

**\*68.** The C83400-red-brass rod *AB* and 2014-T6-aluminum rod *BC* are joined at the collar *B* and fixed connected at their ends. If there is no load in the members when $T_1 = 50°F$, determine the average normal stress in each member when $T_2 = 120°F$. Also, how far will the collar be displaced? The cross-sectional area of each member is 1.75 in².

**Prob. 68**

**69.** The assembly has the diameters and material make-up indicated. If it fits securely between its fixed supports when the temperature is $T_1 = 70°F$, determine the average normal stress in each material when the temperature reaches $T_2 = 110°F$.

**Prob. 69**

**70.** The rod is made of A992 steel and has a diameter of 0.25 in. If the rod is 4 ft long when the springs are compressed 0.5 in. and the temperature of the rod is $T = 40°F$, determine the force in the rod when its temperature is $T = 160°F$.

**Prob. 70**

**71.** If the assembly fits snugly between two rigid supports *A* and *C* when the temperature is at $T_1$, determine the normal stress developed in both rod segments when the temperature rises to $T_2$. Both segments are made of the same material, having a modulus of elasticity of *E* and coefficient of thermal expansion of $\alpha$.

**\*72.** If the assembly fits snugly between the two supports *A* and *C* when the temperature is at $T_1$, determine the normal stress developed in both segments when the temperature rises to $T_2$. Both segments are made of the same material having a modulus of elasticity of *E* and coefficient of the thermal expansion of $\alpha$. The flexible supports at *A* and *C* each have a stiffness *k*.

**Probs. 71/72**

**73.** The pipe is made of A992 steel and is connected to the collars at *A* and *B*. When the temperature is 60°F, there is no axial load in the pipe. If hot gas traveling through the pipe causes its temperature to rise by $\Delta T = (40 + 15x)°F$, where *x* is in feet, determine the average normal stress in the pipe. The inner diameter is 2 in., the wall thickness is 0.15 in.

**74.** The bronze C86100 pipe has an inner radius of 0.5 in. and a wall thickness of 0.2 in. If the gas flowing through it changes the temperature of the pipe uniformly from $T_A = 200°F$ at *A* to $T_B = 60°F$ at *B*, determine the axial force it exerts on the walls. The pipe was fitted between the walls when $T = 60°F$.

**Probs. 73/74**

**75.** The 40-ft-long A-36 steel rails on a train track are laid with a small gap between them to allow for thermal expansion. Determine the required gap $\delta$ so that the rails just touch one another when the temperature is increased from $T_1 = -20°F$ to $T_2 = 90°F$. Using this gap, what would be the axial force in the rails if the temperature were to rise to $T_3 = 110°F$? The cross-sectional area of each rail is 5.10 in². 

**Prob. 75**

**\*76.** The device is used to measure a change in temperature. Bars $AB$ and $CD$ are made of A-36 steel and 2014-T6 aluminum alloy, respectively. When the temperature is at 75°F, $ACE$ is in the horizontal position. Determine the vertical displacement of the pointer at $E$ when the temperature rises to 150°F.

**Prob. 76**

**77.** The bar has a cross-sectional area $A$, length $L$, modulus of elasticity $E$, and coefficient of thermal expansion $\alpha$. The temperature of the bar changes uniformly along its length from $T_A$ at $A$ to $T_B$ at $B$ so that at any point $x$ along the bar $T = T_A + x(T_B - T_A)/L$. Determine the force the bar exerts on the rigid walls. Initially no axial force is in the bar and the bar has a temperature of $T_A$.

**Prob. 77**

**78.** When the temperature is at 30°C, the A-36 steel pipe fits snugly between the two fuel tanks. When fuel flows through the pipe, the temperatures at ends $A$ and $B$ rise to 130°C and 80°C, respectively. If the temperature drop along the pipe is linear, determine the average normal stress developed in the pipe. Assume each tank provides a rigid support at $A$ and $B$.

**Prob. 78**

**79.** When the temperature is at 30°C, the A-36 steel pipe fits snugly between the two fuel tanks. When fuel flows through the pipe, the temperatures at ends $A$ and $B$ rise to 130°C and 80°C, respectively. If the temperature drop along the pipe is linear, determine the average normal stress developed in the pipe. Assume the walls of each tank act as a spring, each having a stiffness of $k = 900$ MN/m.

**\*80.** When the temperature is at 30°C, the A-36 steel pipe fits snugly between the two fuel tanks. When fuel flows through the pipe, it causes the temperature to vary along the pipe as $T = (\frac{5}{3}x^2 - 20x + 120)°C$, where $x$ is in meters. Determine the normal stress developed in the pipe. Assume each tank provides a rigid support at $A$ and $B$.

**Probs. 79/80**

**81.** The 50-mm-diameter cylinder is made from Am 1004-T61 magnesium and is placed in the clamp when the temperature is $T_1 = 20°$ C. If the 304-stainless-steel carriage bolts of the clamp each have a diameter of 10 mm, and they hold the cylinder snug with negligible force against the rigid jaws, determine the force in the cylinder when the temperature rises to $T_2 = 130°$C.

**82.** The 50-mm-diameter cylinder is made from Am 1004-T61 magnesium and is placed in the clamp when the temperature is $T_1 = 15°$C. If the two 304-stainless-steel carriage bolts of the clamp each have a diameter of 10 mm, and they hold the cylinder snug with negligible force against the rigid jaws, determine the temperature at which the average normal stress in either the magnesium or the steel first becomes 12 MPa.

**Probs. 81/82**

**83.** The wires $AB$ and $AC$ are made of steel, and wire $AD$ is made of copper. Before the 150-lb force is applied, $AB$ and $AC$ are each 60 in. long and $AD$ is 40 in. long. If the temperature is increased by 80°F, determine the force in each wire needed to support the load. Take $E_{st} = 29(10^3)$ ksi, $E_{cu} = 17(10^3)$ ksi, $\alpha_{st} = 8(10^{-6})/°$F, $\alpha_{cu} = 9.60(10^{-6})/°$F. Each wire has a cross-sectional area of 0.0123 in$^2$.

**Prob. 83**

**\*84.** The center rod $CD$ of the assembly is heated from $T_1 = 30°$C to $T_2 = 180°$C using electrical resistance heating. At the lower temperature $T_1$ the gap between $C$ and the rigid bar is 0.7 mm. Determine the force in rods $AB$ and $EF$ caused by the increase in temperature. Rods $AB$ and $EF$ are made of steel, and each has a cross-sectional area of 125 mm$^2$. $CD$ is made of aluminum and has a cross-sectional area of 375 mm$^2$. $E_{st} = 200$ GPa, $E_{al} = 70$ GPa, and $\alpha_{al} = 23(10^{-6})/°$C.

**85.** The center rod $CD$ of the assembly is heated from $T_1 = 30°$C to $T_2 = 180°$C using electrical resistance heating. Also, the two end rods $AB$ and $EF$ are heated from $T_1 = 30°$C to $T_2 = 50°$C. At the lower temperature $T_1$ the gap between $C$ and the rigid bar is 0.7 mm. Determine the force in rods $AB$ and $EF$ caused by the increase in temperature. Rods $AB$ and $EF$ are made of steel, and each has a cross-sectional area of 125 mm$^2$. $CD$ is made of aluminum and has a cross-sectional area of 375 mm$^2$. $E_{st} = 200$ GPa, $E_{al} = 70$ GPa, $\alpha_{st} = 12(10^{-6})/°$C and $\alpha_{al} = 23(10^{-6})/°$C.

**Probs. 84/85**

**86.** The metal strap has a thickness $t$ and width $w$ and is subjected to a temperature gradient $T_1$ to $T_2$ ($T_1 < T_2$). This causes the modulus of elasticity for the material to vary linearly from $E_1$ at the top to a smaller amount $E_2$ at the bottom. As a result, for any vertical position $y$, $E = [(E_2 - E_1)/w]y + E_1$. Determine the position $d$ where the axial force $P$ must be applied so that the bar stretches uniformly over its cross section.

**Prob. 86**

## 7 Stress Concentrations

In Sec. 1, it was pointed out that when an axial force is applied to a member, it creates a complex stress distribution within the localized region of the point of load application. Not only do complex stress distributions arise just under a concentrated loading, they can also arise at sections where the member's cross-sectional area changes. For example, consider the bar in Fig. 20a, which is subjected to an axial force $P$. Here the once horizontal and vertical grid lines deflect into an irregular pattern around the hole centered in the bar. The maximum normal stress in the bar occurs on section $a$–$a$, which is taken through the bar's *smallest* cross-sectional area. Provided the material behaves in a linear-elastic manner, the stress distribution acting on this section can be determined either from a mathematical analysis, using the theory of elasticity, or experimentally by measuring the strain normal to section $a$–$a$ and then calculating the stress using Hooke's law, $\sigma = E\epsilon$. Regardless of the method used, the general shape of the stress distribution will be like that shown in Fig. 20b. In a similar manner, if the bar has a reduction in its cross section, achieved using shoulder fillets as in Fig. 21a, then again the maximum normal stress in the bar will occur at the *smallest* cross-sectional area, section $a$–$a$, and the stress distribution will look like that shown in Fig. 21b.

This saw blade has grooves cut into it in order to relieve both the dynamic stress that develops within it as it rotates and the thermal stress that develops as it heats up. Note the small circles at the end of each groove. These serve to reduce the stress concentrations that develop at the end of each groove.

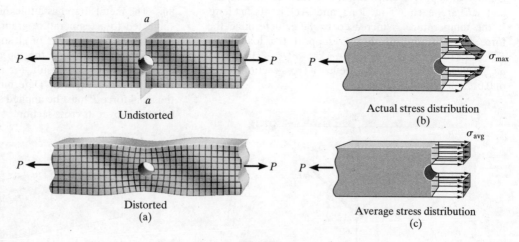

Undistorted

Actual stress distribution
(b)

Distorted
(a)

Average stress distribution
(c)

**Fig. 20**

In both of these cases, *force equilibrium* requires the magnitude of the *resultant force* developed by the stress distribution to be equal to $P$. In other words,

$$P = \int_A \sigma \, dA \tag{5}$$

This integral *graphically* represents the total *volume* under each of the stress-distribution diagrams shown in Fig. 20*b* or Fig. 21*b*. The resultant **P** must act through the *centroid* of each *volume*.

In engineering practice, the actual stress distributions in Fig. 20*b* and Fig. 21*b* do *not* have to be determined. Instead, only the *maximum stress* at these sections must be known, and the member is then designed to resist this stress when the axial load **P** is applied. Specific values of this maximum normal stress can be determined by experimental methods or by advanced mathematical techniques using the theory of elasticity. The results of these investigations are usually reported in graphical form using a ***stress-concentration factor*** $K$. We define $K$ as a ratio of the maximum stress to the average normal stress acting at the cross section; i.e.,

Stress concentrations often arise at sharp corners on heavy machinery. Engineers can mitigate this effect by using stiffeners welded to the corners.

$$K = \frac{\sigma_{max}}{\sigma_{avg}} \tag{6}$$

Provided $K$ is known, and the average normal stress has been calculated from $\sigma_{avg} = P/A$, where $A$ is the *smallest* cross-sectional area, Figs. 20*c* and 21*c*, then the maximum normal stress at the cross section is $\sigma_{max} = K(P/A)$.

a

a

Undistorted

Actual stress distribution
(b)

Distorted
(a)

Average stress distribution
(c)

**Fig. 21**

(c)                    (b)                    (a)

(d)

**Fig. 22**

Specific values of $K$ are generally reported in handbooks related to stress analysis. Examples are given in Figs. 23 and 24. Note that $K$ is independent of the bar's material properties; rather, it *depends* only on the bar's *geometry* and the type of discontinuity. As the size $r$ of the discontinuity is *decreased*, the stress concentration is increased. For example, if a bar requires a change in cross section, it has been determined that a sharp corner, Fig. 22a, produces a stress-concentration factor greater than 3. In other words, the maximum normal stress will be three times greater than the average normal stress on the smallest cross section. However, this can be reduced to, say, 1.5 by introducing a fillet, Fig. 22 *b*. A further reduction can be made by means of small grooves or holes placed at the transition, Fig. 22c and 22d. In all of these cases these designs help to reduce the rigidity of the material surrounding the corners, so that both the strain and the stress are more evenly spread throughout the bar.

The stress-concentration factors given in Figs. 23 and 24 were determined on the basis of a static loading, with the assumption that the stress in the material does not exceed the proportional limit. If the material is *very brittle*, the proportional limit may be at the fracture stress, and so for this material, failure will begin *at* the point of stress concentration. Essentially a crack begins to form at this point, and a higher stress concentration will develop at the *tip* of this crack. This, in turn, causes the crack to propagate over the cross section, resulting in sudden fracture. For this reason, it is very important to use stress-concentration factors in design when using brittle materials. On the other hand, if the material is ductile and subjected to a static load, it is often not necessary to use stress-concentration factors since any stress that exceeds the proportional limit will not result in a crack. Instead, the material will have reserve strength due to yielding and strain-hardening. In the next section we will discuss the effects caused by this phenomenon.

Stress concentrations are also responsible for many failures of structural members or mechanical elements subjected to *fatigue loadings*. For these cases, a stress concentration will cause the material to crack if the stress exceeds the material's endurance limit, whether or not the material is ductile or brittle. Here, the material *localized* at the tip of the crack remains in a *brittle state*, and so the crack continues to grow, leading to a progressive fracture. As a result, one must seek ways to limit the amount of damage that can be caused by fatigue.

**Fig. 23**

**Fig. 24**

Failure of this steel pipe in tension occurred at its smallest cross-sectional area, which is through the hole. Notice how the material yielded around the fractured surface.

## *8   Inelastic Axial Deformation

Up to this point we have only considered loadings that cause the material of a member to behave elastically. Sometimes, however, a member may be designed so that the loading causes the material to yield and thereby permanently deform. Such members are often made from a highly ductile metal such as annealed low-carbon steel having a stress–strain diagram that is similar to that of Fig. 6 and for simplicity can be *modeled* as shown in Fig. 25b. A material that exhibits this behavior is referred to as being *elastic perfectly plastic* or *elastoplastic.*

To illustrate physically how such a material behaves, consider the bar in Fig. 25a, which is subjected to the axial load **P**. If the load causes an *elastic stress* $\sigma = \sigma_1$ to be developed in the bar, then applying Eq. 5, *equilibrium* requires $P = \int \sigma_1 \, dA = \sigma_1 A$. Furthermore, the stress $\sigma_1$ causes the bar to strain $\varepsilon_1$ as indicated on the stress–strain diagram, Fig. 25b. If $P$ is now increased to $P_p$ such that it causes yielding of the material, that is, $\sigma = \sigma_Y$, then again $P_p = \int \sigma_Y \, dA = \sigma_Y A$. The load $P_p$ is called the *plastic load* since it represents the maximum load that can be supported by an elastoplastic material. For this case, the strains are *not* uniquely defined. Instead, at the instant $\sigma_Y$ is attained, the bar is *first* subjected to the yield strain $\epsilon_Y$, Fig. 25b, after which the bar will *continue to yield* (or elongate) such that the strains $\epsilon_2$, then $\epsilon_3$, etc., are generated. Since our "model" of the material exhibits perfectly plastic material behavior, this elongation will continue indefinitely with no increase in load. In reality, however, the material will, after some yielding, actually begin to strain-harden so that the extra strength it attains will *stop* any further straining. As a result, any design based on this behavior will be safe, since strain-hardening provides the potential for the material to support an *additional* load if necessary.

(a)                                            (b)

**Fig. 25**

Consider now the case of a bar having a hole through it as shown in Fig. 26a. As the magnitude of **P** is increased, a stress concentration occurs in the material at the edge of the hole, on section $a$–$a$. The stress here will reach a maximum value of, say, $\sigma_{max} = \sigma_1$ and have a corresponding *elastic strain* of $\epsilon_1$, Fig. 26b. The stresses and corresponding strains at other points on the cross section will be smaller, as indicated by the stress distribution shown in Fig. 26c. Equilibrium requires $P = \int \sigma \, dA$. In other words, $P$ is geometrically equivalent to the "volume" contained within the stress distribution. If the load is now increased to $P'$, so that $\sigma_{max} = \sigma_Y$, then the material will begin to yield outward from the hole, until the equilibrium condition $P' = \int \sigma \, dA$ is satisfied, Fig. 26d. As shown, this produces a stress distribution that has a geometrically *greater* "volume" than that shown in Fig. 26c. A further increase in load will cause the material over the *entire cross section* to yield eventually. When this happens, *no greater load* can be sustained by the bar. This *plastic load* $P_p$ is shown in Fig. 26e. It can be calculated from the equilibrium condition

$$P_p = \int_A \sigma_Y \, dA = \sigma_Y A$$

where $A$ is the bar's cross-sectional area at section $a$–$a$.

The following examples illustrate numerically how these concepts apply to other types of problems for which the material has elastoplastic behavior.

(a)

(b)

(c)  (d)  (e)

**Fig. 26**

## *9  Residual Stress

If an axially loaded member or group of such members forms a statically indeterminate system that can support both tensile and compressive loads, then excessive external loadings, which cause yielding of the material, will create *residual stresses* in the members when the loads are removed. The reason for this has to do with the elastic recovery of the material that occurs during unloading. To show this, consider a prismatic member made from an elastoplastic material having the stress–strain diagram shown in Fig. 27. If an axial load produces a stress $\sigma_Y$ in the material and a corresponding strain $\epsilon_C$, then when the load is *removed*, the material will respond elastically and follow the line $CD$ in order to recover some of the strain. A recovery to zero stress at point $O'$ will be possible only if the member is statically determinate, since the support reactions for the member must be zero when the load is removed. Under these circumstances the member will be permanently deformed so that the permanent set or strain in the member is $\epsilon_{O'}$.

If the member is *statically indeterminate*, however, removal of the external load will cause the support forces to respond to the elastic recovery $CD$. Since these forces will constrain the member from full recovery, they will induce **residual stresses** in the member. To solve a problem of this kind, the complete cycle of loading and then unloading of the member can be considered as the *superposition* of a positive load (loading) on a negative load (unloading). The loading, $O$ to $C$, results in a plastic stress distribution, whereas the unloading, along $CD$, results only in an elastic stress distribution. Superposition requires the loads to cancel; however, the stress distributions will not cancel, and so residual stresses will remain.

**Fig. 27**

# EXAMPLE | 12

The bar in Fig. 28a is made of steel that is assumed to be elastic perfectly plastic, with $\sigma_Y = 250$ MPa. Determine (a) the maximum value of the applied load $P$ that can be applied without causing the steel to yield and (b) the maximum value of $P$ that the bar can support. Sketch the stress distribution at the critical section for each case.

## SOLUTION

**Part (a).** When the material behaves elastically, we must use a stress-concentration factor determined from Fig. 23 that is unique for the bar's geometry. Here

$$\frac{r}{h} = \frac{4 \text{ mm}}{(40 \text{ mm} - 8 \text{ mm})} = 0.125$$

$$\frac{w}{h} = \frac{40 \text{ mm}}{(40 \text{ mm} - 8 \text{ mm})} = 1.25$$

From the figure $K \approx 1.75$. The maximum load, without causing yielding, occurs when $\sigma_{max} = \sigma_Y$. The average normal stress is $\sigma_{avg} = P/A$. Using Eq. 6, we have

$$\sigma_{max} = K\sigma_{avg}; \qquad \sigma_Y = K\left(\frac{P_Y}{A}\right)$$

$$250(10^6) \text{ Pa} = 1.75\left[\frac{P_Y}{(0.002 \text{ m})(0.032 \text{ m})}\right]$$

$$P_Y = 9.14 \text{ kN} \qquad\qquad Ans.$$

This load has been calculated using the *smallest* cross section. The resulting stress distribution is shown in Fig. 28b. For equilibrium, the "volume" contained within this distribution must equal 9.14 kN.

**Part (b).** The maximum load sustained by the bar will cause *all the material* at the smallest cross section to yield. Therefore, as $P$ is increased to the *plastic load* $P_p$, it gradually changes the stress distribution from the elastic state shown in Fig. 28b to the plastic state shown in Fig. 28c. We require

$$\sigma_Y = \frac{P_p}{A}$$

$$250(10^6) \text{ Pa} = \frac{P_p}{(0.002 \text{ m})(0.032 \text{ m})}$$

$$P_p = 16.0 \text{ kN} \qquad\qquad Ans.$$

Here $P_p$ equals the "volume" contained within the stress distribution, which in this case is $P_p = \sigma_Y A$.

(a)

(b)

(c)

**Fig. 28**

## EXAMPLE  13

(b)

**Fig. 29**

The rod shown in Fig. 29a has a radius of 5 mm and is made of an elastic perfectly plastic material for which $\sigma_Y = 420$ MPa, $E = 70$ GPa, Fig. 29c. If a force of $P = 60$ kN is applied to the rod and then removed, determine the residual stress in the rod.

### SOLUTION

The free-body diagram of the rod is shown in Fig. 29b. Application of the load **P** will cause one of three possibilities, namely, both segments $AC$ and $CB$ remain elastic, $AC$ is plastic while $CB$ is elastic, or both $AC$ and $CB$ are plastic.*

An *elastic analysis*, similar to that discussed in Sec. 4, will produce $F_A = 45$ kN and $F_B = 15$ kN at the supports. However, this results in a stress of

$$\sigma_{AC} = \frac{45 \text{ kN}}{\pi(0.005 \text{ m})^2} = 573 \text{ MPa (compression)} > \sigma_Y = 420 \text{ MPa}$$

$$\sigma_{CB} = \frac{15 \text{ kN}}{\pi(0.005 \text{ m})^2} = 191 \text{ MPa (tension)}$$

Since the material in segment $AC$ will yield, we will assume that $AC$ becomes plastic, while $CB$ remains elastic.

For this case, the maximum possible force developed in $AC$ is

$$(F_A)_Y = \sigma_Y A = 420(10^3) \text{ kN/m}^2 [\pi(0.005 \text{ m})^2] = 33.0 \text{ kN}$$

and from the equilibrium of the rod, Fig. 29b,

$$F_B = 60 \text{ kN} - 33.0 \text{ kN} = 27.0 \text{ kN}$$

The stress in each segment of the rod is therefore

$$\sigma_{AC} = \sigma_Y = 420 \text{ MPa (compression)}$$

$$\sigma_{CB} = \frac{27.0 \text{ kN}}{\pi(0.005 \text{ m})^2} = 344 \text{ MPa (tension)} < 420 \text{ MPa (OK)}$$

---

*The possibility of $CB$ becoming plastic before $AC$ will not occur because when point $C$ moves, the strain in $AC$ (since it is shorter) will always be larger than the strain in $CB$.

**Residual Stress.** In order to obtain the residual stress, it is also necessary to know the strain in each segment due to the loading. Since CB responds elastically,

$$\delta_C = \frac{F_B L_{CB}}{AE} = \frac{(27.0 \text{ kN})(0.300 \text{ m})}{\pi(0.005 \text{ m})^2 [70(10^6) \text{ kN/m}^2]} = 0.001474 \text{ m}$$

$$\epsilon_{CB} = \frac{\delta_C}{L_{CB}} = \frac{0.001474 \text{ m}}{0.300 \text{ m}} = +0.004913$$

$$\epsilon_{AC} = \frac{\delta_C}{L_{AC}} = -\frac{0.001474 \text{ m}}{0.100 \text{ m}} = -0.01474$$

Here the yield strain is

$$\epsilon_Y = \frac{\sigma_Y}{E} = \frac{420(10^6) \text{ N/m}^2}{70(10^9) \text{ N/m}^2} = 0.006$$

(c)

**Fig. 29 (cont.)**

Therefore, when **P** is *applied*, the stress–strain behavior for the material in segment CB moves from O to A', Fig. 29c, and the stress-strain behavior for the material in segment AC moves from O to B' If the load **P** is applied in the reverse direction, in other words, the load is removed, then an elastic response occurs and a reverse force of $F_A = 45$ kN and $F_B = 15$ kN must be applied to each segment. As calculated previously, these forces now produce stresses $\sigma_{AC} = 573$ MPa (tension) and $\sigma_{CB} = 191$ MPa (compression), and as a result the residual stress in each member is

$$(\sigma_{AC})_r = -420 \text{ MPa} + 573 \text{ MPa} = 153 \text{ MPa} \qquad Ans.$$

$$(\sigma_{CB})_r = 344 \text{ MPa} - 191 \text{ MPa} = 153 \text{ MPa} \qquad Ans.$$

This residual stress is the *same* for both segments, which is to be expected. Also note that the stress–strain behavior for segment AC moves from B' to D' in Fig. 29c, while the stress–strain behavior for the material in segment CB moves from A' to C' when the load is removed.

## EXAMPLE 14

(a)

$\delta_{AB} = 0.03 \text{ ft} + \delta_{AC}$  — Initial position

$\delta_{AC}$ — Final position

(d)

$\sigma$ (ksi)

50

0.0017

$\epsilon$ (in./in.)

(b)

$T_{AB}$  $T_{AC}$

3 kip

(c)

**Fig. 30**

Two steel wires are used to lift the weight of 3 kip, Fig. 30a. Wire $AB$ has an unstretched length of 20.00 ft and wire $AC$ has an unstretched length of 20.03 ft. If each wire has a cross-sectional area of 0.05 in$^2$, and the steel can be considered elastic perfectly plastic as shown by the $\sigma-\epsilon$ graph in Fig. 30b, determine the force in each wire and its elongation.

## SOLUTION

Once the weight is supported by both wires, then the stress in the wires depends on the corresponding strain. There are three possibilities, namely, the strains in both wires are elastic, wire $AB$ is plastically strained while wire $AC$ is elastically strained, or both wires are plastically strained. We will assume that $AC$ remains *elastic* and $AB$ is plastically strained.

Investigation of the free-body diagram of the suspended weight, Fig. 30c, indicates that the problem is statically indeterminate. The equation of equilibrium is

$$+\uparrow \Sigma F_y = 0; \qquad T_{AB} + T_{AC} - 3 \text{ kip} = 0 \qquad (1)$$

Since $AB$ becomes plastically strained then it must support its maximum load.

$$T_{AB} = \sigma_Y A_{AB} = 50 \text{ ksi} (0.05 \text{ in}^2) = 2.50 \text{ kip} \qquad Ans.$$

Therefore, from Eq. 1,

$$T_{AC} = 0.500 \text{ kip} \qquad Ans.$$

Note that wire $AC$ remains elastic as assumed since the stress in the wire is $\sigma_{AC} = 0.500 \text{ kip}/0.05 \text{ in}^2 = 10 \text{ ksi} < 50 \text{ ksi}$. The corresponding elastic strain is determined by proportion, Fig. 30b; i.e.,

$$\frac{\epsilon_{AC}}{10 \text{ ksi}} = \frac{0.0017}{50 \text{ ksi}}$$

$$\epsilon_{AC} = 0.000340$$

The elongation of $AC$ is thus

$$\delta_{AC} = (0.000340)(20.03 \text{ ft}) = 0.00681 \text{ ft} \qquad Ans.$$

And from Fig. 30d, the elongation of $AB$ is then

$$\delta_{AB} = 0.03 \text{ ft} + 0.00681 \text{ ft} = 0.0368 \text{ ft} \qquad Ans.$$

# PROBLEMS

**87.** Determine the maximum normal stress developed in the bar when it is subjected to a tension of $P = 8$ kN.

***88.** If the allowable normal stress for the bar is $\sigma_{allow} = 120$ MPa, determine the maximum axial force $P$ that can be applied to the bar.

**Probs. 87/88**

**89.** The steel bar has the dimensions shown. Determine the maximum axial force $P$ that can be applied so as not to exceed an allowable tensile stress of $\sigma_{allow} = 150$ MPa.

**Prob. 89**

**90.** Determine the maximum axial force $P$ that can be applied to the steel plate. The allowable stress is $\sigma_{allow} = 21$ ksi.

**Prob. 90**

**91.** Determine the maximum axial force $P$ that can be applied to the bar. The bar is made from steel and has an allowable stress of $\sigma_{allow} = 21$ ksi.

***92.** Determine the maximum normal stress developed in the bar when it is subjected to a tension of $P = 2$ kip.

**Probs. 91/92**

**93.** Determine the maximum normal stress developed in the bar when it is subjected to a tension of $P = 8$ kN.

**Prob. 93**

**94.** The resulting stress distribution along section $AB$ for the bar is shown. From this distribution, determine the approximate resultant axial force $P$ applied to the bar. Also, what is the stress-concentration factor for this geometry?

**Prob. 94**

**95.** The 10-mm-diameter shank of the steel bolt has a bronze sleeve bonded to it. The outer diameter of this sleeve is 20 mm. If the yield stress for the steel is $(\sigma_Y)_{st} = 640$ MPa, and for the bronze $(\sigma_Y)_{br} = 520$ MPa, determine the largest possible value of $P$ that can be applied to the bolt. Assume the materials to be elastic perfectly plastic. $E_{st} = 200$ GPa, $E_{br} = 100$ GPa.

**\*96.** The 10-mm-diameter shank of the steel bolt has a bronze sleeve bonded to it. The outer diameter of this sleeve is 20 mm. If the yield stress for the steel is $(\sigma_Y)_{st} = 640$ MPa, and for the bronze $(\sigma_Y)_{br} = 520$ MPa, determine the magnitude of the largest elastic load $P$ that can be applied to the assembly. $E_{st} = 200$ GPa, $E_{br} = 100$ GPa.

**Probs. 95/96**

**97.** The weight is suspended from steel and aluminum wires, each having the same initial length of 3 m and cross-sectional area of 4 mm². If the materials can be assumed to be elastic perfectly plastic, with $(\sigma_Y)_{st} = 120$ MPa and $(\sigma_Y)_{al} = 70$ MPa, determine the force in each wire if the weight is (a) 600 N and (b) 720 N. $E_{al} = 70$ GPa, $E_{st} = 200$ GPa.

**Prob. 97**

**98.** The bar has a cross-sectional area of 0.5 in² and is made of a material that has a stress–strain diagram that can be approximated by the two line segments shown. Determine the elongation of the bar due to the applied loading.

**Prob. 98**

**99.** The rigid beam is supported by a pin at $A$ and two steel wires, each having a diameter of 4 mm. If the yield stress for the wires is $\sigma_Y = 530$ MPa, and $E_{st} = 200$ GPa, determine the intensity of the distributed load $w$ that can be placed on the beam and will just cause wire $EB$ to yield. What is the displacement of point $G$ for this case? For the calculation, assume that the steel is elastic perfectly plastic.

**\*100.** The rigid beam is supported by a pin at $A$ and two steel wires, each having a diameter of 4 mm. If the yield stress for the wires is $\sigma_Y = 530$ MPa, and $E_{st} = 200$ GPa, determine (a) the intensity of the distributed load $w$ that can be placed on the beam that will cause only one of the wires to start to yield and (b) the smallest intensity of the distributed load that will cause both wires to yield. For the calculation, assume that the steel is elastic perfectly plastic.

**Probs. 99/100**

**101.** The rigid lever arm is supported by two A-36 steel wires having the same diameter of 4 mm. If a force of $P = 3$ kN is applied to the handle, determine the force developed in both wires and their corresponding elongations. Consider A-36 steel as an elastic-perfectly plastic material.

**102.** The rigid lever arm is supported by two A-36 steel wires having the same diameter of 4 mm. Determine the smallest force **P** that will cause (a) only one of the wires to yield; (b) both wires to yield. Consider A-36 steel as an elastic-perfectly plastic material.

**\*104.** The rigid beam is supported by three 25-mm diameter A-36 steel rods. If the beam supports the force of $P = 230$ kN, determine the force developed in each rod. Consider the steel to be an elastic perfectly-plastic material.

**105.** The rigid beam is supported by three 25-mm diameter A-36 steel rods. If the force of $P = 230$ kN is applied on the beam and removed, determine the residual stresses in each rod. Consider the steel to be an elastic perfectly-plastic material.

**Probs. 104/105**

**Probs. 101/102**

**103.** Two steel wires, each having a cross-sectional area of 2 mm² are tied to a ring at $C$, and then stretched and tied between the two pins $A$ and $B$. The initial tension in the wires is 50 N. If a horizontal force **P** is applied to the ring, determine the force in each wire if $P = 20$ N. What is the smallest force $P$ that must be applied to the ring to reduce the force in wire $CB$ to zero? Take $\sigma_Y = 300$ MPa. $E_{st} = 200$ GPa.

**106.** A material has a stress–strain diagram that can be described by the curve $\sigma = c\epsilon^{1/2}$. Determine the deflection of the end of a rod made from this material if it has a length $L$, cross-sectional area $A$, and a specific weight $\gamma$.

**107.** Solve Prob. 106 if the stress–strain diagram is defined by $\sigma = c\epsilon^{3/2}$.

**Prob. 103**

**Probs. 106/107**

**\*108.** The rigid beam is supported by the three posts $A$, $B$, and $C$ of equal length. Posts $A$ and $C$ have a diameter of 75 mm and are made of a material for which $E = 70$ GPa and $\sigma_Y = 20$ MPa. Post $B$ has a diameter of 20 mm and is made of a material for which $E' = 100$ GPa and $\sigma_Y' = 590$ MPa. Determine the smallest magnitude of $\mathbf{P}$ so that (a) only rods $A$ and $C$ yield and (b) all the posts yield.

**109.** The rigid beam is supported by the three posts $A$, $B$, and $C$. Posts $A$ and $C$ have a diameter of 60 mm and are made of a material for which $E = 70$ GPa and $\sigma_Y = 20$ MPa. Post $B$ is made of a material for which $E' = 100$ GPa and $\sigma_Y' = 590$ MPa. If $P = 130$ kN, determine the diameter of post $B$ so that all three posts are about to yield. (Do not assume that the three posts have equal uncompressed lengths.)

**Probs. 108/109**

**110.** The wire $BC$ has a diameter of 0.125 in. and the material has the stress–strain characteristics shown in the figure. Determine the vertical displacement of the handle at $D$ if the pull at the grip is slowly increased and reaches a magnitude of (a) $P = 450$ lb, (b) $P = 600$ lb. Assume the bar is rigid.

**Prob. 110**

**111.** The bar having a diameter of 2 in. is fixed connected at its ends and supports the axial load $\mathbf{P}$. If the material is elastic perfectly plastic as shown by the stress–strain diagram, determine the smallest load $P$ needed to cause segment $CB$ to yield. If this load is released, determine the permanent displacement of point $C$.

**\*112.** Determine the elongation of the bar in Prob. 111 when both the load $\mathbf{P}$ and the supports are removed.

**Probs. 111/112**

**113.** The three bars are pinned together and subjected to the load $\mathbf{P}$. If each bar has a cross-sectional area $A$, length $L$, and is made from an elastic perfectly plastic material, for which the yield stress is $\sigma_Y$, determine the largest load (ultimate load) that can be supported by the bars, i.e., the load $P$ that causes all the bars to yield. Also, what is the horizontal displacement of point $A$ when the load reaches its ultimate value? The modulus of elasticity is $E$.

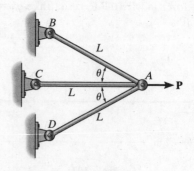

**Prob. 113**

# CHAPTER REVIEW

When a loading is applied at a point on a body, it tends to create a stress distribution within the body that becomes more uniformly distributed at regions removed from the point of application of the load. This is called Saint-Venant's principle.

$$\sigma_{avg} = \frac{P}{A}$$

The relative displacement at the end of an axially loaded member relative to the other end is determined from

$$\delta = \int_0^L \frac{P(x)dx}{A(x)E(x)}$$

If a series of concentrated external axial forces are applied to a member and $AE$ is also piecewise constant, then

$$\delta = \Sigma \frac{PL}{AE}$$

For application, it is necessary to use a sign convention for the internal load $P$ and displacement $\delta$. We considered tension and elongation as positive values. Also, the material must not yield, but rather it must remain linear elastic.

Superposition of load and displacement is possible provided the material remains linear elastic and no significant changes in the geometry of the member occur after loading.

The reactions on a statically indeterminate bar can be determined using the equilibrium equations and compatibility conditions that specify the displacement at the supports. These displacements are related to the loads using a load–displacement relationship such as $\delta = PL/AE$.

| | |
|---|---|
| A change in temperature can cause a member made of homogeneous isotropic material to change its length by $$\delta = \alpha \Delta T L$$ If the member is confined, this change will produce thermal stress in the member. | |
| Holes and sharp transitions at a cross section will create stress concentrations. For the design of a member made of brittle material one obtains the stress concentration factor $K$ from a graph, which has been determined from experiment. This value is then multiplied by the average stress to obtain the maximum stress at the cross section. $$\sigma_{\max} = K\sigma_{\text{avg}}$$ | |
| If the loading in a bar made of ductile material causes the material to yield, then the stress distribution that is produced can be determined from the strain distribution and the stress–strain diagram. Assuming the material is perfectly plastic, yielding will cause the stress distribution at the cross section of a hole or transition to even out and become uniform. | |
| If a member is constrained and an external loading causes yielding, then when the load is released, it will cause residual stress in the member. | |

# CONCEPTUAL PROBLEMS

**C1.** In each photo the concrete footings *A* were poured when the column was already in place. Later the concrete slab was poured. Explain why the 45° cracks formed in the slab at each corner of the square footing and not for the circular footing.

**C2.** The row of bricks, along with mortar and an internal steel reinforcing rod, was intended to serve as a lintel beam to support the bricks above this ventilation opening on an exterior wall of a building. Explain what may have caused the bricks to fail in the manner shown.

C2

C1

# REVIEW PROBLEMS

**114.** The assembly consists of two A992 steel bolts *AB* and *EF* and an 6061-T6 aluminum rod *CD*. When the temperature is at 30° C, the gap between the rod and rigid member *AE* is 0.1 mm. Determine the normal stress developed in the bolts and the rod if the temperature rises to 130° C. Assume *BF* is also rigid.

**115.** The assembly shown consists of two A992 steel bolts *AB* and *EF* and an 6061-T6 aluminum rod *CD*. When the temperature is at 30° C, the gap between the rod and rigid member *AE* is 0.1 mm. Determine the highest temperature to which the assembly can be raised without causing yielding either in the rod or the bolts. Assume *BF* is also rigid.

**Probs. 114/115**

**\*116.** The rods each have the same 25-mm diameter and 600-mm length. If they are made of A992 steel, determine the forces developed in each rod when the temperature increases by 50° C.

**Prob. 116**

**117.** Two A992 steel pipes, each having a cross-sectional area of 0.32 in², are screwed together using a union at *B* as shown. Originally the assembly is adjusted so that no load is on the pipe. If the union is then tightened so that its screw, having a lead of 0.15 in., undergoes two full turns, determine the average normal stress developed in the pipe. Assume that the union at *B* and couplings at *A* and *C* are rigid. Neglect the size of the union. *Note:* The lead would cause the pipe, when *unloaded*, to shorten 0.15 in. when the union is rotated one revolution.

**Prob. 117**

**118.** The force **P** is applied to the bar, which is composed of an elastic perfectly plastic material. Construct a graph to show how the force in each section *AB* and *BC* (ordinate) varies as *P* (abscissa) is increased. The bar has cross-sectional areas of 1 in² in region *AB* and 4 in² in region *BC*, and $\sigma_Y = 30$ ksi.

**Prob. 118**

AXIAL LOAD

**119.** The 2014-T6 aluminum rod has a diameter of 0.5 in and is lightly attached to the rigid supports at $A$ and $B$ when $T_1 = 70°F$. If the temperature becomes $T_2 = -10°F$, and an axial force of $P = 16$ lb is applied to the rigid collar as shown, determine the reactions at $A$ and $B$.

**121.** The rigid link is supported by a pin at $A$ and two A-36 steel wires, each having an unstretched length of 12 in. and cross-sectional area of 0.0125 in². Determine the force developed in the wires when the link supports the vertical load of 350 lb.

**Prob. 119**

**Prob. 121**

**\*120.** The 2014-T6 aluminum rod has a diameter of 0.5 in. and is lightly attached to the rigid supports at $A$ and $B$ when $T_1 = 70°F$. Determine the force $P$ that must be applied to the collar so that, when $T = 0°F$, the reaction at $B$ is zero.

**122.** The joint is made from three A992 steel plates that are bonded together at their seams. Determine the displacement of end $A$ with respect to end $B$ when the joint is subjected to the axial loads shown. Each plate has a thickness of 5 mm.

**Prob. 120**

**Prob. 122**

195

# Solutions and Answers for Preliminary Problems

## P1a.

$N_{ED} = 700$ N

$N_{DC} = 300$ N    400 N

$N_{CB} = 500$ N    200 N    400 N

$N_{BA} = 400$ N    100 N    200 N    400 N

## P1b.

600 N    $N_{AB} = 600$ N

600 N    400 N    $N_{BC} = 200$ N

600 N    400 N    300 N    $N_{CD} = 500$ N

## P2.

900 N    $N_{CB} = 900$ N

400 N    $N_{ED} = 400$ N

400 N    500 N    $N_{DB} = 900$ N

$N_{AB} = 1800$ N    900 N    900 N

## P3.

$(8x)$ N    $x$

$N = 8x$

## P4.

$100x$    800 N    $x$

$N = (800 - 100x)$ N

## P5.

60 kN    2 m    4 m    40 kN    20 kN

$$\Delta_B = \frac{PL}{AE} = \frac{20(10^3)\ \text{N}\ (3\ \text{m})}{2(10^{-3})\ \text{m}^2\,(60(10^9)\ \text{N/m}^2)}$$

$$= 0.5(10^{-3})\ \text{m} = 0.5\ \text{mm}$$

# Selected Answers

1. $\delta_B = 2.31$ mm, $\delta_A = 2.64$ mm
2. $\delta_{A/D} = 0.111$ in. away from end $D$.
3. $\sigma_{AB} = 22.2$ ksi (T), $\sigma_{BC} = 41.7$ ksi (C), $\sigma_{CD} = 25.0$ ksi (C), $\delta_{A/D} = 0.00157$ in. towards end $D$
5. $\delta_B = 1.59$ mm, $\delta_A = 6.14$ mm
6. $\delta_A = 0.0128$ in.
7. $\delta_A = -0.194$ in.
9. $\delta_F = 0.453$ mm
10. $P = 4.97$ kN
11. $\delta_l = 0.0260$ in.
13. $\delta_D = 17.3$ mm
14. $F = 12.0$ kN, $\delta_{A/B} = -0.864$ mm
15. $F = 17.0$ kN, $\delta_{A/B} = -1.03$ mm
17. $P = 59.5$ kN
18. $(\delta_A)_v = 0.0379$ in.
19. $P = 9.24$ kip
21. $\delta = 33.9$ mm
22. $W = 9.69$ kN
25. $\delta = 0.360$ mm
26. $\delta = 0.00257$ in.
27. $\delta = \dfrac{P}{2a\pi r_0^2 E}(1 - e^{-2aL})$
29. $p_0 = 250$ kN/m, $\delta = 2.93$ mm
30. $F = 420$ kN, $\delta = 4.57$ mm
31. $\sigma_{st} = 65.9$ MPa, $\sigma_{con} = 8.24$ MPa
33. $\sigma_{st} = 48.8$ MPa, $\sigma_{con} = 5.85$ MPa
34. $\sigma_{con} = 1.64$ ksi, $\sigma_{st} = 11.3$ ksi
35. $P = 114$ kip
37. $F_C = \left[\dfrac{9(8ka + \pi d^2 E)}{136ka + 18\pi d^2 E}\right]P$, $F_A = \left(\dfrac{64ka + 9\pi d^2 E}{136ka + 18\pi d^2 E}\right)P$
38. $T_{AB} = 1.12$ kip, $T_{AC} = 1.68$ kip
39. $A_{AB} = 0.03$ in$^2$
41. $F_D = 71.4$ kN, $F_C = 329$ kN
42. $F_D = 219$ kN, $F_C = 181$ kN
43. $\sigma_{AB} = \sigma_{CD} = 26.5$ MPa, $\sigma_{EF} = 33.8$ MPa
45. $\sigma_b = 32.4$ MPa, $\sigma_t = 34.5$ MPa
46. $F_D = 20.4$ kN, $F_A = 180$ kN
47. $P = 198$ kN
49. $F_A = 4.09$ kip, $F_B = 2.91$ kip
50. $x = 28.9$ in., $P = 60.4$ kip
51. $T_{CD} = 27.2$ kip, $T_{CB} = 9.06$ kip
53. $F_{BD} = 969$ N, $F_{AB} = F_{BC} = 620$ N
54. $\sigma_{BD} = 45.5$ MPa, $\sigma_{AB} = 69.1$ MPa
55. $\sigma_{BE} = 96.3$ MPa, $\sigma_{AD} = 79.6$ MPa, $\sigma_{CF} = 113$ MPa

57. $\theta = 0.0633°$
58. $\sigma_{AB} = \sigma_{CD} = \dfrac{6P}{\pi d^2}$
59. $\theta = \dfrac{6PL}{\pi d^2 E a}$
61. $\sigma_{AB} = \dfrac{7P}{12A}$, $\sigma_{CD} = \dfrac{P}{3A}$, $\sigma_{EF} = \dfrac{P}{12A}$
62. $\sigma_{AB} = \sigma_{AC} = 10.4$ ksi, $\sigma_{AD} = 13.8$ ksi
63. Use $d = 1\dfrac{5}{8}$ in.
65. $\sigma_s = 45.9$ MPa, $\sigma_b = 180$ MPa
66. $d_b = 59.4$ mm, $F_s = F_b = 502$ kN
67. $d = 4.90$ in.
69. $\sigma_{al} = 2.46$ ksi, $\sigma_{br} = 5.52$ ksi, $\sigma_{st} = 22.1$ ksi
70. $F = 0.510$ kip
71. $\sigma_{AB} = \dfrac{2}{5}\alpha(T_2 - T_1)E$, $\sigma_{BC} = \dfrac{8}{5}\alpha(T_2 - T_1)E$
73. $\sigma = 19.1$ ksi
74. $F = 7.60$ kip
75. $\delta = 0.348$ in., $F = 19.5$ kip
77. $F = \dfrac{\alpha AE}{2}(T_B - T_A)$
78. $\sigma = 180$ MPa
79. $\sigma = 105$ MPa
81. $F = 904$ N
82. $T_2 = 244°$
83. $F_{AC} = F_{AB} = 10.0$ lb, $F_{AD} = 136$ lb
85. $F_{AB} = F_{EF} = 1.85$ kN
86. $d = \left[\dfrac{2E_2 + E_1}{3(E_2 + E_1)}\right]w$
87. $\sigma_{max} = 168$ MPa
89. $P = 49.1$ kN
90. $P = 5.47$ kip
91. $P = 1.34$ kip
93. $\sigma_{max} = 81.7$ MPa
94. $P = 15$ kip, $K = 1.60$
95. $P = 173$ kN
97. (a) $F_{st} = 444$ N, $F_{al} = 156$ N, (b) $F_{st} = 480$ N, $F_{al} = 240$ N
98. $\delta_{Tot} = 0.432$ in.
99. $w = 21.9$ kN/m, $\delta_G = 4.24$ mm
101. $F_{AB} = 3.14$ kN, $F_{CD} = 2.72$ kN, $\delta_{CD} = 0.324$ mm, $\delta_{AB} = 0.649$ mm
102. (a) $P = 2.62$ kN, (b) $P = 3.14$ kN
103. $F_{AC} = 62$ N, $F_{BC} = 42$ N, $P = 125$ N
105. $(\sigma_{CF})_r = 17.7$ MPa (C), $(\sigma_{BE})_r = 53.2$ MPa (T), $(\sigma_{AD})_r = 35.5$ MPa (C)

**106.** $\delta = \dfrac{\gamma^2 L^3}{3c^2}$

**107.** $\delta = \dfrac{3}{5}\left(\dfrac{\gamma}{c}\right)^{\frac{2}{3}} L^{\frac{5}{3}}$

**109.** $d_B = 17.8\,\text{mm}$

**110.** (a) $\delta_D = 0.375\,\text{in.}$,

   (b) $\delta_D = 6.40\,\text{in.}$

**111.** $P = 126\,\text{kip}, \Delta\delta = 0.00720\,\text{in.}$

**113.** $P = \sigma_Y A\,(2\cos\theta + 1), \delta_A = \dfrac{\sigma_\gamma L}{E\cos\theta}$

**114.** $\sigma_b = 33.5\,\text{MPa}, \sigma_r = 16.8\,\text{MPa}$

**115.** $T = 507°\,\text{C}$

**117.** $\sigma_{AB} = \sigma_{BC} = 145\,\text{ksi}$

**119.** $F_B = 2.13\,\text{kip}, F_A = 2.14\,\text{kip}$

**121.** $F_B = 86.6\,\text{lb}, F_C = 195\,\text{lb}$

**122.** $\delta_{A/B} = 0.491\,\text{mm}$

---

# Fundamental Problems Partial Solutions and Answers

**F1**

$A = \dfrac{\pi}{4}(0.02^2) = 0.1(10^{-3})\pi\,\text{m}^2$

$\delta_C = \dfrac{1}{AE}\{40(10^3)(400) + [-60(10^3)(600)]\}$

$= \dfrac{-20(10^6)\,\text{N}\cdot\text{mm}}{AE}$

$= -0.318\,\text{mm}$  *Ans.*

**F2**

$A_{AB} = A_{CD} = \dfrac{\pi}{4}(0.02^2) = 0.1(10^{-3})\pi\,\text{m}^2$

$A_{BC} = \dfrac{\pi}{4}(0.04^2 - 0.03^2) = 0.175(10^{-3})\pi\,\text{m}^2$

$\delta_{D/A} = \dfrac{[-10(10^3)](400)}{[0.1(10^{-3})\pi][68.9(10^9)]}$

$\qquad + \dfrac{[10(10^3)](400)}{[0.175(10^{-3})\pi][68.9(10^9)]}$

$\qquad + \dfrac{[-20(10^3)](400)}{[0.1(10^{-3})\pi][68.9(10^9)]}$

$= -0.449\,\text{mm}$  *Ans.*

**F3**

$A = \dfrac{\pi}{4}(0.03^2) = 0.225(10^{-3})\pi\,\text{m}^2$

$\delta_C = \dfrac{1}{0.225(10^{-3})\pi[200(10^9)]}\left\{\left[-90(10^3)\right.\right.$

$\qquad \left.\left. + 2\left(\dfrac{4}{5}\right)30(10^3)\right](0.4) + [-90(10^3)(0.6)]\right\}$

$= -0.772(10^{-3})\,\text{m} = -0.772\,\text{mm}$  *Ans.*

**F4**

$\delta_{A/B} = \dfrac{PL}{AE} = \dfrac{[60(10^3)](0.8)}{[0.1(10^{-3})\pi][200(10^9)]}$

$= 0.7639(10^{-3})\,\text{m}\downarrow$

$\delta_B = \dfrac{F_{sp}}{k} = \dfrac{60(10^3)}{50(10^6)} = 1.2(10^{-3})\,\text{m}\downarrow$

$+\downarrow \quad \delta_A = \delta_B + \delta_{A/B}$

$\delta_A = 1.2(10^{-3}) + 0.7639(10^{-3})$

$= 1.9639(10^{-3})\,\text{m} = 1.96\,\text{mm}\downarrow$  *Ans.*

**F5**

$A = \dfrac{\pi}{4}(0.02^2) = 0.1(10^{-3})\pi\,\text{m}^2$

Internal load $P(x) = 30(10^3)x$

$\delta_A = \int \dfrac{P(x)dx}{AE}$

$= \dfrac{1}{[0.1(10^{-3})\pi][73.1(10^9)]}\int_0^{0.9\,\text{m}} 30(10^3)x\,dx$

$= 0.529(10^{-3})\,\text{m} = 0.529\,\text{mm}$  *Ans.*

**F6**

Distributed load $P(x) = \dfrac{45(10^3)}{0.9}x = 50(10^3)x\,\text{N/m}$

Internal load $P(x) = \dfrac{1}{2}(50(10^3))x(x) = 25(10^3)x^2$

$\delta_A = \int_0^L \dfrac{P(x)dx}{AE}$

$= \dfrac{1}{[0.1(10^{-3})\pi][73.1(10^9)]}\int_0^{0.9\,\text{m}} [25(10^3)x^2]dx$

$= 0.265\,\text{mm}$  *Ans.*

# Torsion

From Chapter 5 of *Mechanics of Materials*, Ninth Edition. R. C. Hibbeler. Copyright © 2014 by Pearson Education, Inc.
Published by Pearson Prentice Hall. All rights reserved.

The torsional stress and angle of twist of this soil auger depend upon the output of the machine turning the bit as well as the resistance of the soil in contact with the shaft.

# Torsion

## CHAPTER OBJECTIVES

■ In this chapter we will discuss the effects of applying a torsional loading to a long straight member such as a shaft or tube. Initially we will consider the member to have a circular cross section. We will show how to determine both the stress distribution within the member and the angle of twist when the material behaves in a linear elastic manner and also when it is inelastic. Statically indeterminate analysis of shafts and tubes will also be discussed, along with special topics that include those members having noncircular cross sections. Lastly, stress concentrations and residual stress caused by torsional loadings will be given special consideration.

## 1 Torsional Deformation of a Circular Shaft

*Torque* is a moment that tends to twist a member about its longitudinal axis. Its effect is of primary concern in the design of drive shafts used in vehicles and machinery. We can illustrate physically what happens when a torque is applied to a circular shaft by considering the shaft to be made of a highly deformable material such as rubber, Fig. 1*a*. When the torque is applied, the circles and longitudinal grid lines originally marked on the shaft tend to distort into the pattern shown in Fig. 1*b*. Note that twisting causes the circles to *remain circles*, and each longitudinal grid line deforms into a helix that intersects the circles at equal angles. Also, the cross sections at the ends of the shaft will remain *flat* — that is, they do not warp or bulge in or out — and radial lines *remain straight* during the deformation, Fig. 1*b*. From these observations we can assume that if the angle of twist is *small*, the *length of the shaft* and its *radius* will *remain unchanged*.

Before deformation
(a)

Circles remain circular

Longitudinal lines become twisted

*T*

*T*

Radial lines remain straight

After deformation
(b)

**Fig. 1**

If the shaft is fixed at one end and a torque is applied to its other end, the dark green shaded plane in Fig. 2 will distort into a skewed form as shown. Here a radial line located on the cross section at a distance *x* from the fixed end of the shaft will rotate through an angle $\phi(x)$. The angle $\phi(x)$, so defined, is called the *angle of twist*. It depends on the position *x* and will vary along the shaft as shown.

In order to understand how this distortion strains the material, we will now isolate a small element located at a radial distance $\rho$ (rho) from the axis of the shaft, Fig. 3. Due to the deformation as noted in Fig. 2, the front and rear faces of the element will undergo a rotation—the back face by $\phi(x)$, and the front face by $\phi(x) + \Delta\phi$. As a result, the *difference* in these rotations, $\Delta\phi$, causes the element to be subjected to a *shear strain*. To calculate this strain, note that before deformation the angle between the edges *AB* and *AC* is 90°; after deformation, however, the edges of the element are *AD* and *AC* and the angle between them is $\theta'$. From the definition of shear strain, Eq. 3, we have

$$\gamma = \frac{\pi}{2} - \theta'$$

Notice the deformation of the rectangular element when this rubber bar is subjected to a torque.

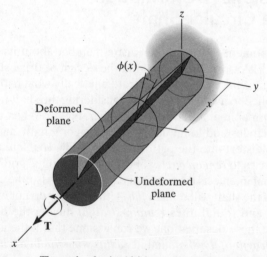

The angle of twist $\phi(x)$ increases as *x* increases.

**Fig. 2**

This angle, $\gamma$, is indicated on the element. It can be related to the length $\Delta x$ of the element and the angle $\Delta \phi$ between the shaded planes by considering the length of arc $BD$, that is

$$BD = \rho \Delta \phi = \Delta x \gamma$$

Therefore, if we let $\Delta x \rightarrow dx$ and $\Delta \phi \rightarrow d\phi$,

$$\gamma = \rho \frac{d\phi}{dx} \qquad (1)$$

Since $dx$ and $d\phi$ are the *same* for *all elements* located at points on the cross section at $x$, then $d\phi/dx$ is constant over the cross section, and Eq. 1 states that the magnitude of the shear strain for any of these elements varies only with its radial distance $\rho$ from the axis of the shaft. In other words, the shear strain within the shaft varies linearly along any radial line, from zero at the axis of the shaft to a maximum $\gamma_{max}$ at its outer boundary, Fig. 4. Since $d\phi/dx = \gamma/\rho = \gamma_{max}/c$, then

$$\gamma = \left( \frac{\rho}{c} \right) \gamma_{max} \qquad (2)$$

The results obtained here are also valid for circular tubes. They depend only on the assumptions regarding the deformations mentioned above.

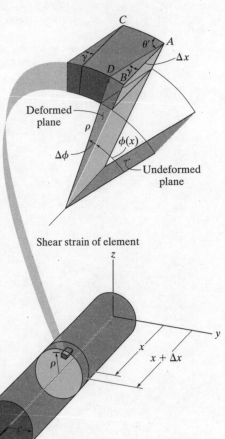

Shear strain of element

**Fig. 3**

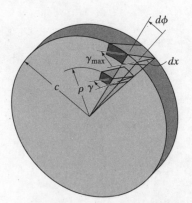

The shear strain at points on the cross section increases linearly with $\rho$, i.e., $\gamma = (\rho/c)\gamma_{max}$.

**Fig. 4**

## 2 The Torsion Formula

When an external torque is applied to a shaft, it creates a corresponding internal torque within the shaft. In this section, we will develop an equation that relates this internal torque to the shear stress distribution on the cross section of a circular shaft or tube.

If the material is linear-elastic, then Hooke's law applies, $\tau = G\gamma$, and consequently a **_linear variation in shear strain_**, as noted in the previous section, leads to a corresponding **_linear variation in shear stress_** along any radial line on the cross section. Hence, $\tau$ will vary from zero at the shaft's longitudinal axis to a maximum value, $\tau_{max}$, at its outer surface. This variation is shown in Fig. 5 on the front faces of a selected number of elements, located at an intermediate radial position $\rho$ and at the outer radius $c$. Due to the proportionality of triangles, we can write

$$\tau = \left(\frac{\rho}{c}\right)\tau_{max} \tag{3}$$

This equation expresses the shear-stress distribution over the cross section in terms of the radial position $\rho$ of the element. Using it, we can now apply the condition that requires the torque produced by the stress distribution over the entire cross section to be equivalent to the resultant internal torque $T$ at the section, which holds the shaft in equilibrium, Fig. 5.

Shear stress varies linearly along
each radial line of the cross section.

**Fig. 5**

Specifically, each element of area $dA$, located at $\rho$, is subjected to a force of $dF = \tau\, dA$. The torque produced by this force is $dT = \rho(\tau\, dA)$. We therefore have for the entire cross section

$$T = \int_A \rho(\tau\, dA) = \int_A \rho\left(\frac{\rho}{c}\right)\tau_{max}\, dA \qquad (4)$$

Since $\tau_{max}/c$ is constant,

$$T = \frac{\tau_{max}}{c} \int_A \rho^2\, dA \qquad (5)$$

The integral depends only on the geometry of the shaft. It represents the **polar moment of inertia** of the shaft's cross-sectional area about the shaft's longitudinal axis. We will symbolize its value as $J$, and therefore the above equation can be rearranged and written in a more compact form, namely,

$$\boxed{\tau_{max} = \frac{Tc}{J}} \qquad (6)$$

Here

$\tau_{max}$ = the maximum shear stress in the shaft, which occurs at the outer surface

$T$ = the resultant *internal torque* acting at the cross section. Its value is determined from the method of sections and the equation of moment equilibrium applied about the shaft's longitudinal axis

$J$ = the polar moment of inertia of the cross-sectional area

$c$ = the outer radius of the shaft

Combining Eqs. 3 and 6, the shear stress at the intermediate distance $\rho$ can be determined from

$$\boxed{\tau = \frac{T\rho}{J}} \qquad (7)$$

The shaft attached to the center of this wheel is subjected to a torque, and the maximum stress it creates must be resisted by the shaft to prevent failure.

Either of the above two equations is often referred to as the **torsion formula**. Recall that it is used only if the shaft is circular and the material is homogeneous and behaves in a linear elastic manner, since the derivation is based on Hooke's law.

**Fig. 6**

**Solid Shaft.** If the shaft has a solid circular cross section, the polar moment of inertia $J$ can be determined using an area element in the form of a *differential ring* or annulus having a thickness $d\rho$ and circumference $2\pi\rho$, Fig. 6. For this ring, $dA = 2\pi\rho \, d\rho$, and so

$$J = \int_A \rho^2 \, dA = \int_0^c \rho^2 (2\pi\rho \, d\rho) = 2\pi \int_0^c \rho^3 \, d\rho = 2\pi \left(\frac{1}{4}\right)\rho^4 \Big|_0^c$$

$$\boxed{J = \frac{\pi}{2}c^4} \tag{8}$$

Note that $J$ is a *geometric property* of the circular area and is always positive. Common units used for its measurement are $mm^4$ or $in^4$.

The shear stress has been shown to vary linearly along each radial line of the cross section of the shaft. However, if an element of material on the cross section is isolated, then due to the complementary property of shear, equal shear stresses must also act on four of its adjacent faces as shown in Fig. 7a. Hence, ***not only does the internal torque T develop a linear distribution of shear stress along each radial line in the plane of the cross-sectional area, but also an associated shear-stress distribution is developed along an axial plane***, Fig. 7b. It is interesting to note that because of this axial distribution of shear stress, shafts made from wood tend to *split* along the axial plane when subjected to excessive torque, Fig. 8. This is because wood is an anisotropic material. Its shear resistance parallel to its grains or fibers, directed along the axis of the shaft, is much less than its resistance perpendicular to the fibers, directed in the plane of the cross section.

(a)

$\tau_{max}$

$\tau_{max}$

Shear stress varies linearly along each radial line of the cross section.

(b)

**Fig. 7**

Failure of a wooden shaft due to torsion.

**Fig. 8**

## Tubular Shaft.

If a shaft has a tubular cross section, with inner radius $c_i$ and outer radius $c_o$, then from Eq. 8 we can determine its polar moment of inertia by subtracting $J$ for a shaft of radius $c_i$ from that determined for a shaft of radius $c_o$. The result is

$$J = \frac{\pi}{2}(c_o^4 - c_i^4) \qquad (9)$$

Like the solid shaft, the shear stress distributed over the tube's cross-sectional area varies linearly along any radial line, Fig. 9a. Furthermore, the shear stress varies along an axial plane in this same manner, Fig. 9b.

## Absolute Maximum Torsional Stress.

If the absolute maximum torsional stress is to be determined, then it becomes important to find the location where the ratio $Tc/J$ is a maximum. In this regard, it may be helpful to show the variation of the internal torque $T$ at each section along the axis of the shaft by drawing a ***torque diagram***, which is a plot of the internal torque $T$ versus its position $x$ along the shaft's length. Once the internal torque throughout the shaft is determined, the maximum ratio of $Tc/J$ can then be identified.

The tubular drive shaft for this truck was subjected to an excessive torque resulting in failure caused by yielding of the material. Engineers deliberately design drive shafts to fail before torsional damage can occur to parts of the engine or transmission.

(a)

Shear stress varies linearly along each radial line of the cross section.

(b)

**Fig. 9**

## Important Points

- When a shaft having a *circular cross section* is subjected to a torque, the cross section *remains plane* while radial lines rotate. This causes a *shear strain* within the material that *varies linearly* along any radial line, from zero at the axis of the shaft to a maximum at its outer boundary.

- For linear elastic homogeneous material the *shear stress* along any radial line of the shaft also *varies linearly*, from zero at its axis to a maximum at its outer boundary. This maximum shear stress *must not* exceed the proportional limit.

- Due to the complementary property of shear, the linear shear stress distribution within the plane of the cross section is also distributed along an adjacent axial plane of the shaft.

- The torsion formula is based on the requirement that the resultant torque on the cross section is equal to the torque produced by the shear stress distribution about the longitudinal axis of the shaft. It is required that the shaft or tube have a *circular* cross section and that it is made of *homogeneous* material which has *linear-elastic* behavior.

## Procedure for Analysis

The torsion formula can be applied using the following procedure.

### Internal Loading.

- Section the shaft perpendicular to its axis at the point where the shear stress is to be determined, and use the necessary free-body diagram and equations of equilibrium to obtain the internal torque at the section.

### Section Property.

- Calculate the polar moment of inertia of the cross-sectional area. For a solid section of radius $c$, $J = \pi c^4/2$, and for a tube of outer radius $c_o$ and inner radius $c_i$, $J = \pi(c_o^4 - c_i^4)/2$.

### Shear Stress.

- Specify the radial distance $\rho$, measured from the center of the cross section to the point where the shear stress is to be found. Then apply the torsion formula $\tau = T\rho/J$, or if the maximum shear stress is to be determined use $\tau_{max} = Tc/J$. When substituting the data, make sure to use a consistent set of units.

- The shear stress acts on the cross section in a direction that is always perpendicular to $\rho$. The force it creates must contribute a torque about the axis of the shaft that is in the *same direction* as the internal resultant torque $\mathbf{T}$ acting on the section. Once this direction is established, a volume element located at the point where $\tau$ is determined can be isolated, and the direction of $\tau$ acting on the remaining three adjacent faces of the element can be shown.

# EXAMPLE | 1

The *solid* shaft of radius $c$ is subjected to a torque **T**, Fig. 10a. Determine the fraction of $T$ that is resisted by the material contained within the outer core of the shaft, which has an inner radius of $c/2$ and outer radius $c$.

(a)

## SOLUTION

The stress in the shaft varies linearly, such that $\tau = (\rho/c)\tau_{max}$, Eq. 3. Therefore, the torque $dT'$ on the ring (area) located within the outer core, Fig. 10b, is

$$dT' = \rho(\tau \, dA) = \rho(\rho/c)\tau_{max}(2\pi\rho \, d\rho)$$

For the entire outer core area the torque is

$$T' = \frac{2\pi\tau_{max}}{c} \int_{c/2}^{c} \rho^3 d\rho$$

$$= \frac{2\pi\tau_{max}}{c} \frac{1}{4} \rho^4 \Big|_{c/2}^{c}$$

(b)

**Fig. 10**

So that

$$T' = \frac{15\pi}{32} \tau_{max}c^3 \qquad (1)$$

This torque $T'$ can be expressed in terms of the applied torque $T$ by first using the torsion formula to determine the maximum stress in the shaft. We have

$$\tau_{max} = \frac{Tc}{J} = \frac{Tc}{(\pi/2)c^4}$$

or

$$\tau_{max} = \frac{2T}{\pi c^3}$$

Substituting this into Eq. 1 yields

$$T' = \frac{15}{16} T \qquad \qquad Ans.$$

**NOTE:** Here, approximately 94% of the torque is resisted by the outer core, and the remaining 6% (or $\frac{1}{16}$) of $T$ is resisted by the inner core of the shaft, $\rho = 0$ to $\rho = c/2$. As a result, the material located at the *outer core* of the shaft is highly effective in resisting torque, which justifies the use of tubular shafts as an efficient means for transmitting torque, and thereby saving material.

## EXAMPLE | 2

42.5 kip·in.

30 kip·in.

12.5 kip·in.

*a*

*a*

(a)

The shaft shown in Fig. 11a is supported by two bearings and is subjected to three torques. Determine the shear stress developed at points A and B, located at section a–a of the shaft, Fig. 11c.

42.5 kip·in.

30 kip·in.

**T**

*x*

(b)

A

18.9 ksi

12.5 kip·in.

B

3.77 ksi

0.75 in.    0.15 in.    *x*

(c)

**Fig. 11**

### SOLUTION

**Internal Torque.** Since the bearing reactions do not offer resistance to shaft rotation, the applied torques satisfy moment equilibrium about the shaft's axis.

The internal torque at section a–a will be determined from the free-body diagram of the left segment, Fig. 11b. We have

$$\Sigma M_x = 0; \quad 42.5 \text{ kip} \cdot \text{in.} - 30 \text{ kip} \cdot \text{in.} - T = 0 \quad T = 12.5 \text{ kip} \cdot \text{in.}$$

**Section Property.** The polar moment of inertia for the shaft is

$$J = \frac{\pi}{2}(0.75 \text{ in.})^4 = 0.497 \text{ in.}^4$$

**Shear Stress.** Since point A is at $\rho = c = 0.75$ in.,

$$\tau_A = \frac{Tc}{J} = \frac{(12.5 \text{ kip} \cdot \text{in.})(0.75 \text{ in.})}{(0.497 \text{ in.}^4)} = 18.9 \text{ ksi} \qquad Ans.$$

Likewise for point B, at $\rho = 0.15$ in., we have

$$\tau_B = \frac{T\rho}{J} = \frac{(12.5 \text{ kip} \cdot \text{in.})(0.15 \text{ in.})}{(0.497 \text{ in.}^4)} = 3.77 \text{ ksi} \qquad Ans.$$

**NOTE:** The directions of these stresses on each element at A and B, Fig. 11c, are established from the direction of the resultant internal torque **T**, shown in Fig. 11b. Note carefully how the shear stress acts on the planes of each of these elements.

## EXAMPLE 3

The pipe shown in Fig. 12a has an inner diameter of 80 mm and an outer diameter of 100 mm. If its end is tightened against the support at A using a torque wrench at B, determine the shear stress developed in the material at the inner and outer walls along the central portion of the pipe when the 80-N forces are applied to the wrench.

### SOLUTION

**Internal Torque.** A section is taken at an intermediate location $C$ along the pipe's axis, Fig. 12b. The only unknown at the section is the internal torque **T**. We require

$$\Sigma M_y = 0; \quad 80\,\text{N}\,(0.3\,\text{m}) + 80\,\text{N}\,(0.2\,\text{m}) - T = 0$$

$$T = 40\,\text{N}\cdot\text{m}$$

**Section Property.** The polar moment of inertia for the pipe's cross-sectional area is

$$J = \frac{\pi}{2}\left[(0.05\,\text{m})^4 - (0.04\,\text{m})^4\right] = 5.796(10^{-6})\,\text{m}^4$$

(a)

**Shear Stress.** For any point lying on the outside surface of the pipe, $\rho = c_o = 0.05$ m, we have

$$\tau_o = \frac{Tc_o}{J} = \frac{40\,\text{N}\cdot\text{m}(0.05\,\text{m})}{5.796(10^{-6})\,\text{m}^4} = 0.345\,\text{MPa} \quad Ans.$$

And for any point located on the inside surface, $\rho = c_i = 0.04$ m, so that

$$\tau_i = \frac{Tc_i}{J} = \frac{40\,\text{N}\cdot\text{m}(0.04\,\text{m})}{5.796(10^{-6})\,\text{m}^4} = 0.276\,\text{MPa} \quad Ans.$$

(b)

**NOTE:** To show how these stresses act at representative points $D$ and $E$ on the cross-section, we will first view the cross section from the front of segment $CA$ of the pipe, Fig. 12a. On this section, Fig. 12c, the resultant internal torque is equal but opposite to that shown in Fig. 12b. The shear stresses at $D$ and $E$ contribute to this torque and therefore act on the shaded faces of the elements in the directions shown. As a consequence, notice how the shear-stress components act on the other three faces. Furthermore, since the top face of $D$ and the inner face of $E$ are in stress-free regions taken from the pipe's outer and inner walls, no shear stress can exist on these faces or on the other corresponding faces of the elements.

(c)

**Fig. 12**

# 3  Power Transmission

The belt drive transmits the torque developed by an electric motor to the shaft at $A$. The stress developed in the shaft depends upon the power transmitted by the motor and the rate of rotation of the shaft. $P = T\omega$.

Shafts and tubes having circular cross sections are often used to transmit power developed by a machine. When used for this purpose, they are subjected to a torque that depends on the power generated by the machine and the angular speed of the shaft. *Power* is defined as the work performed per unit of time. Also, the work transmitted by a rotating shaft equals the torque applied times the angle of rotation. Therefore, if during an instant of time $dt$ an applied torque $\mathbf{T}$ causes the shaft to rotate $d\theta$, then the instantaneous power is

$$P = \frac{T\,d\theta}{dt}$$

Since the shaft's angular velocity is $\omega = d\theta/dt$, we can express the power as

$$\boxed{P = T\omega} \tag{10}$$

In the SI system, power is expressed in *watts* when torque is measured in newton-meters $(\text{N} \cdot \text{m})$ and $\omega$ is in radians per second $(\text{rad/s})$ $(1\,\text{W} = 1\,\text{N} \cdot \text{m/s})$. In the FPS system, the basic units of power are foot-pounds per second $(\text{ft} \cdot \text{lb/s})$; however, horsepower (hp) is often used in engineering practice, where

$$1\,\text{hp} = 550\,\text{ft} \cdot \text{lb/s}$$

For machinery, the *frequency* of a shaft's rotation, $f$, is often reported. This is a measure of the number of revolutions or cycles the shaft makes per second and is expressed in hertz $(1\,\text{Hz} = 1\,\text{cycle/s})$. Since $1\,\text{cycle} = 2\pi\,\text{rad}$, then $\omega = 2\pi f$, and so the above equation for power becomes

$$\boxed{P = 2\pi f T} \tag{11}$$

**Shaft Design.**  When the power transmitted by a shaft and its frequency of rotation are known, the torque developed in the shaft can be determined from Eq. 11; that is, $T = P/2\pi f$. Knowing $T$ and the allowable shear stress for the material, $\tau_{\text{allow}}$, we can determine the size of the shaft's cross section using the torsion formula, provided the material behavior is linear elastic. Specifically, the design or geometric parameter $J/c$ becomes

$$\frac{J}{c} = \frac{T}{\tau_{\text{allow}}} \tag{12}$$

For a *solid shaft*, $J = (\pi/2)c^4$, and thus, upon substitution, a *unique value* for the shaft's radius $c$ can be determined. If the shaft is *tubular*, so that $J = (\pi/2)(c_o^4 - c_i^4)$, design permits a wide range of possibilities for the solution. This is because an *arbitrary choice* can be made for either $c_o$ or $c_i$ and the other radius can then be determined from Eq. 12.

## EXAMPLE | 4

A solid steel shaft $AB$, shown in Fig. 13, is to be used to transmit 5 hp from the motor $M$ to which it is attached. If the shaft rotates at $\omega = 175$ rpm and the steel has an allowable shear stress of $\tau_{\text{allow}} = 14.5$ ksi, determine the required diameter of the shaft to the nearest $\frac{1}{8}$ in.

**Fig. 13**

### SOLUTION

The torque on the shaft is determined from Eq. 10, that is, $P = T\omega$. Expressing $P$ in foot-pounds per second and $\omega$ in radians/second, we have

$$P = 5 \text{ hp} \left( \frac{550 \text{ ft} \cdot \text{lb/s}}{1 \text{ hp}} \right) = 2750 \text{ ft} \cdot \text{lb/s}$$

$$\omega = \frac{175 \text{ rev}}{\text{min}} \left( \frac{2\pi \text{ rad}}{1 \text{ rev}} \right) \left( \frac{1 \text{ min}}{60 \text{ s}} \right) = 18.33 \text{ rad/s}$$

Thus,

$$P = T\omega; \qquad 2750 \text{ ft} \cdot \text{lb/s} = T(18.33 \text{ rad/s})$$
$$T = 150.1 \text{ ft} \cdot \text{lb}$$

Applying Eq. 12 yields

$$\frac{J}{c} = \frac{\pi}{2} \frac{c^4}{c} = \frac{T}{\tau_{\text{allow}}}$$

$$c = \left( \frac{2T}{\pi \tau_{\text{allow}}} \right)^{1/3} = \left( \frac{2(150.1 \text{ ft} \cdot \text{lb})(12 \text{ in./ft})}{\pi (14\,500 \text{ lb/in}^2)} \right)^{1/3}$$

$$c = 0.429 \text{ in.}$$

Since $2c = 0.858$ in., select a shaft having a diameter of

$$d = \frac{7}{8} \text{ in.} = 0.875 \text{ in.} \qquad\qquad Ans.$$

# PRELIMINARY PROBLEMS

**P1.** Determine the internal torque at each section and show the torsional stress on differential volume elements located at $A, B, C$, and $D$.

(a)

**P1**

**P2.** Determine the internal torque at each section and show the torsional stress on differential volume elements located at $A, B, C$, and $D$.

(b)

**P2**

**P3.** The solid and hollow shafts are each subjected to the torque $T$. In each case, sketch the shear stress distribution along the two radial lines.

**P3**

**P4.** The motor delivers 10 hp to the shaft. If it rotates at 1200 rpm, detemine the torque produced by the motor.

**P4**

# FUNDAMENTAL PROBLEMS

**F1.** The solid circular shaft is subjected to an internal torque of $T = 5$ kN · m. Determine the shear stress developed at points $A$ and $B$. Represent each state of stress on a volume element.

**F3.** The shaft is hollow from $A$ to $B$ and solid from $B$ to $C$. Determine the maximum shear stress developed in the shaft. The shaft has an outer diameter of 80 mm, and the thickness of the wall of the hollow segment is 10 mm.

**F1**

**F3**

**F2.** The hollow circular shaft is subjected to an internal torque of $T = 10$ kN · m. Determine the shear stress developed at points $A$ and $B$. Represent each state of stress on a volume element.

**F4.** Determine the maximum shear stress developed in the 40-mm-diameter shaft.

**F2**

**F4**

**F5.** Determine the maximum shear stress developed in the shaft at section $a-a$.

Section $a$–$a$

**F5**

**F6.** Determine the shear stress developed at point $A$ on the surface of the shaft. Represent the state of stress on a volume element at this point. The shaft has a radius of 40 mm.

800 mm

5 kN·m/m

**F6**

**F7.** The solid 50-mm-diameter shaft is used to transmit the torques applied to the gears. Determine the absolute maximum shear stress in the shaft.

**F7**

**F8.** The gear motor can develop 3 hp when it turns at 150 rev/min. If the allowable shear stress for the shaft is $\tau_{\text{allow}} = 12$ ksi, determine the smallest diameter of the shaft to the nearest $\frac{1}{8}$ in. that can be used.

**F8**

# PROBLEMS

**1.** The solid shaft of radius $r$ is subjected to a torque **T**. Determine the radius $r'$ of the inner core of the shaft that resists one-half of the applied torque $(T/2)$. Solve the problem two ways: (a) by using the torsion formula, (b) by finding the resultant of the shear-stress distribution.

**2.** The solid shaft of radius $r$ is subjected to a torque **T**. Determine the radius $r'$ of the inner core of the shaft that resists one-quarter of the applied torque $(T/4)$. Solve the problem two ways: (a) by using the torsion formula, (b) by finding the resultant of the shear-stress distribution.

**T**

**Probs. 1/2**

**3.** The solid shaft is fixed to the support at $C$ and subjected to the torsional loadings shown. Determine the shear stress at points $A$ and $B$ and sketch the shear stress on volume elements located at these points.

**Prob. 3**

**\*4.** The copper pipe has an outer diameter of 40 mm and an inner diameter of 37 mm. If it is tightly secured to the wall at $A$ and three torques are applied to it as shown, determine the absolute maximum shear stress developed in the pipe.

**Prob. 4**

**5.** The copper pipe has an outer diameter of 2.50 in. and an inner diameter of 2.30 in. If it is tightly secured to the wall at $C$ and three torques are applied to it as shown, determine the shear stress developed at points $A$ and $B$. These points lie on the pipe's outer surface. Sketch the shear stress on volume elements located at $A$ and $B$.

**Prob. 5**

**6.** The solid shaft has a diameter of 0.75 in. If it is subjected to the torques shown, determine the maximum shear stress developed in regions *BC* and *DE* of the shaft. The bearings at *A* and *F* allow free rotation of the shaft.

**7.** The solid shaft has a diameter of 0.75 in. If it is subjected to the torques shown, determine the maximum shear stress developed in regions *CD* and *EF* of the shaft. The bearings at *A* and *F* allow free rotation of the shaft.

**9.** The solid shaft is fixed to the support at *C* and subjected to the torsional loadings shown. Determine the shear stress at points *A* and *B* on the surface, and sketch the shear stress on volume elements located at these points.

**Probs. 6/7**

**Prob. 9**

**\*8.** The solid 30-mm-diameter shaft is used to transmit the torques applied to the gears. Determine the absolute maximum shear stress on the shaft.

**10.** The coupling is used to connect the two shafts together. Assuming that the shear stress in the bolts is *uniform*, determine the number of bolts necessary to make the maximum shear stress in the shaft equal to the shear stress in the bolts. Each bolt has a diameter *d*.

**Prob. 8**

**Prob. 10**

**11.** The assembly consists of two sections of galvanized steel pipe connected together using a reducing coupling at *B*. The smaller pipe has an outer diameter of 0.75 in. and an inner diameter of 0.68 in., whereas the larger pipe has an outer diameter of 1 in. and an inner diameter of 0.86 in. If the pipe is tightly secured to the wall at *C*, determine the maximum shear stress developed in each section of the pipe when the couple shown is applied to the handles of the wrench.

**Prob. 11**

**14.** A steel tube having an outer diameter of 2.5 in. is used to transmit 9 hp when turning at 27 rev/min. Determine the inner diameter *d* of the tube to the nearest $\frac{1}{8}$ in. if the allowable shear stress is $\tau_{allow} = 10$ ksi.

**Prob. 14**

**\*12.** The 150-mm-diameter shaft is supported by a smooth journal bearing at *E* and a smooth thrust bearing at *F*. Determine the maximum shear stress developed in each segment of the shaft.

**13.** If the tubular shaft is made from material having an allowable shear stress of $\tau_{allow} = 85$ MPa, determine the required minimum wall thickness of the shaft to the nearest millimeter. The shaft has an outer diameter of 150 mm.

**15.** The solid shaft is made of material that has an allowable shear stress of $\tau_{allow} = 10$ MPa. Determine the required diameter of the shaft to the nearest millimeter.

**\*16.** The solid shaft has a diameter of 40 mm. Determine the absolute maximum shear stress in the shaft and sketch the shear-stress distribution along a radial line of the shaft where the shear stress is maximum.

**Probs. 12/13**

**Probs. 15/16**

**17.** The rod has a diameter of 1 in. and a weight of 10 lb/ft. Determine the maximum torsional stress in the rod at a section located at $A$ due to the rod's weight.

**18.** The rod has a diameter of 1 in. and a weight of 15 lb/ft. Determine the maximum torsional stress in the rod at a section located at $B$ due to the rod's weight.

**Probs. 17/18**

**19.** The shaft consists of solid 80-mm-diameter rod segments $AB$ and $CD$, and the tubular segment $BC$ which has an outer diameter of 100 mm and inner diameter of 80 mm. If the material has an allowable shear stress of $\tau_{allow} = 75$ MPa, determine the maximum allowable torque **T** that can be applied to the shaft.

**\*20.** The shaft consists of rod segments $AB$ and $CD$, and the tubular segment $BC$. If the torque $T = 10$ kN·m is applied to the shaft, determine the required minimum diameter of the rod and the maximum inner diameter of the tube. The outer diameter of the tube is 120 mm, and the material has an allowable shear stress of $\tau_{allow} = 75$ MPa.

**Probs. 19/20**

**21.** If the 40-mm-diameter rod is subjected to a uniform distributed torque of $t_0 = 1.5$ kN·m/m, determine the shear stress developed at point $C$.

**22.** If the rod is subjected to a uniform distributed torque of $t_0 = 1.5$ kN·m/m, determine the rod's minimum required diameter $d$ if the material has an allowable shear stress of $\tau_{allow} = 75$ MPa.

**23.** If the 40-mm diameter rod is made from a material having an allowable shear stress of $\tau_{allow} = 75$ MPa, determine the maximum allowable intensity $t_0$ of the uniform distributed torque.

**Probs. 21/22/23**

**\*24.** The copper pipe has an outer diameter of 2.50 in. and an inner diameter of 2.30 in. If it is tightly secured to the wall at $C$ and a uniformly distributed torque is applied to it as shown, determine the shear stress developed at points $A$ and $B$. These points lie on the pipe's outer surface. Sketch the shear stress on volume elements located at $A$ and $B$.

**25.** The copper pipe has an outer diameter of 2.50 in. and an inner diameter of 2.30 in. If it is tightly secured to the wall at $C$ and it is subjected to the uniformly distributed torque along its entire length, determine the absolute maximum shear stress in the pipe. Discuss the validity of this result.

**Probs. 24/25**

**26.** A cylindrical spring consists of a rubber annulus bonded to a rigid ring and shaft. If the ring is held fixed and a torque **T** is applied to the shaft, determine the maximum shear stress in the rubber.

**Prob. 26**

**27.** The assembly consists of the solid rod $AB$, tube $BC$, and the lever arm. If the rod and the tube are made of material having an allowable shear stress of $\tau_{allow} = 12$ ksi, determine the maximum allowable torque **T** that can be applied to the end of the rod and from there the couple forces $P$ that can be applied to the lever arm. The diameter of the rod is 2 in., and the outer and inner diameters of the tube are 4 in. and 2 in., respectively.

**\*28.** The assembly consists of the solid rod $AB$, tube $BC$, and the lever arm. If a torque of $T = 20$ kip·in. is applied to the rod and couple forces of $P = 5$ kip are applied to the lever arm, determine the required diameter for the rod, and the outer and inner diameters of the tube, if the ratio of the inner diameter $d_i$, to outer diameter $d_o$, is required to be $d_i/d_o = 0.75$. The rod and the tube are made of material having an allowable shear stress of $\tau_{allow} = 12$ ksi.

**Probs. 27/28**

**29.** The steel shafts are connected together using a fillet weld as shown. Determine the average shear stress in the weld along section $a$–$a$ if the torque applied to the shafts is $T = 60$ N·m. *Note:* The critical section where the weld fails is along section $a$–$a$.

**Prob. 29**

**30.** The shaft has a diameter of 80 mm. Due to friction at its surface within the hole, it is subjected to a variable torque described by the function $t = (25xe^{x^2})$ N·m/m, where $x$ is in meters. Determine the minimum torque $T_0$ needed to overcome friction and cause it to twist. Also, determine the absolute maximum stress in the shaft.

**Prob. 30**

**31.** The solid steel shaft $AC$ has a diameter of 25 mm and is supported by smooth bearings at $D$ and $E$. It is coupled to a motor at $C$, which delivers 3 kW of power to the shaft while it is turning at 50 rev/s. If gears $A$ and $B$ remove 1 kW and 2 kW, respectively, determine the maximum shear stress developed in the shaft within regions $AB$ and $BC$. The shaft is free to turn in its support bearings $D$ and $E$.

**33.** The motor $M$ is connected to the speed reducer $C$ by the tubular shaft and coupling. If the motor supplies 20 hp and rotates the shaft at a rate of 600 rpm, determine the minimum inner and outer diameters $d_i$ and $d_o$ of the shaft if $d_i/d_o = 0.75$. The shaft is made from a material having an allowable shear stress of $\tau_{allow} = 12$ ksi.

**34.** The motor $M$ is connected to the speed reducer $C$ by the tubular shaft and coupling. The shaft has an outer and inner diameter of 1 in. and 0.75 in., respectively, and is made from a material having an allowable shear stress of $\tau_{allow} = 12$ ksi, when the motor supplies 20 hp of power. Determine the smallest allowable angular velocity of the shaft.

**Prob. 31**

**Probs. 33/34**

**35.** The 25-mm-diameter shaft on the motor is made of a material having an allowable shear stress of $\tau_{allow} = 75$ MPa. If the motor is operating at its maximum power of 5 kW, determine the minimum allowable rotation of the shaft.

**\*36.** The drive shaft of the motor is made of a material having an allowable shear stress of $\tau_{allow} = 75$ MPa. If the outer diameter of the tubular shaft is 20 mm and the wall thickness is 2.5 mm, determine the maximum allowable power that can be supplied to the motor when the shaft is operating at an angular velocity of 1500 rev/min.

**\*32.** The pump operates using the motor that has a power of 85 W. If the impeller at $B$ is turning at 150 rev/min, determine the maximum shear stress developed in the 20-mm-diameter transmission shaft at $A$.

**Prob. 32**

**Probs. 35/36**

**37.** A ship has a propeller drive shaft that is turning at 1500 rev/min while developing 1800 hp. If it is 8 ft long and has a diameter of 4 in., determine the maximum shear stress in the shaft caused by torsion.

**38.** The motor $A$ develops a power of 300 W and turns its connected pulley at 90 rev/min. Determine the required diameters of the steel shafts on the pulleys at $A$ and $B$ if the allowable shear stress is $\tau_{allow} = 85$ MPa.

Prob. 38

**39.** The solid steel shaft $DF$ has a diameter of 25 mm and is supported by smooth bearings at $D$ and $E$. It is coupled to a motor at $F$, which delivers 12 kW of power to the shaft while it is turning at 50 rev/s. If gears $A$, $B$, and $C$ remove 3 kW, 4 kW, and 5 kW respectively, determine the maximum shear stress developed in the shaft within regions $CF$ and $BC$. The shaft is free to turn in its support bearings $D$ and $E$.

**\*40.** Determine the absolute maximum shear stress developed in the shaft in Prob. 39.

Probs. 39/40

**41.** The A-36 steel tubular shaft is 2 m long and has an outer diameter of 50 mm. When it is rotating at 40 rad/s, it transmits 25 kW of power from the motor $M$ to the pump $P$. Determine the smallest thickness of the tube if the allowable shear stress is $\tau_{allow} = 80$ MPa.

**42.** The A-36 solid steel shaft is 2 m long and has a diameter of 60 mm. It is required to transmit 60 kW of power from the motor $M$ to the pump $P$. Determine the smallest angular velocity the shaft can have if the allowable shear stress is $\tau_{allow} = 80$ MPa.

Probs. 41/42

**43.** The solid shaft has a linear taper from $r_A$ at one end to $r_B$ at the other. Derive an equation that gives the maximum shear stress in the shaft at a location $x$ along the shaft's axis.

Prob. 43

**\*44.** The rod has a diameter of 0.5 in. and weight of 5 lb/ft. Determine the maximum torsional stress in the rod at a section located at $A$ due to the rod's weight.

**45.** Solve Prob. 44 for the maximum torsional stress at $B$.

Probs. 44/45

**46.** A motor delivers 500 hp to the shaft, which is tubular and has an outer diameter of 2 in. If it is rotating at 200 rad/s, determine its largest inner diameter to the nearest $\frac{1}{8}$ in. if the allowable shear stress for the material is $\tau_{allow} = 25$ ksi.

Prob. 46

Long shafts subjected to torsion can, in some cases, have a noticeable elastic twist.

# 4  Angle of Twist

Occasionally the design of a shaft depends on restricting the amount of rotation or twist that may occur when the shaft is subjected to a torque. Furthermore, being able to compute the angle of twist for a shaft is important when analyzing the reactions on statically indeterminate shafts.

In this section we will develop a formula for determining the *angle of twist* $\phi$ (phi) of one end of a shaft with respect to its other end. The shaft is assumed to have a circular cross section that can gradually vary along its length, Fig. 14a. Also, the material is assumed to be homogeneous and to behave in a linear-elastic manner when the torque is applied. As with the case of an axially loaded bar, we will neglect the localized deformations that occur at points of application of the torques and where the cross section changes abruptly. By Saint-Venant's principle, these effects occur within small regions of the shaft's length and generally they will have only a slight effect on the final result.

Using the method of sections, a differential disk of thickness $dx$, located at position $x$, is isolated from the shaft, Fig. 14b. The internal resultant torque is $T(x)$, since the external loading may cause it to vary along the axis of the shaft. Due to $T(x)$, the disk will twist, such that the *relative rotation* of one of its faces with respect to the other face is $d\phi$, Fig. 14b. As a result an element of material located at an arbitrary radius $\rho$ within the disk will undergo a shear strain $\gamma$. The values of $\gamma$ and $d\phi$ are related by Eq. 1, namely,

$$d\phi = \gamma \frac{dx}{\rho} \qquad (13)$$

(a)

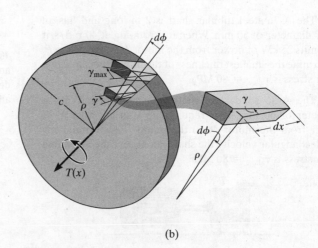

(b)

**Fig. 14**

Since Hooke's law, $\gamma = \tau/G$, applies and the shear stress can be expressed in terms of the applied torque using the torsion formula $\tau = T(x)\rho/J(x)$, then $\gamma = T(x)\rho/J(x)G(x)$. Substituting this into Eq. 13, the angle of twist for the disk is

$$d\phi = \frac{T(x)}{J(x)G(x)}\,dx$$

Integrating over the entire length $L$ of the shaft, we obtain the angle of twist for the entire shaft, namely,

$$\phi = \int_0^L \frac{T(x)\,dx}{J(x)G(x)} \qquad (14)$$

When computing both the stress and the angle of twist of this soil auger, it is necessary to consider the variable torsional loading which acts along its length.

Here

$\phi$ = the angle of twist of one end of the shaft with respect to the other end, measured in radians

$T(x)$ = the *internal torque* at the arbitrary position $x$, found from the method of sections and the equation of moment equilibrium applied about the shaft's axis

$J(x)$ = the shaft's polar moment of inertia expressed as a function of $x$.

$G(x)$ = the shear modulus of elasticity for the material expressed as a function of $x$.

## Constant Torque and Cross-Sectional Area.

Usually in engineering practice the material is homogeneous so that $G$ is constant. Also, the shaft's cross-sectional area and the external torque are constant along the length of the shaft, Fig. 15. If this is the case, the internal torque $T(x) = T$, the polar moment of inertia $J(x) = J$, and Eq. 14 can be integrated, which gives

$$\phi = \frac{TL}{JG} \qquad (15)$$

The similarities between the above two equations and those for an axially loaded bar ($\delta = \int P(x)dx/A(x)E(x)$ and $\delta = PL/AE$) should be noted.

**Fig. 15**

Load
dial

Load
range
selector

Torque
strain
recorder

Motor
controls

Specimen

Fixed
head

Turning
head

Motor

Movable unit
on rails

**Fig. 16**

Equation 15 is often used to determine the shear modulus of elasticity $G$ of a material. To do so, a specimen of known length and diameter is placed in a torsion testing machine like the one shown in Fig. 16. The applied torque $T$ and angle of twist $\phi$ are then measured along the length $L$. Using Eq. 15, $G = TL/J\phi$. Usually, to obtain a more reliable value of $G$, several of these tests are performed and the average value is used.

**Multiple Torques.** If the shaft is subjected to several different torques, or the cross-sectional area or shear modulus changes abruptly from one region of the shaft to the next, Eq. 15 can be applied to each segment of the shaft where these quantities are all constant. The angle of twist of one end of the shaft with respect to the other is then found from the vector addition of the angles of twist of each segment. For this case,

$$\phi = \sum \frac{TL}{JG} \tag{16}$$

**Sign Convention.** In order to apply this equation, we must develop a sign convention for both the internal torque and the angle of twist of one end of the shaft with respect to the other end. To do this, we will use the right-hand rule, whereby both the torque and angle will be *positive*, provided the *thumb* is directed *outward* from the shaft when the fingers curl to give the tendency for rotation, Fig. 17.

To illustrate the use of this sign convention, consider the shaft shown in Fig. 18a. The angle of twist of end $A$ with respect to end $D$ is to be determined. Three segments of the shaft must be considered, since the internal torque will change at $B$ and at $C$. Using the method of sections,

Positive sign convention
for $T$ and $\phi$.

**Fig. 17**

the *internal torques* are found for each segment, Fig. 18*b*. By the right-hand rule, with positive torques directed away from the *sectioned end* of the shaft, we have $T_{AB} = +80 \, \text{N} \cdot \text{m}$, $T_{BC} = -70 \, \text{N} \cdot \text{m}$, and $T_{CD} = -10 \, \text{N} \cdot \text{m}$. These results are also shown on the *torque diagram* for the shaft, Fig. 18*c*. Applying Eq. 16, we have

$$\phi_{A/D} = \frac{(+80 \, \text{N} \cdot \text{m}) \, L_{AB}}{JG} + \frac{(-70 \, \text{N} \cdot \text{m}) \, L_{BC}}{JG} + \frac{(-10 \, \text{N} \cdot \text{m}) \, L_{CD}}{JG}$$

If the other data is substituted and the answer is found as a *positive* quantity, it means that end $A$ will rotate as indicated by the curl of the right-hand fingers when the thumb is directed *away* from the shaft, Fig. 18*a*. The double subscript notation is used to indicate this relative angle of twist $(\phi_{A/D})$; however, if the angle of twist is to be determined relative to a *fixed support*, then only a single subscript will be used. For example, if $D$ is a fixed support, then the angle of twist will be denoted as $\phi_A$.

(b)

(a)

(c)

**Fig. 18**

## Important Point

- When applying Eq. 14 to determine the angle of twist, it is important that the applied torques do not cause yielding of the material and that the material is homogeneous and behaves in a linear elastic manner.

## Procedure for Analysis

The angle of twist of one end of a shaft or tube with respect to the other end can be determined using the following procedure.

Internal Torque.

- The *internal torque* is found at a point on the axis of the shaft by using the method of sections and the equation of moment equilibrium, applied along the shaft's axis.

- If the torque varies along the shaft's length, a section should be made at the arbitrary position $x$ along the shaft and the *internal torque* represented as a function of $x$, i.e., $T(x)$.

- If several constant external torques act on the shaft between its ends, the internal torque in each *segment* of the shaft, between any two external torques, must be determined. The results can be represented graphically as a torque diagram.

Angle of Twist.

- When the circular cross-sectional area of the shaft varies along the shaft's axis, the polar moment of inertia must be expressed as a function of its position $x$ along the axis, $J(x)$.

- If the polar moment of inertia or the internal torque *suddenly changes* between the ends of the shaft, then $\phi = \int (T(x)/J(x)G(x))\,dx$ or $\phi = TL/JG$ must be applied to *each segment* for which $J$, $G$, and $T$ are continuous or constant.

- When the internal torque in each segment is determined, be sure to use a consistent sign convention for the shaft, such as the one discussed in Fig. 17. Also make sure that a consistent set of units is used when substituting numerical data into the equations.

# EXAMPLE 5

The gears attached to the fixed-end steel shaft are subjected to the torques shown in Fig. 19a. If the shear modulus of elasticity is 80 GPa and the shaft has a diameter of 14 mm, determine the displacement of the tooth $P$ on gear $A$. The shaft turns freely within the bearing at $B$.

(a)

## SOLUTION

**Internal Torque.** By inspection, the torques in segments $AC$, $CD$, and $DE$ are different yet *constant* throughout each segment. Free-body diagrams of appropriate segments of the shaft along with the calculated internal torques are shown in Fig. 19b. Using the right-hand rule and the established sign convention that positive torque is directed away from the sectioned end of the shaft, we have

$$T_{AC} = +150 \text{ N} \cdot \text{m} \quad T_{CD} = -130 \text{ N} \cdot \text{m} \quad T_{DE} = -170 \text{ N} \cdot \text{m}$$

These results are also shown on the torque diagram, Fig. 19c.

**Angle of Twist.** The polar moment of inertia for the shaft is

$$J = \frac{\pi}{2}(0.007 \text{ m})^4 = 3.771(10^{-9}) \text{ m}^4$$

Applying Eq. 16 to each segment and adding the results algebraically, we have

$$\phi_A = \sum \frac{TL}{JG} = \frac{(+150 \text{ N} \cdot \text{m})(0.4 \text{ m})}{3.771(10^{-9})\text{m}^4 [80(10^9)\text{N/m}^2]}$$

$$+ \frac{(-130 \text{ N} \cdot \text{m})(0.3 \text{ m})}{3.771(10^{-9})\text{m}^4 [80(10^9)\text{N/m}^2]}$$

$$+ \frac{(-170 \text{ N} \cdot \text{m})(0.5 \text{ m})}{3.771(10^{-9})\text{m}^4 [80(10^9) \text{N/m}^2]} = -0.2121 \text{ rad}$$

(b)

(c)

Since the answer is negative, by the right-hand rule the thumb is directed *toward* the end $E$ of the shaft, and therefore gear $A$ will rotate as shown in Fig. 19d.

The displacement of tooth $P$ on gear $A$ is

$$s_P = \phi_A r = (0.2121 \text{ rad})(100 \text{ mm}) = 21.2 \text{ mm} \quad \textit{Ans.}$$

**NOTE:** Remember that this analysis is valid only if the shear stress does not exceed the proportional limit of the material.

(d)

**Fig. 19**

## EXAMPLE | 6

**Fig. 20**

The two solid steel shafts shown in Fig. 20a are coupled together using the meshed gears. Determine the angle of twist of end A of shaft AB when the torque $T = 45$ N·m is applied. Take $G = 80$ GPa. Shaft AB is free to rotate within bearings E and F, whereas shaft DC is fixed at D. Each shaft has a diameter of 20 mm. Ignore lateral flexing of the shafts.

### SOLUTION

**Internal Torque.** Free-body diagrams for each shaft are shown in Fig. 20b and 20c. Summing moments along the x axis of shaft AB yields the tangential reaction between the gears of $F = 45$ N·m/0.15 m = 300 N. Summing moments about the x axis of shaft DC, this force then creates a torque of $(T_D)_x = 300$ N (0.075 m) = 22.5 N·m on shaft DC.

**Angle of Twist.** To solve the problem, we will first calculate the rotation of gear C due to the torque of 22.5 N·m in shaft DC, Fig. 20c. This angle of twist is

$$\phi_C = \frac{TL_{DC}}{JG} = \frac{(+22.5 \text{ N·m})(1.5 \text{ m})}{(\pi/2)(0.010 \text{ m})^4 [80(10^9)\text{N/m}^2]} = +0.0269 \text{ rad}$$

Since the gears at the end of the shaft are in mesh, the rotation $\phi_C$ of gear C causes gear B to rotate $\phi_B$, Fig. 20d, where

$$\phi_B(0.15 \text{ m}) = (0.0269 \text{ rad})(0.075 \text{ m})$$
$$\phi_B = 0.0134 \text{ rad}$$

We will now determine the angle of twist of end A with respect to end B of shaft AB caused by the 45 N·m torque, Fig. 20b. We have

$$\phi_{A/B} = \frac{T_{AB}L_{AB}}{JG} = \frac{(+45 \text{ N·m})(2 \text{ m})}{(\pi/2)(0.010 \text{ m})^4 [80(10^9) \text{ N/m}^2]} = +0.0716 \text{ rad}$$

The rotation of end A is therefore determined by adding $\phi_B$ and $\phi_{A/B}$, since both angles are in the *same direction*, Fig. 20b. We have

$$\phi_A = \phi_B + \phi_{A/B} = 0.0134 \text{ rad} + 0.0716 \text{ rad} = +0.0850 \text{ rad} \quad Ans.$$

## EXAMPLE 7

The 2-in.-diameter solid cast-iron post shown in Fig. 21a is buried 24 in. in soil. If a torque is applied to its top using a rigid wrench, determine the maximum shear stress in the post and the angle of twist at its top. Assume that the torque is about to turn the post, and the soil exerts a uniform torsional resistance of $t$ lb·in./in. along its 24-in. buried length. $G = 5.5(10^3)$ ksi.

(a)

### SOLUTION

**Internal Torque.** The internal torque in segment $AB$ of the post is constant. From the free-body diagram, Fig. 21b, we have

$$\Sigma M_z = 0; \qquad T_{AB} = 25 \text{ lb } (12 \text{ in.}) = 300 \text{ lb} \cdot \text{in.}$$

The magnitude of the uniform distribution of torque along the buried segment $BC$ can be determined from equilibrium of the entire post, Fig. 21c. Here

$$\Sigma M_z = 0 \qquad 25 \text{ lb } (12 \text{ in.}) - t(24 \text{ in.}) = 0$$
$$t = 12.5 \text{ lb} \cdot \text{in./in.}$$

Hence, from a free-body diagram of a section of the post located at the position $x$, Fig. 21d, we have

$$\Sigma M_z = 0; \qquad T_{BC} - 12.5x = 0$$
$$T_{BC} = 12.5x$$

(b)

**Maximum Shear Stress.** The largest shear stress occurs in region $AB$, since the torque is largest there and $J$ is constant for the post. Applying the torsion formula, we have

$$\tau_{max} = \frac{T_{AB}\, c}{J} = \frac{(300 \text{ lb} \cdot \text{in.})(1 \text{ in.})}{(\pi/2)(1 \text{ in.})^4} = 191 \text{ psi} \qquad Ans.$$

**Angle of Twist.** The angle of twist at the top can be determined relative to the bottom of the post, since it is fixed and yet is about to turn. Both segments $AB$ and $BC$ twist, and so in this case we have

$$\phi_A = \frac{T_{AB}\, L_{AB}}{JG} + \int_0^{L_{BC}} \frac{T_{BC}\, dx}{JG}$$

$$= \frac{(300 \text{ lb} \cdot \text{in.})\, 36 \text{ in.}}{JG} + \int_0^{24 \text{ in.}} \frac{12.5x\, dx}{JG}$$

$$= \frac{10\,800 \text{ lb} \cdot \text{in}^2}{JG} + \frac{12.5[(24)^2/2] \text{ lb} \cdot \text{in}^2}{JG}$$

(d)

(c)

**Fig. 21**

$$= \frac{14\,400 \text{ lb} \cdot \text{in}^2}{(\pi/2)(1 \text{ in.})^4\, 5500(10^3) \text{ lb/in}^2} = 0.00167 \text{ rad} \qquad Ans.$$

## FUNDAMENTAL PROBLEMS

**F9.** The 60-mm-diameter steel shaft is subjected to the torques shown. Determine the angle of twist of end $A$ with respect to $C$. Take $G = 75$ GPa.

400 mm
600 mm
3 kN·m
2 kN·m

**F9**

**F10.** Determine the angle of twist of wheel $B$ with respect to wheel $A$. The shaft has a diameter of 40 mm and is made of steel for which $G = 75$ GPa.

150 mm
450 mm
100 mm
150 mm
150 mm
6 kN
4 kN  10 kN
2 kN

**F10**

**F11.** The hollow 6061-T6 aluminum shaft has an outer and inner radius of $c_o = 40$ mm and $c_i = 30$ mm, respectively. Determine the angle of twist of end $A$. The flexible support at $B$ has a torsional stiffness of $k = 90$ kN·m/rad.

900 mm
3 kN·m

**F11**

**F12.** A series of gears are mounted on the 40-mm-diameter steel shaft. Determine the angle of twist of gear $B$ relative to gear $A$. Take $G = 75$ GPa.

600 N·m
900 N·m
500 N·m
300 N·m
500 N·m
200 mm
200 mm
200 mm
200 mm

**F12**

**F13.** The 80-mm-diameter shaft is made of steel. If it is subjected to the uniform distributed torque, determine the angle of twist of end $A$ with respect to $B$. Take $G = 75$ GPa.

800 mm
5 kN·m/m

**F13**

**F14.** The 80-mm-diameter shaft is made of steel. If it is subjected to the triangular distributed load, determine the angle of twist of end $A$ with respect to $C$. Take $G = 75$ GPa.

400 mm
600 mm
15 kN·m/m

**F14**

# PROBLEMS

**47.** The propellers of a ship are connected to an A-36 steel shaft that is 60 m long and has an outer diameter of 340 mm and inner diameter of 260 mm. If the power output is 4.5 MW when the shaft rotates at 20 rad/s, determine the maximum torsional stress in the shaft and its angle of twist.

**\*48.** The solid shaft of radius $c$ is subjected to a torque **T** at its ends. Show that the maximum shear strain developed in the shaft is $\gamma_{\max} = Tc/JG$. What is the shear strain on an element located at point $A$, $c/2$ from the center of the shaft? Sketch the strain distortion of this element.

**Prob. 48**

**49.** The A-36 steel axle is made from tubes $AB$ and $CD$ and a solid section $BC$. It is supported on smooth bearings that allow it to rotate freely. If the gears, fixed to its ends, are subjected to 85-N · m torques, determine the angle of twist of gear $A$ relative to gear $D$. The tubes have an outer diameter of 30 mm and an inner diameter of 20 mm. The solid section has a diameter of 40 mm.

**50.** The hydrofoil boat has an A992 steel propeller shaft that is 100 ft long. It is connected to an in-line diesel engine that delivers a maximum power of 2500 hp and causes the shaft to rotate at 1700 rpm. If the outer diameter of the shaft is 8 in. and the wall thickness is $\frac{3}{8}$ in., determine the maximum shear stress developed in the shaft. Also, what is the "wind up," or angle of twist in the shaft at full power?

**Prob. 50**

**51.** The 60-mm-diameter shaft is made of 6061-T6 aluminum having an allowable shear stress of $\tau_{\text{allow}} = 80$ MPa. Determine the maximum allowable torque **T**. Also, find the corresponding angle of twist of disk $A$ relative to disk $C$.

**\*52.** The 60-mm-diameter shaft is made of 6061-T6 aluminum. If the allowable shear stress is $\tau_{\text{allow}} = 80$ MPa, and the angle of twist of disk $A$ relative to disk $C$ is limited so that it does not exceed 0.06 rad, determine the maximum allowable torque **T**.

**Prob. 49**

**Probs. 51/52**

**53.** The 20-mm-diameter A-36 steel shaft is subjected to the torques shown. Determine the angle of twist of the end B.

**Prob. 53**

**54.** The shaft is made of A992 steel with the allowable shear stress of $\tau_{allow} = 75$ MPa. If gear B supplies 15 kW of power, while gears A, C and D withdraw 6 kW, 4 kW and 5 kW, respectively, determine the required minimum diameter d of the shaft to the nearest millimeter. Also, find the corresponding angle of twist of gear A relative to gear D. The shaft is rotating at 600 rpm.

**55.** Gear B supplies 15 kW of power, while gears A, C and D withdraw 6 kW, 4 kW and 5 kW, respectively. If the shaft is made of steel with the allowable shear stress of $\tau_{allow} = 75$ MPa, and the relative angle of twist between any two gears cannot exceed 0.05 rad, determine the required minimum diameter d of the shaft to the nearest millimeter. The shaft is rotating at 600 rpm.

**Probs. 54/55**

**\*56.** The A-36 steel axle is made from tubes AB and CD and a solid section BC. It is supported on smooth bearings that allow it to rotate freely. If the gears, fixed to its ends, are subjected to 85-N · m torques, determine the angle of twist of the end B of the solid section relative to end C. The tubes have an outer diameter of 30 mm and an inner diameter of 20 mm. The solid section has a diameter of 40 mm.

**Prob. 56**

**57.** The turbine develops 150 kW of power, which is transmitted to the gears such that C receives 70% and D receives 30%. If the rotation of the 100-mm-diameter A-36 steel shaft is $\omega = 800$ rev/min., determine the absolute maximum shear stress in the shaft and the angle of twist of end E of the shaft relative to B. The journal bearing at E allows the shaft to turn freely about its axis.

**58.** The turbine develops 150 kW of power, which is transmitted to the gears such that both C and D receive an equal amount. If the rotation of the 100-mm-diameter A-36 steel shaft is $\omega = 500$ rev/min., determine the absolute maximum shear stress in the shaft and the rotation of end B of the shaft relative to E. The journal bearing at E allows the shaft to turn freely about its axis.

**Probs. 57/58**

**59.** The shaft is made of A992 steel. It has a diameter of 1 in. and is supported by bearings at $A$ and $D$, which allow free rotation. Determine the angle of twist of $B$ with respect to $D$.

**\*60.** The shaft is made of A-36 steel. It has a diameter of 1 in. and is supported by bearings at $A$ and $D$, which allow free rotation. Determine the angle of twist of gear $C$ with respect to $B$.

**Probs. 59/60**

**61.** The two shafts are made of A992 steel. Each has a diameter of 1 in., and they are supported by bearings at $A$, $B$, and $C$, which allow free rotation. If the support at $D$ is fixed, determine the angle of twist of end $B$ when the torques are applied to the assembly as shown.

**62.** The two shafts are made of A992 steel. Each has a diameter of 1 in., and they are supported by bearings at $A$, $B$, and $C$, which allow free rotation. If the support at $D$ is fixed, determine the angle of twist of end $A$ when the torques are applied to the assembly as shown.

**Probs. 61/62**

**63.** If the shaft is made of red brass C83400 copper with an allowable shear stress of $\tau_{allow} = 20$ MPa, determine the maximum allowable torques $T_1$ and $T_2$ that can be applied at $A$ and $B$. Also, find the corresponding angle of twist of end $A$. Set $L = 0.75$ m.

**\*64.** If the shaft is made of red brass C83400 copper and is subjected to torques $T_1 = 20$ kN·m and $T_2 = 50$ kN·m, determine the distance $L$ so that the angle of twist at end $A$ is zero.

**Probs. 63/64**

**65.** The 8-mm-diameter A-36 steel bolt is screwed tightly into a block at $A$. Determine the couple forces $F$ that should be applied to the wrench so that the maximum shear stress in the bolt becomes 18 MPa. Also, compute the corresponding displacement of each force $F$ needed to cause this stress. Assume that the wrench is rigid.

**Prob. 65**

**66.** The A-36 hollow steel shaft is 2 m long and has an outer diameter of 40 mm. When it is rotating at 80 rad/s, it transmits 32 kW of power from the engine $E$ to the generator $G$. Determine the smallest thickness of the shaft if the allowable shear stress is $\tau_{allow} = 140$ MPa and the shaft is restricted not to twist more than 0.05 rad.

**67.** The A-36 solid steel shaft is 3 m long and has a diameter of 50 mm. It is required to transmit 35 kW of power from the engine $E$ to the generator $G$. Determine the smallest angular velocity the shaft can have if it is restricted not to twist more than 1°.

**69.** The A-36 steel bolt is tightened within a hole so that the reactive torque on the shank $AB$ can be expressed by the equation $t = (kx^2)$ N $\cdot$ m/m, where $x$ is in meters. If a torque of $T = 50$ N $\cdot$ m is applied to the bolt head, determine the constant $k$ and the amount of twist in the 50-mm length of the shank. Assume the shank has a constant radius of 4 mm.

**70.** Solve Prob. 69 if the distributed torque is $t = (kx^{2/3})$ N $\cdot$ m/m.

Probs. 69/70

Probs. 66/67

**\*68.** If the shaft is subjected to a uniform distributed torque $t_0$, determine the angle of twist at $A$. The material has a shear modulus $G$. The shaft is hollow for exactly half its length.

**■71.** Consider the general problem of a circular shaft made from $m$ segments, each having a radius of $c_m$ and shear modulus $G_m$. If there are $n$ torques on the shaft as shown, write a computer program that can be used to determine the angle of twist of its end $A$. Show an application of the program using the values $L_1 = 0.5$ m, $c_1 = 0.02$ m, $G_1 = 30$ GPa, $L_2 = 1.5$ m, $c_2 = 0.05$ m, $G_2 = 15$ GPa, $T_1 = -450$ N $\cdot$ m, $d_1 = 0.25$ m, $T_2 = 600$ N $\cdot$ m, $d_2 = 0.8$ m.

Prob. 68

Prob. 71

**\*72.** The 80-mm diameter shaft is made of 6061-T6 aluminum alloy and subjected to the torsional loading shown. Determine the angle of twist at end $A$.

**Prob. 72**

**73.** The contour of the surface of the shaft is defined by the equation $y = e^{ax}$, where $a$ is a constant. If the shaft is subjected to a torque $T$ at its ends, determine the angle of twist of end $A$ with respect to end $B$. The shear modulus is $G$.

**Prob. 73**

**74.** The rod $ABC$ of radius $c$ is embedded into a medium where the distributed torque reaction varies linearly from zero at $C$ to $t_0$ at $B$. If couple forces $P$ are applied to the lever arm, determine the value of $t_0$ for equilibrium. Also, find the angle of twist of end $A$. The rod is made from material having a shear modulus of $G$.

**Prob. 74**

**75.** The A992 steel posts are "drilled" at constant angular speed into the soil using the rotary installer. If the post has an inner diameter of 200 mm and an outer diameter of 225 mm, determine the relative angle of twist of end $A$ of the post with respect to end $B$ when the post reaches the depth indicated. Due to soil friction, assume the torque along the post varies linearly as shown, and a concentrated torque of 80 kN · m acts at the bit.

**Prob. 75**

**\*76.** A cylindrical spring consists of a rubber annulus bonded to a rigid ring and shaft. If the ring is held fixed and a torque $T$ is applied to the rigid shaft, determine the angle of twist of the shaft. The shear modulus of the rubber is $G$. *Hint:* As shown in the figure, the deformation of the element at radius $r$ can be determined from $r d\theta = dr\gamma$. Use this expression, along with $\tau = T/(2\pi r^2 h)$ from Prob. 26, to obtain the result.

**Prob. 76**

# 5 Statically Indeterminate Torque-Loaded Members

A torsionally loaded shaft may be classified as statically indeterminate if the moment equation of equilibrium, applied about the axis of the shaft, is not adequate to determine the unknown torques acting on the shaft. An example of this situation is shown in Fig. 22a. As shown on the free-body diagram, Fig. 22b, the reactive torques at the supports A and B are unknown. We require that

$$\Sigma M_x = 0; \qquad\qquad T - T_A - T_B = 0$$

In order to obtain a solution, we will use the method of analysis discussed in Sec. 4. The necessary condition of compatibility, or the kinematic condition, requires the angle of twist of one end of the shaft with respect to the other end to be equal to zero, since the end supports are fixed. Therefore,

$$\phi_{A/B} = 0$$

Provided the material is linear elastic, we can apply the load–displacement relation $\phi = TL/JG$ to express the compatibility condition in terms of the unknown torques. Realizing that the internal torque in segment $AC$ is $+T_A$ and in segment $CB$ it is $-T_B$, Fig. 22c, we have

$$\frac{T_A L_{AC}}{JG} - \frac{T_B L_{BC}}{JG} = 0$$

(a)

(b)

(c)

**Fig. 22**

Solving the above two equations for the reactions, realizing that $L = L_{AC} + L_{BC}$, we get

$$T_A = T\left(\frac{L_{BC}}{L}\right) \quad \text{and} \quad T_B = T\left(\frac{L_{AC}}{L}\right)$$

## Procedure for Analysis

The unknown torques in statically indeterminate shafts are determined by satisfying equilibrium, compatibility, and torque-displacement requirements for the shaft.

### Equilibrium.

- Draw a free-body diagram of the shaft in order to identify all the external torques that act on it. Then write the equation of moment equilibrium about the axis of the shaft.

### Compatibility.

- Write the compatibility equation between two points along the shaft. Give consideration as to how the supports constrain the shaft when it is twisted.

### Load-Displacement.

- Express the angles of twist in the compatibility condition in terms of the torques, using a torque-displacement relation, such as $\phi = TL/JG$.

- Solve the equations for the unknown reactive torques. If any of the magnitudes have a negative numerical value, it indicates that this torque acts in the opposite sense of direction to that shown on the free-body diagram.

The shaft of this cutting machine is fixed at its ends and subjected to a torque at its center, allowing it to act as a torsional spring.

# EXAMPLE | 8

The solid steel shaft shown in Fig. 23a has a diameter of 20 mm. If it is subjected to the two torques, determine the reactions at the fixed supports $A$ and $B$.

(a)                                    (b)

## SOLUTION

**Equilibrium.** By inspection of the free-body diagram, Fig. 23b, it is seen that the problem is statically indeterminate since there is only *one* available equation of equilibrium and there are two unknowns. We require

$$\Sigma M_x = 0; \quad -T_B + 800 \text{ N} \cdot \text{m} - 500 \text{ N} \cdot \text{m} - T_A = 0 \quad (1)$$

**Compatibility.** Since the ends of the shaft are fixed, the angle of twist of one end of the shaft with respect to the other must be zero. Hence, the compatibility equation becomes

$$\phi_{A/B} = 0$$

**Load-Displacement.** This condition can be expressed in terms of the unknown torques by using the load-displacement relationship, $\phi = TL/JG$. Here there are three regions of the shaft where the internal torque is constant. On the free-body diagrams in Fig. 23c we have shown the internal torques acting on the left segments of the shaft which are sectioned in each of these regions. This way the internal torque is only a function of $T_B$. Using the sign convention established in Sec. 4, we have

$$\frac{-T_B(0.2 \text{ m})}{JG} + \frac{(800 - T_B)(1.5 \text{ m})}{JG} + \frac{(300 - T_B)(0.3 \text{ m})}{JG} = 0$$

so that

$$T_B = 645 \text{ N} \cdot \text{m} \qquad \qquad Ans.$$

Using Eq. 1,

$$T_A = -345 \text{ N} \cdot \text{m} \qquad \qquad Ans.$$

The negative sign indicates that $\mathbf{T}_A$ acts in the opposite direction of that shown in Fig. 23b.

**Fig. 23**

## EXAMPLE 9

The shaft shown in Fig. 24a is made from a steel tube, which is bonded to a brass core. If a torque of $T = 250$ lb·ft is applied at its end, plot the shear-stress distribution along a radial line of its cross-sectional area. Take $G_{st} = 11.4(10^3)$ ksi, $G_{br} = 5.20(10^3)$ ksi.

### SOLUTION

**Equilibrium.** A free-body diagram of the shaft is shown in Fig. 24b. The reaction at the wall has been represented by the unknown amount of torque resisted by the steel, $T_{st}$, and by the brass, $T_{br}$. Working in units of pounds and inches, equilibrium requires

$$-T_{st} - T_{br} + (250 \text{ lb·ft})(12 \text{ in./ft}) = 0 \qquad (1)$$

**Compatibility.** We require the angle of twist of end $A$ to be the same for both the steel and brass since they are bonded together. Thus,

$$\phi = \phi_{st} = \phi_{br}$$

**Load-Displacement.** Applying the load–displacement relationship, $\phi = TL/JG$,

$$\frac{T_{st}L}{(\pi/2)[(1 \text{ in.})^4 - (0.5 \text{ in.})^4] \, 11.4(10^3) \text{ kip/in}^2} =$$

$$\frac{T_{br}L}{(\pi/2)(0.5 \text{ in.})^4 \, 5.20(10^3) \text{ kip/in}^2}$$

$$T_{st} = 32.88 \, T_{br} \qquad (2)$$

Solving Eqs. 1 and 2, we get

$$T_{st} = 2911.5 \text{ lb·in.} = 242.6 \text{ lb·ft}$$
$$T_{br} = 88.5 \text{ lb·in.} = 7.38 \text{ lb·ft}$$

The shear stress in the brass core varies from zero at its center to a maximum at the interface where it contacts the steel tube. Using the torsion formula,

$$(\tau_{br})_{max} = \frac{(88.5 \text{ lb·in.})(0.5 \text{ in.})}{(\pi/2)(0.5 \text{ in.})^4} = 451 \text{ psi}$$

For the steel, the minimum and maximum shear stresses are

$$(\tau_{st})_{min} = \frac{(2911.5 \text{ lb·in.})(0.5 \text{ in.})}{(\pi/2)[(1 \text{ in.})^4 - (0.5 \text{ in.})^4]} = 989 \text{ psi}$$

$$(\tau_{st})_{max} = \frac{(2911.5 \text{ lb·in.})(1 \text{ in.})}{(\pi/2)[(1 \text{ in.})^4 - (0.5 \text{ in.})^4]} = 1977 \text{ psi}$$

The results are plotted in Fig. 24c. Note the discontinuity of *shear stress* at the brass and steel interface. This is to be expected, since the materials have different moduli of rigidity; i.e., steel is stiffer than brass $(G_{st} > G_{br})$ and thus it carries more shear stress at the interface. Although the shear stress is discontinuous here, the *shear strain* is not. Rather, the shear strain is the *same* for both the brass and the steel.

Shear–stress distribution

(c)

**Fig. 24**

## PROBLEMS

**77.** The steel shaft has a diameter of 40 mm and is fixed at its ends $A$ and $B$. If it is subjected to the couple determine the maximum shear stress in regions $AC$ and $CB$ of the shaft. $G_{st} = 75$ GPa.

**Prob. 77**

**78.** The A992 steel shaft has a diameter of 60 mm and is fixed at its ends $A$ and $B$. If it is subjected to the torques shown, determine the absolute maximum shear stress in the shaft.

**Prob. 78**

**79.** The steel shaft is made from two segments: $AC$ has a diameter of 0.5 in, and $CB$ has a diameter of 1 in. If the shaft is fixed at its ends $A$ and $B$ and subjected to a torque of 500 lb·ft, determine the maximum shear stress in the shaft. $G_{st} = 10.8(10^3)$ ksi.

**Prob. 79**

**\*80.** The shaft is made of A-36 steel and is fixed at its ends $A$ and $D$. Determine the torsional reactions at these supports.

**81.** The shaft is made of A-36 steel and is fixed at end $D$, while end $A$ is allowed to rotate 0.005 rad when the torque is applied. Determine the torsional reactions at these supports.

**Probs. 80/81**

**82.** The shaft is made from a solid steel section $AB$ and a tubular portion made of steel and having a brass core. If it is fixed to a rigid support at $A$, and a torque of $T = 50$ lb · ft is applied to it at $C$, determine the angle of twist that occurs at $C$ and compute the maximum shear stress and maximum shear strain in the brass and steel. Take $G_{st} = 11.5(10^3)$ ksi, $G_{br} = 5.6(10^3)$ ksi.

**Prob. 82**

**83.** The motor $A$ develops a torque at gear $B$ of 450 lb · ft, which is applied along the axis of the 2-in.-diameter steel shaft $CD$. This torque is to be transmitted to the pinion gears at $E$ and $F$. If these gears are temporarily fixed, determine the maximum shear stress in segments $CB$ and $BD$ of the shaft. Also, what is the angle of twist of each of these segments? The bearings at $C$ and $D$ only exert force reactions on the shaft and do not resist torque. $G_{st} = 12(10^3)$ ksi.

**Prob. 83**

**86.** The two shafts are made of A-36 steel. Each has a diameter of 25 mm and they are connected using the gears fixed to their ends. Their other ends are attached to fixed supports at $A$ and $B$. They are also supported by journal bearings at $C$ and $D$, which allow free rotation of the shafts along their axes. If a torque of 500 N · m is applied to the gear at $E$ as shown, determine the reactions at $A$ and $B$.

**87.** Determine the rotation of the gear at $E$ in Prob. 86.

**Probs. 86/87**

**\*84.** The Am1004-T61 magnesium tube is bonded to the A-36 steel rod. If the allowable shear stresses for the magnesium and steel are $(\tau_{allow})_{mg} = 45$ MPa and $(\tau_{allow})_{st} = 75$ MPa, respectively, determine the maximum allowable torque that can be applied at $A$. Also, find the corresponding angle of twist of end $A$.

**85.** The Am1004-T61 magnesium tube is bonded to the A-36 steel rod. If a torque of $T = 5$ kN · m is applied to end $A$, determine the maximum shear stress in each material. Sketch the shear stress distribution.

**Probs. 84/85**

**\*88.** A rod is made from two segments: $AB$ is steel and $BC$ is brass. It is fixed at its ends and subjected to a torque of $T = 680$ N · m. If the steel portion has a diameter of 30 mm, determine the required diameter of the brass portion so the reactions at the walls will be the same. $G_{st} = 75$ GPa, $G_{br} = 39$ GPa.

**89.** Determine the absolute maximum shear stress in the shaft of Prob. 88.

**Probs. 88/89**

**90.** The composite shaft consists of a mid-section that includes the 1-in. diameter solid shaft and a tube that is welded to the rigid flanges at *A* and *B*. Neglect the thickness of the flanges and determine the angle of twist of end *C* of the shaft relative to end *D*. The shaft is subjected to a torque of 800 lb · ft. The material is A-36 steel.

**Prob. 90**

**91.** The A992 steel shaft is made from two segments. *AC* has a diameter of 0.5 in. and *CB* has a diameter of 1 in. If the shaft is fixed at its ends *A* and *B* and subjected to a uniform distributed torque of 60 lb · in./in. along segment *CB*, determine the absolute maximum shear stress in the shaft.

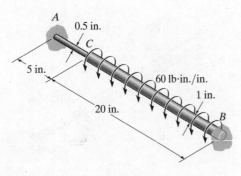

**Prob. 91**

**\*92.** If the shaft is subjected to a uniform distributed torque of *t* = 20 kN · m/m, determine the maximum shear stress developed in the shaft. The shaft is made of 2014-T6 aluminum alloy and is fixed at *A* and *C*.

**Prob. 92**

**93.** The tapered shaft is confined by the fixed supports at *A* and *B*. If a torque **T** is applied at its mid-point, determine the reactions at the supports.

**Prob. 93**

**94.** The shaft of radius *c* is subjected to a distributed torque *t*, measured as torque/length of shaft. Determine the reactions at the fixed supports *A* and *B*.

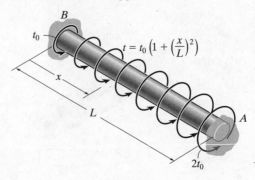

$$t = t_0 \left(1 + \left(\frac{x}{L}\right)^2\right)$$

**Prob. 94**

# *6  Solid Noncircular Shafts

It was demonstrated in Sec. 1 that when a torque is applied to a shaft having a circular cross section—that is, one that is axisymmetric—the shear strains vary linearly from zero at its center to a maximum at its outer surface. Furthermore, due to the uniformity of the shear strain at all points on the same radius, the cross sections do not deform, but rather remain plane after the shaft has twisted. Shafts that have a noncircular cross section, however, are *not* axisymmetric, and so their cross sections will *bulge* or *warp* when the shaft is twisted. Evidence of this can be seen from the way grid lines deform on a shaft having a square cross section when the shaft is twisted, Fig. 25. As a consequence of this deformation the torsional analysis of *noncircular* shafts becomes considerably more complicated and will not be considered in this text.

Using a mathematical analysis based on the theory of elasticity, however, it is possible to determine the shear-stress distribution within a shaft of square cross section. Examples of how this shear stress varies along two radial lines of the shaft are shown in Fig. 26a. Because these shear-stress distributions vary in a complex manner, the shear strains they create will *warp* the cross section as shown in Fig. 26b. In particular notice that the corner points of the shaft must be subjected to zero shear stress and therefore zero shear strain. The reason for this can be shown by considering an element of material located at one of these points, Fig. 26c. One would expect the top face of this element to be subjected to a shear stress in order to aid in resisting the applied torque **T**. This, however, cannot occur since the complementary shear stresses $\tau$ and $\tau'$, acting on the *outer surface* of the shaft, must be *zero*.

Shear stress distribution
along two radial lines

(a)

Warping of
cross-sectional area

(b)

(c)

**Fig. 26**

Undeformed

Deformed

**Fig. 25**

Notice the deformation of the square element when this rubber bar is subjected to a torque.

The results of the analysis for square cross sections, along with other results from the theory of elasticity, for shafts having triangular and elliptical cross sections, are reported in Table 1. In all cases the *maximum shear stress* occurs at a point on the edge of the cross section that is *closest to* the center axis of the shaft. In Table 1 these points are indicated as "dots" on the cross sections. Also given are formulas for the angle of twist of each shaft. By extending these results to a shaft having an *arbitrary* cross section, it can also be shown that the *most efficient shaft* has a *circular cross section*, since it is subjected to both a *smaller* maximum shear stress and a *smaller* angle of twist than one having the same cross sectional area, but not circular, and subjected to the same torque.

The drill shaft is connected to the soil auger using a shaft having a square cross section.

| TABLE 1 | | |
| --- | --- | --- |
| **Shape of cross section** | $\tau_{max}$ | $\phi$ |
| Square | $\dfrac{4.81\,T}{a^3}$ | $\dfrac{7.10\,TL}{a^4 G}$ |
| Equilateral triangle | $\dfrac{20\,T}{a^3}$ | $\dfrac{46\,TL}{a^4 G}$ |
| Ellipse | $\dfrac{2\,T}{\pi a b^2}$ | $\dfrac{(a^2+b^2)TL}{\pi a^3 b^3 G}$ |

246

## EXAMPLE | 10

The 6061-T6 aluminum shaft shown in Fig. 27 has a cross-sectional area in the shape of an equilateral triangle. Determine the largest torque **T** that can be applied to the end of the shaft if the allowable shear stress is $\tau_{allow} = 8$ ksi and the angle of twist at its end is restricted to $\phi_{allow} = 0.02$ rad. How much torque can be applied to a shaft of circular cross section made from the same amount of material?

### SOLUTION
By inspection, the resultant internal torque at any cross section along the shaft's axis is also **T**. Using the formulas for $\tau_{max}$ and $\phi$ in Table 1, we require

$$\tau_{allow} = \frac{20T}{a^3}; \qquad 8(10^3)\ \text{lb/in}^2 = \frac{20T}{(1.5\ \text{in.})^3}$$
$$T = 1350\ \text{lb}\cdot\text{in.}$$

Also,

$$\phi_{allow} = \frac{46TL}{a^4 G_{al}}; \qquad 0.02\ \text{rad} = \frac{46T(4\ \text{ft})(12\ \text{in./ft})}{(1.5\ \text{in.})^4 [3.7(10^6)\ \text{lb/in}^2]}$$
$$T = 170\ \text{lb}\cdot\text{in.} \qquad\qquad Ans.$$

By comparison, the torque is limited due to the angle of twist.

**Circular Cross Section.** If the same amount of aluminum is to be used in making the same length of shaft having a circular cross section, then the radius of the cross section can be calculated. We have

$$A_{circle} = A_{triangle}; \qquad \pi c^2 = \frac{1}{2}(1.5\ \text{in.})(1.5\sin 60°)$$
$$c = 0.557\ \text{in.}$$

**Fig. 27**

The limitations of stress and angle of twist then require

$$\tau_{allow} = \frac{Tc}{J}; \qquad 8(10^3)\ \text{lb/in}^2 = \frac{T(0.557\ \text{in.})}{(\pi/2)(0.557\ \text{in.})^4}$$
$$T = 2170\ \text{lb}\cdot\text{in.}$$

$$\phi_{allow} = \frac{TL}{JG_{al}}; \qquad 0.02\ \text{rad} = \frac{T(4\ \text{ft})(12\ \text{in./ft})}{(\pi/2)(0.557\ \text{in.})^4 [3.7(10^6)\ \text{lb/in}^2]}$$
$$T = 233\ \text{lb}\cdot\text{in.} \qquad\qquad Ans.$$

Again, the angle of twist limits the applied torque.

**NOTE:** Comparing this result (233 lb·in.) with that given above (170 lb·in.), it is seen that a shaft of circular cross section can support 37% more torque than the one having a triangular cross section.

## *7  Thin-Walled Tubes Having Closed Cross Sections

Thin-walled tubes of noncircular cross section are often used to construct light-weight frameworks such as those used in aircraft. In some applications, they may be subjected to a torsional loading. In this section we will analyze the effects of applying a torque to a thin-walled tube having a *closed* cross section, that is, a tube that does not have any breaks or slits along its length. Such a tube, having a constant yet arbitrary cross-sectional shape, and variable thickness $t$, is shown in Fig. 28a. Since the walls are thin, we will obtain the average shear stress by assuming that this stress is *uniformly distributed* across the thickness of the tube at any given point. Before we do this, however, we will first discuss some preliminary concepts regarding the action of shear stress over the cross section.

**Shear Flow.**   Shown in Figs. 28a and 28b is a small element of the tube having a finite length $s$ and differential width $dx$. At one end the element has a thickness $t_A$, and at the other end the thickness is $t_B$. Due to the internal torque **T**, shear stress is developed on the front face of the element. Specifically, at end $A$ the shear stress is $\tau_A$, and at end $B$ it is $\tau_B$. These stresses can be related by noting that equivalent shear stresses $\tau_A$ and $\tau_B$ must also act on the longitudinal sides of the element. Since these sides have a *constant* width $dx$, the forces acting on them are $dF_A = \tau_A(t_A \, dx)$ and $dF_B = \tau_B(t_B \, dx)$. Equilibrium requires these forces to be of equal magnitude but opposite direction, so that

$$\tau_A \, t_A = \tau_B \, t_B$$

This important result states that **the product of the average shear stress times the thickness of the tube is the same at each point on the tube's cross-sectional area**. This product is called **shear flow**,* $q$, and in general terms we can express it as

$$q = \tau_{\text{avg}} t \qquad (17)$$

Since $q$ is constant over the cross section, the *largest* average shear stress must occur where the tube's thickness is the *smallest*.

(a)

(b)

**Fig. 28**

---

*The terminology "flow" is used since $q$ is analogous to water flowing through a tube of rectangular cross section having a constant depth and variable width $w$ Although the water's velocity $v$ at each point along the tube will be different (like $\tau_{\text{avg}}$), the flow $q = vw$ will be constant.

Now if a differential element having a thickness $t$, length $ds$, and width $dx$ is isolated from the tube, Fig. 28$c$, it is seen that the front face over which the average shear stress acts is $dA = t\,ds$. Hence, $dF = \tau_{avg}(t\,ds) = q\,ds$, or $q = dF/ds$. In other words, *the shear flow measures the force per unit length along the tube's cross-sectional area.*

It is important to realize that the shear-stress components shown in Fig. 28$c$ are the only ones acting on the tube. Components acting in the other direction, as shown in Fig. 28$d$, cannot exist. This is because the top and bottom faces of the element are at the inner and outer walls of the tube, and these boundaries must be free of stress. Instead, as noted above, the applied torque causes *the shear flow and the average stress to always be directed tangent to the wall of the tube, such that it contributes to the resultant internal torque* **T**.

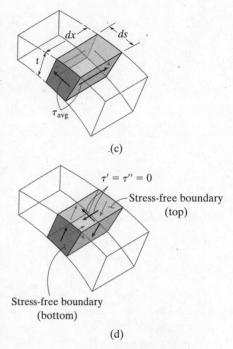

.(c)

(d)

## Average Shear Stress.

The average shear stress can be related to the torque $T$ by considering the torque produced by this shear stress about a selected point $O$ within the tube's boundary, Fig. 28$e$. As shown, the shear stress develops a force $dF = \tau_{avg}\,dA = \tau_{avg}(t\,ds)$ on an element of the tube. This force acts tangent to the centerline of the tube's wall, and if the moment arm is $h$, the torque is

$$dT = h(dF) = h(\tau_{avg}\,t\,ds)$$

For the entire cross section, we require

$$T = \oint h\tau_{avg}\,t\,ds$$

(e)

Here the "line integral" indicates that integration must be performed *around* the entire boundary of the area. Since the shear flow $q = \tau_{avg}\,t$ is *constant*, it can be factored out of the integral, so that

$$T = \tau_{avg}t \oint h\,ds$$

A graphical simplification can be made for evaluating the integral by noting that the *mean area*, shown by the blue colored triangle in Fig. 28$e$, is $dA_m = (1/2)h\,ds$. Thus,

$$T = 2\tau_{avg}\,t \int dA_m = 2\tau_{avg}\,tA_m$$

(f)

**Fig. 28 (cont.)**

249

Solving for $\tau_{avg}$, we have

$$\tau_{avg} = \frac{T}{2tA_m} \qquad (18)$$

Here

$\tau_{avg}$ = the average shear stress acting over a particular thickness of the tube

$T$ = the resultant internal torque at the cross section

$t$ = the thickness of the tube where $\tau_{avg}$ is to be determined

$A_m$ = the mean area enclosed within the boundary of the *centerline* of the tube's thickness. $A_m$ is shown shaded in Fig. 28*f*

Since $q = \tau_{avg}\, t$, then the shear flow throughout the cross section becomes

$$q = \frac{T}{2A_m} \qquad (19)$$

### Angle of Twist.

The angle of twist of a thin-walled tube of length $L$ can be determined using energy methods. If the material behaves in a linear elastic manner and $G$ is the shear modulus, then this angle $\phi$, given in radians, can be expressed as

$$\phi = \frac{TL}{4A_m^2\, G} \oint \frac{ds}{t} \qquad (20)$$

Here again the integration must be performed around the entire boundary of the tube's cross-sectional area.

## Important Points

- Shear flow $q$ is the product of the tube's thickness and the average shear stress. This value is the same at all points along the tube's cross section. As a result, the *largest* average shear stress on the cross section occurs where the thickness is *smallest*.

- Both shear flow and the average shear stress act *tangent* to the wall of the tube at all points and in a direction so as to contribute to the resultant internal torque.

## EXAMPLE | 11

Calculate the average shear stress in a thin-walled tube having a circular cross section of mean radius $r_m$ and thickness $t$, which is subjected to a torque $T$, Fig. 29a. Also, what is the relative angle of twist if the tube has a length $L$?

(a)

### SOLUTION

**Average Shear Stress.** The mean area for the tube is $A_m = \pi r_m^2$. Applying Eq. 18 gives

$$\tau_{avg} = \frac{T}{2tA_m} = \frac{T}{2\pi t r_m^2} \qquad Ans.$$

We can check the validity of this result by applying the torsion formula. In this case, using Eq. 9, we have

$$J = \frac{\pi}{2}\left(r_o^4 - r_i^4\right)$$

$$= \frac{\pi}{2}\left(r_o^2 + r_i^2\right)\left(r_o^2 - r_i^2\right)$$

$$= \frac{\pi}{2}\left(r_o^2 + r_i^2\right)\left(r_o + r_i\right)\left(r_o - r_i\right)$$

Since $r_m \approx r_o \approx r_i$ and $t = r_o - r_i$, $J = \frac{\pi}{2}\left(2r_m^2\right)\left(2r_m\right)t = 2\pi r_m^3 t$

$$\tau_{avg} = \frac{Tr_m}{J} = \frac{Tr_m}{2\pi r_m^3 t} = \frac{T}{2\pi t r_m^2} \qquad Ans.$$

which agrees with the previous result.

The average shear-stress distribution acting throughout the tube's cross section is shown in Fig. 29b. Also shown is the shear-stress distribution acting on a radial line as calculated using the torsion formula. Notice how each $\tau_{avg}$ acts in a direction such that it contributes to the resultant torque $\mathbf{T}$ at the section. As the tube's thickness decreases, the shear stress throughout the tube becomes more uniform.

Actual shear-stress distribution (torsion formula)

Average shear-stress distribution (thin-wall approximation)

(b)

**Fig. 29**

**Angle of Twist.** Applying Eq. 20, we have

$$\phi = \frac{TL}{4A_m^2 G}\oint \frac{ds}{t} = \frac{TL}{4(\pi r_m^2)^2 Gt}\oint ds$$

The integral represents the length around the centerline boundary, which is $2\pi r_m$. Substituting, the final result is

$$\phi = \frac{TL}{2\pi r_m^3 Gt} \qquad Ans.$$

Show that one obtains this same result using Eq. 15.

EXAMPLE | 12

The tube is made of C86100 bronze and has a rectangular cross section as shown in Fig. 30a. If it is subjected to the two torques, determine the average shear stress in the tube at points $A$ and $B$. Also, what is the angle of twist of end $C$? The tube is fixed at $E$.

(a)

**Fig. 30**

SOLUTION

**Average Shear Stress.** If the tube is sectioned through points $A$ and $B$, the resulting free-body diagram is shown in Fig. 30b. The internal torque is 35 N·m. As shown in Fig. 30d, the mean area is

$$A_m = (0.035 \text{ m})(0.057 \text{ m}) = 0.00200 \text{ m}^2$$

Applying Eq. 18 for point $A$, $t_A = 5$ mm, so that

$$\tau_A = \frac{T}{2tA_m} = \frac{35 \text{ N} \cdot \text{m}}{2(0.005 \text{ m})(0.00200 \text{ m}^2)} = 1.75 \text{ MPa} \qquad \textit{Ans.}$$

And for point $B$, $t_B = 3$ mm, and therefore

$$\tau_B = \frac{T}{2tA_m} = \frac{35 \text{ N} \cdot \text{m}}{2(0.003 \text{ m})(0.00200 \text{ m}^2)} = 2.92 \text{ MPa} \qquad \textit{Ans.}$$

These results are shown on elements of material located at points $A$ and $B$, Fig. 30e. Note carefully how the 35-N·m torque in Fig. 30b creates these stresses on the back sides of each element.

(b)                    (c)

**Angle of Twist.** From the free-body diagrams in Fig. 30b and 30c, the internal torques in regions DE and CD are 35 N·m and 60 N·m, respectively. Following the sign convention outlined in Sec. 4, these torques are both positive. Thus, Eq. 20 becomes

$$\phi = \sum \frac{TL}{4A_m^2 G} \oint \frac{ds}{t}$$

$$= \frac{60 \text{ N} \cdot \text{m } (0.5 \text{ m})}{4(0.00200 \text{ m}^2)^2 (38(10^9) \text{ N/m}^2)} \left[ 2\left(\frac{57 \text{ mm}}{5 \text{ mm}}\right) + 2\left(\frac{35 \text{ mm}}{3 \text{ mm}}\right) \right]$$

$$+ \frac{35 \text{ N} \cdot \text{m } (1.5 \text{ m})}{4(0.00200 \text{ m}^2)^2 (38(10^9) \text{ N/m}^2)} \left[ 2\left(\frac{57 \text{ mm}}{5 \text{ mm}}\right) + 2\left(\frac{35 \text{ mm}}{3 \text{ mm}}\right) \right]$$

$$= 6.29(10^{-3}) \text{ rad} = 0.360° \qquad\qquad Ans.$$

(d)                    (e)

**Fig. 30 (cont.)**

## PROBLEMS

**95.** The aluminum rod has a square cross section of 10 mm by 10 mm. If it is 8 m long, determine the torque $T$ that is required to rotate one end relative to the other end by 90°. $G_{al} = 28$ GPa, $(\tau_Y)_{al} = 240$ MPa.

**Prob. 95**

**\*96.** The shafts have elliptical and circular cross sections and are to be made from the same amount of a similar material. Determine the percent of increase in the maximum shear stress and the angle of twist for the elliptical shaft compared to the circular shaft when both shafts are subjected to the same torque and have the same length.

**Prob. 96**

**97.** It is intended to manufacture a circular bar to resist torque; however, the bar is made elliptical in the process of manufacturing, with one dimension smaller than the other by a factor $k$ as shown. Determine the factor by which the maximum shear stress is increased.

**Prob. 97**

**98.** The shaft is made of red brass C83400 and has an elliptical cross section. If it is subjected to the torsional loading shown, determine the maximum shear stress within regions $AC$ and $BC$, and the angle of twist $\phi$ of end $B$ relative to end $A$.

**99.** Solve Prob. 98 for the maximum shear stress within regions $AC$ and $BC$, and the angle of twist $\phi$ of end $B$ relative to $C$.

**Probs. 98/99**

**\*100.** If end $B$ of the shaft, which has an equilateral triangle cross section, is subjected to a torque of $T = 900$ lb · ft, determine the maximum shear stress developed in the shaft. Also, find the angle of twist of end $B$. The shaft is made from 6061-T1 aluminum.

**101.** If the shaft has an equilateral triangle cross section and is made from an alloy that has an allowable shear stress of $\tau_{allow} = 12$ ksi, determine the maximum allowable torque $T$ that can be applied to end $B$. Also, find the corresponding angle of twist of end $B$.

**Probs. 100/101**

**102.** The aluminum strut is fixed between the two walls at $A$ and $B$. If it has a 2 in. by 2 in. square cross section, and it is subjected to the torque of 80 lb·ft at $C$, determine the reactions at the fixed supports. Also, what is the angle of twist at $C$? $G_{al} = 3.8(10^3)$ ksi.

**Probs. 102**

**103.** A torque of 2 kip · in. is applied to the tube. If the wall thickness is 0.1 in., determine the average shear stress in the tube.

**Probs. 103**

**\*104.** The 6061-T6 aluminum bar has a square cross section of 25 mm by 25 mm. If it is 2 m long, determine the maximum shear stress in the bar and the rotation of one end relative to the other end.

**Prob. 104**

**105.** If the shaft is subjected to the torque of 3 kN·m, determine the maximum shear stress developed in the shaft. Also, find the angle of twist of end $B$. The shaft is made from A-36 steel. Set $a = 50$ mm.

**106.** If the shaft is made from A-36 steel having an allowable shear stress of $\tau_{allow} = 75$ MPa, determine the minimum dimension $a$ for the cross-section to the nearest millimeter. Also, find the corresponding angle of twist at end $B$.

**Probs. 105/106**

**107.** If the solid shaft is made from red brass C83400 copper having an allowable shear stress of $\tau_{allow} = 4$ ksi, determine the maximum allowable torque **T** that can be applied at $B$.

**\*108.** If the solid shaft is made from red brass C83400 copper and it is subjected to a torque $T = 6$ kip · ft at $B$, determine the maximum shear stress developed in segments $AB$ and $BC$.

**Probs. 107/108**

**109.** For a given maximum average shear stress, determine the factor by which the torque carrying capacity is increased if the half-circular section is reversed from the dashed-line position to the section shown. The tube is 0.1 in. thick.

**Prob. 109**

**110.** For a given maximum average shear stress, determine the factor by which the torque-carrying capacity is increased if the half-circular sections are reversed from the dashed-line positions to the section shown. The tube is 0.1 in. thick.

**Prob. 110**

**111.** A torque $T$ is applied to two tubes having the cross sections shown. Compare the shear flow developed in each tube.

**Prob. 111**

**\*112.** Due to a fabrication error the inner circle of the tube is eccentric with respect to the outer circle. By what percentage is the torsional strength reduced when the eccentricity $e$ is one-fourth of the difference in the radii?

**Prob. 112**

**113.** Determine the constant thickness of the rectangular tube if average stress is not to exceed 12 ksi when a torque of $T = 20$ kip · in. is applied to the tube. Neglect stress concentrations at the corners. The mean dimensions of the tube are shown.

**114.** Determine the torque $T$ that can be applied to the rectangular tube if the average shear stress is not to exceed 12 ksi. Neglect stress concentrations at the corners. The mean dimensions of the tube are shown and the tube has a thickness of 0.125 in.

**Probs. 113/114**

**115.** The steel tube has an elliptical cross section of mean dimensions shown and a constant thickness of $t = 0.2$ in. If the allowable shear stress is $\tau_{allow} = 8$ ksi, and the tube is to resist a torque of $T = 250$ lb · ft, determine the necessary dimension $b$. The mean area for the ellipse is $A_m = \pi b(0.5b)$.

**Prob. 115**

**\*116.** The tube is made of plastic, is 5 mm thick, and has the mean dimensions shown. Determine the average shear stress at points $A$ and $B$ if the tube is subjected to the torque of $T = 500$ N · m. Show the shear stress on volume elements located at these points. Neglect stress concentrations at the corners.

**Prob. 116**

**117.** The mean dimensions of the cross section of the leading edge and torsion box of an airplane wing can be approximated as shown. If the wing is made of 2014-T6 aluminum alloy having an allowable shear stress of $\tau_{allow} = 125$ MPa and the wall thickness is 10 mm, determine the maximum allowable torque and the corresponding angle of twist per meter length of the wing.

**118.** The mean dimensions of the cross section of the leading edge and torsion box of an airplane wing can be approximated as shown. If the wing is subjected to a torque of 4.5 MN · m and the wall thickness is 10 mm, determine the average shear stress developed in the wing and the angle of twist per meter length of the wing. The wing is made of 2014-T6 aluminum alloy.

**Probs. 117/118**

**119.** The symmetric tube is made from a high-strength steel, having the mean dimensions shown and a thickness of 5 mm. If it is subjected to a torque of $T = 40$ N · m, determine the average shear stress developed at points $A$ and $B$. Indicate the shear stress on volume elements located at these points.

**Prob. 119**

# 8 Stress Concentration

The torsion formula, $\tau_{max} = Tc/J$, cannot be applied to regions of a shaft having a sudden change in the cross section. Here the shear-stress and shear-strain distributions in the shaft become complex and can be obtained only by using experimental methods or possibly by a mathematical analysis based on the theory of elasticity. Three common discontinuities of the cross section that occur in practice are shown in Fig. 31. They are at *couplings*, which are used to connect two collinear shafts together, Fig. 31*a*, *keyways*, used to connect gears or pulleys to a shaft, Fig. 31*b*, and a step shaft which is fabricated or machined from a single shaft, Fig. 31*c*. In each case the maximum shear stress will occur at the point (dot) indicated on the cross section.

The necessity to perform a complex stress analysis at a shaft discontinuity to obtain the maximum shear stress can be eliminated by using a *torsional stress-concentration factor*, $K$. As in the case of axially loaded members, Sec. 7, $K$ is usually taken from a graph based on experimental data. An example, for the shoulder-fillet shaft, is shown in Fig. 32. To use this graph, one first finds the geometric ratio $D/d$ to define the appropriate curve, and then once the abscissa $r/d$ is calculated, the value of $K$ is found along the ordinate.

(a)

(b)

(c)

**Fig. 31**

**Fig. 32**

The maximum shear stress is then determined from

$$\tau_{max} = K \frac{Tc}{J} \qquad (21)$$

Here the torsion formula is applied to the *smaller* of the two connected shafts, since $\tau_{max}$ occurs at the base of the fillet, Fig. 31c.

Note from the graph that an *increase* in radius $r$ causes a *decrease* in $K$. Hence the maximum shear stress in the shaft can be *reduced* by *increasing* the radius. Also, if the diameter of the larger section is reduced, the $D/d$ ratio will be lower and so the value of $K$ and therefore $\tau_{max}$ will be lower.

Like the case of axially loaded members, torsional stress concentration factors should *always* be used when designing shafts made from *brittle materials*, or when designing shafts that will be subjected to *fatigue or cyclic torsional loadings*. These conditions give rise to the formation of cracks at the stress concentration, and this can often lead to a sudden fracture. On the other hand, if large *static* torsional loadings are applied to a shaft made from *ductile material*, then *inelastic strains* will develop within the shaft. Yielding of the material will cause the stress distribution to become more *evenly distributed* throughout the shaft, so that the maximum stress will not be limited to the region of stress concentration. This phenomenon will be discussed further in the next section.

Stress concentrations can arise at the coupling of these shafts, and this must be taken into account when the shaft is designed.

## Important Points

- *Stress concentrations* in shafts occur at points of sudden cross-sectional change, such as couplings, keyways, and step shafts. The more severe the change in geometry, the larger the stress concentration.

- For design or analysis, it is not necessary to know the exact shear-stress distribution on the cross section. Instead, it is possible to obtain the maximum shear stress using a stress concentration factor, $K$, that has been determined through experiment, and is only a function of the geometry of the shaft.

- Normally a stress concentration in a ductile shaft subjected to a static torque will *not* have to be considered in design; however, if the material is *brittle*, or subjected to *fatigue* loadings, then stress concentrations become important.

# EXAMPLE 13

The stepped shaft shown in Fig. 33a is supported by bearings at A and B. Determine the maximum stress in the shaft due to the applied torques. The shoulder fillet at the junction of each shaft has a radius of r = 6 mm.

(a)

**Figure 33**

(b)

$\tau_{max} = 3.10$ MPa

Shear-stress distribution predicted by torsion formula

Actual shear-stress distribution caused by stress concentration

(c)

## SOLUTION

**Internal Torque.** By inspection, moment equilibrium about the axis of the shaft is satisfied. Since the maximum shear stress occurs at the rooted ends of the *smaller* diameter shafts, the internal torque (30 N·m) can be found there by applying the method of sections, Fig. 33b.

**Maximum Shear Stress.** The stress-concentration factor can be determined by using Fig. 32. From the shaft geometry we have

$$\frac{D}{d} = \frac{2(40 \text{ mm})}{2(20 \text{ mm})} = 2$$

$$\frac{r}{d} = \frac{6 \text{ mm}}{2(20 \text{ mm})} = 0.15$$

Thus, the value of K = 1.3 is obtained.
Applying Eq. 21, we have

$$\tau_{max} = K\frac{Tc}{J}; \quad \tau_{max} = 1.3\left[\frac{30 \text{ N} \cdot \text{m} (0.020 \text{ m})}{(\pi/2)(0.020 \text{ m})^4}\right] = 3.10 \text{ MPa} \qquad \textit{Ans.}$$

**NOTE:** From experimental evidence, the actual stress distribution along a radial line of the cross section at the critical section looks similar to that shown in Fig. 33c. Notice how this compares with the linear stress distribution found from the torsion formula.

# *9   Inelastic Torsion

If the torsional loadings applied to the shaft are excessive, then the material may yield, and, consequently, a "plastic analysis" must be used to determine the shear-stress distribution and the angle of twist. To perform this analysis, then as before, it is necessary to meet the conditions of both deformation and equilibrium for the shaft.

It was shown in Sec. 1 that regardless of the material behavior, the shear strains that develop in a circular shaft will vary *linearly*, from zero at the center of the shaft to a maximum at its outer boundary, Fig. 34a. Also, the resultant internal torque at the section must be equivalent to the torque caused by the entire shear-stress distribution over the cross section. This condition can be expressed mathematically by considering the shear stress $\tau$ acting on an element of area $dA$ located a distance $\rho$ from the center of the shaft, Fig. 34b. The force produced by this stress is $dF = \tau \, dA$, and the torque produced is $dT = \rho \, dF = \rho(\tau \, dA)$. For the entire shaft we require

Severe twist of an aluminum specimen caused by the application of a plastic torque.

$$T = \int_A \rho\tau \, dA \qquad (22)$$

Linear shear–strain distribution

(a)

If the area $dA$ over which $\tau$ acts can be defined as a *differential ring* having an area of $dA = 2\pi\rho \, d\rho$, Fig. 34c, then the above equation can be written as

$$T = 2\pi \int_0^c \tau\rho^2 \, d\rho \qquad (23)$$

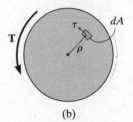

(b)

These conditions of geometry and loading will now be used to determine the shear-stress distribution in a shaft when the shaft is subjected to two types of torque.

## Elastic-Plastic Torque.

Let us consider the material in the shaft to exhibit an elastic-perfectly plastic behavior. As shown in Fig. 35a, this is characterized by a shear stress–strain diagram for which the material undergoes an increasing amount of shear strain when the shear stress reaches the yield point $\tau_Y$.

(c)

**Fig. 34**

(a)

Shear–strain distribution

(b)

Shear–stress distribution

(c)

**Fig. 35**

If the internal torque produces the maximum *elastic* shear strain $\gamma_Y$, at the outer boundary of the shaft, then the maximum elastic torque $T_Y$ that produces this distribution can be found from the torsion formula, $\tau_Y = T_Y c / [(\pi/2)c^4]$, so that

$$T_Y = \frac{\pi}{2}\tau_Y c^3 \qquad (24)$$

Furthermore, the angle of twist can be determined from Eq. 13, namely,

$$d\phi = \gamma \frac{dx}{\rho} \qquad (25)$$

If the applied torque increases in magnitude above $T_Y$, it will begin to cause yielding. It will begin at the outer boundary of the shaft, $\rho = c$, and then, as the maximum shear strain increases to, say, $\gamma'$ in Fig. 35a, the yielding boundary will progress inward toward the shaft's center, Fig. 35b. As shown, this produces an *elastic core*, where, by proportion, the radius of the core is $\rho_Y = (\gamma_Y/\gamma')c$. Also, the outer portion of the material forms a *plastic annulus* or ring, since the shear strains $\gamma$ within this region are greater than $\gamma_Y$. The corresponding shear-stress distribution along a radial line of the shaft is shown in Fig. 35c. It is established by taking successive points on the shear-strain distribution in Fig. 35b and finding the corresponding value of shear stress from the $\tau$–$\gamma$ diagram, Fig. 35a. For example, at $\rho = c$, $\gamma'$ gives $\tau_Y$, and at $\rho = \rho_Y$, $\gamma_Y$ also gives $\tau_Y$; etc.

Since $\tau$ in Fig. 35c can now be expressed as a function of $\rho$, we can apply Eq. 23 to determine the torque. We have

$$T = 2\pi \int_0^c \tau \rho^2 \, d\rho$$

$$= 2\pi \int_0^{\rho_Y} \left(\tau_Y \frac{\rho}{\rho_Y}\right)\rho^2 \, d\rho + 2\pi \int_{\rho_Y}^c \tau_Y \rho^2 \, d\rho$$

$$= \frac{2\pi}{\rho_Y} \tau_Y \int_0^{\rho_Y} \rho^3 \, d\rho + 2\pi\tau_Y \int_{\rho_Y}^c \rho^2 \, d\rho$$

$$= \frac{\pi}{2\rho_Y} \tau_Y \rho_Y^4 + \frac{2\pi}{3}\tau_Y (c^3 - \rho_Y^3)$$

$$= \frac{\pi\tau_Y}{6} (4c^3 - \rho_Y^3) \qquad (26)$$

**Plastic Torque.** Further increases in $T$ tend to shrink the radius of the elastic core until all the material yields, i.e., $\rho_Y \to 0$, Fig. 35b. The material of the shaft will then be subjected to *perfectly plastic behavior* and the shear-stress distribution becomes uniform, so that $\tau = \tau_Y$, Fig. 35d. We can now apply Eq. 23 to determine the *plastic torque* $T_p$, which represents the largest possible torque the shaft will support.

$$T_p = 2\pi \int_0^c \tau_Y \rho^2 d\rho$$

$$= \frac{2\pi}{3} \tau_Y c^3 \qquad (27)$$

Compared with the maximum elastic torque $T_Y$, Eq. 24, it can be seen that

$$T_p = \frac{4}{3} T_Y$$

In other words, the plastic torque is 33% greater than the maximum elastic torque.

Unfortunately, the angle of twist $\phi$ for the shear-stress distribution *cannot* be uniquely defined. This is because $\tau = \tau_Y$ does not correspond to any unique value of shear strain $\gamma \geq \gamma_Y$. As a result, once $\mathbf{T}_p$ is applied, the shaft will continue to deform or twist with no corresponding increase in shear stress.

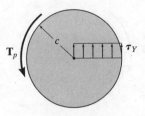

Fully plastic torque

(d)

**Figure 35 (cont.)**

# *10   Residual Stress

When a shaft is subjected to plastic shear strains caused by torsion, removal of the torque will cause some shear stress to remain in the shaft. This stress is referred to as ***residual stress***, and its distribution can be calculated using superposition and elastic recovery. (See Sec. 9.)

For example, if $T_p$ causes the material at the outer boundary of the shaft to be strained to $\gamma_1$, shown as point $C$ on the $\tau - \gamma$ curve in Fig. 36, the release of $T_p$ will cause a reverse shear stress, such that the material behavior will follow the straight-lined segment $CD$, creating some *elastic recovery* of the shear strain $\gamma_1$. This line is parallel to the initial straight-lined portion $AB$ of the $\tau - \gamma$ diagram, and thus both lines have a slope $G$ as indicated.

**Fig. 36**

Plastic torque applied
causing plastic shear strains
throughout the shaft
(a)

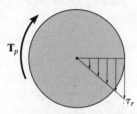

Plastic torque reversed
causing elastic shear strains
throughout the shaft
(b)

Residual shear–stress
distribution in shaft
(c)

Since elastic recovery occurs, we can superimpose on the plastic torque stress distribution in Fig. 37a a *linear stress distribution* caused by applying the plastic torque $T_p$ in the *opposite* direction, Fig. 37b. Here the maximum shear stress $\tau_r$, for this stress distribution, is called the *modulus of rupture* for torsion. It is determined from the torsion formula,* which gives

$$\tau_r = \frac{T_p c}{J} = \frac{T_p c}{(\pi/2)c^4}$$

Using Eq. 27,

$$\tau_r = \frac{[(2/3)\pi \tau_Y c^3]c}{(\pi/2)c^4} = \frac{4}{3}\tau_Y$$

Note that reversed application of $T_p$ using the linear shear-stress distribution in Fig. 37b is possible here, since the maximum recovery for the elastic shear strain is $2\gamma_Y$, as noted in Fig. 37. This corresponds to a maximum applied shear stress of $2\tau_Y$, which is *greater* than the maximum shear stress of $\frac{4}{3}\tau_Y$ calculated above. Hence, by superimposing the stress distributions involving applications and then removal of the plastic torque, we obtain the residual shear-stress distribution in the shaft as shown in Fig. 37c. It should be noted from this diagram that the shear stress at the center of the shaft, shown as $\tau_Y$, must actually be *zero*, since the material along the axis of the shaft is never strained. The reason this is not zero is that we assumed *all* the material of the shaft to have been strained beyond the yield point in order to determine the plastic torque, Fig. 37a. To be more realistic, an elastic–plastic torque should be considered when modeling the material behavior. Doing so leads to the superposition of the stress distribution shown in Fig. 37d.

Elastic–plastic torque applied

Elastic–plastic torque reversed

Residual shear–stress
distribution in shaft

(d)

**Fig. 37**

*The torsion formula is valid only when the material behaves in a linear elastic manner; however, the modulus of rupture is so named because it assumes that the material behaves elastically and then suddenly *ruptures* at the proportional limit.

## Ultimate Torque.

In the general case, most engineering materials will have a shear stress–strain diagram as shown in Fig. 38a. Consequently, if $T$ is increased so that the maximum shear strain in the shaft becomes $\gamma = \gamma_u$, Fig. 38b, then, by proportion $\gamma_Y$ occurs at $\rho_Y = (\gamma_Y/\gamma_u)c$. Likewise, the shear strains at, say, $\rho = \rho_1$ and $\rho = \rho_2$, can be found by proportion, i.e., $\gamma_1 = (\rho_1/c)\gamma_u$ and $\gamma_2 = (\rho_2/c)\gamma_u$. If the corresponding values of $\tau_1$, $\tau_Y$, $\tau_2$, and $\tau_u$ are taken from the $\tau$–$\gamma$ diagram and plotted, we obtain the shear-stress distribution, which acts along a radial line on the cross section, Fig. 38c. The torque produced by this stress distribution is called the *ultimate torque*, $T_u$.

The magnitude of $\mathbf{T}_u$ can be determined by "graphically" integrating Eq. 23. To do this, the cross-sectional area of the shaft is segmented into a finite number of rings, such as the one shown shaded in Fig. 38d. The area of this ring, $\Delta A = 2\pi\rho\,\Delta\rho$, is multiplied by the shear stress $\tau$ that acts on it, so that the force $\Delta F = \tau\,\Delta A$ can be determined. The torque created by this force is then $\Delta T = \rho\,\Delta F = \rho(\tau\,\Delta A)$. The addition of all the torques for the entire cross section, as determined in this manner, gives the ultimate torque $T_u$; that is, Eq. 23 becomes $T_u \approx 2\pi\Sigma\tau\rho^2\,\Delta\rho$. If, however, the stress distribution can be expressed as an analytical function, $\tau = f(\rho)$, as in the elastic and plastic torque cases, then the integration of Eq. 23 can be carried out directly.

(a)

Ultimate shear-strain distribution

(b)

Ultimate shear-stress distribution

(c)

(d)

**Fig. 38**

---

## Important Points

- The *shear-strain distribution* along a radial line on the cross section of a shaft is based on geometric considerations, and it is found to *always* vary linearly along the radial line. Once it is established, the shear-stress distribution can then be determined using the shear stress–strain diagram.

- If the shear-stress distribution for the shaft is established, it produces a torque about the axis of the shaft that is equivalent to the resultant internal torque acting on the cross section.

- *Perfectly plastic behavior* assumes the shear-stress distribution is *constant*. When it occurs, the shaft will continue to twist with no increase in torque. This torque is called the *plastic torque*.

## EXAMPLE | 14

50 mm

30 mm

**T**

$\tau$ (MPa)

20

0.286 $(10^{-3})$

$\gamma$ (rad)

(a)

The tubular shaft in Fig. 39a is made of an aluminum alloy that is assumed to have an elastic-plastic $\tau$–$\gamma$ diagram as shown. Determine the maximum torque that can be applied to the shaft without causing the material to yield, and the maximum torque or plastic torque that can be applied to the shaft. Also, what should the minimum shear strain at the outer wall be in order to develop a fully plastic torque?

### SOLUTION

**Maximum Elastic Torque.** We require the shear stress at the outer fiber to be 20 MPa. Using the torsion formula, we have

$$\tau_Y = \frac{T_Y c}{J}; \qquad 20(10^6)\,\text{N/m}^2 = \frac{T_Y(0.05\,\text{m})}{(\pi/2)\big[(0.05\,\text{m})^4 - (0.03\,\text{m})^4\big]}$$

$$T_Y = 3.42\,\text{kN}\cdot\text{m} \qquad\qquad Ans.$$

The shear-stress and shear-strain distributions for this case are shown in Fig. 39b. The values at the tube's inner wall have been obtained by proportion.

**Plastic Torque.** The shear-stress distribution in this case is shown in Fig. 39c. Application of Eq. 23 requires $\tau = \tau_Y$. We have

$$T_p = 2\pi \int_{0.03\,\text{m}}^{0.05\,\text{m}} \big[20(10^6)\,\text{N/m}^2\big]\rho^2\,d\rho = 125.66(10^6)\frac{1}{3}\rho^3 \bigg|_{0.03\,\text{m}}^{0.05\,\text{m}}$$

$$= 4.11\,\text{kN}\cdot\text{m} \qquad\qquad Ans.$$

For this tube $T_p$ represents a 20% increase in torque capacity compared with the elastic torque $T_Y$.

**Outer Radius Shear Strain.** The tube becomes fully plastic when the shear strain at the *inner wall* becomes $0.286(10^{-3})$ rad, as shown in Fig. 39c. Since the shear strain *remains linear* over the cross section, the plastic strain at the outer fibers of the tube in Fig. 39c is determined by proportion.

$$\frac{\gamma_o}{50\,\text{mm}} = \frac{0.286(10^{-3})\,\text{rad}}{30\,\text{mm}}$$

$$\gamma_o = 0.477(10^{-3})\,\text{rad} \qquad\qquad Ans.$$

50 mm   12 MPa

20 MPa

30 mm

Elastic shear–stress distribution

0.286 $(10^{-3})$ rad

0.172 $(10^{-3})$ rad

Elastic shear–strain distribution

(b)

**Fig. 39**

20 MPa

0.477 $(10^{-3})$ rad

0.286 $(10^{-3})$ rad

Plastic shear–stress distribution          Initial plastic shear–strain distribution

(c)

# EXAMPLE | 15

A solid circular shaft has a radius of 20 mm and length of 1.5 m. The material has an elastic-plastic $\tau$–$\gamma$ diagram as shown in Fig. 40a. Determine the torque needed to twist the shaft $\phi = 0.6$ rad.

(a)

## SOLUTION

We will first obtain the shear-strain distribution, then establish the shear-stress distribution. Once this is known, the applied torque can be determined.

The maximum shear strain occurs at the surface of the shaft, $\rho = c$. Since the angle of twist is $\phi = 0.6$ rad for the entire 1.5-m length of the shaft, then using Eq. 25, for the entire length we have

$$\phi = \gamma \frac{L}{\rho}; \qquad 0.6 = \frac{\gamma_{max}(1.5 \text{ m})}{0.02 \text{ m}}$$

$$\gamma_{max} = 0.008 \text{ rad}$$

Shear–strain distribution

(b)

The shear-strain distribution is shown in Fig. 40b. Note that yielding of the material occurs since $\gamma_{max} > \gamma_Y = 0.0016$ rad in Fig. 40a. The radius of the elastic core, $\rho_Y$, can be obtained by proportion. From Fig. 40b,

$$\frac{\rho_Y}{0.0016} = \frac{0.02 \text{ m}}{0.008}$$

$$\rho_Y = 0.004 \text{ m} = 4 \text{ mm}$$

Based on the shear-strain distribution, the shear-stress distribution, plotted over a radial line segment, is shown in Fig. 40c. The torque can now be obtained using Eq. 26. Substituting in the numerical data yields

Shear–stress distribution

(c)

**Fig. 40**

$$T = \frac{\pi \tau_Y}{6}(4c^3 - \rho_Y^3)$$

$$= \frac{\pi\left[75(10^6) \text{ N/m}^2\right]}{6}[4(0.02 \text{ m})^3 - (0.004 \text{ m})^3]$$

$$= 1.25 \text{ kN} \cdot \text{m} \qquad\qquad\qquad Ans.$$

## EXAMPLE | 16

(a)

A tube in Fig. 41a has a length of 5 ft and the material has an elastic-plastic $\tau-\gamma$ diagram, also shown in Fig. 41a. Determine the plastic torque $T_p$. What is the residual shear-stress distribution if $\mathbf{T}_p$ is removed *just after* the tube becomes fully plastic?

### SOLUTION

**Plastic Torque.** The plastic torque $\mathbf{T}_p$ will strain the tube such that all the material yields. Hence the stress distribution will appear as shown in Fig. 41b. Applying Eq. 23, we have

$$T_p = 2\pi \int_{c_i}^{c_o} \tau_Y \rho^2 \, d\rho = \frac{2\pi}{3} \tau_Y (c_o^3 - c_i^3)$$

$$= \frac{2\pi}{3} (12(10^3) \text{ lb/in}^2)[(2 \text{ in.})^3 - (1 \text{ in.})^3] = 175.9 \text{ kip} \cdot \text{in.} \quad Ans.$$

Plastic torque applied

(b)

When the tube just becomes fully plastic, yielding has started at the inner wall, i.e., at $c_i = 1$ in., $\gamma_Y = 0.002$ rad, Fig. 41a. The angle of twist that occurs can be determined from Eq. 25, which for the entire tube becomes

$$\phi_p = \gamma_Y \frac{L}{c_i} = \frac{(0.002)(5 \text{ ft})(12 \text{ in./ft})}{(1 \text{ in.})} = 0.120 \text{ rad} \, \circlearrowright$$

Plastic torque reversed

(c)

When $\mathbf{T}_p$ is *removed,* or in effect reapplied in the opposite direction, then the "fictitious" linear shear-stress distribution shown in Fig. 41c must be superimposed on the one shown in Fig. 41b. In Fig. 41c the maximum shear stress or the modulus of rupture is found from the torsion formula

$$\tau_r = \frac{T_p c_o}{J} = \frac{(175.9 \text{ kip} \cdot \text{in.})(2 \text{ in.})}{(\pi/2)[(2 \text{ in.})^4 - (1 \text{ in.})^4]} = 14.93 \text{ ksi}$$

Also, at the inner wall of the tube the shear stress is

$$\tau_i = (14.93 \text{ ksi})\left(\frac{1 \text{ in.}}{2 \text{ in.}}\right) = 7.47 \text{ ksi} \quad Ans.$$

The resultant residual shear-stress distribution is shown in Fig. 41d.

Residual shear–stress distribution

**Fig. 41**

# PROBLEMS

**\*120.** The steel step shaft has an allowable shear stress of $\tau_{allow} = 8$ MPa. If the transition between the cross sections has a radius $r = 4$ mm, determine the maximum torque $T$ that can be applied.

**Prob. 120**

**123.** The transition at the cross sections of the step shaft has a radius of 2.8 mm. Determine the maximum shear stress developed in the shaft.

**Prob. 123**

**121.** The step shaft is to be designed to rotate at 720 rpm while transmitting 30 kW of power. Is this possible? The allowable shear stress is $\tau_{allow} = 12$ MPa and the radius at the transition on the shaft is 7.5 mm.

**122.** The built-up shaft is designed to rotate at 540 rpm. If the radius at the transition on the shaft is $r = 7.2$ mm, and the allowable shear stress for the material is $\tau_{allow} = 55$ MPa, determine the maximum power the shaft can transmit.

**\*124.** The steel used for the step shaft has an allowable shear stress of $\tau_{allow} = 8$ MPa. If the radius at the transition between the cross sections is $r = 2.25$ mm, determine the maximum torque $T$ that can be applied.

**Probs. 121/122**

**Prob. 124**

**125.** The step shaft is subjected to a torque of 710 lb · in. If the allowable shear stress for the material is $\tau_{allow} = 12$ ksi, determine the smallest radius at the junction between the cross sections that can be used to transmit the torque.

**129.** The solid shaft is made of an elastic-perfectly plastic material as shown. Determine the torque $T$ needed to form an elastic core in the shaft having a radius of $\rho_Y = 20$ mm. If the shaft is 3 m long, through what angle does one end of the shaft twist with respect to the other end? When the torque is removed, determine the residual stress distribution in the shaft and the permanent angle of twist.

**Prob. 129**

**Prob. 125**

**130.** The shaft is subjected to a maximum shear strain of 0.0048 rad. Determine the torque applied to the shaft if the material has strain hardening as shown by the shear stress–strain diagram.

**126.** A solid shaft has a diameter of 40 mm and length of 1 m. It is made from an elastic-plastic material having a yield stress of $\tau_Y = 100$ MPa. Determine the maximum elastic torque $T_Y$ and the corresponding angle of twist. What is the angle of twist if the torque is increased to $T = 1.2T_Y$? $G = 80$ GPa.

**127.** Determine the torque needed to twist a short 2-mm-diameter steel wire through several revolutions if it is made from steel assumed to be elastic-plastic and having a yield stress of $\tau_Y = 50$ MPa. Assume that the material becomes fully plastic.

**\*128.** A bar having a circular cross section of 3 in.-diameter is subjected to a torque of 100 in. · kip. If the material is elastic-plastic, with $\tau_Y = 16$ ksi, determine the radius of the elastic core.

**Prob. 130**

**131.** An 80-mm-diameter solid circular shaft is made of an elastic-perfectly plastic material having a yield shear stress of $\tau_Y = 125$ MPa. Determine (a) the maximum elastic torque $T_Y$; and (b) the plastic torque $T_p$.

**\*132.** The hollow shaft has the cross section shown and is made of an elastic-perfectly plastic material having a yield shear stress of $\tau_Y$. Determine the ratio of the plastic torque $T_p$ to the maximum elastic torque $T_Y$.

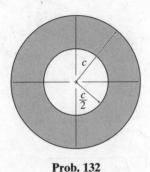

**Prob. 132**

**133.** If the step shaft is elastic-plastic as shown, determine the largest torque $T$ that can be applied to the shaft. Also, draw the shear-stress distribution over a radial line for each section. Neglect the effect of stress concentration.

**Prob. 133**

**134.** The solid shaft is made from an elastic-plastic material as shown. Determine the torque $T$ needed to form an elastic core in the shaft having a radius of $\rho_Y = 23$ mm. If the shaft is 2 m long, through what angle does one end of the shaft twist with respect to the other end? When the torque is removed, determine the residual stress distribution in the shaft and the permanent angle of twist.

**Prob. 134**

**135.** A 1.5-in.-diameter shaft is made from an elastic-plastic material as shown. Determine the radius of its elastic core if it is subjected to a torque of $T = 200$ lb · ft. If the shaft is 10 in. long, determine the angle of twist.

**Prob. 135**

**\*136.** The tubular shaft is made of a strain-hardening material having a $\tau$–$\gamma$ diagram as shown. Determine the torque $T$ that must be applied to the shaft so that the maximum shear strain is 0.01 rad.

**Prob. 136**

**137.** The shaft is made from a strain-hardening material having a $\tau$–$\gamma$ diagram as shown. Determine the torque $T$ that must be applied to the shaft in order to create an elastic core in the shaft having a radius of $\rho_c = 0.5$ in.

**Prob. 137**

**138.** The tube is made of elastic-perfectly plastic material, which has the $\tau$–$\gamma$ diagram shown. Determine the torque $T$ that just causes the inner surface of the shaft to yield. Also, find the residual shear-stress distribution in the shaft when the torque is removed.

**Prob. 138**

**139.** The shear stress–strain diagram for a solid 50-mm-diameter shaft can be approximated as shown in the figure. Determine the torque required to cause a maximum shear stress in the shaft of 125 MPa. If the shaft is 3 m long, what is the corresponding angle of twist?

**Prob. 139**

**\*140.** The 2-m-long tube is made of an elastic-perfectly plastic material as shown. Determine the applied torque $T$ that subjects the material at the tube's outer edge to a shear strain of $\gamma_{max} = 0.006$ rad. What would be the permanent angle of twist of the tube when this torque is removed? Sketch the residual stress distribution in the tube.

**142.** The 2-m-long tube is made from an elastic-plastic material as shown. Determine the applied torque $T$, which subjects the material of the tube's outer edge to a shearing strain, of $\gamma_{max} = 0.008$ rad. What would be the permanent angle of twist of the tube when the torque is removed? Sketch the residual stress distribution of the tube.

**Prob. 140**

**Prob. 142**

**141.** A steel alloy core is bonded firmly to the copper alloy tube to form the shaft shown. If the materials have the $\tau-\gamma$ diagrams shown, determine the torque resisted by the core and the tube.

**Prob. 141**

# CHAPTER REVIEW

Torque causes a shaft having a circular cross section to twist, such that the shear strain in the shaft is proportional to its radial distance from the center of the shaft. Provided the material is homogeneous and linear elastic, then the shear stress is determined from the torsion formula,

$$\tau = \frac{T\rho}{J}$$

The design of a shaft requires finding the geometric parameter,

$$\frac{J}{c} = \frac{T}{\tau_{\text{allow}}}$$

Often the power $P$ supplied to a shaft rotating at $\omega$ is reported, in which case the torque is determined from $P = T\omega$.

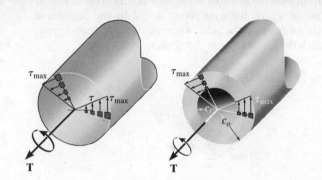

The angle of twist of a circular shaft is determined from

$$\phi = \int_0^L \frac{T(x)\,dx}{J(x)G(x)}$$

If the internal torque and $JG$ are constant within each segment of the shaft then

$$\phi = \sum \frac{TL}{JG}$$

For application, it is necessary to use a sign convention for the internal torque and to be sure the material remains linear elastic.

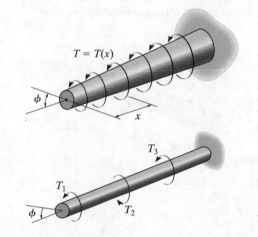

If the shaft is statically indeterminate, then the reactive torques are determined from equilibrium, compatibility of twist, and a torque-twist relationship, such as $\phi = TL/JG$.

Solid non-circular shafts tend to warp out of plane when subjected to a torque. Formulas are available to determine the maximum elastic shear stress and the twist for these cases.

The average shear stress in thin-walled tubes is determined by assuming the shear flow across each thickness $t$ of the tube is constant. The average shear stress value is determined from $\tau_{avg} = \dfrac{T}{2t A_m}$.

Stress concentrations occur in shafts when the cross section suddenly changes. The maximum shear stress is determined using a stress concentration factor $K$, which is determined from experiment and represented in graphical form. Once obtained, $\tau_{max} = K\left(\dfrac{Tc}{J}\right)$.

If the applied torque causes the material to exceed the elastic limit, then the stress distribution will not be proportional to the radial distance from the centerline of the shaft. Instead, the internal torque is related to the stress distribution using the shear-stress–shear-strain diagram and equilibrium.

If a shaft is subjected to a plastic torque, which is then released, it will cause the material to respond elastically, thereby causing residual shear stress to be developed in the shaft.

# REVIEW PROBLEMS

**143.** The shaft is made of A992 steel and has an allowable shear stress of $\tau_{allow} = 75$ MPa. When the shaft is rotating at 300 rpm, the motor supplies 8 kW of power, while gears $A$ and $B$ withdraw 5 kW and 3 kW, respectively. Determine the required minimum diameter of the shaft to the nearest millimeter. Also, find the rotation of gear $A$ relative to $C$.

**\*144.** The shaft is made of A992 steel and has an allowable shear stress of $\tau_{allow} = 75$ MPa. When the shaft is rotating at 300 rpm, the motor supplies 8 kW of power, while gears $A$ and $B$ withdraw 5 kW and 3 kW, respectively. If the angle of twist of gear $A$ relative to $C$ is not allowed to exceed 0.03 rad, determine the required minimum diameter of the shaft to the nearest millimeter.

**Probs. 143/144**

**145.** The A-36 steel circular tube is subjected to a torque of 10 kN · m. Determine the shear stress at the mean radius $\rho = 60$ mm and compute the angle of twist of the tube if it is 4 m long and fixed at its far end. Solve the problem using Eqs. 7 and 15 and by using Eqs. 18 and 20.

**Prob. 145**

**146.** A portion of an airplane fuselage can be approximated by the cross section shown. If the thickness of its 2014-T6-aluminum skin is 10 mm, determine the maximum wing torque **T** that can be applied if $\tau_{allow} = 4$ MPa. Also, in a 4-m long section, determine the angle of twist.

**Prob. 146**

**147.** The material of which each of three shafts is made has a yield stress of $\tau_Y$ and a shear modulus of $G$. Determine which shaft geometry will resist the largest torque without yielding. What percentage of this torque can be carried by the other two shafts? Assume that each shaft is made of the same amount of material and that it has the same cross-sectional area $A$.

**Prob. 147**

**\*148.** Segments $AB$ and $BC$ of the assembly are made from 6061-T6 aluminum and A992 steel, respectively. If couple forces $P = 3$ kip are applied to the lever arm, determine the maximum shear stress developed in each segment. The assembly is fixed at $A$ and $C$.

**150.** The tapered shaft is made from 2014-T6 aluminum alloy, and has a radius which can be described by the function $r = 0.02(1 + x^{3/2})$ m, where $x$ is in meters. Determine the angle of twist of its end $A$ if it is subjected to a torque of $450$ N · m.

**Prob. 148**

**Prob. 150**

**149.** Segments $AB$ and $BC$ of the assembly are made from 6061-T6 aluminum and A992 steel, respectively. If the allowable shear stress for the aluminum is $(\tau_{allow})_{al} = 12$ ksi and for the steel $(\tau_{allow})_{st} = 10$ ksi, determine the maximum allowable couple forces $P$ that can be applied to the lever arm. The assembly is fixed at $A$ and $C$.

**151.** The 60-mm-diameter shaft rotates at 300 rev/min. This motion is caused by the unequal belt tensions on the pulley of 800 N and 450 N. Determine the power transmitted and the maximum shear stress developed in the shaft.

**Prob. 149**

**Prob. 151**

# Solutions and Answers for Preliminary Problems

**P1.**

300 N·m

300 N·m

A

B

300 N·m

Equilibrium

500 N·m

C D

500 N·m

300 N·m

800 N·m

Equilibrium

**P2.**

400 N·m

A

B

C

200 N·m

D

**P3.**

$\tau_{max}$

$\tau_{max}$

T

$\tau_{max}$

$\tau_{max}$

T

**P4.**

$$P = T\omega$$

$$(10\ hp)\left(\frac{550\ ft \cdot lb/s}{1\ hp}\right) = T\left(1200\ \frac{rev}{min}\right)\left(\frac{1\ min}{60\ s}\right)\frac{2\pi\ rad}{1\ rev}$$

$$T = 43.8\ lb \cdot ft$$

# Selected Answers

**1.** $r' = 0.841r$

**2.** $r' = 0.707r$

**3.** $\tau_B = 6.04 \text{ MPa}, \tau_A = 6.04 \text{ MPa}$

**5.** $\tau_A = 3.45 \text{ ksi}, \tau_B = 2.76 \text{ ksi}$

**6.** $(\tau_{BC})_{max} = 5.07 \text{ ksi}, (\tau_{DE})_{max} = 3.62 \text{ ksi}$

**7.** $(\tau_{EF})_{max} = 0, (\tau_{CD})_{max} = 2.17 \text{ ksi}$

**9.** $\tau_B = 6.79 \text{ MPa}, \tau_A = 7.42 \text{ MPa}$

**10.** $n = \dfrac{2r^3}{Rd^2}$

**11.** $\tau_{AB} = 7.82 \text{ ksi}, \tau_{BC} = 2.36 \text{ ksi}$

**13.** Use $t = 25 \text{ mm}$

**14.** Use $d = 1\dfrac{3}{4}$ in.

**15.** Use $d = 33 \text{ mm}$

**17.** $\tau_{max} = 4.89 \text{ ksi}$

**18.** $\tau_{max} = 7.33 \text{ ksi}$

**19.** $T = 7.54 \text{ kN} \cdot \text{m}$

**21.** $\tau_C = 35.8 \text{ MPa}$

**22.** $d = 39.4 \text{ mm}$

**23.** $t_0 = 1.57 \text{ kN} \cdot \text{m/m}$

**25.** $\tau_{\max}^{abs} = 3.59 \text{ ksi}$

**26.** $\tau_{max} = \dfrac{T}{2\pi r_i^2 h}$

**27.** $T = 1.57 \text{ kip} \cdot \text{ft}, P = 5.11 \text{ kip}$

**29.** $\tau_{avg} = 1.44 \text{ MPa}$

**30.** $T_0 = 670 \text{ N} \cdot \text{m}, \tau_{\max}^{abs} = 6.66 \text{ MPa}$

**31.** $(\tau_{AB})_{max} = 1.04 \text{ MPa}, (\tau_{BC})_{max} = 3.11 \text{ MPa}$

**33.** $d_o = 1.09 \text{ in.}, d_i = 0.819 \text{ in.}$

**34.** $\omega = 82.0 \text{ rad/s}$

**35.** $\omega = 21.7 \text{ rad/s}$

**37.** $\tau_{max} = 6.02 \text{ ksi}$

**38.** $d_A = 12.4 \text{ mm}, d_B = 16.8 \text{ mm}$

**39.** $(\tau_{max})_{CF} = 12.5 \text{ MPa}, (\tau_{max})_{BC} = 7.26 \text{ MPa}$

**41.** $t = 2.3 \text{ mm}$

**42.** $\omega = 17.7 \text{ rad/s}$

**43.** $\tau_{max} = \dfrac{2TL^3}{\pi[r_A(L-x)+r_Bx]^3}$

**45.** $(\tau_B)_{max} = 18.3 \text{ ksi}$

**46.** Use $d_i = 1\dfrac{5}{8}$ in.

**47.** $\tau_{max} = 44.3 \text{ MPa}, \phi = 11.9°$

**49.** $\phi_{A/D} = 0.879°$

**50.** $\tau_{max} = 2.83 \text{ ksi}, \phi = 4.43°$

**51.** $T = 5.09 \text{ kN} \cdot \text{m}, \phi_{A/C} = 3.53°$

**53.** $\phi_B = 5.74°$

**54.** Use $d = 22 \text{ mm}, \phi_{A/D} = 2.54°$

**55.** Use $d = 25 \text{ mm}$

**57.** $\tau_{max} = 9.12 \text{ MPa}, \phi_{E/B} = 0.585°$

**58.** $\tau_{max} = 14.6 \text{ MPa}, \phi_{B/E} = 1.11°$

**59.** $\phi_{B/D} = 1.15°$

**61.** $\phi_B = 1.53°$

**62.** $\phi_A = 1.78°$

**63.** $T_1 = 18.5 \text{ kN} \cdot \text{m}, T_2 = 50.0 \text{ kN} \cdot \text{m},$ $\phi_{A/C} = 0.155°$

**65.** $F = 6.03 \text{ N}, s = 0.720 \text{ mm}$

**66.** $t = 7.53 \text{ mm}$

**67.** $\omega = 131 \text{ rad/s}$

**69.** $k = 1.20(10^6) \text{ N/m}^2, \phi = 3.56°$

**70.** $k = 12.28(10^3) \text{ N/m}^{2/3}, \phi = 2.97°$

**73.** $\phi = \dfrac{T}{2a\pi G}(1 - e^{-4aL})$

**74.** $t_0 = \dfrac{4Pd}{L}, \phi = \dfrac{4PLd}{3\pi c^4 G}$

**75.** $\phi_{A/B} = 5.62°$

**77.** $(\tau_{AC})_{max} = 14.3 \text{ MPa}, (\tau_{CB})_{max} = 9.55 \text{ MPa}$

**78.** $\tau_{\max}^{abs} = 9.77 \text{ MPa}$

**79.** $\tau_{max} = 29.3 \text{ ksi}$

**81.** $T_A = 12.3 \text{ kip} \cdot \text{ft}, T_D = 7.72 \text{ kip} \cdot \text{ft}$

**82.** $\phi_C = 0.116°, (\tau_{st})_{max} = 395 \text{ psi},$ $(\gamma_{st})_{max} = 34.3(10^{-6}) \text{ rad}, (\tau_{br})_{max} = 96.1 \text{ psi},$ $(\gamma_{br})_{max} = 17.2(10^{-6}) \text{ rad}$

**83.** $(\tau_{BC})_{max} = 1.47 \text{ ksi}, (\tau_{BD})_{max} = 1.96 \text{ ksi},$ $\phi_{B/C} = \phi_{B/D} = 0.338°$

**85.** $(\tau_{st})_{max} = 86.5 \text{ MPa}, (\tau_{mg})_{max} = 41.5 \text{ MPa},$ $(\tau_{mg})|_{\rho = 0.02\,m} = 20.8 \text{ MPa}$

**86.** $T_B = 222 \text{ N} \cdot \text{m}, T_A = 55.6 \text{ N} \cdot \text{m}$

**87.** $\phi_E = 1.66°$

**89.** $\tau_{\max}^{abs} = 64.1 \text{ MPa}$

**90.** $\phi_{C/D} = 6.22°$

**91.** $\tau_{\max}^{abs} = 5.50 \text{ ksi}$

**93.** $T_B = \dfrac{37}{189}T, T_A = \dfrac{152}{189}T$

**94.** $T_B = \dfrac{7t_0 L}{12}, T_A = \dfrac{3t_0 L}{4}$

**95.** $T = 7.74 \text{ N} \cdot \text{m}$

**97.** Factor of increase in max. shear stress $= \dfrac{1}{k^2}$

**98.** $(\tau_{BC})_{max} = 0.955 \text{ MPa}, (\tau_{AC})_{max} = 1.59 \text{ MPa},$ $\phi_{B/A} = 0.207°$

**99.** $(\tau_{BC})_{max} = 0.955 \text{ MPa}, (\tau_{AC})_{max} = 1.59 \text{ MPa},$ $\phi_{B/C} = 0.0643°$

**101.** $T = 1.35 \text{ kip} \cdot \text{ft}, \phi = 3.42°$

**102.** $T_B = 32 \text{ lb} \cdot \text{ft}, T_A = 48 \text{ lb} \cdot \text{ft}, \phi_C = 0.0925°$

**103.** $\tau_{avg} = 3.35 \text{ ksi}$

**105.** $\tau_{max} = 61.1 \text{ MPa}, \phi_B = 0.700°$

**106.** Use $a = 47 \text{ mm}, \phi_B = 0.897°$

| | | | | |
|---|---|---|---|---|
| **107.** | $T = 6.65 \text{ kip} \cdot \text{ft}$ | | **131.** | $T_Y = 12.6 \text{ kN} \cdot \text{m}, T_p = 16.8 \text{ kN} \cdot \text{m}$ |
| **109.** | Factor of increase $= 1.66$ | | **133.** | $T = 110 \text{ lb} \cdot \text{ft}$ |
| **110.** | Factor of increase $= 2.85$ | | **134.** | $T = 19.2 \text{ kN} \cdot \text{m}, \phi = 24.9°, \phi_r = 6.72°$ |
| **111.** | $q_{sq} = \dfrac{\pi}{4} q_{cr}$ | | **135.** | $\rho_Y = 0.542 \text{ in.}, \phi = 6.34°$ |
| | | | **137.** | $T = 331 \text{ lb} \cdot \text{ft}$ |
| **113.** | $t = 0.104 \text{ in.}$ | | **138.** | $T = 41.2 \text{ kip} \cdot \text{ft}, (\tau_r)_{\rho = c_o} = 2.44 \text{ ksi},$ |
| **114.** | $T = 2 \text{ kip} \cdot \text{ft}$ | | | $(\tau_r)_{\rho = c_i} = -3.78 \text{ ksi}$ |
| **115.** | $b = 0.773 \text{ in.}$ | | **139.** | $T = 3.27 \text{ kN} \cdot \text{m}, \phi = 68.8°$ |
| **117.** | $T = 4.73 \text{ MN} \cdot \text{m}, \phi = 0.428°/\text{m}$ | | **141.** | $T_t = 7.39 \text{ kN} \cdot \text{m}, T_c = 7.61 \text{ kN} \cdot \text{m}$ |
| **118.** | $\tau_{avg} = 119 \text{ MPa}, \phi = 0.407°/\text{m}$ | | **142.** | $T_p = 13.6 \text{ kN} \cdot \text{m}, \phi_r = 12.3°$ |
| **119.** | $(\tau_{avg})_A = (\tau_{avg})_B = 357 \text{ kPa}$ | | **143.** | Use $d = 26 \text{ mm}, \phi_{A/C} = 2.11°$ |
| **121.** | No, it is not possible. | | **145.** | $\tau = 88.3 \text{ MPa}, \phi = 4.50°$ |
| **122.** | $P = 101 \text{ kW}$ | | **146.** | $T = 381 \text{ kN} \cdot \text{m}, \phi = 0.0310°$ |
| **123.** | $\tau_{max} = 50.6 \text{ MPa}$ | | **147.** | The circular shaft will resist the largest torque. |
| **125.** | $r = 0.075 \text{ in.}$ | | | For the square shaft: 73.7%, |
| **126.** | $T_Y = 1.26 \text{ kN} \cdot \text{m}, \phi = 3.58°, \phi' = 4.86°$ | | | For the triangular shaft: 62.2% |
| **127.** | $T_p = 0.105 \text{ N} \cdot \text{m}$ | | **149.** | $P = 2.80 \text{ kip}$ |
| **129.** | $T = 20.8 \text{ kN} \cdot \text{m}, \phi = 34.4°, \phi_r = 12.2°$ | | **150.** | $\phi_A = 1.59°$ |
| **130.** | $T = 14.4 \text{ kip} \cdot \text{ft}$ | | **151.** | $P = 1.10 \text{ kW}, \tau_{max} = 825 \text{ kPa}$ |

# Fundamental Problems Partial Solutions and Answers

**F1**    $J = \dfrac{\pi}{2}(0.04^4) = 1.28(10^{-6})\pi \text{ m}^4$

$$\tau_A = \tau_{max} = \frac{Tc}{J} = \frac{5(10^3)(0.04)}{1.28(10^{-6})\pi} = 49.7 \text{ MPa}$$
*Ans.*

$$\tau_B = \frac{T\rho_B}{J} = \frac{5(10^3)(0.03)}{1.28(10^{-6})\pi} = 37.3 \text{ MPa}$$
*Ans.*

**F2**    $J = \dfrac{\pi}{2}(0.06^4 - 0.04^4) = 5.2(10^{-6})\pi \text{ m}^4$

$$\tau_B = \tau_{max} = \frac{Tc}{J} = \frac{10(10^3)(0.06)}{5.2(10^{-6})\pi} = 36.7 \text{ MPa}$$
*Ans.*

$$\tau_A = \frac{T\rho_A}{J} = \frac{10(10^3)(0.04)}{5.2(10^{-6})\pi} = 24.5 \text{ MPa}$$
*Ans.*

**F3**    $J_{AB} = \dfrac{\pi}{2}(0.04^4 - 0.03^4) = 0.875(10^{-6})\pi \text{ m}^4$

$$J_{BC} = \frac{\pi}{2}(0.04^4) = 1.28(10^{-6})\pi \text{ m}^4$$

$$(\tau_{AB})_{max} = \frac{T_{AB}\,c_{AB}}{J_{AB}} = \frac{[2(10^3)](0.04)}{0.875(10^{-6})\pi} = 29.1 \text{ MPa}$$

$$(\tau_{BC})_{max} = \frac{T_{BC}\,c_{BC}}{J_{BC}} = \frac{[6(10^3)](0.04)}{1.28(10^{-6})\pi}$$
$$= 59.7 \text{ MPa}$$
*Ans.*

**F4**    $T_{AB} = 0, T_{BC} = 600 \text{ N} \cdot \text{m}, T_{CD} = 0$

$$J = \frac{\pi}{2}(0.02^4) = 80(10^{-9})\pi \text{ m}^4$$

$$\tau_{max} = \frac{Tc}{J} = \frac{600(0.02)}{80(10^{-9})\pi} = 47.7 \text{ MPa}$$
*Ans.*

**F5**    $J_{BC} = \dfrac{\pi}{2}(0.04^4 - 0.03^4) = 0.875(10^{-6})\pi \text{ m}^4$

$$(\tau_{BC})_{max} = \frac{T_{BC}\,c_{BC}}{J_{BC}} = \frac{2100(0.04)}{0.875(10^{-6})\pi}$$
$$= 30.6 \text{ MPa}$$
*Ans.*

**F6**    $t = 5(10^3) \text{ N} \cdot \text{m/m}$

Internal torque is $T = 5(10^3)(0.8) = 4000 \text{ N} \cdot \text{m}$

$$J = \frac{\pi}{2}(0.04^4) = 1.28(10^{-6})\pi \text{ m}^4$$

$$\tau_{AB} = \frac{T_A c}{J} = \frac{4000(0.04)}{1.28(10^{-6})\pi} = 39.8 \text{ MPa}$$
*Ans.*

**F7**    Maximum internal torque is in region $AB$.

$T_{AB} = 250 \text{ N} \cdot \text{m}$

$$\tau_{max}^{abs} = \frac{T_{AB}\,c}{J} = \frac{250(0.025)}{\dfrac{\pi}{2}(0.025)^4} = 10.2 \text{ MPa}$$
*Ans.*

**F8** $\qquad P = T\omega; \quad 3(550) \text{ ft} \cdot \text{lb/s} = T\left[150\left(\dfrac{2\pi}{60}\right) \text{rad/s}\right]$

$T = 105.04 \text{ ft} \cdot \text{lb}$

$\tau_{\text{allow}} = \dfrac{Tc}{J}; \quad 12(10^3) = \dfrac{105.04(12)(d/2)}{\dfrac{\pi}{2}(d/2)^4}$

$$d = 0.812 \text{ in.}$$

$$\text{Use } d = \dfrac{7}{8} \text{ in.} \qquad \qquad Ans.$$

**F9** $\qquad J = \dfrac{\pi}{2}(0.03^4) = 0.405(10^{-6})\pi \text{ m}^4$

$\phi_{A/C} = \dfrac{-2(10^3)(0.6) + (10^3)(0.4)}{[0.405(10^{-6})\pi][75(10^9)]}$

$\qquad = -0.00838 \text{ rad} = -0.480° \qquad Ans.$

**F10** $\qquad J = \dfrac{\pi}{2}(0.02^4) = 80(10^{-9})\pi \text{ m}^4$

$\phi_{B/A} = \dfrac{600(0.45)}{[80(10^{-9})\pi][75(10^9)]}$

$\qquad = 0.01432 \text{ rad} = 0.821° \qquad Ans.$

**F11** $\qquad J = \dfrac{\pi}{2}(0.04^4 - 0.03^4) = 0.875(10^{-6})\pi \text{ m}^4$

$\phi_{A/B} = \dfrac{T_{AB} \, L_{AB}}{JG} = \dfrac{3(10^3)(0.9)}{[0.875(10^{-6})\pi][26(10^9)]}$

$\qquad = 0.03778 \text{ rad}$

$\phi_B = \dfrac{T_B}{k} = \dfrac{3(10^3)}{90(10^3)} = 0.03333 \text{ rad}$

$\phi_A = \phi_B + \phi_{A/B}$

$\qquad = 0.03333 + 0.03778$

$\qquad = 0.07111 \text{ rad} = 4.07° \qquad Ans.$

**F12** $\qquad J = \dfrac{\pi}{2}(0.02^4) = 80(10^{-9})\pi \text{ m}^4$

$\phi_{B/A} = \dfrac{0.02[600 + (-300) + 200 + 500]}{[80(10^{-9})\pi][75(10^9)]}$

$\qquad = 0.01061 \text{ rad} = 0.608° \qquad Ans.$

**F13** $\qquad J = \dfrac{\pi}{2}(0.04^4) = 1.28(10^{-6})\pi \text{ m}^4$

$t = 5(10^3) \text{ N} \cdot \text{m/m}$

Internal torque is $5(10^3)x \text{ N} \cdot \text{m}$

$\phi_{A/B} = \displaystyle\int_0^L \dfrac{T(x)dx}{JG}$

$\qquad = \dfrac{1}{[1.28(10^{-6})\pi][75(10^9)]}\displaystyle\int_0^{0.8 \text{ m}} 5(10^3)x\,dx$

$\qquad = 0.00531 \text{ rad} = 0.304° \qquad Ans.$

**F14** $\qquad J = \dfrac{\pi}{2}(0.04^4) = 1.28(10^{-6})\pi \text{ m}^4$

Distributed torque is $t = \dfrac{15(10^3)}{0.6}(x)$

$\qquad = 25(10^3)x \text{ N} \cdot \text{m/m}$

Internal torque is $T(x) = \dfrac{1}{2}(25x)(10^3)(x)$

$\qquad = 12.5(10^3)x^2 \text{ N} \cdot \text{m}$

$\phi_{A/C} = \displaystyle\int_0^L \dfrac{T(x)dx}{JG} + \dfrac{T_{BC}L_{BC}}{JG}$

$= \dfrac{1}{[1.28(10^{-6})\pi][75(10^9)]}\left[\displaystyle\int_0^{0.6 \text{ m}} 12.5(10^3)x^2\,dx + 4500(0.4)\right]$

$= 0.008952 \text{ rad} = 0.513° \qquad Ans.$

# Bending

From Chapter 6 of *Mechanics of Materials*, Ninth Edition. R. C. Hibbeler. Copyright © 2014 by Pearson Education, Inc. Published by Pearson Prentice Hall. All rights reserved.

The deck of this bridge has been designed on the basis of its ability to resist bending stress.

# Bending

## CHAPTER OBJECTIVES

■ Beams and shafts are important structural and mechanical elements in engineering. In this chapter we will determine the stress in these members caused by bending. The chapter begins with a discussion of how to establish the shear and moment diagrams for a beam or shaft. Like the normal-force and torque diagrams, the shear and moment diagrams provide a useful means for determining the largest shear and moment in a member, and they specify where these maximums occur. Once the internal moment at a section is determined, the bending stress can then be calculated. First we will consider members that are straight, have a symmetric cross section, and are made of homogeneous linear elastic material. Afterward we will discuss special cases involving unsymmetric bending and members made of composite materials. Consideration will also be given to curved members, stress concentrations, inelastic bending, and residual stresses.

## 1 Shear and Moment Diagrams

Members that are slender and support loadings that are applied perpendicular to their longitudinal axis are called *beams*. In general, beams are long, straight bars having a constant cross-sectional area. Often they are classified as to how they are supported. For example, a *simply supported beam* is pinned at one end and roller supported at the other, Fig. 1, a *cantilevered beam* is fixed at one end and free at the other, and an *overhanging beam* has one or both of its ends freely extended over the supports. Beams are considered among the most important of all structural elements. They are used to support the floor of a building, the deck of a bridge, or the wing of an aircraft. Also, the axle of an automobile, the boom of a crane, even many of the bones of the body act as beams.

Simply supported beam

Cantilevered beam

Overhanging beam

**Fig. 1**

Because of the applied loadings, beams develop an internal shear force and bending moment that, in general, vary from point to point along the axis of the beam. In order to properly design a beam it therefore becomes necessary to determine the *maximum* shear and moment in the beam. One way to do this is to express $V$ and $M$ as functions of their arbitrary position $x$ along the beam's axis. These *shear and moment functions* can then be plotted and represented by graphs called **shear and moment diagrams.** The maximum values of $V$ and $M$ can then be obtained from these graphs. Also, since the shear and moment diagrams provide detailed information about the *variation* of the shear and moment along the beam's axis, they are often used by engineers to decide where to place reinforcement materials within the beam or how to proportion the size of the beam at various points along its length.

In order to formulate $V$ and $M$ in terms of $x$ we must choose the origin and the positive direction for $x$. Although the choice is arbitrary, most often the origin is located at the left end of the beam and the positive direction is to the right.

In general, the internal shear and moment functions of $x$ will be *discontinuous,* or their slope will be discontinuous, at points where a distributed load changes or where concentrated forces or couple moments are applied. Because of this, the shear and moment functions must be determined for *each region* of the beam *between* any two discontinuities of loading. For example, coordinates $x_1$, $x_2$, and $x_3$ will have to be used to describe the variation of $V$ and $M$ throughout the length of the beam in Fig. 2. These coordinates will be valid *only* within the regions from $A$ to $B$ for $x_1$, from $B$ to $C$ for $x_2$, and from $C$ to $D$ for $x_3$.

**Fig. 2**

Positive external distributed load

Positive internal shear

Positive internal moment

Beam sign convention

**Fig. 3**

**Beam Sign Convention.** Before presenting a method for determining the shear and moment as functions of $x$ and later plotting these functions (shear and moment diagrams), it is first necessary to establish a *sign convention* so as to define "positive" and "negative" values for $V$ and $M$. Although the choice of a sign convention is arbitrary, here we will use the one often used in engineering practice and shown in Fig. 3. The *positive directions* are as follows: the *distributed load* acts *upward* on the beam; the internal *shear force* causes a *clockwise* rotation of the beam segment on which it acts; and the internal *moment* causes *compression* in the *top fibers* of the segment such that it bends the segment so that it "holds water". Loadings that are opposite to these are considered negative.

## Important Points

- *Beams* are long straight members that are subjected to loads perpendicular to their longitudinal axis. They are classified according to the way they are supported, e.g., simply supported, cantilevered, or overhanging.

- In order to properly design a beam, it is important to know the *variation* of the internal shear and moment along its axis in order to find the points where these values are a maximum.

- Using an established sign convention for positive shear and moment, the shear and moment in the beam can be determined as a function of its position $x$ on the beam, and then these functions can be plotted to form the shear and moment diagrams.

## Procedure for Analysis

The shear and moment diagrams for a beam can be constructed using the following procedure.

Support Reactions.

- Determine all the reactive forces and couple moments acting on the beam, and resolve all the forces into components acting perpendicular and parallel to the beam's axis.

Shear and Moment Functions.

- Specify separate coordinates $x$ having an origin at the beam's *left end* and extending to regions of the beam between concentrated forces and/or couple moments, or where there is no discontinuity of distributed loading.

- Section the beam at each distance $x$, and draw the free-body diagram of one of the segments. Be sure **V** and **M** are shown acting in their positive sense, in accordance with the sign convention given in Fig. 3.

- The shear is obtained by summing forces perpendicular to the beam's axis.

- To eliminate $V$, the moment is obtained directly by summing moments about the sectioned end of the segment.

Shear and Moment Diagrams.

- Plot the shear diagram ($V$ versus $x$) and the moment diagram ($M$ versus $x$). If numerical values of the functions describing $V$ and $M$ are *positive,* the values are plotted above the $x$ axis, whereas negative values are plotted below the axis.

- Generally it is convenient to show the shear and moment diagrams below the free-body diagram of the beam.

## EXAMPLE | 1

Draw the shear and moment diagrams for the beam shown in Fig. 4a.

### SOLUTION

**Support Reactions.**   The support reactions are shown in Fig. 4c.

**Shear and Moment Functions.**   A free-body diagram of the left segment of the beam is shown in Fig. 4b. The distributed loading on this segment, $wx$, is represented by its resultant force only *after* the segment is isolated as a free-body diagram. This force acts through the centroid of the area comprising the distributed loading, a distance of $x/2$ from the right end. Applying the two equations of equilibrium yields

$$+\uparrow\Sigma F_y = 0; \qquad\qquad \frac{wL}{2} - wx - V = 0$$

$$V = w\left(\frac{L}{2} - x\right) \qquad (1)$$

$$\zeta +\Sigma M = 0; \qquad\qquad -\left(\frac{wL}{2}\right)x + (wx)\left(\frac{x}{2}\right) + M = 0$$

$$M = \frac{w}{2}(Lx - x^2) \qquad (2)$$

**Shear and Moment Diagrams.**   The shear and moment diagrams shown in Fig. 4c are obtained by plotting Eqs. 1 and 2. The point of *zero shear* can be found from Eq. 1:

$$V = w\left(\frac{L}{2} - x\right) = 0$$

$$x = \frac{L}{2}$$

**NOTE:** From the moment diagram, this value of $x$ represents the point on the beam where the *maximum moment* occurs, since by Eq. 2 (see Sec. 2) the *slope* $V = dM/dx = 0$. From Eq. 2, we have

$$M_{max} = \frac{w}{2}\left[L\left(\frac{L}{2}\right) - \left(\frac{L}{2}\right)^2\right]$$

$$= \frac{wL^2}{8}$$

(a)

(b)

(c)

**Fig. 4**

## EXAMPLE 2

Draw the shear and moment diagrams for the beam shown in Fig. 5a.

(a)

(b)

### SOLUTION

**Support Reactions.** The distributed load is replaced by its resultant force and the reactions have been determined as shown in Fig. 5b.

**Shear and Moment Functions.** A free-body diagram of a beam segment of length $x$ is shown in Fig. 5c. Note that the intensity of the triangular load at the section is found by proportion, that is, $w/x = w_0/L$ or $w = w_0 x/L$. With the load intensity known, the resultant of the distributed loading is determined from the area under the diagram. Thus,

(c)

$$+\uparrow \Sigma F_y = 0; \qquad \frac{w_0 L}{2} - \frac{1}{2}\left(\frac{w_0 x}{L}\right)x - V = 0$$

$$V = \frac{w_0}{2L}(L^2 - x^2) \tag{1}$$

$$\zeta + \Sigma M = 0; \qquad \frac{w_0 L^2}{3} - \frac{w_0 L}{2}(x) + \frac{1}{2}\left(\frac{w_0 x}{L}\right)x\left(\frac{1}{3}x\right) + M = 0$$

$$M = \frac{w_0}{6L}(-2L^3 + 3L^2 x - x^3) \tag{2}$$

These results can be checked by applying Eqs. 1 and 2 of Sec. 2, that is,

$$w = \frac{dV}{dx} = \frac{w_0}{2L}(0 - 2x) = -\frac{w_0 x}{L} \qquad \text{OK}$$

$$V = \frac{dM}{dx} = \frac{w_0}{6L}(0 + 3L^2 - 3x^2) = \frac{w_0}{2L}(L^2 - x^2) \qquad \text{OK}$$

**Shear and Moment Diagrams.** The graphs of Eqs. 1 and 2 are shown in Fig. 5d.

(d)

**Fig. 5**

# EXAMPLE 3

Draw the shear and moment diagrams for the beam shown in Fig. 6a.

(a)

## SOLUTION

**Support Reactions.** The distributed load is divided into triangular and rectangular component loadings and these loadings are then replaced by their resultant forces. The reactions have been determined as shown on the beam's free-body diagram, Fig. 6b.

(b)

(c)

**Shear and Moment Functions.** A free-body diagram of the left segment is shown in Fig. 6c. As above, the trapezoidal loading is replaced by rectangular and triangular distributions. Note that the intensity of the triangular load at the section is found by proportion. The resultant force and the location of each distributed loading are also shown. Applying the equilibrium equations, we have

$$+\uparrow \Sigma F_y = 0; \quad 30 \text{ kip} - (2 \text{ kip/ft})x - \frac{1}{2}(4 \text{ kip/ft})\left(\frac{x}{18 \text{ ft}}\right)x - V = 0$$

$$V = \left(30 - 2x - \frac{x^2}{9}\right) \text{kip} \qquad (1)$$

$$\zeta + \Sigma M = 0;$$

$$-30 \text{ kip}(x) + (2 \text{ kip/ft})x\left(\frac{x}{2}\right) + \frac{1}{2}(4 \text{ kip/ft})\left(\frac{x}{18 \text{ ft}}\right)x\left(\frac{x}{3}\right) + M = 0$$

$$M = \left(30x - x^2 - \frac{x^3}{27}\right) \text{kip} \cdot \text{ft} \qquad (2)$$

Equation 2 may be checked by noting that $dM/dx = V$, that is, Eq. 1. Also, $w = dV/dx = -2 - \frac{2}{9}x$. This equation checks, since when $x = 0$, $w = -2$ kip/ft, and when $x = 18$ ft, $w = -6$ kip/ft, Fig. 6a.

**Shear and Moment Diagrams.** Equations 1 and 2 are plotted in Fig. 6d. Since the point of maximum moment occurs when $dM/dx = V = 0$ (Eq. 2), then, from Eq. 1,

$$V = 0 = 30 - 2x - \frac{x^2}{9}$$

Choosing the positive root,

$$x = 9.735 \text{ ft}$$

Thus, from Eq. 2,

$$M_{\text{max}} = 30(9.735) - (9.735)^2 - \frac{(9.735)^3}{27}$$

$$= 163 \text{ kip} \cdot \text{ft}$$

(d)

**Fig. 6**

290

## EXAMPLE 4

Draw the shear and moment diagrams for the beam shown in Fig. 7a.

(a)

(b)

### SOLUTION

**Support Reactions.** The reactions at the supports have been determined and are shown on the free-body diagram of the beam, Fig. 7d.

**Shear and Moment Functions.** Since there is a discontinuity of distributed load and also a concentrated load at the beam's center, two regions of $x$ must be considered in order to describe the shear and moment functions for the entire beam.

$0 \le x_1 < 5$ m, Fig. 7b:

$+\uparrow \Sigma F_y = 0;$        $5.75$ kN $- V = 0$

$$V = 5.75 \text{ kN} \qquad (1)$$

$\zeta + \Sigma M = 0;$    $-80$ kN $\cdot$ m $- 5.75$ kN $x_1 + M = 0$

$$M = (5.75x_1 + 80) \text{ kN} \cdot \text{m} \qquad (2)$$

$5$ m $< x_2 \le 10$ m, Fig. 7c:

$+\uparrow \Sigma F_y = 0;$    $5.75$ kN $- 15$ kN $- 5$ kN/m$(x_2 - 5$ m$) - V = 0$

$$V = (15.75 - 5x_2) \text{ kN} \qquad (3)$$

$\zeta + \Sigma M = 0;$    $-80$ kN $\cdot$ m $- 5.75$ kN $x_2 + 15$ kN$(x_2 - 5$ m$)$

$$+ 5 \text{ kN/m}(x_2 - 5 \text{ m})\left(\frac{x_2 - 5 \text{ m}}{2}\right) + M = 0$$

$$M = (-2.5x_2^2 + 15.75x_2 + 92.5) \text{ kN} \cdot \text{m} \qquad (4)$$

These results can be checked in part by noting that $w = dV/dx$ and $V = dM/dx$. Also, when $x_1 = 0$, Eqs. 1 and 2 give $V = 5.75$ kN and $M = 80$ kN $\cdot$ m; when $x_2 = 10$ m, Eqs. 3 and 4 give $V = -34.25$ kN and $M = 0$. These values check with the support reactions shown on the free-body diagram, Fig. 7d.

**Shear and Moment Diagrams.** Equations 1 through 4 are plotted in Fig. 7d.

(c)

(d)

Fig. 7

# 2 Graphical Method for Constructing Shear and Moment Diagrams

In cases where a beam is subjected to *several* different loadings, determining $V$ and $M$ as functions of $x$ and then plotting these equations can become quite tedious. In this section a simpler method for constructing the shear and moment diagrams is discussed—a method based on two differential relations, one that exists between distributed load and shear, and the other between shear and moment.

## Regions of Distributed Load.
For purposes of generality, consider the beam shown in Fig. 8*a*, which is subjected to an arbitrary loading. A free-body diagram for a very small segment $\Delta x$ of the beam is shown in Fig. 8*b*. Since this segment has been chosen at a position $x$ where there is no concentrated force or couple moment, the results to be obtained will *not* apply at these points of concentrated loading.

Notice that all the loadings shown on the segment act in their positive directions according to the established sign convention, Fig. 3. Also, both the internal resultant shear and moment, acting on the right face of the segment, must be changed by a small amount in order to keep the segment in equilibrium. The distributed load, which is approximately constant over $\Delta x$, has been replaced by a resultant force $w(x)\Delta x$ that acts at $\frac{1}{2}(\Delta x)$ from the right side. Applying the equations of equilibrium to the segment, we have

Failure of this table occurred at the brace support on its right side. If drawn, the bending moment diagram for the table loading would indicate this to be the point of maximum internal moment.

(a)

Free-body diagram
of segment $\Delta x$

(b)

**Fig. 8**

$$+\uparrow \Sigma F_y = 0; \qquad V + w(x)\,\Delta x - (V + \Delta V) = 0$$

$$\Delta V = w(x)\,\Delta x$$

$$\zeta + \Sigma M_O = 0; \qquad -V\,\Delta x - M - w(x)\,\Delta x\left[\tfrac{1}{2}(\Delta x)\right] + (M + \Delta M) = 0$$

$$\Delta M = V\,\Delta x + w(x)\tfrac{1}{2}(\Delta x)^2$$

Dividing by $\Delta x$ and taking the limit as $\Delta x \to 0$, the above two equations become

$$\frac{dV}{dx} = w(x)$$

$$\begin{array}{ccc}
\text{slope of} & & \text{distributed} \\
\text{shear diagram} & = & \text{load intensity} \\
\text{at each point} & & \text{at each point}
\end{array} \tag{1}$$

$$\frac{dM}{dx} = V(x)$$

$$\begin{array}{ccc}
\text{slope of} & & \text{shear} \\
\text{moment diagram} & = & \text{at each} \\
\text{at each point} & & \text{point}
\end{array} \tag{2}$$

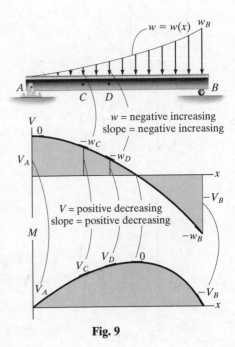

Fig. 9

These two equations provide a convenient means for quickly obtaining the shear and moment diagrams for a beam. Equation 1 states that at a point the *slope* of the shear diagram equals the intensity of the distributed loading. For example, consider the beam in Fig. 9a. The distributed loading is negative and increases from zero to $w_B$. Therefore, the shear diagram will be a curve that has a *negative slope,* increasing from zero to $-w_B$. Specific slopes $w_A = 0$, $-w_C$, $-w_D$, and $-w_B$ are shown in Fig. 9b.

In a similar manner, Eq. 2 states that at a point the *slope* of the moment diagram is equal to the shear. Notice that the shear diagram in Fig. 9b starts at $+V_A$, decreases to zero, and then becomes negative and decreases to $-V_B$. The moment diagram will then have an initial slope of $+V_A$ which decreases to zero, then the slope becomes negative and decreases to $-V_B$. Specific slopes $V_A$, $V_C$, $V_D$, 0, and $-V_B$ are shown in Fig. 9c.

Equations 1 and 2 may also be rewritten in the form $dV = w(x)dx$ and $dM = V dx$. Noting that $w(x) \, dx$ and $V \, dx$ represent differential areas under the distributed loading and shear diagram, respectively, we can integrate these areas between any two points $C$ and $D$ on the beam, Fig. 9d, and write

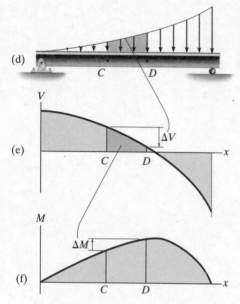

(d)

(e)

(f)

**Fig. 9 (cont.)**

$$\Delta V = \int w(x)dx$$

$$\text{change in} \atop \text{shear} = {\text{area under} \atop \text{distributed loading}}$$

(3)

$$\Delta M = \int V(x)dx$$

$$\text{change in} \atop \text{moment} = {\text{area under} \atop \text{shear diagram}}$$

(4)

Equation 3 states that the *change in shear* between $C$ and $D$ is equal to the *area* under the distributed-loading curve between these two points, Fig. 9d. In this case the change is negative since the distributed load acts downward. Similarly, from Eq. 4, the change in moment between $C$ and $D$, Fig. 9f, is equal to the area under the shear diagram within the region from $C$ to $D$. Here the change is positive.

Since the above equations do not apply at points where a concentrated force or couple moment acts, we will now consider each of these cases.

## Regions of Concentrated Force and Moment.
A free-body diagram of a small segment of the beam in Fig. 8a taken from under the force is shown in Fig. 10a. Here it can be seen that force equilibrium requires

$$+\uparrow \Sigma F_y = 0; \qquad V + F - (V + \Delta V) = 0$$
$$\Delta V = F \qquad (5)$$

Thus, when **F** acts *upward* on the beam, $\Delta V$ is *positive* so the shear will "jump" *upward*. Likewise, if **F** acts *downward*, the jump ($\Delta V$) will be *downward*.

When the beam segment includes the couple moment $M_0$, Fig. 10b, then moment equilibrium requires the change in moment to be

$$\zeta +\Sigma M_O = 0; \qquad M + \Delta M - M_0 - V \, \Delta x - M = 0$$

Letting $\Delta x \to 0$, we get

$$\Delta M = M_0 \qquad (6)$$

In this case, if **M**$_0$ is applied *clockwise*, $\Delta M$ is *positive* so the moment diagram will "jump" *upward*. Likewise, when **M**$_0$ acts *counterclockwise*, the jump ($\Delta M$) will be *downward*.

(a)

(b)

**Fig. 10**

## Procedure for Analysis

The following procedure provides a method for constructing the shear and moment diagrams for a beam based on the relations among distributed load, shear, and moment.

### Support Reactions.

- Determine the support reactions and resolve the forces acting on the beam into components that are perpendicular and parallel to the beam's axis.

### Shear Diagram.

- Establish the $V$ and $x$ axes and plot the known values of the shear at the two *ends* of the beam.

- Notice how the values of the distributed load vary along the beam, and realize that each of these values indicates the way the shear diagram will slope ($dV/dx = w$). Here $w$ is positive when it acts upward.

- If a numerical value of the shear is to be determined at a point, one can find this value either by using the method of sections and the equation of force equilibrium, or by using $\Delta V = \int w(x)\,dx$, which states that the *change in the shear* between any two points is equal to the *area under the load diagram* between the two points.

### Moment Diagram.

- Establish the $M$ and $x$ axes and plot the known values of the moment at the *ends* of the beam.

- Notice how the values of the shear diagram vary along the beam, and realize that each of these values indicates the way the moment diagram will slope ($dM/dx = V$).

- At the point where the shear is zero, $dM/dx = 0$, and therefore this would be a point of maximum or minimum moment.

- If a numerical value of the moment is to be determined at the point, one can find this value either by using the method of sections and the equation of moment equilibrium, or by using $\Delta M = \int V(x)\,dx$, which states that the *change in moment* between any two points is equal to the *area under the shear diagram* between the two points.

- Since $w(x)$ must be *integrated* to obtain $\Delta V$, and $V(x)$ is integrated to obtain $M(x)$, then if $w(x)$ is a curve of degree $n$, $V(x)$ will be a curve of degree $n + 1$ and $M(x)$ will be a curve of degree $n + 2$. For example, if $w(x)$ is uniform, $V(x)$ will be linear and $M(x)$ will be parabolic.

# EXAMPLE 5

(a)

Draw the shear and moment diagrams for the beam shown in Fig. 11a.

## SOLUTION

**Support Reactions.** The reaction at the fixed support is shown on the free-body diagram, Fig. 11b.

**Shear Diagram.** The shear at each end of the beam is plotted first, Fig. 11c. Since there is no distributed loading on the beam, the slope of the shear diagram is zero as indicated. Note how the force $P$ at the center of the beam causes the shear diagram to jump downward an amount $P$, since this force acts downward.

**Moment Diagram.** The moments at the ends of the beam are plotted, Fig. 11d. Here the moment diagram consists of two sloping lines, one with a slope of $+2P$ and the other with a slope of $+P$.

The value of the moment in the center of the beam can be determined by the method of sections, or from the area under the shear diagram. If we choose the left half of the shear diagram,

$$M\big|_{x=L} = M\big|_{x=0} + \Delta M$$

$$M\big|_{x=L} = -3PL + (2P)(L) = -PL$$

**Fig. 11**

## EXAMPLE | 6

Draw the shear and moment diagrams for the beam shown in Fig. 12a.

(a)

## SOLUTION

**Support Reactions.** The reactions are shown on the free-body diagram in Fig. 12b.

**Shear Diagram.** The shear at each end is plotted first, Fig. 12c. Since there is no distributed load on the beam, the shear diagram has zero slope and is therefore a horizontal line.

**Moment Diagram.** The moment is zero at each end, Fig. 12d. The moment diagram has a constant negative slope of $-M_0/2L$ since this is the shear in the beam at each point. Note that the couple moment $M_0$ causes a jump in the moment diagram at the beam's center, but it does not affect the shear diagram at this point.

**Fig. 12**

## EXAMPLE | 7

Draw the shear and moment diagrams for each of the beams shown in Figs. 13a and 14a.

### SOLUTION

**Support Reactions.** The reactions at the fixed support are shown on each free-body diagram, Figs. 13b and 14b.

**Shear Diagram.** The shear at each end point is plotted first, Figs. 13c and 14c. The distributed loading on each beam indicates the slope of the shear diagram and thus produces the shapes shown.

**Moment Diagram.** The moment at each end point is plotted first, Figs. 13d and 14d. Various values of the shear at each point on the beam indicate the slope of the moment diagram at the point. Notice how this variation produces the curves shown.

**NOTE:** Observe how the degree of the curves from $w$ to $V$ to $M$ increases by one due to the integration of $dV = w\,dx$ and $dM = V\,dx$. For example, in Fig. 14, the linear distributed load produces a parabolic shear diagram and cubic moment diagram.

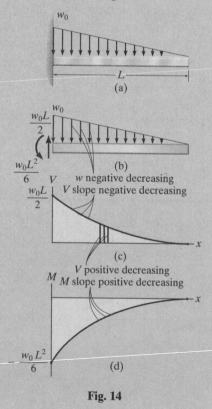

**Fig. 13**

**Fig. 14**

## EXAMPLE | 8

Draw the shear and moment diagrams for the cantilever beam in Fig. 15a.

(a)

(b)

(c)

(d)

(e)

**Fig. 15**

### SOLUTION

**Support Reactions.** The support reactions at the fixed support $B$ are shown in Fig. 15b.

**Shear Diagram.** The shear at end $A$ is $-2$ kN. This value is plotted at $x = 0$, Fig. 15c. Notice how the shear diagram is constructed by following the slopes defined by the loading $w$. The shear at $x = 4$ m is $-5$ kN, the reaction on the beam. This value can be verified by finding the area under the distributed loading, Eq. 3.

$$V|_{x=4\,m} = V|_{x=2\,m} + \Delta V = -2 \text{ kN} - (1.5 \text{ kN/m})(2 \text{ m}) = -5 \text{ kN}$$

**Moment Diagram.** The moment of zero at $x = 0$ is plotted in Fig. 15d. Notice how the moment diagram is constructed based on knowing its slope, which is equal to the shear at each point. The change of moment from $x = 0$ to $x = 2$ m is determined from the area under the shear diagram. Hence, the moment at $x = 2$ m is

$$M|_{x=2\,m} = M|_{x=0} + \Delta M = 0 + [-2 \text{ kN}(2 \text{ m})] = -4 \text{ kN} \cdot \text{m}$$

This same value can be determined from the method of sections, Fig. 15e.

EXAMPLE 9

Draw the shear and moment diagrams for the overhang beam in Fig. 16a.

(a)

## SOLUTION

**Support Reactions.** The support reactions are shown in Fig. 16b.

**Shear Diagram.** The shear of –2 kN at end $A$ of the beam is plotted at $x = 0$, Fig. 16c. The slopes are determined from the loading and from this the shear diagram is constructed, as indicated in the figure. In particular, notice the positive jump of 10 kN at $x = 4$ m due to the force $B_y$, as indicated in the figure.

**Moment Diagram.** The moment of zero at $x = 0$ is plotted, Fig. 16d. Then following the behavior of the slope found from the shear diagram, the moment diagram is constructed. The moment at $x = 4$ m is found from the area under the shear diagram.

$$M\big|_{x=4\,\mathrm{m}} = M\big|_{x=0} + \Delta M = 0 + [-2\ \mathrm{kN}(4\ \mathrm{m})] = -8\ \mathrm{kN\cdot m}$$

We can also obtain this value by using the method of sections, as shown in Fig. 16e.

**Fig. 16**

(e)

300

## EXAMPLE 10

The shaft in Fig. 17a is supported by a thrust bearing at A and a journal bearing at B. Draw the shear and moment diagrams.

120 lb/ft

12 ft

(a)

## SOLUTION

**Support Reactions.** The support reactions are shown in Fig. 17b.

**Shear Diagram.** As shown in Fig. 17c, the shear at $x = 0$ is +240 lb. Following the slope defined by the loading, the shear diagram is constructed, where at B its value is −480 lb. Since the shear changes sign, the point where $V = 0$ must be located. To do this we will use the method of sections. The free-body diagram of the left segment of the shaft, sectioned at an arbitrary position $x$, is shown in Fig. 17e. Notice that the intensity of the distributed load at $x$ is $w = 10x$, which has been found by proportional triangles, i.e., $120/12 = w/x$.

Thus, for $V = 0$,

$$+\uparrow \Sigma F_y = 0; \qquad 240 \text{ lb} - \tfrac{1}{2}(10x)x = 0$$
$$x = 6.93 \text{ ft}$$

**Moment Diagram.** The moment diagram starts at 0 since there is no moment at A; then it is constructed based on the slope as determined from the shear diagram. The maximum moment occurs at $x = 6.93$ ft, where the shear is equal to zero, since $dM/dx = V = 0$, Fig. 17d,

$$\zeta + \Sigma M = 0;$$
$$M_{max} + \tfrac{1}{2}[(10)(6.93)] \, 6.93 \left(\tfrac{1}{3}(6.93)\right) - 240(6.93) = 0$$
$$M_{max} = 1109 \text{ lb} \cdot \text{ft}$$

Finally, notice how integration, first of the loading $w$ which is linear, produces a shear diagram which is parabolic, and then a moment diagram which is cubic.

**NOTE:** Having studied these examples, test yourself by covering over the shear and moment diagrams in Examples 1 through 4 and see if you can construct them using the concepts discussed here.

120 lb/ft

12 ft

(b)

$A_y = 240$ lb    $w$ negative increasing
                  $V$ slope negative increasing
$V$ (lb)          $B_y = 480$ lb

240                6.93          12
0                               $x$ (ft)

$V$ positive (c)
decreasing
$M$ slope positive
decreasing    $V$ negative increasing
              $M$ slope negative increasing
$M$ (lb·ft)   $V = 0$
              $M$ slope = 0

              1109

0                             $x$ (ft)
              6.93      12
              (d)

$\tfrac{1}{2}[10x]x$
$\tfrac{x}{3}$  10 $x$
                V
                M
x
$A_y = 240$ lb
              (e)

**Fig. 17**

# PRELIMINARY PROBLEMS

**P1.** In each case, the beam is subjected to the loadings shown. Draw the free-body-diagram of the beam, and sketch the general shape of the shear and moment diagrams. The loads and geometry are assumed to be known.

(a)

(b)

(c)

(d)

(e)

(f)

(g)

(h)

**P1**

# FUNDAMENTAL PROBLEMS

In each case, express the shear and moment functions in terms of *x*, and then draw the shear and moment diagrams for the beam.

**F1.**

**F1**

**F2.**

**F2**

**F3.**

**F3**

**F4.**

**F4**

In each case, draw the shear and moment diagrams for the beam.

**F5.**

**F5**

**F6.**

**F6**

**F7.**

**F7**

**F8.**

**F8**

# PROBLEMS

**1.** The load binder is used to support a load. If the force applied to the handle is 50 lb, determine the tensions $T_1$ and $T_2$ in each end of the chain and then draw the shear and moment diagrams for the arm $ABC$.

**Prob. 1**

**2.** Draw the shear and moment diagrams for the shaft The bearings at $A$ and $D$ exert only vertical reaction on the shaft. The loading is applied to the pulleys at $B$ and $C$ and $E$.

**Prob. 2**

**3.** The engine crane is used to support the engine, which has a weight of 1200 lb. Draw the shear and moment diagrams of the boom $ABC$ when it is in the horizontal position shown.

**Prob. 3**

**\*4.** Draw the shear and moment diagrams for the beam.

**Prob. 4**

**•5.** Draw the shear and moment diagrams for the beam.

**Prob. 5**

304

**6.** Express the internal shear and moment in terms of $x$ and then draw the shear and moment diagrams.

**Prob. 6**

**7.** Draw the shear and moment diagrams for the compound beam which is pin connected at $B$. (This structure is not fully stable. But with the given loading, it is balanced and will remain as shown if not disturbed.)

**Prob. 7**

**\*8.** Express the internal shear and moment in terms of $x$ and then draw the shear and moment diagrams for the beam.

**Prob. 8**

**9.** Express the internal shear and moment in terms of $x$ and then draw the shear and moment diagrams for the overhanging beam.

**Prob. 9**

**10.** Members $ABC$ and $BD$ of the counter chair are rigidly connected at $B$ and the smooth collar at $D$ is allowed to move freely along the vertical slot. Draw the shear and moment diagrams for member $ABC$.

**Prob. 10**

**11.** Draw the shear and moment diagrams for the pipe. The end screw is subjected to a horizontal force of 5 kN. *Hint:* The reactions at the pin $C$ must be replaced by an equivalent loading at point $B$ on the axis of the pipe.

**Prob. 11**

305

**\*12.** A reinforced concrete pier is used to support the stringers for a bridge deck. Draw the shear and moment diagrams for the pier when it is subjected to the stringer loads shown. Assume the columns at *A* and *B* exert only vertical reactions on the pier.

**Prob. 12**

**13.** Draw the shear and moment diagrams for the rod. It is supported by a pin at *A* and a smooth plate at *B*. The plate slides within the groove and so it cannot support a vertical force, although it can support a moment.

**Prob. 13**

**14.** The industrial robot is held in the stationary position shown. Draw the shear and moment diagrams of the arm *ABC* if it is pin connected at *A* and connected to a hydraulic cylinder (two-force member) *BD*. Assume the arm and grip have a uniform weight of 1.5 lb/in. and support the load of 40 lb at *C*.

**Prob. 14**

**■15.** Consider the general problem of the beam subjected to *n* concentrated loads. Write a computer program that can be used to determine the internal shear and moment at any specified location *x* along the beam, and plot the shear and moment diagrams for the beam. Show an application of the program using the values $P_1 = 500$ lb, $d_1 = 5$ ft, $P_2 = 800$ lb, $d_2 = 15$ ft, $L_1 = 10$ ft, $L = 15$ ft.

**Prob. 15**

**\*16.** Determine the placement distance *a* of the roller support so that the largest absolute value of the moment is a minimum. Draw the shear and moment diagrams for this condition.

**Prob. 16**

**17.** Express the internal shear and moment in the cantilevered beam as a function of *x* and then draw the shear and moment diagrams.

**Prob. 17**

306

**18.** Draw the shear and moment diagrams for the beam, and determine the shear and moment throughout the beam as functions of $x$.

**Prob. 18**

**19.** Draw the shear and moment diagrams for the beam.

**Prob. 19**

***20.** Draw the shear and moment diagrams for the overhanging beam.

**Prob. 20**

**21.** The 150-lb man sits in the center of the boat, which has a uniform width and a weight per linear foot of 3 lb/ft. Determine the maximum bending moment exerted on the boat. Assume that the water exerts a uniform distributed load upward on the bottom of the boat.

**Prob. 21**

**22.** Draw the shear and moment diagrams for the overhang beam.

**Prob. 22**

**23.** The footing supports the load transmitted by the two columns. Draw the shear and moment diagrams for the footing if the reaction of soil pressure on the footing is assumed to be uniform.

**Prob. 23**

***24.** Express the shear and moment in terms of $x$ and then draw the shear and moment diagrams for the simply supported beam.

**Prob. 24**

**25.** Draw the shear and moment diagrams for the beam and determine the shear and moment in the beam as functions of $x$, where 4 ft $< x <$ 10 ft.

**Prob. 25**

**■26.** Consider the general problem of a cantilevered beam subjected to $n$ concentrated loads and a constant distributed loading $w$. Write a computer program that can be used to determine the internal shear and moment at any specified location $x$ along the beam, and plot the shear and moment diagrams for the beam. Show an application of the program using the values $P_1 = 4$ kN, $d_1 = 2$ m, $w = 800$ N/m, $a_1 = 2$ m, $a_2 = 4$ m, $L = 4$ m.

**Prob. 26**

**27.** Draw the shear and moment diagrams for the beam.

**Prob. 27**

***28.** Draw the shear and moment diagrams for the beam.

**Prob. 28**

**29.** Draw the shear and moment diagrams for the double overhanging beam.

**Prob. 29**

**30.** The beam is bolted or pinned at $A$ and rests on a bearing pad at $B$ that exerts a uniform distributed loading on the beam over its 2-ft length. Draw the shear and moment diagrams for the beam if it supports a uniform loading of 2 kip/ft.

**Prob. 30**

**31.** The support at $A$ allows the beam to slide freely along the vertical guide so that it cannot support a vertical force. Draw the shear and moment diagrams for the beam.

**Prob. 31**

***32.** The smooth pin is supported by two leaves $A$ and $B$ and subjected to a compressive load of 0.4 kN/m caused by bar $C$. Determine the intensity of the distributed load $w_0$ of the leaves on the pin and draw the shear and moment diagram for the pin.

**Prob. 32**

**33.** The shaft is supported by a smooth thrust bearing at $A$ and smooth journal bearing at $B$. Draw the shear and moment diagrams for the shaft.

**Prob. 33**

**34.** Draw the shear and moment diagrams for the cantilever beam.

**Prob. 34**

**35.** Draw the shear and moment diagrams for the beam and determine the shear and moment as functions of $x$.

**Prob. 35**

**\*36.** Thae shaft is supported by a smooth thrust bearing at $A$ and a smooth journal bearing at $B$. Draw the shear and moment diagrams for the shaft.

**Prob. 36**

**37.** Draw the shear and moment diagrams for the beam.

**Prob. 37**

**38.** The beam is used to support a uniform load along $CD$ due to the 6-kN weight of the crate. If the reaction at bearing support $B$ can be assumed uniformly distributed along its width, draw the shear and moment diagrams for the beam.

**Prob. 38**

**39.** Draw the shear and moment diagrams for the double overhanging beam.

**Prob. 39**

**\*40.** Draw the shear and moment diagrams for the simply supported beam.

**Prob. 40**

**41.** The compound beam is fixed at $A$, pin connected at $B$, and supported by a roller at $C$. Draw the shear and moment diagrams for the beam.

600 N

400 N/m

A

B

C

2 m — 2 m — 2 m

**Prob. 41**

**42.** Draw the shear and moment diagrams for the compound beam.

5 kN/m

A

B

C

D

2 m — 1 m — 1 m

**Prob. 42**

**43.** The compound beam is fixed at $A$, pin connected at $B$, and supported by a roller at $C$. Draw the shear and moment diagrams for the beam.

2 kN

3 kN/m

A

B

C

3 m — 3 m

**Prob. 43**

***44.** Draw the shear and moment diagrams for the beam.

$w$

8 kip/ft

$w = \dfrac{1}{8}x^2$

$A$

$B$

$x$

8 ft

**Prob. 44**

**45.** A short link at $B$ is used to connect beams $AB$ and $BC$ to form the compound beam shown. Draw the shear and moment diagrams for the beam if the supports at $A$ and $B$ are considered fixed and pinned, respectively.

15 kN

3 kN/m

A

B

C

4.5 m — 1.5 m — 1.5 m

**Prob. 45**

**46.** Determine the placement $b$ of the hooks to minimize the largest moment when the concrete member is being hoisted. Draw the shear and moment diagrams. The member has a square cross section of dimension $a$ on each side. The specific weight of concrete is $\gamma$.

60° 60°

$b$ — $b$

$L$

**Prob. 46**

# 3 Bending Deformation of a Straight Member

In this section, we will discuss the deformations that occur when a straight prismatic beam, made of homogeneous material, is subjected to bending. The discussion will be limited to beams having a cross-sectional area that is symmetrical with respect to an axis, and the bending moment is applied about an axis perpendicular to this axis of symmetry as shown in Fig. 18. The behavior of members that have unsymmetrical cross sections, or are made from several different materials, is based on similar observations and will be discussed separately in later sections of this chapter.

By using a highly deformable material such as rubber, we can illustrate what happens when a straight prismatic member is subjected to a bending moment. Consider, for example, the undeformed bar in Fig. 19a, which has a square cross section and is marked with longitudinal and transverse grid lines. When a bending moment is applied, it tends to distort these lines into the pattern shown in Fig. 19b. Notice that the longitudinal lines become *curved* and the vertical transverse lines *remain straight* and yet undergo a *rotation*.

The bending moment causes the material within the *bottom* portion of the bar to *stretch* and the material within the *top* portion to *compress*. Consequently, between these two regions there must be a surface, called the *neutral surface,* in which longitudinal fibers of the material will not undergo a change in length, Fig. 18.

Fig. 18

Before deformation

(a)

Horizontal lines become curved

Vertical lines remain straight, yet rotate

After deformation

(b)

Fig. 19

Note the distortion of the lines due to bending of this rubber bar. The top line stretches, the bottom line compresses, and the center line remains the same length. Furthermore the vertical lines rotate and yet remain straight.

From these observations we will make the following three assumptions regarding the way the stress deforms the material. First, the *longitudinal axis x*, which lies within the neutral surface, Fig. 20*a*, does *not* experience any *change in length.* Rather the moment will tend to deform the beam so that this line *becomes a curve* that lies in the *x–y* plane of symmetry, Fig. 20*b*. Second, all **cross sections** of the beam **remain plane** and perpendicular to the longitudinal axis during the deformation. And third, *any deformation* of the *cross section* within its own plane, as noticed in Fig. 19*b*, will be *neglected.* In particular, the *z* axis, lying in the plane of the cross section and about which the cross section rotates, is called the *neutral axis*, Fig. 20*b*.

In order to show how this distortion will strain the material, we will isolate a small segment of the beam located a distance *x* along the beam's length and having an undeformed thickness Δ*x*, Fig. 20*a*. This element, taken from the beam, is shown in profile view in the undeformed and

(a)

neutral
axis

**M**

*z*

longitudinal
axis

*x*

neutral
surface

*y*

*z*

(b)

**Fig. 20**

312

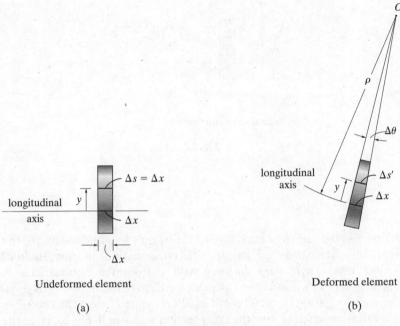

Undeformed element

(a)

Deformed element

(b)

**Fig. 21**

deformed positions in Fig. 21. Notice that any line segment $\Delta x$, located on the neutral surface, does not change its length, whereas any line segment $\Delta s$, located at the arbitrary distance $y$ above the neutral surface, will contract and become $\Delta s'$ after deformation. By definition, the normal strain along $\Delta s$ is determined from Eq. 2, namely,

$$\epsilon = \lim_{\Delta s \to 0} \frac{\Delta s' - \Delta s}{\Delta s}$$

We will now represent this strain in terms of the location $y$ of the segment and the radius of curvature $\rho$ of the longitudinal axis of the element. Before deformation, $\Delta s = \Delta x$, Fig. 21a. After deformation $\Delta x$ has a radius of curvature $\rho$, with center of curvature at point $O'$, Fig. 21b. Since $\Delta \theta$ defines the angle between the sides of the element, $\Delta x = \Delta s = \rho \Delta \theta$. In the same manner, the deformed length of $\Delta s$ becomes $\Delta s' = (\rho - y)\Delta \theta$. Substituting into the above equation, we get

$$\epsilon = \lim_{\Delta \theta \to 0} \frac{(\rho - y)\Delta \theta - \rho \Delta \theta}{\rho \Delta \theta}$$

or

$$\epsilon = -\frac{y}{\rho} \tag{7}$$

This important result indicates that the longitudinal normal strain of any element within the beam depends on its location $y$ on the cross

Normal strain distribution

**Fig. 22**

section and the radius of curvature of the beam's longitudinal axis at the point. In other words, for any specific cross section, the ***longitudinal normal strain will vary linearly*** with $y$ from the neutral axis. A contraction $(-\epsilon)$ will occur in fibers located above the neutral axis $(+y)$, whereas elongation $(+\epsilon)$ will occur in fibers located below the axis $(-y)$. This variation in strain over the cross section is shown in Fig. 22. Here the maximum strain occurs at the outermost fiber, located a distance of $y = c$ from the neutral axis. Using Eq. 7, since $\epsilon_{max} = c/\rho$, then by division,

$$\frac{\epsilon}{\epsilon_{max}} = -\left(\frac{y/\rho}{c/\rho}\right)$$

So that

$$\epsilon = -\left(\frac{y}{c}\right)\epsilon_{max} \tag{8}$$

This normal strain depends only on the assumptions made with regards to the *deformation*. When a moment is applied to the beam, therefore, it will only cause a *normal stress* in the longitudinal or $x$ direction. All the other components of normal and shear stress will be zero. It is this uniaxial state of stress that causes the material to have the longitudinal normal strain component $\epsilon_x$, defined by Eq. 8. Furthermore, by Poisson's ratio, there must *also* be associated strain components $\epsilon_y = -\nu\epsilon_x$ and $\epsilon_z = -\nu\epsilon_x$, which deform the plane of the cross-sectional area, although here we have neglected these deformations. Such deformations will, however, cause the *cross-sectional dimensions* to become smaller below the neutral axis and larger above the neutral axis. For example, if the beam has a square cross section, it will actually deform as shown in Fig. 23.

**Fig. 23**

# 4   The Flexure Formula

In this section, we will develop an equation that relates the stress distribution in a beam to the internal resultant bending moment acting on the beam's cross section. To do this we will assume that the material behaves in a linear-elastic manner and therefore a *linear variation of normal strain,* Fig. 24a, must then be the result of a *linear variation in normal stress,* Fig. 24b. Hence, like the normal strain variation, $\sigma$ will vary from zero at the member's neutral axis to a maximum value, $\sigma_{max}$, a distance $c$ farthest from the neutral axis. Because of the proportionality of triangles, Fig. 23b, or by using Hooke's law, $\sigma = E\epsilon$, and Eq. 8, we can write

$$\sigma = -\left(\frac{y}{c}\right)\sigma_{max} \qquad (9)$$

This equation describes the stress distribution over the cross-sectional area. The sign convention established here is significant. For positive **M,** which acts in the $+z$ direction, positive values of $y$ give negative values for $\sigma$, that is, a compressive stress since it acts in the negative $x$ direction. Similarly, negative $y$ values will give positive or tensile values for $\sigma$. If a volume element of material is selected at a specific point on the cross section, only these tensile or compressive normal stresses will act on it. For example, the element located at $+y$ is shown in Fig. 24c.

We can locate the position of the neutral axis on the cross section by satisfying the condition that the *resultant force* produced by the stress distribution over the cross-sectional area must be equal to *zero.* Noting that the force $dF = \sigma\, dA$ acts on the arbitrary element $dA$ in Fig. 24c, we require

$$F_R = \Sigma F_x; \qquad 0 = \int_A dF = \int_A \sigma\, dA$$

$$= \int_A -\left(\frac{y}{c}\right)\sigma_{max}\, dA$$

$$= \frac{-\sigma_{max}}{c}\int_A y\, dA$$

Normal strain variation
(profile view)

(a)

Bending stress variation
(profile view)

(b)

**Fig. 24**

This wood specimen failed in bending due to its fibers being crushed at its top and torn apart at its bottom.

Bending stress variation

(c)

**Fig. 24 (cont.)**

Since $\sigma_{max}/c$ is not equal to zero, then

$$\int_A y \, dA = 0 \qquad (10)$$

In other words, the first moment of the member's cross-sectional area about the neutral axis must be zero. This condition can only be satisfied if the *neutral axis* is also the horizontal *centroidal axis* for the cross section.* Consequently, once the centroid for the member's cross-sectional area is determined, the location of the neutral axis is known.

We can determine the stress in the beam from the requirement that the resultant internal moment $M$ must be equal to the moment produced by the stress distribution about the neutral axis. The moment of $d\mathbf{F}$ in Fig. 24c about the neutral axis is $dM = y \, dF$. Since $dF = \sigma \, dA$, using Eq. 9, we have for the entire cross section,

$$(M_R)_z = \Sigma M_z; \qquad M = \int_A y \, dF = \int_A y(\sigma \, dA) = \int_A y\left(\frac{y}{c}\sigma_{max}\right)dA$$

or

$$M = \frac{\sigma_{max}}{c}\int_A y^2 \, dA \qquad (11)$$

---

*Recall that the location $\bar{y}$ for the centroid of the cross-sectional area is defined from the equation $\bar{y} = \int y \, dA / \int dA$. If $\int y \, dA = 0$, then $\bar{y} = 0$, and so the centroid lies on the reference (neutral) axis.

The integral represents the *moment of inertia* of the cross-sectional area about the neutral axis. We will symbolize its value as $I$. Hence, Eq. 11 can be solved for $\sigma_{max}$ and written as

$$\sigma_{max} = \frac{Mc}{I} \tag{12}$$

Here

$\sigma_{max} =$ the the maximum normal stress in the member, which occurs at a point on the cross-sectional area *farthest away* from the neutral axis

$M =$ the resultant internal moment, determined from the method of sections and the equations of equilibrium, and calculated about the neutral axis of the cross section

$c =$ perpendicular distance from the neutral axis to a point farthest away from the neutral axis. This is where $\sigma_{max}$ acts.

$I =$ moment of inertia of the cross-sectional area about the neutral axis

Since $\sigma_{max}/c = -\sigma/y$, Eq. 9, the normal stress at the location distance $y$ can be determined from an equation similar to Eq. 12. We have

$$\sigma = -\frac{My}{I} \tag{13}$$

Note that the negative sign is necessary since it agrees with the established $x$, $y$, $z$ axes. By the right-hand rule, $M$ is positive along the $+z$ axis, $y$ is positive upward, and $\sigma$ therefore must be negative (compressive) since it acts in the negative $x$ direction, Fig. 24c.

Either of the above two equations is often referred to as the ***flexure formula***. It is used to determine the normal stress in a straight member, having a cross section that is symmetrical with respect to an axis, and the moment is applied perpendicular to this axis. Although we have assumed that the member is prismatic, we can in most cases of engineering design also use the flexure formula to determine the normal stress in members that have a *slight taper*. For example, using a mathematical analysis based on the theory of elasticity, a member having a rectangular cross section and a length that is tapered 15° will have an actual maximum normal stress that is about 5.4% *less* than that calculated using the flexure formula.

## Important Points

- The cross section of a straight beam *remains plane* when the beam deforms due to bending. This causes tensile stress on one portion of the cross section and compressive stress on the other portion. In between these portions, there exists the *neutral axis* which is subjected to *zero stress*.

- Due to the deformation, the *longitudinal strain* varies *linearly* from zero at the neutral axis to a maximum at the outer fibers of the beam. Provided the material is homogeneous and linear elastic, then the *stress* also varies in a *linear* fashion over the cross section.

- The neutral axis passes through the *centroid* of the cross-sectional area. This result is based on the fact that the resultant normal force acting on the cross section must be zero.

- The flexure formula is based on the requirement that the resultant internal moment on the cross section is equal to the moment produced by the normal stress distribution about the neutral axis.

## Procedure for Analysis

In order to apply the flexure formula, the following procedure is suggested.

### Internal Moment.

- Section the member at the point where the bending or normal stress is to be determined, and obtain the internal moment $M$ at the section. The centroidal or neutral axis for the cross section must be known, since $M$ *must* be calculated about this axis.

- If the absolute maximum bending stress is to be determined, then draw the moment diagram in order to determine the maximum moment in the member.

### Section Property.

- Determine the moment of inertia of the cross-sectional area about the neutral axis.

### Normal Stress.

- Specify the location $y$, measured perpendicular to the neutral axis to the point where the normal stress is to be determined. Then apply the equation $\sigma = -My/I$, or if the maximum bending stress is to be calculated, use $\sigma_{\max} = Mc/I$. When substituting the data, make sure the units are consistent.

- The stress acts in a direction such that the force it creates at the point contributes a moment about the neutral axis that is in the same direction as the internal moment **M**, Fig. 24c. In this manner the stress distribution acting over the entire cross section can be sketched, or a volume element of the material can be isolated and used to graphically represent the normal stress acting at the point.

## EXAMPLE | 11

A beam has a rectangular cross section and is subjected to the stress distribution shown in Fig. 25a. Determine the internal moment **M** at the section caused by the stress distribution (a) using the flexure formula, (b) by finding the resultant of the stress distribution using basic principles.

(a)

### SOLUTION

**Part (a).**  The flexure formula is $\sigma_{max} = Mc/I$. From Fig. 25a, $c = 6$ in. and $\sigma_{max} = 2$ ksi. The neutral axis is defined as line $NA$, because the stress is zero along this line. Since the cross section has a rectangular shape, the moment of inertia for the area about $NA$ is determined from the formula for a rectangle given on the inside front cover; i.e.,

$$I = \frac{1}{12}bh^3 = \frac{1}{12}(6 \text{ in.})(12 \text{ in.})^3 = 864 \text{ in}^4$$

Therefore,

$$\sigma_{max} = \frac{Mc}{I}; \qquad 2 \text{ kip/in}^2 = \frac{M(6 \text{ in.})}{864 \text{ in}^4}$$

$$M = 288 \text{ kip} \cdot \text{in.} = 24 \text{ kip} \cdot \text{ft} \qquad \textit{Ans.}$$

(b)

**Fig. 25**

**Part (b).**  The resultant force for each of the two *triangular* stress distributions in Fig. 25b is graphically equivalent to the *volume* contained within each stress distribution. Thus, each volume is

$$F = \frac{1}{2}(6 \text{ in.})(2 \text{ kip/in}^2)(6 \text{ in.}) = 36 \text{ kip}$$

These forces, which form a couple, act in the same direction as the stresses within each distribution, Fig. 25b. Furthermore, they act through the *centroid* of each volume, i.e., $\frac{2}{3}(6 \text{ in.}) = 4$ in. from the neutral axis of the beam. Hence the distance between them is 8 in. as shown. The moment of the couple is therefore

$$M = 36 \text{ kip}(8 \text{ in.}) = 288 \text{ kip} \cdot \text{in.} = 24 \text{ kip} \cdot \text{ft} \qquad \textit{Ans.}$$

**NOTE:** This result can also be obtained by choosing a horizontal strip of area $dA = (6 \text{ in.}) \, dy$ and using integration by applying Eq. 11.

## EXAMPLE 12

The simply supported beam in Fig. 26a has the cross-sectional area shown in Fig. 26b. Determine the absolute maximum bending stress in the beam and draw the stress distribution over the cross section at this location.

(a)

(c)

(b)

(d)

**Fig. 26**

### SOLUTION

**Maximum Internal Moment.** The maximum internal moment in the beam, $M = 22.5$ kN·m, occurs at the center.

**Section Property.** By reasons of symmetry, the neutral axis passes through the centroid $C$ at the midheight of the beam, Fig. 26b. The area is subdivided into the three parts shown, and the moment of inertia of each part is calculated about the neutral axis using the parallel-axis theorem. Choosing to work in meters, we have

$$I = \Sigma(\bar{I} + Ad^2)$$

$$= 2\left[\frac{1}{12}(0.25 \text{ m})(0.020 \text{ m})^3 + (0.25 \text{ m})(0.020 \text{ m})(0.160 \text{ m})^2\right]$$

$$+ \left[\frac{1}{12}(0.020 \text{ m})(0.300 \text{ m})^3\right]$$

$$= 301.3(10^{-6}) \text{ m}^4$$

$$\sigma_{max} = \frac{Mc}{I}; \quad \sigma_{max} = \frac{22.5(10^3) \text{ N} \cdot \text{m}(0.170 \text{ m})}{301.3(10^{-6}) \text{ m}^4} = 12.7 \text{ MPa} \quad Ans.$$

A three-dimensional view of the stress distribution is shown in Fig. 26d. Notice how the stress at points $B$ and $D$ on the cross section develops a force that contributes a moment about the neutral axis that has the same direction as **M**. Specifically, at point $B$, $y_B = 150$ mm, and so as shown in Fig. 26d,

$$\sigma_B = -\frac{My_B}{I}; \quad \sigma_B = -\frac{22.5(10^3) \text{ N} \cdot \text{m}(0.150 \text{ m})}{301.3(10^{-6}) \text{ m}^4} = -11.2 \text{ MPa}$$

## EXAMPLE | 13

The beam shown in Fig. 27a has a cross-sectional area in the shape of a channel, Fig. 27b. Determine the maximum bending stress that occurs in the beam at section a–a.

(a)

### SOLUTION

**Internal Moment.** Here the beam's support reactions do not have to be determined. Instead, by the method of sections, the segment to the left of section a–a can be used, Fig. 27c. In particular, note that the resultant internal axial force **N** passes through the centroid of the cross section. Also, realize that *the resultant internal moment must be calculated about the beam's neutral axis* at section a–a.

To find the location of the neutral axis, the cross-sectional area is subdivided into three composite parts as shown in Fig. 27b. We have

(b)

$$\bar{y} = \frac{\Sigma \tilde{y}A}{\Sigma A} = \frac{2[0.100 \text{ m}](0.200 \text{ m})(0.015 \text{ m}) + [0.010 \text{ m}](0.02 \text{ m})(0.250 \text{ m})}{2(0.200 \text{ m})(0.015 \text{ m}) + 0.020 \text{ m}(0.250 \text{ m})}$$

$$= 0.05909 \text{ m} = 59.09 \text{ mm}$$

This dimension is shown in Fig. 27c.

Applying the moment equation of equilibrium about the neutral axis, we have

$$\zeta + \Sigma M_{NA} = 0; \quad 2.4 \text{ kN}(2 \text{ m}) + 1.0 \text{ kN}(0.05909 \text{ m}) - M = 0$$

$$M = 4.859 \text{ kN} \cdot \text{m}$$

(c)

**Fig. 27**

**Section Property.** The moment of inertia about the neutral axis is determined using $I = \Sigma (\bar{I} + Ad^2)$ applied to each of the three composite parts of the cross-sectional area. Working in meters, we have

$$I = \left[ \frac{1}{12}(0.250 \text{ m})(0.020 \text{ m})^3 + (0.250 \text{ m})(0.020 \text{ m})(0.05909 \text{ m} - 0.010 \text{ m})^2 \right]$$

$$+ 2\left[ \frac{1}{12}(0.015 \text{ m})(0.200 \text{ m})^3 + (0.015 \text{ m})(0.200 \text{ m})(0.100 \text{ m} - 0.05909 \text{ m})^2 \right]$$

$$= 42.26(10^{-6}) \text{ m}^4$$

**Maximum Bending Stress.** The maximum bending stress occurs at points farthest away from the neutral axis. This is at the bottom of the beam, $c = 0.200 \text{ m} - 0.05909 \text{ m} = 0.1409 \text{ m}$. Thus,

$$\sigma_{max} = \frac{Mc}{I} = \frac{4.859(10^3) \text{ N} \cdot \text{m}(0.1409 \text{ m})}{42.26(10^{-6}) \text{ m}^4} = 16.2 \text{ MPa} \qquad Ans.$$

Show that at the top of the beam the bending stress is $\sigma' = 6.79$ MPa.

**NOTE:** The normal force of $N = 1$ kN and shear force $V = 2.4$ kN will also contribute additional stress on the cross section.

## EXAMPLE | 14

(a)

(b)

**Fig. 28**

The member having a rectangular cross section, Fig. 28a, is designed to resist a moment of 40 N·m. In order to increase its strength and rigidity, it is proposed that two small ribs be added at its bottom, Fig. 28b. Determine the maximum normal stress in the member for both cases.

### SOLUTION

**Without Ribs.** Clearly the neutral axis is at the center of the cross section, Fig. 28a, so $\bar{y} = c = 15$ mm $= 0.015$ m. Thus,

$$I = \frac{1}{12}bh^3 = \frac{1}{12}(0.060 \text{ m})(0.030 \text{ m})^3 = 0.135(10^{-6}) \text{ m}^4$$

Therefore the maximum normal stress is

$$\sigma_{max} = \frac{Mc}{I} = \frac{(40 \text{ N} \cdot \text{m})(0.015 \text{ m})}{0.135(10^{-6}) \text{ m}^4} = 4.44 \text{ MPa} \qquad Ans.$$

**With Ribs.** From Fig. 28b, segmenting the area into the large main rectangle and the bottom two rectangles (ribs), the location $\bar{y}$ of the centroid and the neutral axis is determined as follows:

$$\bar{y} = \frac{\Sigma \tilde{y} A}{\Sigma A}$$

$$= \frac{[0.015 \text{ m}](0.030 \text{ m})(0.060 \text{ m}) + 2[0.0325 \text{ m}](0.005 \text{ m})(0.010 \text{ m})}{(0.03 \text{ m})(0.060 \text{ m}) + 2(0.005 \text{ m})(0.010 \text{ m})}$$

$$= 0.01592 \text{ m}$$

This value does not represent $c$. Instead

$$c = 0.035 \text{ m} - 0.01592 \text{ m} = 0.01908 \text{ m}$$

Using the parallel-axis theorem, the moment of inertia about the neutral axis is

$$I = \left[\frac{1}{12}(0.060 \text{ m})(0.030 \text{ m})^3 + (0.060 \text{ m})(0.030 \text{ m})(0.01592 \text{ m} - 0.015 \text{ m})^2\right]$$

$$+ 2\left[\frac{1}{12}(0.010 \text{ m})(0.005 \text{ m})^3 + (0.010 \text{ m})(0.005 \text{ m})(0.0325 \text{ m} - 0.01592 \text{ m})^2\right]$$

$$= 0.1642(10^{-6}) \text{ m}^4$$

Therefore, the maximum normal stress is

$$\sigma_{max} = \frac{Mc}{I} = \frac{40 \text{ N} \cdot \text{m}(0.01908 \text{ m})}{0.1642(10^{-6}) \text{ m}^4} = 4.65 \text{ MPa} \qquad Ans.$$

**NOTE:** This surprising result indicates that the addition of the ribs to the cross section will *increase* the maximum normal stress rather than decrease it, and for this reason they should be omitted.

# PRELIMINARY PROBLEMS

**P2.** Determine the moment of inertia of the cross section about the neutral axis.

**P2**

**P3.** Determine the location of the centroid, $\bar{y}$ and the moment of inertia of the cross section about the neutral axis.

**P3**

**P4.** In each case, show how the bending stress acts on a differential volume element located at point $A$ and point $B$.

(a)

(b)

**P4**

**P5.** Sketch the bending stress distribution over each cross section.

(a)　　　　(b)

**P5**

# FUNDAMENTAL PROBLEMS

**F9.** If the beam is subjected to a bending moment of $M = 20$ kN · m, determine the maximum bending stress in the beam.

F9

**F10.** If the beam is subjected to a bending moment of $M = 50$ kN · m, sketch the bending stress distribution over the beam's cross section.

F10

**F11.** If the beam is subjected to a bending moment of $M = 50$ kN · m, determine the maximum bending stress in the beam.

F11

**F12.** If the beam is subjected to a bending moment of $M = 10$ kN · m, determine the bending stress in the beam at points $A$ and $B$, and sketch the results on a differential element at each of these points.

F12

**F13.** If the beam is subjected to a bending moment of $M = 5$ kN · m, determine the bending stress developed at point $A$ and sketch the result on a differential element at this point.

F13

## PROBLEMS

**47.** If the A-36 steel sheet roll is supported as shown and the allowable bending stress is 165 MPa, determine the smallest radius $r$ of the spool if the steel sheet has a width of 1 m and a thickness of 1.5 mm. Also, find the corresponding maximum internal moment developed in the sheet.

**Prob. 47**

**\*48.** Determine the moment $M$ that will produce a maximum stress of 10 ksi on the cross section.

**49.** Determine the maximum tensile and compressive bending stress in the beam if it is subjected to a moment of $M = 4$ kip $\cdot$ ft.

**Probs. 48/49**

**50.** A member has the triangular cross section shown. Determine the largest internal moment $M$ that can be applied to the cross section without exceeding allowable tensile and compressive stresses of $(\sigma_{allow})_t = 22$ ksi and $(\sigma_{allow})_c = 15$ ksi, respectively.

**51.** A member has the triangular cross section shown. If a moment of $M = 800$ lb $\cdot$ ft is applied to the cross section, determine the maximum tensile and compressive bending stresses in the member. Also, sketch a three-dimensional view of the stress distribution action over the cross section.

**Probs. 50/51**

**\*52.** If the beam is subjected to an internal moment of $M = 30$ kN $\cdot$ m, determine the maximum bending stress in the beam. The beam is made from A992 steel. Sketch the bending stress distribution on the cross section.

**53.** If the beam is subjected to an internal moment of $M = 30$ kN $\cdot$ m, determine the resultant force caused by the bending stress distribution acting on the top flange $A$.

**Probs. 52/53**

**54.** If the built-up beam is subjected to an internal moment of $M = 75$ kN·m, determine the maximum tensile and compressive stress acting in the beam.

**55.** If the built-up beam is subjected to an internal moment of $M = 75$ kN·m, determine the amount of this internal moment resisted by plate $A$.

**58.** The aluminum machine part is subjected to a moment of $M = 75$ N·m. Determine the bending stress created at points $B$ and $C$ on the cross section. Sketch the results on a volume element located at each of these points.

**59.** The aluminum machine part is subjected to a moment of $M = 75$ N·m. Determine the maximum tensile and compressive bending stresses in the part.

**Probs. 54/55**

**Probs. 58/59**

**\*56.** The aluminum strut has a cross-sectional area in the form of a cross. If it is subjected to the moment $M = 8$ kN·m, determine the bending stress acting at points $A$ and $B$, and show the results acting on volume elements located at these points.

**57.** The aluminum strut has a cross-sectional area in the form of a cross. If it is subjected to the moment $M = 8$ kN·m, determine the maximum bending stress in the beam, and sketch a three-dimensional view of the stress distribution acting over the entire cross-sectional area.

**\*60.** The beam is subjected to a moment of 15 kip·ft. Determine the resultant force the bending stress produces on the top flange $A$ and bottom flange $B$. Also compute the maximum bending stress developed in the beam.

**61.** The beam is subjected to a moment of 15 kip·ft. Determine the percentage of this moment that is resisted by the web $D$ of the beam.

**Probs. 56/57**

**Probs. 60/61**

**62.** A box beam is constructed from four pieces of wood, glued together as shown. If the moment acting on the cross section is 10 kN · m, determine the stress at points $A$ and $B$ and show the results acting on volume elements located at these points.

**Prob. 62**

**63.** The beam is subjected to a moment of $M = 30$ lb · ft. Determine the bending stress acting at point $A$ and $B$. Also, stetch a three-dimensional view of the stress distribution acting over the entire cross-sectional area.

**Prob. 63**

**\*64.** The axle of the freight car is subjected to wheel loading of 20 kip. If it is supported by two journal bearings at $C$ and $D$, determine the maximum bending stress developed at the center of the axle, where the diameter is 5.5 in.

**Prob. 64**

**65.** A shaft is made of a polymer having an elliptical cross-section. If it resists an internal moment of $M = 50$ N · m, determine the maximum bending stress developed in the material (a) using the flexure formula, where $I_z = \frac{1}{4}\pi(0.08$ m)$(0.04$ m)$^3$, (b) using integration. Sketch a three-dimensional view of the stress distribution acting over the cross-sectional area.

**66.** Solve Prob. 65 if the moment $M = 50$ N · m is applied about the $y$ axis instead of the $x$ axis. Here $I_y = \frac{1}{4}\pi(0.04$ m)$(0.08$ m)$^3$.

**Probs. 65/66**

**67.** The shaft is supported by smooth journal bearings at $A$ and $B$ that only exert vertical reactions on the shaft. If $d = 90$ mm, determine the absolute maximum bending stress in the beam, and sketch the stress distribution acting over the cross section.

**\*68.** The shaft is supported by smooth journal bearings at $A$ and $B$ that only exert vertical reactions on the shaft. Determine its smallest diameter $d$ if the allowable bending stress is $\sigma_{allow} = 180$ MPa.

**Probs. 67/68**

**69.** Two designs for a beam are to be considered. Determine which one will support a moment of $M = 150 \text{ kN} \cdot \text{m}$ with the least amount of bending stress. What is that stress?

(a)          (b)

**Prob. 69**

**70.** The simply supported truss is subjected to the central distributed load. Neglect the effect of the diagonal lacing and determine the absolute maximum bending stress in the truss. The top member is a pipe having an outer diameter of 1 in. and thickness of $\frac{3}{16}$ in., and the bottom member is a solid rod having a diameter of $\frac{1}{2}$ in.

**Prob. 70**

**71.** The boat has a weight of 2300 lb and a center of gravity at $G$. If it rests on the trailer at the smooth contact $A$ and can be considered pinned at $B$, determine the absolute maximum bending stress developed in the main strut of the trailer. Consider the strut to be a box-beam having the dimensions shown and pinned at $C$.

**Prob. 71**

**\*72.** Determine the absolute maximum bending stress in the 1.5-in.-diameter shaft which is subjected to the concentrated forces. The sleeve bearings at $A$ and $B$ support only vertical forces.

**73.** Determine the smallest allowable diameter of the shaft which is subjected to the concentrated forces. The sleeve bearings at $A$ and $B$ support only vertical forces, and the allowable bending stress is $\sigma_{\text{allow}} = 22$ ksi.

**Probs. 72/73**

**74.** The pin is used to connect the three links together. Due to wear, the load is distributed over the top and bottom of the pin as shown on the free-body diagram. If the diameter of the pin is 0.40 in., determine the maximum bending stress on the cross-sectional area at the center section $a–a$. For the solution it is first necessary to determine the load intensities $w_1$ and $w_2$.

**Prob. 74**

**75.** The shaft is supported by a smooth thrust bearing at $A$ and smooth journal bearing at $D$. If the shaft has the cross section shown, determine the absolute maximum bending stress in the shaft.

**Prob. 75**

**\*76.** Determine the moment **M** that must be applied to the beam in order to create a maximum stress of 80 MPa. Also sketch the stress distribution acting over the cross section.

**Prob. 76**

**77.** If the beam is subjected to an internal moment of $M = 2\,\text{kip}\cdot\text{ft}$, determine the maximum tensile and compressive stress in the beam. Also, sketch the bending stress distribution on the cross section.

**78.** If the allowable tensile and compressive stress for the beam are $(\sigma_{allow})_t = 2$ ksi and $(\sigma_{allow})_c = 3$ ksi, respectively, determine the maximum allowable internal moment **M** that can be applied on the cross section.

**79.** If the beam is subjected to an internal moment of $M = 2\,\text{kip}\cdot\text{ft}$, determine the resultant force of the bending stress distribution acting on the top vertical board $A$.

**Probs. 77/78/79**

**\*80.** If the beam is subjected to an internal moment of $M = 100\,\text{kN}\cdot\text{m}$, determine the bending stress developed at points $A$, $B$ and $C$. Sketch the bending stress distribution on the cross section.

**81.** If the beam is made of material having an allowable tensile and compressive stress of $(\sigma_{allow})_t = 125$ MPa and $(\sigma_{allow})_c = 150$ MPa, respectively, determine the maximum allowable internal moment **M** that can be applied to the beam.

**Probs. 80/81**

**82.** The shaft is supported by a smooth thrust bearing at $A$ and smooth journal bearing at $C$. If $d = 3$ in., determine the absolute maximum bending stress in the shaft.

**83.** The shaft is supported by a smooth thrust bearing at $A$ and smooth journal bearing at $C$. If the material has an allowable bending stress of $\sigma_{allow} = 24$ ksi, determine the required minimum diameter $d$ of the shaft to the nearest $1/16$ in.

**Probs. 82/83**

**\*84.** If the intensity of the load $w = 15$ kN/m, determine the absolute maximum tensile and compressive stress in the beam.

**85.** If the material of the beam has an allowable bending stress of $\sigma_{allow} = 150$ MPa, determine the maximum allowable intensity $w$ of the uniform distributed load.

**Probs. 84/85**

**86.** Determine the absolute maximum bending stress in the 2-in.-diameter shaft which is subjected to the concentrated forces. The journal bearings at $A$ and $B$ only support vertical forces.

**87.** Determine the smallest allowable diameter of the shaft which is subjected to the concentrated forces. The journal bearings at $A$ and $B$ only support vertical forces. The allowable bending stress is $\sigma_{allow} = 22$ ksi.

**Probs. 86/87**

**\*88.** If the beam has a square cross section of 9 in. on each side, determine the absolute maximum bending stress in the beam.

**Prob. 88**

**89.** If the compound beam in Prob. 42 has a square cross section of side length $a$, determine the minimum value of $a$ if the allowable bending stress is $\sigma_{allow} = 150$ MPa.

**90.** If the beam in Prob. 28 has a rectangular cross section with a width $b$ and a height $h$, determine the absolute maximum bending stress in the beam.

**91.** Determine the absolute maximum bending stress in the 80-mm-diameter shaft which is subjected to the concentrated forces. The journal bearings at $A$ and $B$ only support vertical forces.

**\*92.** Determine, to the nearest millimeter, the smallest allowable diameter of the shaft which is subjected to the concentrated forces. The journal bearings at $A$ and $B$ only support vertical forces. The allowable bending stress is $\sigma_{allow} = 150$ MPa.

**Probs. 91/92**

**93.** The wing spar $ABD$ of a light plane is made from 2014–T6 aluminum and has a cross-sectional area of 1.27 in.$^2$, a depth of 3 in., and a moment of inertia about its neutral axis of 2.68 in$^4$. Determine the absolute maximum bending stress in the spar if the anticipated loading is to be as shown. Assume $A$, $B$, and $C$ are pins. Connection is made along the central longitudinal axis of the spar.

**Prob. 93**

**94.** The beam has a rectangular cross section as shown. Determine the largest load $P$ that can be supported on its overhanging ends so that the bending stress does not exceed $\sigma_{max} = 10$ MPa.

**95.** The beam has the rectangular cross section shown. If $P = 12$ kN, determine the absolute maximum bending stress in the beam. Sketch the stress distribution acting over the cross section.

Probs. 94/95

**\*96.** A log that is 2 ft in diameter is to be cut into a rectangular section for use as a simply supported beam. If the allowable bending stress for the wood is $\sigma_{allow} = 8$ ksi, determine the required width $b$ and height $h$ of the beam that will support the largest load possible. What is this load?

**97.** A log that is 2 ft in diameter is to be cut into a rectangular section for use as a simply supported beam. If the allowable bending stress for the wood is $\sigma_{allow} = 8$ ksi, determine the largest load $P$ that can be supported if the width of the beam is $b = 8$ in.

Probs. 96/97

**98.** If the beam in Prob. 18 has a rectangular cross section with a width of 8 in. and a height of 16 in., determine the absolute maximum bending stress in the beam.

**99.** If the beam has a square cross section of 6 in. on each side, determine the absolute maximum bending stress in the beam.

Prob. 99

**\*100.** If $d = 450$ mm, determine the absolute maximum bending stress in the overhanging beam.

**101.** If wood used for the beam has an allowable bending stress of $\sigma_{allow} = 6$ MPa, determine the minimum dimension $d$ of the beam's cross sectional area to the nearest mm.

Probs. 100/101

**102.** If the concentrated force $P = 2$ kN is applied at the free end of the overhanging beam, determine the absolute maximum tensile and compressive stress developed in the beam.

**103.** If the overhanging beam is made of wood having the allowable tensile and compressive stresses of $(\sigma_{allow})_t = 4$ MPa and $(\sigma_{allow})_c = 5$ MPa, determine the maximum concentrated force **P** that can applied at the free end.

Probs. 102/103

# 5 Unsymmetric Bending

When developing the flexure formula we imposed a condition that the cross-sectional area be *symmetric* about an axis perpendicular to the neutral axis; furthermore, the resultant internal moment **M** acts along the neutral axis. Such is the case for the "T" or channel sections shown in Fig. 29. These conditions, however, are unnecessary, and in this section we will show that the flexure formula can also be applied either to a beam having a cross-sectional area of any shape or to a beam having a resultant internal moment that acts in any direction.

**Moment Applied About Principal Axis.** Consider the beam's cross section to have the unsymmetrical shape shown in Fig. 30a. As in Sec. 4, the right-handed $x$, $y$, $z$ coordinate system is established such that the origin is located at the centroid $C$ on the cross section, and the resultant internal moment **M** acts along the $+z$ axis. We require the stress distribution acting over the entire cross-sectional area to have a zero force resultant, the resultant internal moment about the $y$ axis to be zero, and the resultant internal moment about the $z$ axis to equal **M**.* These three conditions can be expressed mathematically by considering the force acting on the differential element $dA$ located at $(0, y, z)$, Fig. 30a. This force is $dF = \sigma\, dA$, and therefore we have

Axis of symmetry

Neutral axis

**M**

Axis of symmetry

Neutral axis

**M**

**Fig. 29**

$$F_R = \Sigma F_x; \qquad\qquad 0 = -\int_A \sigma\, dA \qquad\qquad (14)$$

$$(M_R)_y = \Sigma M_y; \qquad\qquad 0 = -\int_A z\sigma\, dA \qquad\qquad (15)$$

$$(M_R)_z = \Sigma M_z; \qquad\qquad M = \int_A y\sigma\, dA \qquad\qquad (16)$$

$dF = \sigma dA$

$dA$

$C$

**M**

$\sigma_{max}$

$\sigma$

$c$

$y$

**M**

Bending-stress distribution
(profile view)

(a)

(b)

**Fig. 30**

*The condition that moments about the $y$ axis be equal to zero was not considered in Sec. 4, since the bending-stress distribution was *symmetric* with respect to the $y$ axis and such a distribution of stress automatically produces zero moment about the $y$ axis. See Fig. 24c.

As shown in Sec. 4, Eq. 14 is satisfied since the $z$ axis passes through the *centroid* of the area. Also, since the $z$ axis represents the *neutral axis* for the cross section, the normal stress will vary linearly from zero at the neutral axis, to a maximum at $|y| = c$, Fig. 30b. Hence the stress distribution is defined by $\sigma = -(y/c)\sigma_{max}$. When this equation is substituted into Eq. 16 and integrated, it leads to the flexure formula $\sigma_{max} = Mc/I$. When it is substituted into Eq. 15, we get

$$0 = \frac{-\sigma_{max}}{c}\int_A yz \, dA$$

which requires

$$\int_A yz \, dA = 0$$

Zee sectioned members are often in light-gage metal building construction to support roofs. To design them to support bending loads, it is necessary to determine their principal axes of inertia.

This integral is called the ***product of inertia*** for the area. It will indeed be zero provided the $y$ and $z$ axes are chosen as ***principal axes of inertia*** for the area. For an arbitrarily shaped area, the orientation of the principal axes can always be determined, using either the inertia transformation equations or Mohr's circle of inertia. If the area has an axis of symmetry, however, the ***principal axes*** can easily be established ***since they will always be oriented along the axis of symmetry and perpendicular to it***.

For example, consider the members shown in Fig. 31. In each of these cases, $y$ and $z$ must define the principal axes of inertia for the cross section in order to satisfy Eqs. 14 through 16. In Fig. 31a the principal axes are located by symmetry. Since **M** is applied about one of the principal axes ($z$ axis), the stress distribution is determined from the flexure formula, $\sigma = -My/I_z$, and is shown for each case.

(a)

(b)

(c)

**Fig. 31**

(a)

=

$M_z = M \cos \theta$

(b)

+

$M_y = M \sin \theta$

(c)

**Fig. 32**

**Moment Arbitrarily Applied.** Sometimes a member may be loaded such that **M** does not act about one of the principal axes of the cross section. When this occurs, the moment should first be resolved into components directed along the principal axes, then the flexure formula can be used to determine the normal stress caused by *each* moment component. Finally, using the principle of superposition, the resultant normal stress at the point can be determined.

To show this, consider the beam to have a rectangular cross section and to be subjected to the moment **M,** Fig. 32*a*. Here **M** makes an angle $\theta$ with the *maximum principal z* axis, i.e., the axis of maximum moment of inertia for the cross section. We will assume $\theta$ is positive when it is directed from the $+z$ axis toward the $+y$ axis, the minimum pricipal axis, as shown. Resolving **M** into components along the $z$ and $y$ axes, we have $M_z = M \cos \theta$ and $M_y = M \sin \theta$, as shown in Figs. 32*b* and 32*c*. The normal-stress distributions that produce **M** and its components **M**$_z$ and **M**$_y$ are shown in Figs. 32*d*, 32*e*, and 32*f*, where it is assumed that $(\sigma_x)_{max} > (\sigma'_x)_{max}$. By inspection, the maximum tensile and compressive stresses $[(\sigma_x)_{max} + (\sigma'_x)_{max}]$ occur at two opposite corners of the cross section, Fig. 32*d*.

Applying the flexure formula to each moment component in Figs. 32*b* and 32*c*, and adding the results algebraically, the resultant normal stress at any point on the cross section, Fig. 32*d*, is then

$$\sigma = -\frac{M_z y}{I_z} + \frac{M_y z}{I_y} \qquad (17)$$

Here,

$\sigma = $ the normal stress at the point

$y, z = $ the coordinates of the point measured from $x, y, z$ axes having their origin at the centroid of the cross-sectional area and forming a right-handed coordinate system
The $x$ axis is directed outward from the cross-section and the $y$ and $z$ axes represent respectively the principal axes of minimum and maximum moment of inertia for the area

$M_y, M_z = $ the resultant internal moment components directed along the maximum $z$ and minimum $y$ principal axes. They are positive if directed along the $+y$ and $+z$ axes, otherwise they are negative. Or, stated another way, $M_y = M \sin \theta$ and $M_z = M \cos \theta$, where $\theta$ is measured positive from the $+z$ axis toward the $+y$ axis

$I_y, I_z = $ the maximum and minimum *principal moments of inertia* calculated about the $z$ and $y$ axes, respectively.

The $x$, $y$, $z$ axes form a right-handed system, and the proper algebraic signs must be assigned to the moment components and the coordinates when applying this equation. When this is the case, the resulting stress will be *tensile* if it is *positive* and *compressive* if it is *negative*.

## Orientation of the Neutral Axis.

The angle $\alpha$ of the neutral axis in Fig. 32d can be determined by applying Eq. 17 with $\sigma = 0$, since by definition no normal stress acts on the neutral axis. We have

$$y = \frac{M_y I_z}{M_z I_y} z$$

Since $M_z = M \cos \theta$ and $M_y = M \sin \theta$, then

$$y = \left( \frac{I_z}{I_y} \tan \theta \right) z \tag{18}$$

This equation defines the neutral axis for the cross section. Since the slope of this line is $\tan \alpha = y/z$, then

$$\boxed{\tan \alpha = \frac{I_z}{I_y} \tan \theta} \tag{19}$$

Here it can be seen that unless $I_z = I_y$ the angle $\theta$, defining the direction of the moment **M**, Fig. 32a, will *not equal* $\alpha$, the angle defining the inclination of the neutral axis, Fig. 32d.

(d)

||

(e)

+

(f)

**Fig. 32 (cont.)**

## Important Points

- The flexure formula can be applied only when bending occurs about axes that represent the *principal axes of inertia* for the cross section. These axes have their origin at the centroid and are oriented along an axis of symmetry, if there is one, and perpendicular to it.

- If the moment is applied about some arbitrary axis, then the moment must be resolved into components along each of the principal axes, and the stress at a point is determined by superposition of the stress caused by each of the moment components.

EXAMPLE | 15

The rectangular cross section shown in Fig. 33a is subjected to a bending moment of $M = 12 \text{ kN} \cdot \text{m}$. Determine the normal stress developed at each corner of the section, and specify the orientation of the neutral axis.

## SOLUTION

**Internal Moment Components.** By inspection it is seen that the $y$ and $z$ axes represent the principal axes of inertia since they are axes of symmetry for the cross section. As required we have established the $z$ axis as the principal axis for *maximum* moment of inertia. The moment is resolved into its $y$ and $z$ components, where

$$M_y = -\frac{4}{5}(12 \text{ kN} \cdot \text{m}) = -9.60 \text{ kN} \cdot \text{m}$$

$$M_z = \frac{3}{5}(12 \text{ kN} \cdot \text{m}) = 7.20 \text{ kN} \cdot \text{m}$$

**Section Properties.** The moments of inertia about the $y$ and $z$ axes are

$$I_y = \frac{1}{12}(0.4 \text{ m})(0.2 \text{ m})^3 = 0.2667(10^{-3}) \text{ m}^4$$

$$I_z = \frac{1}{12}(0.2 \text{ m})(0.4 \text{ m})^3 = 1.067(10^{-3}) \text{ m}^4$$

**Bending Stress.** Thus,

$$\sigma = -\frac{M_z y}{I_z} + \frac{M_y z}{I_y}$$

$$\sigma_B = -\frac{7.20(10^3) \text{ N} \cdot \text{m}(0.2 \text{ m})}{1.067(10^{-3}) \text{ m}^4} + \frac{-9.60(10^3) \text{ N} \cdot \text{m}(-0.1 \text{ m})}{0.2667(10^{-3}) \text{ m}^4} = 2.25 \text{ MPa} \qquad Ans.$$

$$\sigma_C = -\frac{7.20(10^3) \text{ N} \cdot \text{m}(0.2 \text{ m})}{1.067(10^{-3}) \text{ m}^4} + \frac{-9.60(10^3) \text{ N} \cdot \text{m}(0.1 \text{ m})}{0.2667(10^{-3}) \text{ m}^4} = -4.95 \text{ MPa} \qquad Ans.$$

$$\sigma_D = -\frac{7.20(10^3) \text{ N} \cdot \text{m}(-0.2 \text{ m})}{1.067(10^{-3}) \text{ m}^4} + \frac{-9.60(10^3) \text{ N} \cdot \text{m}(0.1 \text{ m})}{0.2667(10^{-3}) \text{ m}^4} = -2.25 \text{ MPa} \qquad Ans.$$

$$\sigma_E = -\frac{7.20(10^3) \text{ N} \cdot \text{m}(-0.2 \text{ m})}{1.067(10^{-3}) \text{ m}^4} + \frac{-9.60(10^3) \text{ N} \cdot \text{m}(-0.1 \text{ m})}{0.2667(10^{-3}) \text{ m}^4} = 4.95 \text{ MPa} \qquad Ans.$$

The resultant normal-stress distribution has been sketched using these values, Fig. 33b. Since superposition applies, the distribution is linear as shown.

(a)                                              (b)

**Fig. 33**

**Orientation of Neutral Axis.** The location $z$ of the neutral axis ($NA$), Fig. 33b, can be established by proportion. Along the edge $BC$, we require

$$\frac{2.25 \text{ MPa}}{z} = \frac{4.95 \text{ MPa}}{(0.2 \text{ m} - z)}$$

$$0.450 - 2.25z = 4.95z$$

$$z = 0.0625 \text{ m}$$

In the same manner this is also the distance from $D$ to the neutral axis in Fig. 33b.

We can also establish the orientation of the $NA$ using Eq. 19, which is used to specify the angle $\alpha$ that the axis makes with the $z$ or *maximum* principal axis. According to our sign convention, $\theta$ must be measured from the $+z$ axis toward the $+y$ axis. By comparison, in Fig. 33c, $\theta = -\tan^{-1}\frac{4}{3} = -53.1°$ (or $\theta = +306.9°$). Thus,

$$\tan \alpha = \frac{I_z}{I_y} \tan \theta$$

$$\tan \alpha = \frac{1.067(10^{-3}) \text{ m}^4}{0.2667(10^{-3}) \text{ m}^4} \tan(-53.1°)$$

$$\alpha = -79.4° \qquad\qquad Ans.$$

(c)

This result is shown in Fig. 33c. Using the value of $z$ calculated above, verify, using the geometry of the cross section, that one obtains the same answer.

## EXAMPLE | 16

The Z-section shown in Fig. 34a is subjected to the bending moment of $M = 20$ kN·m. The principal axes $y$ and $z$ are oriented as shown, such that they represent the minimum and maximum principal moments of inertia, $I_y = 0.960(10^{-3})$ m⁴ and $I_z = 7.54(10^{-3})$ m⁴, respectively. Determine the normal stress at point $P$ and the orientation of the neutral axis.

### SOLUTION

For use of Eq. 19, it is important that the $z$ axis represent the principal axis for the *maximum* moment of inertia. (Note that most of the area is located furthest from this axis.)

**Internal Moment Components.** From Fig. 34a,

$$M_y = 20 \text{ kN·m} \sin 57.1° = 16.79 \text{ kN·m}$$
$$M_z = 20 \text{ kN·m} \cos 57.1° = 10.86 \text{ kN·m}$$

**Bending Stress.** The $y$ and $z$ coordinates of point $P$ must be determined first. Note that the $y'$, $z'$ coordinates of $P$ are $(-0.2 \text{ m}, 0.35 \text{ m})$. Using the colored triangles from the construction shown in Fig. 34b, we have

$$y_P = -0.35 \sin 32.9° - 0.2 \cos 32.9° = -0.3580 \text{ m}$$

$$z_P = 0.35 \cos 32.9° - 0.2 \sin 32.9° = 0.1852 \text{ m}$$

Applying Eq. 17,

$$\sigma_P = -\frac{M_z y_P}{I_z} + \frac{M_y z_P}{I_y}$$

$$= -\frac{(10.86(10^3) \text{ N·m})(-0.3580 \text{ m})}{7.54(10^{-3}) \text{ m}^4} + \frac{(16.79(10^3) \text{ N·m})(0.1852 \text{ m})}{0.960(10^{-3}) \text{ m}^4}$$

$$= 3.76 \text{ MPa} \qquad\qquad Ans.$$

**Orientation of Neutral Axis.** The angle $\theta = 57.1°$ is shown in Fig. 34a. Thus,

$$\tan \alpha = \left[ \frac{7.54(10^{-3}) \text{ m}^4}{0.960(10^{-3}) \text{ m}^4} \right] \tan 57.1°$$

$$\alpha = 85.3° \qquad\qquad Ans.$$

The neutral axis is oriented as shown in Fig. 34b.

(a)

(b)

**Fig. 34**

# FUNDAMENTAL PROBLEMS

**F14.** Determine the bending stress developed at corners $A$ and $B$. What is the orientation of the neutral axis?

**F14**

**F15.** Determine the maximum stress in the beam's cross section.

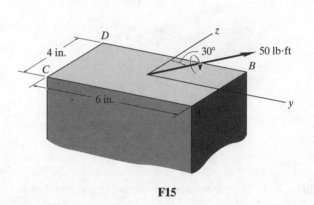

**F15**

# PROBLEMS

**\*104.** The member has a square cross section and is subjected to a resultant internal bending moment of $M = 850\ \text{N} \cdot \text{m}$ as shown. Determine the stress at each corner and sketch the stress distribution produced by **M**. Set $\theta = 45°$.

**Prob. 104**

**105.** The member has a square cross section and is subjected to a resultant internal bending moment of $M = 850\ \text{N} \cdot \text{m}$ as shown. Determine the stress at each corner and sketch the stress distribution produced by **M**. Set $\theta = 30°$.

**Prob. 105**

**106.** Consider the general case of a prismatic beam subjected to bending-moment components $M_y$ and $M_z$, as shown, when the $x, y, z$ axes pass through the centroid of the cross section. If the material is linear-elastic, the normal stress in the beam is a linear function of position such that $\sigma = a + by + cz$. Using the equilibrium conditions $0 = \int_A \sigma \, dA$, $M_y = \int_A z\sigma \, dA$, $M_z = \int_A -y\sigma \, dA$, determine the constants $a$, $b$, and $c$, and show that the normal stress can be determined from the equation $\sigma = [-(M_z I_y + M_y I_{yz})y + (M_y I_z + M_z I_{yz})z]/(I_y I_z - I_{yz}^2)$.

**Prob. 106**

**107.** If the beam is subjected to the internal moment of $M = 2$ kN·m, determine the maximum bending stress developed in the beam and the orientation of the neutral axis.

**\*108.** If the wood used for the T-beam has an allowable tensile and compressive stress of $(\sigma_{\text{allow}})_t = 4$ MPa and $(\sigma_{\text{allow}})_c = 6$ MPa, respectively, determine the maximum allowable internal moment **M** that can be applied to the beam.

**Probs. 107/108**

**109.** The box beam is subjected to the internal moment of $M = 4$ kN·m, which is directed as shown. Determine the maximum bending stress developed in the beam and the orientation of the neutral axis.

**110.** If the wood used for the box beam has an allowable bending stress of $(\sigma_{\text{allow}}) = 6$ MPa, determine the maximum allowable internal moment **M** that can be applied to the beam.

**Probs. 109/110**

**111.** If the beam is subjected to the internal moment of $M = 1200$ kN·m, determine the maximum bending stress acting on the beam and the orientation of the neutral axis.

**\*112.** If the beam is made from a material having an allowable tensile and compressive stress of $(\sigma_{\text{allow}})_t = 125$ MPa and $(\sigma_{\text{allow}})_c = 150$ MPa, respectively, determine the maximum allowable internal moment **M** that can be applied to the beam.

**Probs. 111/112**

**113.** The board is used as a simply supported floor joist. If a bending moment of $M = 800$ lb·ft is applied 3° from the $z$ axis, determine the stress developed in the board at the corner $A$. Compare this stress with that developed by the same moment applied along the $z$ axis ($\theta = 0°$). What is the angle $\alpha$ for the neutral axis when $\theta = 3°$? *Comment:* Normally, floor boards would be nailed to the top of the beams so that $\theta \approx 0°$ and the high stress due to misalignment would not occur.

**Prob. 113**

**114.** The T-beam is subjected to a bending moment of $M = 150$ kip·in. directed as shown. Determine the maximum bending stress in the beam and the orientation of the neutral axis. The location $\bar{y}$ of the centroid, $C$, must be determined.

**Prob. 114**

**115.** The beam has a rectangular cross section. If it is subjected to a bending moment of $M = 3500$ N·m directed as shown, determine the maximum bending stress in the beam and the orientation of the neutral axis.

**Prob. 115**

**\*116.** For the section, $I_{y'} = 31.7(10^{-6})$ m⁴, $I_{z'} = 114(10^{-6})$ m⁴, $I_{y'z'} = 15.1(10^{-6})$ m⁴. The member's cross-sectional area has principal moments of inertia of $I_y = 29.0(10^{-6})$ m⁴ and $I_z = 117(10^{-6})$ m⁴, computed about the principal axes of inertia $y$ and $z$, respectively. If the section is subjected to a moment of $M = 2500$ N·m directed as shown, determine the stress produced at point $A$, using Eq. 17.

**117.** Solve Prob. 116 using the equation developed in Prob. 106.

**Probs. 116/117**

**118.** If the applied distributed loading of $w = 4$ kN/m can be assumed to pass through the centroid of the beam's cross sectional area, determine the absolute maximum bending stress in the joist and the orientation of the neutral axis. The beam can be considered simply-supported at $A$ and $B$.

**119.** Determine the maximum allowable intensity $w$ of the uniform distributed load that can be applied to the beam. Assume $w$ passes through the centroid of the beam's cross sectional area and the beam is simply supported at $A$ and $B$. The beam is made of material having an allowable bending stress of $\sigma_{allow} = 165$ MPa.

**Probs. 118/119**

## *6 Composite Beams

Beams constructed of two or more different materials are referred to as
***composite beams***. For example, a beam can be made of wood with straps
of steel at its top and bottom, Fig. 35. Engineers purposely design beams in
this manner in order to develop a more efficient means for supporting
loads.

Since the flexure formula was developed only for beams having
homogeneous material, this formula cannot be applied directly to
determine the normal stress in a composite beam. In this section,
however, we will develop a method for modifying or "transforming" a
composite beam's cross section into one made of a single material.
Once this has been done, the flexure formula can then be used for the
stress analysis.

To explain how to do this we will consider a composite beam made of
two materials, 1 and 2, bonded together and having the cross-sectional
areas shown in Fig. 36a. If a bending moment is applied to this beam,
then, like one that is homogeneous, the total cross-sectional area will
*remain plane* after bending, and hence the displacement is continuous so
that normal strains will vary linearly from zero at the neutral axis to a
maximum in the material located farthest from this axis, Fig. 36b.
Provided the material is linear elastic, then at any point the normal stress
in material 1 is determined from $\sigma = E_1\epsilon$, and for material 2 the stress
distribution is found from $\sigma = E_2\epsilon$. Assuming material 1 is stiffer than
material 2, then $E_1 > E_2$ and so the stress distribution will look like that
shown in Fig. 36c or 36d. In particular, notice the jump in stress that
occurs at the juncture of the two materials. Here the *strain* is the *same,*
but since the modulus of elasticity for the materials suddenly changes,
so does the stress. It is possible to determine the location of the
neutral axis and the maximum stress based on a trial-and-error procedure.

Steel plates

**Fig. 35**

This requires satisfying the conditions that the stress distribution produces a zero resultant force on the cross section and the moment of the stress distribution about the neutral axis must be equal to **M.**

A simpler way to satisfy these two conditions is to use the *transformed section method*, which transforms the beam into one made of a *single material*. For example, if the beam is thought to consist entirely of the less stiff material 2, then the cross section will look like that shown in Fig. 36*e*. Here the height *h* of the beam remains the *same,* since the strain distribution in Fig. 36*b* must be preserved. However, the upper portion of the beam must be widened in order to carry a load *equivalent* to that carried by the stiffer material 1 in Fig. 36*d*. The necessary width can be determined by considering the force $d\mathbf{F}$ acting on an area $dA = dz\,dy$ of the beam in Fig. 36*a*. It is $dF = \sigma\,dA = (E_1\epsilon)\,dz\,dy$. Assuming the width of a *corresponding element* of height $dy$ in Fig. 36*e* is $n\,dz$, then $dF' = \sigma'dA' = (E_2\epsilon)n\,dz\,dy$. Equating these forces, so that they produce the same moment about the $z$ (neutral) axis, we have

$$E_1\epsilon\,dz\,dy = E_2\epsilon n\,dz\,dy$$

or

$$n = \frac{E_1}{E_2} \tag{20}$$

(a)

Normal strain variation
(profile view)

(b)

Bending stress variation
(profile view)

(c)

Bending stress variation

(d)

**Fig. 36**

343

Beam transformed to material ②

(e)

Beam transformed to material ①

(f)

Bending-stress variation for
beam transformed to material ②

(g)

Bending-stress variation for
beam transformed to material ①

(h)

**Fig. 36 (cont.)**

This dimensionless number $n$ is called the **transformation factor**. It indicates that the cross section, having a width $b$ on the original beam, Fig. 36a, must be increased in width to $b_2 = nb$ in the region where material 1 is being transformed into material 2, Fig. 36e.

In a similar manner, if the less stiff material 2 is transformed into the stiffer material 1, the cross section will look like that shown in Fig. 36f. Here the width of material 2 has been changed to $b_1 = n'b$, where $n' = E_2/E_1$. In this case the transformation factor $n'$ will be *less than one* since $E_1 > E_2$. In other words, we need less of the stiffer material to support the moment.

Once the beam has been transformed into one having a *single material,* the normal-stress distribution over the transformed cross section will be linear as shown in Fig. 36g or Fig. 36h. Consequently, the centroid (neutral axis) and moment of inertia for the transformed area can be determined and the flexure formula applied in the usual manner to determine the stress at each point on the transformed beam. The stress in the transformed beam will be equivalent to the stress in the *same material* of the actual beam; however, the stress found on the transformed material has to be multiplied by the transformation factor $n$ (or $n'$), since the area of the transformed material, $dA' = n\, dz\, dy$, is $n$ times the area of actual material $dA = dz\, dy$. That is,

$$dF = \sigma\, dA = \sigma'\, dA'$$
$$\sigma\, dz\, dy = \sigma' n\, dz\, dy$$
$$\sigma = n\sigma' \tag{21}$$

Example 17 numerically illustrates application of the transformed section method.

## Important Points

- *Composite beams* are made from different materials in order to efficiently carry a load. Application of the flexure formula requires the material to be homogeneous, and so the cross section of the beam must be transformed into a single material if this formula is to be used to calculate the bending stress.

- The *transformation factor n* is a ratio of the moduli of the different materials that make up the beam. Used as a multiplier, it converts the width of the cross section of the composite beam into a beam made from a single material so that this beam has the same strength as the composite beam. Stiff material will thus be replaced by more of the softer material and vice versa.

- Once the stress in the transformed material is determined, then it must be multiplied by the transformation factor to obtain the stress in the actual beam.

## *7  Reinforced Concrete Beams

All beams subjected to pure bending must resist both tensile and compressive stresses. Concrete, however, is very susceptible to cracking when it is in tension, and therefore by itself it will not be suitable for resisting a bending moment.* In order to circumvent this shortcoming, engineers place steel reinforcing rods within a concrete beam at a location where the concrete is in tension, Fig. 37a. To be most effective, these rods are located farthest from the beam's neutral axis, so that the moment created by the forces developed in them is greatest about the neutral axis. Furthermore, the rods are required to have some concrete coverage to protect them from corrosion or loss of strength in the event of a fire. Codes used for actual reinforced concrete design assume the concrete will not support any tensile loading, since the possible cracking of concrete is unpredictable. As a result, the normal stress distribution acting on the cross-sectional area of a reinforced concrete beam is assumed to look like that shown in Fig. 37b.

The stress analysis requires locating the neutral axis and determining the maximum stress in the steel and concrete. To do this, the area of steel $A_{st}$ is first transformed into an equivalent area of concrete using the transformation factor $n = E_{st}/E_{conc}$. This ratio, which gives $n > 1$, requires a "greater" amount of concrete to replace the steel. The transformed area is $nA_{st}$ and the transformed section looks like that shown in Fig. 37c. Here $d$ represents the distance from the top of the beam to the thin strip of (transformed) steel, $b$ is the beam's width, and $h'$ is the yet unknown distance from the top of the beam to the neutral axis. To obtain $h'$, we require the centroid $C$ of the cross-sectional area of the transformed section to lie on the neutral axis, Fig. 37c. With reference to the neutral axis, therefore, the moment of the two areas together, $\Sigma \tilde{y} A$, must be zero, since $\bar{y} = \Sigma \tilde{y} A / \Sigma A = 0$. Thus,

$$bh'\left(\frac{h'}{2}\right) - nA_{st}(d - h') = 0$$

$$\frac{b}{2}h'^2 + nA_{st}h' - nA_{st}d = 0$$

Once $h'$ is obtained from this quadratic equation, the solution proceeds in the usual manner for obtaining the stress in the beam. Example 18 numerically illustrates application of this method.

(a)

Concrete assumed cracked within this region.

(b)

(c)

**Fig. 37**

---

*Inspection of its particular stress-strain diagram in Fig. 11 reveals that concrete can be 12.5 times stronger in compression than in tension.

EXAMPLE 17

A composite beam is made of wood and reinforced with a steel strap located on its bottom side. It has the cross-sectional area shown in Fig. 38a. If the beam is subjected to a bending moment of $M = 2$ kN $\cdot$ m , determine the normal stress at points $B$ and $C$. Take $E_w = 12$ GPa and $E_{st} = 200$ GPa.

Fig. 38

## SOLUTION

**Section Properties.** Although the choice is arbitrary, here we will transform the section into one made entirely of steel. Since steel has a greater stiffness than wood ($E_{st} > E_w$), the width of the wood is *reduced* to an equivalent width for steel. For this to be the case, $n = E_w/E_{st}$, so that

$$b_{st} = nb_w = \frac{12 \text{ GPa}}{200 \text{ GPa}}(150 \text{ mm}) = 9 \text{ mm}$$

The transformed section is shown in Fig. 38b.

The location of the centroid (neutral axis), calculated from a reference axis located at the *bottom* of the section, is

$$\bar{y} = \frac{\Sigma\bar{y}A}{\Sigma A} = \frac{[0.01 \text{ m}](0.02 \text{ m})(0.150 \text{ m}) + [0.095 \text{ m}](0.009 \text{ m})(0.150 \text{ m})}{0.02 \text{ m}(0.150 \text{ m}) + 0.009 \text{ m}(0.150 \text{ m})} = 0.03638 \text{ m}$$

The moment of inertia about the neutral axis is therefore

$$I_{NA} = \left[\frac{1}{12}(0.150 \text{ m})(0.02 \text{ m})^3 + (0.150 \text{ m})(0.02 \text{ m})(0.03638 \text{ m} - 0.01 \text{ m})^2\right]$$

$$+ \left[\frac{1}{12}(0.009 \text{ m})(0.150 \text{ m})^3 + (0.009 \text{ m})(0.150 \text{ m})(0.095 \text{ m} - 0.03638 \text{ m})^2\right]$$

$$= 9.358(10^{-6}) \text{ m}^4$$

**Fig. 38 (cont.)**

**Normal Stress.** Applying the flexure formula, the normal stress at $B'$ and $C$ is

$$\sigma_{B'} = \frac{2(10^3)\ \text{N} \cdot \text{m}(0.170\ \text{m} - 0.03638\ \text{m})}{9.358(10^{-6})\ \text{m}^4} = 28.6\ \text{MPa}$$

$$\sigma_C = \frac{2(10^3)\ \text{N} \cdot \text{m}(0.03638\ \text{m})}{9.358(10^{-6})\ \text{m}^4} = 7.78\ \text{MPa} \qquad \textit{Ans.}$$

The normal-stress distribution on the transformed (all steel) section is shown in Fig. 38c.

The normal stress in the wood at $B$ in Fig. 38a, is determined from Eq. 21; that is,

$$\sigma_B = n\sigma_{B'} = \frac{12\ \text{GPa}}{200\ \text{GPa}}(28.56\ \text{MPa}) = 1.71\ \text{MPa} \qquad \textit{Ans.}$$

Using these concepts, show that the normal stress in the steel and the wood at the point where they are in contact is $\sigma_{st} = 3.50\ \text{MPa}$ and $\sigma_w = 0.210\ \text{MPa}$, respectively. The normal-stress distribution in the actual beam is shown in Fig. 38d.

## EXAMPLE 18

The reinforced concrete beam has the cross-sectional area shown in Fig. 39a. If it is subjected to a bending moment of $M = 60$ kip·ft, determine the normal stress in each of the steel reinforcing rods and the maximum normal stress in the concrete. Take $E_{st} = 29(10^3)$ ksi and $E_{conc} = 3.6(10^3)$ ksi.

### SOLUTION

Since the beam is made from concrete, in the following analysis we will neglect its strength in supporting a tensile stress.

**Section Properties.** The total area of steel, $A_{st} = 2[\pi(0.5 \text{ in.})^2] = 1.571 \text{ in}^2$ will be transformed into an equivalent area of concrete, Fig. 39b. Here

$$A' = nA_{st} = \frac{29(10^3) \text{ ksi}}{3.6(10^3) \text{ ksi}}(1.571 \text{ in}^2) = 12.65 \text{ in}^2$$

We require the centroid to lie on the neutral axis. Thus $\Sigma \tilde{y}A = 0$, or

$$12 \text{ in. } (h')\frac{h'}{2} - 12.65 \text{ in}^2(16 \text{ in.} - h') = 0$$
$$h'^2 + 2.11h' - 33.7 = 0$$

Solving for the positive root,

$$h' = 4.85 \text{ in.}$$

Using this value for $h'$, the moment of inertia of the transformed section about the neutral axis is

$$I = \left[\frac{1}{12}(12 \text{ in.})(4.85 \text{ in.})^3 + 12 \text{ in. }(4.85 \text{ in.})\left(\frac{4.85 \text{ in.}}{2}\right)^2\right] +$$
$$12.65 \text{ in}^2(16 \text{ in.} - 4.85 \text{ in.})^2 = 2029 \text{ in}^4$$

**Normal Stress.** Applying the flexure formula to the transformed section, the maximum normal stress in the concrete is

$$(\sigma_{conc})_{max} = \frac{[60 \text{ kip·ft}(12 \text{ in./ft})](4.85 \text{ in.})}{2029 \text{ in}^4} = 1.72 \text{ ksi} \qquad Ans.$$

The normal stress resisted by the "concrete" strip, which replaced the steel, is

$$\sigma'_{conc} = \frac{[60 \text{ kip·ft}(12 \text{ in./ft})](16 \text{ in.} - 4.85 \text{ in.})}{2029 \text{ in}^4} = 3.96 \text{ ksi}$$

The normal stress in each of the two reinforcing rods is therefore

$$\sigma_{st} = n\sigma'_{conc} = \left(\frac{29(10^3) \text{ ksi}}{3.6(10^3) \text{ ksi}}\right)3.96 \text{ ksi} = 31.9 \text{ ksi} \qquad Ans.$$

The normal-stress distribution is shown graphically in Fig. 39c.

(a)

(b)

(c)

**Fig. 39**

# *8  Curved Beams

The flexure formula applies to a straight member, since it was shown that the normal strain within the member varies linearly from the neutral axis. If the member is *curved*, however, the strain will not be linear, and so we must develop another method to describe the stress distribution. In this section we will consider the analysis of a *curved beam*, that is, a member that has a curved axis and is subjected to bending. Typical examples include hooks and chain links. In all these cases, the members are not slender, but rather have a sharp curve, and their cross-sectional dimensions are large compared with their radius of curvature.

The following analysis assumes that the cross section is constant and has an axis of symmetry that is perpendicular to the direction of the applied moment **M,** Fig. 40a. Also, the material is homogeneous and isotropic, and it behaves in a linear-elastic manner when the load is applied. Like the case of a straight beam, we will also assume that the *cross sections* of the member *remain plane* after the moment is applied. Furthermore, any distortion of the cross section within its own plane will be neglected.

To perform the analysis, three radii, extending from the center of curvature $O'$ of the member, are identified in Fig. 40a. Here $\bar{r}$ references the known location of the *centroid* for the cross-sectional area, $R$ references the yet unspecified location of the *neutral axis,* and $r$ locates the *arbitrary point* or area element $dA$ on the cross section.

This crane hook represents a typical example of a curved beam.

(a)

**Fig. 40**

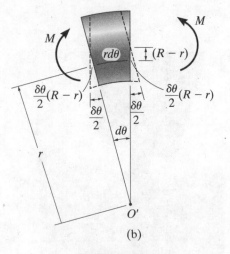

(b)

**Fig. 40 (cont.)**

If we isolate a differential segment of the beam, Fig. 40b, the stress tends to deform the material such that each cross section will rotate through an angle $\delta\theta/2$. The normal strain $\epsilon$ in the strip (or line) of material located at $r$ will now be determined. This strip has an original length $r\,d\theta$, Fig. 40b. However, due to the rotations $\delta\theta/2$ the strip's total change in length is $\delta\theta(R - r)$. Consequently, $\epsilon = \delta\theta(R - r)/r\,d\theta$. If we let $k = \delta\theta/d\theta$, which is the same for any particular strip, we have $\epsilon = k(R - r)/r$. Unlike the case of straight beams, here it can be seen that the ***normal strain*** is a nonlinear function of $r$, in fact it varies in a ***hyperbolic fashion.*** This occurs even though the cross section of the beam remains plane after deformation. If the material remains linearly elastic then $\sigma = E\epsilon$ and so

$$\sigma = Ek\left(\frac{R - r}{r}\right) \tag{22}$$

This variation is also hyperbolic, and since it has now been established, we can determine the location of the neutral axis and relate the stress distribution to the resultant internal moment $M$.

To obtain the location $R$ of the neutral axis, we require the resultant internal force caused by the stress distribution acting over the cross section to be equal to zero; i.e.,

$$F_R = \Sigma F_x; \qquad \int_A \sigma\,dA = 0$$

$$\int_A Ek\left(\frac{R - r}{r}\right)dA = 0$$

Since $Ek$ and $R$ are constants, we have

$$R\int_A \frac{dA}{r} - \int_A dA = 0$$

Solving for $R$ yields

$$R = \frac{A}{\displaystyle\int_A \frac{dA}{r}} \tag{23}$$

Here

$R$ = the location of the neutral axis, specified from the center of curvature $O'$ of the member

$A$ = the cross-sectional area of the member

$r$ = the arbitrary position of the area element $dA$ on the cross section, specified from the center of curvature $O'$ of the member

The integral in Eq. 23 has been evaluated for various cross-sectional geometries, and the results for some common cross sections are listed in Table 1.

| Shape | $\int_A \dfrac{dA}{r}$ |
|---|---|
| **TABLE 1** | |
| $b$, $r_1$, $r_2$ (rectangle) | $b\ln\dfrac{r_2}{r_1}$ |
| $r_1$, $b$, $r_2$ (triangle) | $\dfrac{b\,r_2}{(r_2 - r_1)}\left(\ln\dfrac{r_2}{r_1}\right) - b$ |
| $2c$, $\bar{r}$ (circle) | $2\pi\left(\bar{r} - \sqrt{\bar{r}^2 - c^2}\right)$ |
| $2a$, $2b$, $\bar{r}$ (ellipse) | $\dfrac{2\pi b}{a}\left(\bar{r} - \sqrt{\bar{r}^2 - a^2}\right)$ |

In order to relate the stress distribution to the resultant bending moment, we require the resultant internal moment to be equal to the moment of the stress distribution calculated about the neutral axis. From Fig. 40$a$, the stress $\sigma$, acting on the area element $dA$ and located a distance $y$ from the neutral axis, creates a moment about the neutral axis of $dM = y(\sigma\,dA)$. For the entire cross section, we require $M = \int y\sigma\,dA$. Since $y = R - r$, and $\sigma$ is defined by Eq. 22, we have

$$M = \int_A (R - r)Ek\left(\frac{R - r}{r}\right) dA$$

Expanding, realizing that $Ek$ and $R$ are constants, then

$$M = Ek\left( R^2 \int_A \frac{dA}{r} - 2R \int_A dA + \int_A r\,dA \right)$$

The first integral is equivalent to $A/R$ as determined from Eq. 23, and the second integral is simply the cross-sectional area $A$. Realizing that the location of the centroid of the cross section is determined from $\bar{r} = \int r\,dA/A$, the third integral can be replaced by $\bar{r}A$. Thus,

$$M = EkA(\bar{r} - R)$$

Finally, solving for $Ek$ in Eq. 22, substituting into the above equation, and solving for $\sigma$, we have

$$\boxed{\sigma = \frac{M(R - r)}{Ar(\bar{r} - R)}} \tag{24}$$

Here

$\sigma$ = the normal stress in the member

$M$ = the internal moment, determined from the method of sections and the equations of equilibrium and calculated about the neutral axis for the cross section. This moment is *positive* if it tends to increase the member's radius of curvature, i.e., it tends to straighten out the member.

$A$ = the cross-sectional area of the member

$R$ = the distance measured from the center of curvature to the neutral axis, determined from Eq. 23

$\bar{r}$ = the distance measured from the center of curvature to the centroid of the cross section

$r$ = the distance measured from the center of curvature to the point where the stress $\sigma$ is to be determined

$\sigma_{max}$

Bending stress variation
(profile view)

(c)

(d)

(e)

**Fig. 40 (cont.)**

From Fig. 40a, $r = R - y$. Also, the constant and usually very small distance between the neutral axis and the centroid is $e = \bar{r} - R$. When these results are substituted into Eq. 24, we can also write

$$\sigma = \frac{My}{Ae(R - y)}$$ (25)

These two equations represent two forms of the so-called *curved-beam formula,* which like the flexure formula can be used to determine the normal-stress distribution in a curved member. This distribution is, as previously stated, hyperbolic; an example is shown in Figs. 40c and 40d. Since the stress acts along the circumference of the beam, it is sometimes called **circumferential stress**. Note that due to the curvature of the beam, the circumferential stress will create a corresponding component of **radial stress**, so called since this component acts in the radial direction. To show how it is developed, consider the free-body diagram of the segment shown in Fig. 40e. Here the radial stress $\sigma_r$ is necessary since it creates the force $dF_r$ that is required to balance the two components of circumferential forces $dF$ which act along the line $O'B$.

Sometimes the radial stresses within curved members may become significant, especially if the member is constructed from thin plates and has, for example, the shape of an I-section. In this case the radial stress can become as large as the circumferential stress, and consequently the member must be designed to resist both stresses. For most cases, however, these stresses can be neglected, especially if the member has a *solid section*. Here the curved-beam formula gives results that are in very close agreement with those determined either by experiment or by a mathematical analysis based on the theory of elasticity.

The curved-beam formula is normally used when the curvature of the member is very pronounced, as in the case of hooks or rings. However, if the radius of curvature is greater than five times the depth of the member, the *flexure formula* can normally be used to determine the stress. For example, for rectangular sections for which this ratio equals 5, the maximum normal stress, when determined by the flexure formula, will be about 7% *less* than its value when determined by the curved-beam formula. This error is further reduced when the radius of curvature-to-depth ratio is more than 5.*

---

*See, for example, Boresi, A. P., et al., *Advanced Mechanics of Materials*, John Wiley & Sons, New York.

## Important Points

- The *curved-beam formula* should be used to determine the circumferential stress in a beam when the radius of curvature is less than five times the depth of the beam.

- Due to the curvature of the beam, the normal strain in the beam *does not* vary linearly with depth as in the case of a straight beam. As a result, the neutral axis generally does not pass through the centroid of the cross section.

- The radial stress component caused by bending can generally be neglected, especially if the cross section is a solid section and not made from thin plates.

## Procedure for Analysis

In order to apply the curved-beam formula the following procedure is suggested.

### Section Properties.

- Determine the cross-sectional area $A$ and the location of the centroid, $\bar{r}$, measured from the center of curvature.
- Find the location of the neutral axis, $R$, using Eq. 23 or Table 1. If the cross-sectional area consists of $n$ "composite" parts, determine $\int dA/r$ for *each part*. Then, from Eq. 23, for the entire section, $R = \Sigma A / \Sigma(\int dA/r)$. In all cases, $R < \bar{r}$.

### Normal Stress.

- The normal stress located at a point $r$ away from the center of curvature is determined from Eq. 24. If the distance $y$ to the point is measured from the neutral axis, then find $e = \bar{r} - R$ and use Eq. 25.
- Since $\bar{r} - R$ generally produces a very *small number*, it is best to calculate $\bar{r}$ and $R$ with sufficient accuracy so that the subtraction leads to a number $e$ having at least four significant figures.
- If the stress is positive it will be tensile, whereas if it is negative it will be compressive.
- The stress distribution over the entire cross section can be graphed, or a volume element of the material can be isolated and used to represent the stress acting at the point on the cross section where it has been calculated.

EXAMPLE | 19

The curved bar has a cross-sectional area shown in Fig. 41a. If it is subjected to bending moments of 4 kN · m, determine the maximum normal stress developed in the bar.

(a)

**Fig. 41**

### SOLUTION

**Internal Moment.**  Each section of the bar is subjected to the same resultant internal moment of 4 kN · m. Since this moment tends to decrease the bar's radius of curvature, it is negative. Thus, $M = -4$ kN · m.

**Section Properties.**  Here we will consider the cross section to be composed of a rectangle and triangle. The total cross-sectional area is

$$\Sigma A = (0.05\text{ m})^2 + \frac{1}{2}(0.05\text{ m})(0.03\text{ m}) = 3.250(10^{-3})\text{ m}^2$$

The location of the centroid is determined with reference to the center of curvature, point $O'$, Fig. 41a.

$$\bar{r} = \frac{\Sigma \tilde{r} A}{\Sigma A}$$

$$= \frac{[0.225\text{ m}](0.05\text{ m})(0.05\text{ m}) + [0.260\text{ m}]\frac{1}{2}(0.050\text{ m})(0.030\text{ m})}{3.250(10^{-3})\text{ m}^2}$$

$$= 0.23308\text{ m}$$

We can find $\int_A dA/r$ for each part using Table 1. For the rectangle,

$$\int_A \frac{dA}{r} = 0.05 \text{ m} \left( \ln \frac{0.250 \text{ m}}{0.200 \text{ m}} \right) = 0.011157 \text{ m}$$

And for the triangle,

$$\int_A \frac{dA}{r} = \frac{(0.05 \text{ m})(0.280 \text{ m})}{(0.280 \text{ m} - 0.250 \text{ m})} \left( \ln \frac{0.280 \text{ m}}{0.250 \text{ m}} \right) - 0.05 \text{ m} = 0.0028867 \text{ m}$$

Thus the location of the neutral axis is determined from

$$R = \frac{\Sigma A}{\Sigma \int_A dA/r} = \frac{3.250(10^{-3}) \text{ m}^2}{0.011157 \text{ m} + 0.0028867 \text{ m}} = 0.23142 \text{ m}$$

Note that $R < \bar{r}$ as expected. Also, the calculations were performed with sufficient accuracy so that $(\bar{r} - R) = 0.23308 \text{ m} - 0.23142 \text{ m} = 0.00166 \text{ m}$ is now accurate to three significant figures.

**Normal Stress.** The maximum normal stress occurs either at $A$ or $B$. Applying the curved-beam formula to calculate the normal stress at $B$, $r_B = 0.200$ m, we have

$$\sigma_B = \frac{M(R - r_B)}{A r_B (\bar{r} - R)} = \frac{(-4 \text{ kN} \cdot \text{m})(0.23142 \text{ m} - 0.200 \text{ m})}{3.250(10^{-3}) \text{ m}^2 (0.200 \text{ m})(0.00166 \text{ m})}$$

$$= -116 \text{ MPa}$$

At point $A$, $r_A = 0.280$ m and the normal stress is

$$\sigma_A = \frac{M(R - r_A)}{A r_A (\bar{r} - R)} = \frac{(-4 \text{ kN} \cdot \text{m})(0.23142 \text{ m} - 0.280 \text{ m})}{3.250(10^{-3}) \text{ m}^2 (0.280 \text{ m})(0.00166 \text{ m})}$$

$$= 129 \text{ MPa} \qquad\qquad Ans.$$

By comparison, the maximum normal stress is at $A$. A two-dimensional representation of the stress distribution is shown in Fig. 41b.

Fig. 41 (cont.)

**Fig. 42**

# 9 Stress Concentrations

The flexure formula cannot be used to determine the stress distribution within regions of a member where the cross-sectional area suddenly changes, since the normal-stress and strain distributions at the section become *nonlinear*. The results can only be obtained through experiment or, in some cases, by using the theory of elasticity. Common discontinuities include members having notches on their surfaces, Fig. 42*a*, holes for passage of fasteners or other items, Fig. 42*b*, or abrupt changes in the outer dimensions of the member's cross section, Fig. 42*c*. The *maximum* normal stress at each of these discontinuities occurs at the section taken through the *smallest* cross-sectional area.

For design, it is generally important to only know the maximum normal stress developed at these sections, not the actual stress distribution. As in the previous cases of axially loaded bars and torsionally loaded shafts, we can obtain the maximum normal stress due to bending using a stress-concentration factor $K$. For example, Fig. 43 gives values of $K$ for a flat bar that has a change in cross section using shoulder fillets. To use this graph simply find the geometric ratios $w/h$

**Fig. 43**

**Fig. 44**

and $r/h$ and then find the corresponding value of $K$ for a particular geometry. Once $K$ is obtained, the maximum bending stress shown in Fig. 45 is determined using

**Fig. 45**

$$\sigma_{max} = K\frac{Mc}{I} \tag{26}$$

In the same manner, Fig. 44 can be used if the discontinuity consists of circular grooves or notches.

Like axial load and torsion, stress concentration for bending should always be considered when designing members made of brittle materials or those that are subjected to fatigue or cyclic loadings. Also, realize that stress-concentration factors apply *only* when the material is subjected to *elastic behavior*. If the applied moment causes yielding of the material, as is the case with ductile materials, the stress becomes redistributed throughout the member, and the maximum stress that results will be *lower* than that determined using stress-concentration factors. This phenomenon is discussed further in the next section.

Stress concentrations caused by bending occur at the sharp corners of this window lintel and are responsible for the crack at the corner.

## Important Points

- Stress concentrations occur at points of sudden cross-sectional change, caused by notches and holes, because here the stress and strain become nonlinear. The more severe the change, the larger the stress concentration.

- For design or analysis, the maximum normal stress occurs on the *smallest* cross-sectional area. This stress can be obtained by using a stress concentration factor, $K$, that has been determined through experiment and is only a function of the geometry of the member.

- Normally, the stress concentration in a ductile material subjected to a static moment will not have to be considered in design; however, if the material is *brittle*, or subjected to *fatigue* loading, then stress concentrations become important.

## EXAMPLE | 20

The transition in the cross-sectional area of the steel bar is achieved using shoulder fillets as shown in Fig. 46a. If the bar is subjected to a bending moment of 5 kN · m, determine the maximum normal stress developed in the steel. The yield stress is $\sigma_Y = 500$ MPa.

### SOLUTION

The moment creates the largest stress in the bar at the base of the fillet, where the cross-sectional area is smallest. The stress-concentration factor can be determined by using Fig. 43. From the geometry of the bar, we have $r = 16$ mm, $h = 80$ mm, $w = 120$ mm. Thus,

$$\frac{r}{h} = \frac{16 \text{ mm}}{80 \text{ mm}} = 0.2 \qquad \frac{w}{h} = \frac{120 \text{ mm}}{80 \text{ mm}} = 1.5$$

These values give $K = 1.45$. Applying Eq. 26, we have

$$\sigma_{max} = K\frac{Mc}{I} = (1.45)\frac{(5(10^3) \text{ N} \cdot \text{m})(0.04 \text{ m})}{\left[\frac{1}{12}(0.020 \text{ m})(0.08 \text{ m})^3\right]} = 340 \text{ MPa} \qquad Ans.$$

This result indicates that the steel remains elastic since the stress is below the yield stress (500 MPa).

**NOTE:** The normal-stress distribution is nonlinear and is shown in Fig. 46b. Realize, however, that by Saint-Venant's principle, Sec. 1, these localized stresses smooth out and become linear when one moves (approximately) a distance of 80 mm or more to the right of the transition. In this case, the flexure formula gives $\sigma_{max} = 234$ MPa, Fig. 46c. Also note that the choice of a larger-radius fillet will significantly reduce $\sigma_{max}$, since as $r$ increases in Fig. 43, $K$ will decrease.

(b)

(c)

**Fig. 46**

# PROBLEMS

**\*120.** The composite beam is made of steel ($A$) bonded to brass ($B$) and has the cross section shown. If it is subjected to a moment of $M = 6.5$ kN·m, determine the maximum bending stress in the brass and steel. Also, what is the stress in each material at the seam where they are bonded together? $E_{br} = 100$ GPa, $E_{st} = 200$ GPa.

**121.** The composite beam is made of steel ($A$) bonded to brass ($B$) and has the cross section shown. If the allowable bending stress for the steel is $(\sigma_{allow})_{st} = 180$ MPa, and for the brass $(\sigma_{allow})_{br} = 60$ MPa, determine the maximum moment $M$ that can be applied to the beam. $E_{br} = 100$ GPa, $E_{st} = 200$ GPa.

**Probs. 120/121**

**122.** Segment $A$ of the composite beam is made from 2014-T6 aluminum alloy and segment $B$ is A-36 steel. If $w = 0.9$ kip/ft, determine the absolute maximum bending stress developed in the aluminum and steel. Sketch the stress distribution on the cross section.

**123.** Segment $A$ of the composite beam is made from 2014-T6 aluminum alloy and segment $B$ is A-36 steel. The allowable bending stress for the aluminum and steel are $(\sigma_{allow})_{al} = 15$ ksi and $(\sigma_{allow})_{st} = 22$ ksi. Determine the maximum allowable intensity $w$ of the uniform distributed load.

**Probs. 122/123**

**\*124.** The Z section has principal moments of inertia of $I_y = 0.060(10^{-3})$ m$^4$ and $I_z = 0.471(10^{-3})$ m$^4$, computed about the principal axes of inertia $y$ and $z$, respectively. If the section is subjected to an internal moment of $M = 250$ N·m directed horizontally as shown, determine the stress produced at point $B$. Solve the problem using Eq. 17.

**Prob. 124**

**125.** The wooden section of the beam is reinforced with two steel plates as shown. Determine the maximum internal moment $M$ that the beam can support if the allowable stresses for the wood and steel are $(\sigma_{allow})_w = 6$ MPa, and $(\sigma_{allow})_{st} = 150$ MPa, respectively. Take $E_w = 10$ GPa and $E_{st} = 200$ GPa.

**126.** The wooden section of the beam is reinforced with two steel plates as shown. If the beam is subjected to an internal moment of $M = 30$ kN·m, determine the maximum bending stresses developed in the steel and wood. Sketch the stress distribution over the cross section. Take $E_w = 10$ GPa and $E_{st} = 200$ GPa.

**Probs. 125/126**

**127.** The member has a brass core bonded to a steel casing. If a couple moment of 8 kN·m is applied at its end, determine the maximum bending stress in the member. $E_{br} = 100$ GPa, $E_{st} = 200$ GPa.

8 kN·m

3 m

20 mm
100 mm
20 mm

20 mm
100 mm
20 mm

**Prob. 127**

**\*128.** The steel channel is used to reinforce the wood beam. Determine the maximum stress in the steel and in the wood if the beam is subjected to a moment of $M = 850$ lb·ft. $E_{st} = 29(10^3)$ ksi, $E_w = 1600$ ksi.

4 in.
0.5 in.
15 in.
$M = 850$ lb·ft
0.5 in.
0.5 in.

**Prob. 128**

**129.** A wood beam is reinforced with steel straps at its top and bottom as shown. Determine the maximum bending stress developed in the wood and steel if the beam is subjected to a bending moment of $M = 5$ kN·m. Sketch the stress distribution acting over the cross section. Take $E_w = 11$ GPa, $E_{st} = 200$ GPa.

y
20 mm
300 mm
$M = 5$ kN·m
20 mm
x
200 mm
z

**Prob. 129**

**130.** The beam is made from three types of plastic that are identified and have the moduli of elasticity shown in the figure. Determine the maximum bending stress in the PVC.

500 lb    500 lb

PVC $E_{PVC} = 450$ ksi
Escon $E_E = 160$ ksi
Bakelite $E_B = 800$ ksi

3 ft    4 ft    3 ft

1 in.
2 in.
2 in.

3 in.

**Prob. 130**

**131.** The concrete beam is reinforced with three 20-mm-diameter steel rods. Assume that the concrete cannot support tensile stress. If the allowable compressive stress for concrete is $(\sigma_{allow})_{con} = 12.5$ MPa and the allowable tensile stress for steel is $(\sigma_{allow})_{st} = 220$ MPa, determine the required dimension $d$ so that both the concrete and steel achieve their allowable stress simultaneously. This condition is said to be 'balanced'. Also, compute the corresponding maximum allowable internal moment **M** that can be applied to the beam. The moduli of elasticity for concrete and steel are $E_{con} = 25$ GPa and $E_{st} = 200$ GPa, respectively.

200 mm
**M**
d

**Prob. 131**

**\*132.** The wide-flange section is reinforced with two wooden boards as shown. If this composite beam is subjected to an internal moment of $M = 100$ kN·m, determine the maximum bending stress developed in the steel and the wood. Take $E_w = 10$ GPa and $E_{st} = 200$ GPa.

**133.** The wide-flange section is reinforced with two wooden boards as shown. If the steel and wood have an allowable bending stress of $(\sigma_{allow})_{st} = 150$ MPa and $(\sigma_{allow})_w = 6$ MPa, determine the maximum allowable internal moment **M** that can be applied to the beam. Take $E_w = 10$ GPa and $E_{st} = 200$ GPa.

**Probs. 132/133**

**134.** If the beam is subjectd to an internal moment of $M = 45$ kN·m, determine the maximum bending stress developed in the A-36 steel section $A$ and the 2014-T6 aluminum alloy section $B$.

**Prob. 134**

**135.** The Douglas fir beam is reinforced wizth A-36 straps at its center and sides. Determine the maximum stress developed in the wood and steel if the beam is subjected to a bending moment of $M_z = 7.50$ kip·ft. Sketch the stress distribution acting over the cross section.

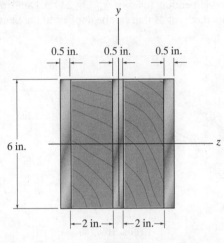

**Prob. 135**

**\*136.** For the curved beam in Fig. 40a, show that when the radius of curvature approaches infinity, the curved-beam formula, Eq. 24, reduces to the flexure formula, Eq. 13.

**137.** The curved member is subjected to the internal moment of $M = 50$ kN·m. Determine the percentage error introduced in the computation of maximum bending stress using the flexure formula for straight members.

**138.** The curved member is made from material having an allowable bending stress of $\sigma_{allow} = 100$ MPa. Determine the maximum allowable internal moment $M$ that can be applied to the member.

**Probs. 137/138**

**139.** The curved beam is subjected to a bending moment of $M = 40$ lb · ft. Determine the maximum bending stress in the beam. Also, sketch a two-dimensional view of the stress distribution acting on section a–a.

**\*140.** The curved beam is made from material having an allowable bending stress of $\sigma_{allow} = 24$ ksi. Determine the maximum moment $M$ that can be applied to the beam.

Probs. 139/140

**141.** If $P = 3$ kN, determine the bending stress developed at points $A$, $B$ and $C$ of the cross section at section a–a. Using these results, sketch the stress distribution on section a–a.

**142.** If the maximum bending stress at section a–a is not allowed to exceed $\sigma_{allow} = 150$ MPa, determine the maximum allowable force **P** that can be applied to the end $E$.

Probs. 141/142

**143.** The elbow of the pipe has an outer radius of 0.75 in. and an inner radius of 0.63 in. If the assembly is subjected to the moments of $M = 25$ lb · in., determine the maximum stress developed at section a–a.

Prob. 143

**\*144.** The curved member is symmetric and is subjected to a moment of $M = 600$ lb · ft. Determine the bending stress in the member at points $A$ and $B$. Show the stress acting on volume elements located at these points.

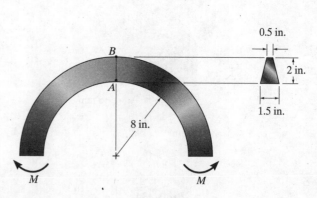

Prob. 144

362

**145.** The curved bar used on a machine has a rectangular cross section. If the bar is subjected to a couple as shown, determine the maximum tensile and compressive stress acting at section *a–a*. Sketch the stress distribution on the section in three dimensions.

**Prob. 145**

**146.** The fork is used as part of a nosewheel assembly for an airplane. If the maximum wheel reaction at the end of the fork is 840 lb, determine the maximum bending stress in the curved portion of the fork at section *a–a*. There the cross-sectional area is circular, having a diameter of 2 in.

**Prob. 146**

**147.** If the curved member is subjected to the internal moment of $M = 600$ lb·ft, determine the bending stress developed at points $A$, $B$ and $C$. Using these results, sketch the stress distribution on the cross section.

**\*148.** If the curved member is made from material having an allowable bending stress of $\sigma_{allow} = 15$ ksi, determine the maximum allowable internal moment **M** that can be applied to the member.

**Probs. 147/148**

**149.** A 100-mm-diameter circular rod is bent into an **S** shape. If it is subjected to the applied moments $M = 125$ N·m at its ends, determine the maximum tensile and compressive stress developed in the rod.

**Prob. 149**

**150.** The bar is subjected to a moment of $M = 153$ N·m. Determine the smallest radius $r$ of the fillets so that an allowable bending stress of $\sigma_{allow} = 120$ MPa is not exceeded.

**151.** The bar is subjected to a moment of $M = 17.5$ N·m. If $r = 6$ mm determine the maximum bending stress in the material.

**Probs. 150/151**

**\*152.** The bar is subjected to a moment of $M = 40$ N·m. Determine the smallest radius $r$ of the fillets so that an allowable bending stress of $\sigma_{allow} = 124$ MPa is not exceeded.

**153.** The bar is subjected to a moment of $M = 17.5$ N·m. If $r = 5$ mm, determine the maximum bending stress in the material.

**Probs. 152/153**

**154.** The simply supported notched bar is subjected to two forces **P**. Determine the largest magnitude of **P** that can be applied without causing the material to yield. The material is A-36 steel. Each notch has a radius of $r = 0.125$ in.

**Probs. 154**

**155.** The simply supported notched bar is subjected to the two loads, each having a magnitude of $P = 100$ lb. Determine the maximum bending stress developed in the bar, and sketch the bending-stress distribution acting over the cross section at the center of the bar. Each notch has a radius of $r = 0.125$ in.

**Prob. 155**

**\*156.** Determine the length $L$ of the center portion of the bar so that the maximum bending stress at $A, B$, and $C$ is the same. The bar has a thickness of 10 mm.

**Prob. 156**

**157.** The stepped bar has a thickness of 15 mm. Determine the maximum moment that can be applied to its ends if it is made of a material having an allowable bending stress of $\sigma_{allow} = 200$ MPa.

**Prob. 157**

# *10  Inelastic Bending

The equations for determining the normal stress due to bending that have previously been developed are valid only if the material behaves in a linear-elastic manner. If the applied moment causes the material to *yield,* a plastic analysis must then be used to determine the stress distribution. For bending of straight members three conditions must be met.

### Linear Normal-Strain Distribution.
Based only on geometric considerations, it was shown in Sec. 3 that the normal strains always vary *linearly* from zero at the neutral axis of the cross section to a maximum at the farthest point from the neutral axis.

### Resultant Force Equals Zero.
Since there is only a resultant internal moment acting on the cross section, the resultant force caused by the stress distribution must be equal to zero. Since $\sigma$ creates a force on the area $dA$ of $dF = \sigma \, dA$, Fig. 47, then for the entire cross-sectional area $A$, we have

**Fig. 47**

$$F_R = \Sigma F_x; \qquad \int_A \sigma \, dA = 0 \qquad (27)$$

This equation provides a means for obtaining the *location of the neutral axis.*

### Resultant Moment.
The resultant moment at the section must be equivalent to the moment caused by the stress distribution about the neutral axis. Since the moment of the force $dF = \sigma \, dA$ about the neutral axis is $dM = y(\sigma \, dA)$, Fig 47, then summing the results over the entire cross section, we have,

$$(M_R)_z = \Sigma M_z; \qquad M = \int_A y(\sigma \, dA) \qquad (28)$$

These conditions of geometry and loading will now be used to show how to determine the stress distribution in a beam when it is subjected to a resultant internal moment that causes yielding of the material. Throughout the discussion we will assume that the material has a stress–strain diagram that is the *same* in tension as it is in compression. For simplicity, we will begin by considering the beam to have a cross-sectional area with two axes of symmetry; in this case, a rectangle of height $h$ and width $b$, as shown in Fig. 48$a$. Two cases of loading that are of special interest will be considered.

(a)

Strain distribution
(profile view)

(b)

**Plastic Moment.** Some materials, such as steel, tend to exhibit elastic-perfectly plastic behavior when the stress in the material reaches $\sigma_Y$. If the applied moment $M = M_Y$ is just sufficient to produce yielding in the top and bottom fibers of the beam as shown in Fig. 48b, then we can determine $M_Y$ using the flexure formula $\sigma_Y = M_Y(h/2)/[bh^3/12]$ or

$$M_Y = \frac{1}{6}bh^2\sigma_Y \tag{29}$$

If the internal moment $M > M_Y$, the material at the top and bottom of the beam will begin to yield, causing a redistribution of stress over the cross section until the required internal moment $M$ is developed. If this causes normal-strain distribution as shown in Fig. 48b, then the corresponding normal-stress distribution is determined from the stress–strain diagram shown in Fig. 48c. Here the strains $\epsilon_1, \epsilon_Y, \epsilon_2$, correspond to stresses $\sigma_1, \sigma_Y, \sigma_Y$, respectively. When these and other stresses like them are plotted on the cross section, we obtain the stress distribution shown in Fig. 48d or 48e. Here the tension and compression stress "blocks" each consist of component rectangular and triangular blocks. The resultant forces they produce are equivalent to their volumes.

$$T_1 = C_1 = \frac{1}{2}y_Y\,\sigma_Y b$$

$$T_2 = C_2 = \left(\frac{h}{2} - y_Y\right)\sigma_Y b$$

Because of the symmetry, Eq. 27 is satisfied and the neutral axis passes through the centroid of the cross section as shown. The applied moment $M$ can be related to the yield stress $\sigma_Y$ using Eq. 28. From Fig. 48e, we require

$$M = T_1\left(\frac{2}{3}y_Y\right) + C_1\left(\frac{2}{3}y_Y\right) + T_2\left[y_Y + \frac{1}{2}\left(\frac{h}{2} - y_Y\right)\right]$$

$$+ C_2\left[y_Y + \frac{1}{2}\left(\frac{h}{2} - y_Y\right)\right]$$

$$= 2\left(\frac{1}{2}y_Y\,\sigma_Y b\right)\left(\frac{2}{3}y_Y\right) + 2\left[\left(\frac{h}{2} - y_Y\right)\sigma_Y b\right]\left[\frac{1}{2}\left(\frac{h}{2} + y_Y\right)\right]$$

$$= \frac{1}{4}bh^2\sigma_Y\left(1 - \frac{4}{3}\frac{y_Y^2}{h^2}\right)$$

Stress–strain diagram
(elastic-plastic region)

(c)

Stress distribution
(profile view)

(d)

Plastic
yielding

(e)

**Fig. 48**

Or using Eq. 29,

$$M = \frac{3}{2}M_Y\left(1 - \frac{4}{3}\frac{y_Y^2}{h^2}\right) \tag{30}$$

As noted in Fig. 48e, **M** produces two zones of plastic yielding and an elastic core in the member. The boundary between them is located a distance $\pm y_Y$ from the neutral axis. As **M** increases in magnitude, $y_Y$ approaches zero. This would render the material entirely plastic and the stress distribution will then look like that shown in Fig. 48f. From Eq. 30 with $y_Y = 0$, or by finding the moments of the stress "blocks" around the neutral axis, we can write this limiting value as

$$M_p = \frac{1}{4}bh^2\sigma_Y \tag{31}$$

Using Eq. 29, or Eq. 30 with $y = 0$, we have

$$M_p = \frac{3}{2}M_Y \tag{32}$$

This moment is referred to as the ***plastic moment***. Its value applies only for a rectangular section, since the analysis depends on the geometry of the cross section.

Beams used in steel buildings are sometimes designed to resist a plastic moment. When this is the case, codes usually list a design property for a beam called the shape factor. The ***shape factor*** is defined as the ratio

$$k = \frac{M_p}{M_Y} \tag{33}$$

This value specifies the additional moment capacity that a beam can support beyond its maximum elastic moment. For example, from Eq. 32, a beam having a rectangular cross section has a shape factor of $k = 1.5$. Therefore this section will support 50% more bending moment than its maximum elastic moment when it becomes fully plastic.

Plastic moment

(f)

**Fig. 48 (cont.)**

**Residual Stress.**   When the plastic moment is removed from the beam then it will cause *residual stress* to be developed in the beam. These stresses are often important when considering fatigue and other types of mechanical behavior, and so we will discuss a method used for their computation. To explain how this is done, we will assume that $M_p$ causes the material at the top and bottom of the beam to be strained to $\epsilon_1(\gg\epsilon_Y)$, as shown by point $B$ on the $\sigma-\epsilon$ curve in Fig. 49a. A release of this moment will cause this material to recover some of this strain elastically by following the dashed path $BC$. Since this recovery is elastic, we can superimpose on the stress distribution in Fig. 49b a linear stress distribution caused by applying the plastic moment in the opposite direction, Fig. 49c. Here the maximum stress, which is called the *modulus of rupture* for bending, $\sigma_r$, can be determined from the flexure formula when the beam is loaded with the plastic moment. We have

$$\sigma_{\max} = \frac{Mc}{I} = \frac{M_p\left(\frac{1}{2}h\right)}{\left(\frac{1}{12}bh^3\right)} = \frac{\left(\frac{1}{4}bh^2\sigma_Y\right)\left(\frac{1}{2}h\right)}{\left(\frac{1}{12}bh^3\right)} = 1.5\sigma_Y$$

(a)

**Fig. 49**

Plastic moment applied
causing plastic strain
(b)

Plastic moment reversal
causing elastic strain
(c)

Residual stress
distribution in beam
(d)

**Fig. 49 (cont.)**

This reversed application of the plastic moment is possible here, since maximum elastic recovery strain at the top and bottom of the beam is $2\epsilon_Y$ as shown in Fig. 49a. This corresponds to a maximum stress of $2\sigma_Y$ which is greater than the *required* stress of $1.5\sigma_Y$ as calculated above, Fig. 49c.

The superposition of the plastic moment, Fig. 49b, and its removal, Fig. 49c, gives the residual-stress distribution shown in Fig. 49d. As an exercise, use the component triangular "blocks" that represent this stress distribution and show that it results in a zero-force and zero-moment resultant on the member as required.

## Ultimate Moment.

Consider now the more general case of a beam having a cross section that is symmetrical only with respect to the vertical axis, while the moment is applied about the horizontal axis, Fig. 50a. We will assume that the material exhibits strain hardening and that its stress–strain diagrams for tension and compression are different, Fig. 50b.

If the moment **M** produces yielding of the beam, difficulty arises in finding *both* the location of the neutral axis and the maximum strain that is produced in the beam. This is because the cross section is unsymmetrical about the horizontal axis and the stress–strain behavior of the material is not the same in tension and compression. To solve this problem, a trial-and-error procedure requires the following steps:

1. For a given moment **M**, *assume* the location of the neutral axis and the slope of the "linear" strain distribution, Fig. 50c.

2. Graphically establish the stress distribution on the member's cross section using the $\sigma-\epsilon$ curve to plot values of stress corresponding to values of strain. The resulting stress distribution, Fig. 50d, will then have the same shape as the $\sigma-\epsilon$ curve.

(a)

(b)

**Fig. 50**

Strain distribution
(profile view)

(c)

Stress distribution
(profile view)

(d)

(e)

**Fig. 50 (cont.)**

3. Determine the volumes enclosed by the tensile and compressive stress "blocks." (As an approximation, this may require dividing each block into composite regions.) Equation 27 requires the volumes of these blocks to be *equal*, since they represent the resultant tensile force **T** and resultant compressive force **C** on the section, Fig. 50*e*. If these forces are unequal, an adjustment as to the *location* of the neutral axis must be made (point of *zero strain*) and the process repeated until Eq. 27 ($T = C$) is satisfied.

4. Once $T = C$, the moments produced by **T** and **C** can be calculated about the neutral axis. Here the moment arms for **T** and **C** are measured from the neutral axis to the *centroids of the volumes* defined by the stress distributions, Fig. 50*e*. Equation 28 requires $M = Ty' + Cy''$. If this equation is not satisfied, the *slope* of the *strain distribution* must be adjusted and the computations for $T$ and $C$ and the moment must be repeated until close agreement is obtained.

This trial-and-error procedure is obviously very tedious, and fortunately it does not occur very often in engineering practice. Most beams are symmetric about two axes, and they are constructed from materials that are assumed to have similar tension-and-compression stress–strain diagrams. Whenever this occurs, the neutral axis will pass through the centroid of the cross section, and the process of relating the stress distribution to the resultant moment is thereby simplified.

## Important Points

- The *normal strain distribution* over the cross section of a beam is based only on geometric considerations and has been found to always remain *linear,* regardless of the applied load. The normal stress distribution, however, must be determined from the material behavior, or stress–strain diagram once the strain distribution is established.

- The *location of the neutral axis* is determined from the condition that the *resultant force* on the cross section is *zero.*

- The resultant internal moment on the cross section must be equal to the moment of the stress distribution about the neutral axis.

- Perfectly plastic behavior assumes the normal stress distribution is *constant* over the cross section, and the beam will continue to bend, with no increase in moment. This moment is called the *plastic moment.*

## EXAMPLE | 21

The steel wide-flange beam has the dimensions shown in Fig. 51a. If it is made of an elastic perfectly plastic material having a tensile and compressive yield stress of $\sigma_Y = 36$ ksi, determine the shape factor for the beam.

0.5 in.

0.5 in.

9 in.

0.5 in.

8 in.

(a)

### SOLUTION

In order to determine the shape factor, it is first necessary to calculate the maximum elastic moment $M_Y$ and the plastic moment $M_p$.

**Maximum Elastic Moment.** The normal-stress distribution for the maximum elastic moment is shown in Fig. 51b. The moment of inertia about the neutral axis is

$$I = \left[ \frac{1}{12}(0.5 \text{ in.})(9 \text{ in.})^3 \right] + 2\left[ \frac{1}{12}(8 \text{ in.})(0.5 \text{ in.})^3 + 8 \text{ in. }(0.5 \text{ in.})(4.75 \text{ in.})^2 \right] = 211.0 \text{ in}^4$$

Applying the flexure formula, we have

$$\sigma_{max} = \frac{Mc}{I}; \qquad 36 \text{ kip/in}^2 = \frac{M_Y(5 \text{ in.})}{211.0 \text{ in}^4} \qquad M_Y = 1519.5 \text{ kip} \cdot \text{in.}$$

**Plastic Moment.** The plastic moment causes the steel over the entire cross section of the beam to yield, so that the normal-stress distribution looks like that shown in Fig. 51c. Due to symmetry of the cross-sectional area and since the tension and compression stress–strain diagrams are the same, the neutral axis passes through the centroid of the cross section. In order to determine the plastic moment, the stress distribution is divided into four composite rectangular "blocks," and the force produced by each "block" is equal to the volume of the block. Therefore, we have

36 ksi

A

36 ksi

$M_Y$

(b)

$$C_1 = T_1 = 36 \text{ kip/in}^2 (0.5 \text{ in.})(4.5 \text{ in.}) = 81 \text{ kip}$$
$$C_2 = T_2 = 36 \text{ kip/in}^2 (0.5 \text{ in.})(8 \text{ in.}) = 144 \text{ kip}$$

These forces act through the *centroid* of the volume for each block. Calculating the moments of these forces about the neutral axis, we obtain the plastic moment:

$$M_p = 2[(2.25 \text{ in.})(81 \text{ kip})] + 2[(4.75 \text{ in.})(144 \text{ kip})] = 1732.5 \text{ kip} \cdot \text{in.}$$

**Shape Factor.** Applying Eq. 33 gives

36 ksi

A

$C_2$

$C_1$

$T_1$

$M_p$

$T_2$

36 ksi

(c)

**Fig. 51**

$$k = \frac{M_p}{M_Y} = \frac{1732.5 \text{ kip} \cdot \text{in.}}{1519.5 \text{ kip} \cdot \text{in.}} = 1.14 \qquad Ans.$$

**NOTE:** This value indicates that a wide-flange beam provides a very efficient section for resisting an *elastic moment*. Most of the moment is developed in the flanges, i.e., in the top and bottom segments, whereas the web or vertical segment contributes very little. In this particular case, only 14% additional moment can be supported by the beam beyond that which can be supported elastically.

EXAMPLE | 22

A T-beam has the dimensions shown in Fig. 52a. If it is made of an elastic perfectly plastic material having a tensile and compressive yield stress of $\sigma_Y = 250$ MPa, determine the plastic moment that can be resisted by the beam.

Fig. 52

SOLUTION

The "plastic" stress distribution acting over the beam's cross-sectional area is shown in Fig. 52b. In this case the cross section is not symmetric with respect to a horizontal axis, and consequently, the neutral axis will *not* pass through the centroid of the cross section. To determine the *location* of the neutral axis, $d$, we require the stress distribution to produce a zero resultant force on the cross section. Assuming that $d \leq 120$ mm, we have

$$\int_A \sigma \, dA = 0; \qquad T - C_1 - C_2 = 0$$

$$250 \text{ MPa } (0.015 \text{ m})(d) - 250 \text{ MPa } (0.015 \text{ m})(0.120 \text{ m} - d)$$
$$- 250 \text{ MPa } (0.015 \text{ m})(0.100 \text{ m}) = 0$$
$$d = 0.110 \text{ m} < 0.120 \text{ m} \quad \text{OK}$$

Using this result, the forces acting on each segment are

$$T = 250 \text{ MN/m}^2 (0.015 \text{ m})(0.110 \text{ m}) = 412.5 \text{ kN}$$
$$C_1 = 250 \text{ MN/m}^2 (0.015 \text{ m})(0.010 \text{ m}) = 37.5 \text{ kN}$$
$$C_2 = 250 \text{ MN/m}^2 (0.015 \text{ m})(0.100 \text{ m}) = 375 \text{ kN}$$

Hence the resultant plastic moment about the neutral axis is

$$M_p = 412.5 \text{ kN} \left( \frac{0.110 \text{ m}}{2} \right) + 37.5 \text{ kN} \left( \frac{0.01 \text{ m}}{2} \right) + 375 \text{ kN} \left( 0.01 \text{ m} + \frac{0.015 \text{ m}}{2} \right)$$

$$M_p = 29.4 \text{ kN} \cdot \text{m} \qquad \qquad Ans.$$

BENDING

## EXAMPLE 23

The steel wide-flange beam shown in Fig. 53a is subjected to a fully plastic moment of $M_p$. If this moment is removed, determine the residual-stress distribution in the beam. The material is elastic perfectly plastic and has a yield stress of $\sigma_Y = 36$ ksi.

(a)

### SOLUTION

The normal-stress distribution in the beam caused by $M_p$ is shown in Fig. 53b. When $M_p$ is removed, the material responds elastically. Removal of $M_p$ requires applying $M_p$ in its reverse direction and therefore leads to an assumed elastic stress distribution as shown in Fig. 53c. The modulus of rupture $\sigma_r$ is computed from the flexure formula. Using $M_p = 1732.5$ kip·in. and $I = 211.0$ in$^4$ from Example 21, we have

$$\sigma_{max} = \frac{Mc}{I};$$

$$\sigma_r = \frac{1732.5 \text{ kip·in. (5 in.)}}{211.0 \text{ in}^4} = 41.1 \text{ ksi}$$

As expected, $\sigma_r < 2\sigma_Y$.

Superposition of the stresses gives the residual-stress distribution shown in Fig. 53d. Note that the point of zero normal stress was determined by proportion; i.e., from Figs. 53b and 53c, we require that

$$\frac{41.1 \text{ ksi}}{5 \text{ in.}} = \frac{36 \text{ ksi}}{y}$$

$$y = 4.38 \text{ in.}$$

Plastic moment applied (profile view)

(b)

Plastic moment reversed (profile view)

(c)

Residual stress distribution

(d)

**Fig. 53**

373

**EXAMPLE | 24**

The beam in Fig. 54a is made of an alloy of titanium that has a stress–strain diagram that can in part be approximated by two straight lines. If the material behavior is the *same* in both tension and compression, determine the bending moment that can be applied to the beam that will cause the material at the top and bottom of the beam to be subjected to a strain of 0.050 in./in.

(a)

Strain distribution

(b)

**Fig. 54**

## SOLUTION I
By inspection of the stress–strain diagram, the material is said to exhibit "elastic-plastic behavior with strain hardening." Since the cross section is symmetric and the tension–compression $\sigma$–$\epsilon$ diagrams are the same, the neutral axis must pass through the centroid of the cross section. The strain distribution, which is always linear, is shown in Fig. 54b. In particular, the point where maximum elastic strain (0.010 in./in.) occurs has been determined by proportion, such that $0.05/1.5$ in. $= 0.010/y$ or $y = 0.3$ in.

The corresponding normal-stress distribution acting over the cross section is shown in Fig. 54c. The moment produced by this distribution can be calculated by finding the "volume" of the stress blocks. To do so we will subdivide this distribution into two triangular blocks and a rectangular block in both the tension and compression regions, Fig. 54d. Since the beam is 2 in. wide, the resultants and their locations are determined as follows:

$$T_1 = C_1 = \frac{1}{2}(1.2 \text{ in.})(40 \text{ kip/in}^2)(2 \text{ in.}) = 48 \text{ kip}$$

$$y_1 = 0.3 \text{ in.} + \frac{2}{3}(1.2 \text{ in.}) = 1.10 \text{ in.}$$

$$T_2 = C_2 = (1.2 \text{ in.})(150 \text{ kip/in}^2)(2 \text{ in.}) = 360 \text{ kip}$$

$$y_2 = 0.3 \text{ in.} + \frac{1}{2}(1.2 \text{ in.}) = 0.90 \text{ in.}$$

$$T_3 = C_3 = \frac{1}{2}(0.3 \text{ in.})(150 \text{ kip/in}^2)(2 \text{ in.}) = 45 \text{ kip}$$

$$y_3 = \frac{2}{3}(0.3 \text{ in.}) = 0.2 \text{ in.}$$

The moment produced by this normal-stress distribution about the neutral axis is therefore

190 ksi

$y = 0.3$ in.

150 ksi

150 ksi

1.5 in.

190 ksi

Stress distribution

(c)

$$M = 2[48 \text{ kip } (1.10 \text{ in.}) + 360 \text{ kip } (0.90 \text{ in.}) + 45 \text{ kip } (0.2 \text{ in.})]$$

$$= 772 \text{ kip} \cdot \text{in.} \qquad Ans.$$

## SOLUTION II

Rather than using the above semigraphical technique, it is also possible to find the moment analytically. To do this we must express the stress distribution in Fig. 54c as a function of position y along the beam. Note that $\sigma = f(\epsilon)$ has been given in Fig. 54a. Also, from Fig. 54b, the normal strain can be determined as a function of position y by proportional triangles; i.e.,

$C_1$
$C_2$
$y_3$
$C_3$
$T_3$
0.3 in.
$y_1$ $y_2$
$T_2$
1.2 in.
$T_1$

150 ksi
40 ksi

(d)

$$\epsilon = \frac{0.05}{1.5}y \qquad 0 \le y \le 1.5 \text{ in.}$$

Substituting this into the $\sigma-\epsilon$ functions shown in Fig. 54a gives

$$\sigma = 500y \qquad\qquad 0 \le y \le 0.3 \text{ in.} \qquad (1)$$

$$\sigma = 33.33y + 140 \qquad 0.3 \text{ in.} \le y \le 1.5 \text{ in.} \qquad (2)$$

From Fig. 54e, the moment caused by $\sigma$ acting on the area strip $dA = 2 \, dy$ is

$$dM = y(\sigma \, dA) = y\sigma(2 \, dy)$$

Using Eqs. 1 and 2, the moment for the entire cross section is thus

2 in.

N

$\sigma$

y $dy$

A

(e)

**Fig. 54 (cont.)**

$$M = 2\left[ 2\int_0^{0.3 \text{ in.}} 500y^2 \, dy + 2\int_{0.3 \text{ in.}}^{1.5 \text{ in.}} (33.3y^2 + 140y) \, dy \right]$$

$$= 772 \text{ kip} \cdot \text{in.} \qquad Ans.$$

## PROBLEMS

**158.** Determine the shape factor for the wide-flange beam.

**Prob. 158**

**159.** The beam is made of an elastic plastic material for which $\sigma_Y = 250$ MPa. Determine the residual stress in the beam at its top and bottom after the plastic moment $M_p$ is applied and then released.

**Prob. 159**

*\*160.** Determine the shape factor for the cross section of the H-beam.

**161.** The H-beam is made of an elastic-plastic material for which $\sigma_Y = 250$ MPa. Determine the residual stress in the top and bottom of the beam after the plastic moment $M_p$ is applied and then released.

**Probs. 160/161**

**162.** The box beam is made of an elastic perfectly plastic material for which $\sigma_Y = 250$ MPa. Determine the residual stress in the top and bottom of the beam after the plastic moment $M_p$ is applied and then released.

**Prob. 162**

**163.** Determine the plastic moment $M_p$ that can be supported by a beam having the cross section shown. $\sigma_Y = 30$ ksi.

**Prob. 163**

**165.** The beam is made of elastic-perfectly plastic material. Determine the maximum elastic moment and the plastic moment that can be applied to the cross section. Take $\sigma_Y = 36$ ksi.

**Prob. 165**

**\*164.** Determine the shape factor of the beam's cross section.

**Prob. 164**

**166.** Determine the shape factor for the cross section of the beam.

**Prob. 166**

**167.** The beam is made of an elastic-plastic material for which $\sigma_Y = 200$ MPa. If the largest moment in the beam occurs within the center section *a–a*, determine the magnitude of each force **P** that causes this moment to be (a) the largest elastic moment and (b) the largest plastic moment.

**Prob. 167**

**\*168.** Determine the shape factor of the cross section.

**Prob. 168**

**169.** The beam is made of elastic-perfectly plastic material. Determine the maximum elastic moment and the plastic moment that can be applied to the cross section. Take $\sigma_Y = 36$ ksi.

**Prob. 169**

**170.** The box beam is made from an elastic-plastic material for which $\sigma_Y = 36$ ksi. Determine the magnitude of each concentrated force **P** that will cause the moment to be (a) the largest elastic moment and (b) the largest plastic moment.

**Prob. 170**

**171.** The beam is made from elastic-perfectly plastic material. Determine the shape factor for the thick-walled tube.

**173.** The member is made from an elastic-plastic material. Determine the maximum elastic moment and the plastic moment that can be applied to the cross section. Take $b = 4$ in., $h = 6$ in., $\sigma_Y = 36$ ksi.

**Prob. 171**

**Prob. 173**

**\*172.** Determine the shape factor for the member.

**174.** The beam is made of an elastic plastic material for which $\sigma_Y = 30$ ksi. If the largest moment in the beam occurs at the center section $a$–$a$, determine the intensity of the distributed load $w$ that causes this moment to be (a) the largest elastic moment and (b) the largest plastic moment.

**Prob. 172**

**Prob. 174**

**175.** The box beam is made from an elastic-plastic material for which $\sigma_Y = 25$ ksi. Determine the intensity of the distributed load $w_0$ that will cause the moment to be (a) the largest elastic moment and (b) the largest plastic moment.

**177.** The beam is made of a polyester that has the stress–strain curve shown. If the curve can be represented by the equation $\sigma = [20 \tan^{-1}(15\epsilon)]$ ksi, where $\tan^{-1}(15\epsilon)$ is in radians, determine the magnitude of the force **P** that can be applied to the beam without causing the maximum strain in its fibers at the critical section to exceed $\epsilon_{max} = 0.003$ in./in.

**Prob. 177**

**Prob. 175**

***176.** The wide-flange member is made from an elastic-plastic material. Determine the shape factor.

**178.** The plexiglass bar has a stress–strain curve that can be approximated by the straight-line segments shown. Determine the largest moment $M$ that can be applied to the bar before it fails.

**Prob. 176**

**Prob. 178**

**179.** The stress–strain diagram for a titanium alloy can be approximated by the two straight lines. If a strut made of this material is subjected to bending, determine the moment resisted by the strut if the maximum stress reaches a value of (a) $\sigma_A$ and (b) $\sigma_B$.

**Prob. 179**

**\*180.** A beam is made from polypropylene plastic and has a stress–strain diagram that can be approximated by the curve shown. If the beam is subjected to a maximum tensile and compressive strain of $\epsilon = 0.02$ mm/mm, determine the moment $M$.

**Prob. 180**

**181.** The bar is made of an aluminum alloy having a stress–strain diagram that can be approximated by the straight line segments shown. Assuming that this diagram is the same for both tension and compression, determine the moment the bar will support if the maximum strain at the top and bottom fibers of the beam is $\epsilon_{max} = 0.03$.

**Prob. 181**

**182.** The bar is made of an aluminum alloy having a stress–strain diagram that can be approximated by the straight line segments shown. Assuming that this diagram is the same for both tension and compression, determine the moment the bar will support if the maximum strain at the top and bottom fibers of the beam is $\epsilon_{max} = 0.05$.

**Prob. 182**

381

# CHAPTER REVIEW

Shear and moment diagrams are graphical representations of the internal shear and moment within a beam. They can be constructed by sectioning the beam an arbitrary distance $x$ from the left end, using the equilibrium equations to find $V$ and $M$ as functions of $x$, and then plotting the results. A sign convention for positive distributed load, shear, and moment must be followed.

Positive external distributed load

Positive internal shear

Positive internal moment

Beam sign convention

It is also possible to plot the shear and moment diagrams by realizing that at each point the slope of the shear diagram is equal to the intensity of the distributed loading at the point.

$$w = \frac{dV}{dx}$$

Likewise, the slope of the moment diagram is equal to the shear at the point.

$$V = \frac{dM}{dx}$$

The area under the distributed loading diagram between the points represents the change in shear.

$$\Delta V = \int w \, dx$$

The area under the shear diagram represents the change in moment.

$$\Delta M = \int V \, dx$$

The shear and moment at any point can be obtained using the method of sections. The maximum (or minimum) moment occurs where the shear is zero.

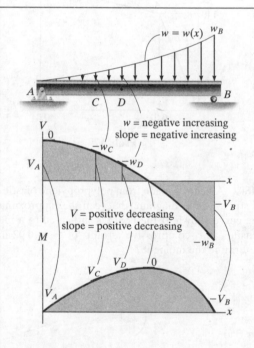

A bending moment tends to produce a linear variation of normal strain within a straight beam. Provided the material is homogeneous, and linear elastic, then equilibrium can be used to relate the internal moment in the beam to the stress distribution. The result is the flexure formula,

$$\sigma_{max} = \frac{Mc}{I}$$

where $I$ and $c$ are determined from the neutral axis that passes through the centroid of the cross section.

If the cross-sectional area of the beam is not symmetric about an axis that is perpendicular to the neutral axis, then unsymmetrical bending will occur. The maximum stress can be determined from formulas, or the problem can be solved by considering the superposition of bending caused by the moment components $\mathbf{M}_y$ and $\mathbf{M}_z$ about the principal axes of inertia for the area.

$$\sigma = -\frac{M_z y}{I_z} + \frac{M_y z}{I_y}$$

Beams made from composite materials can be "transformed" so their cross section is considered as if it were made from a single material. To do this, the transformation factor $n$, which is a ratio of the moduli of elasticity of the materials, is used to change the width $b$ of the beam.

Once the cross section is transformed, then the stress in the transformed material is determined using the flexure formula multiplied by $n$.

$$n = \frac{E_1}{E_2}$$

| Curved beams deform such that the normal strain does not vary linearly from the neutral axis. Provided the material is homogeneous and linear elastic and the cross section has an axis of symmetry, then the curved beam formula can be used to determine the bending stress. | $$\sigma = \frac{M(R - r)}{Ar(\bar{r} - R)}$$ or $$\sigma = \frac{My}{Ae(R - y)}$$ | |
| --- | --- | --- |
| Stress concentrations occur in members having a sudden change in their cross section, caused, for example, by holes and notches. The maximum bending stress at these locations is determined using a stress concentration factor $K$ that is found from graphs determined from experiment. | $$\sigma_{max} = K\frac{Mc}{I}$$ | |
| If the bending moment causes the stress in the material to exceed its elastic limit, then the normal strain will remain linear; however, the stress distribution will vary in accordance with the stress–strain diagram. The plastic and ultimate moments supported by the beam can be determined by requiring the resultant force to be zero and the resultant moment to be equivalent to the moment of the stress distribution. | | |
| If an applied plastic or ultimate moment is released, it will cause the material to respond elastically, thereby inducing residual stresses in the beam. | | |

## CONCEPTUAL PROBLEMS

**C1.** The steel saw blade passes over the drive wheel of the band saw. Using appropriate measurements and data, explain how to determine the bending stress in the blade.

C1

**C2.** The crane boom has a noticeable taper along its length. Explain why. To do so, assume the boom is in the horizontal position and in the process of hoisting a load at its end, so that the reaction on the support *A* becomes zero. Use realistic dimensions and a load, to justify your reasoning.

C2

**C3.** Use reasonable dimensions for this hammer and a loading to show through an analysis why this hammer failed in the manner shown.

C3

**C4.** These garden shears were manufactured using an inferior material. Using a loading of 50 lb applied normal to the blades, and appropriate dimensions for the shears, determine the absolute maximum bending stress in the material and show why the failure occurred at the critical location on the handle.

(a)                                    (b)

C4

# REVIEW PROBLEMS

**183.** Determine the shape factor for the wide-flange beam.

**\*184.** The beam is made of an elastic plastic material for which $\sigma_Y = 250$ MPa. Determine the residual stress in the beam at its top and bottom after the plastic moment $M_p$ is applied and then released.

**Probs. 183/184**

**185.** The compound beam consists of two segments that are pinned together at $B$. Draw the shear and moment diagrams if it supports the distributed loading shown.

**Prob. 185**

**186.** The composite beam consists of a wood core and two plates of steel. If the allowable bending stress for the wood is $(\sigma_{allow})_w = 20$ MPa, and for the steel $(\sigma_{allow})_{st} = 130$ MPa, determine the maximum moment that can be applied to the beam. $E_w = 11$ GPa, $E_{st} = 200$ GPa.

**187.** Solve Prob. 186 if the moment is applied about the $y$ axis instead of the $z$ axis as shown.

**Probs. 186/187**

**\*188.** A shaft is made of a polymer having a parabolic upper and lower cross section. If it resists an internal moment of $M = 125$ N · m, determine the maximum bending stress developed in the material (a) using the flexure formula and (b) using integration. Sketch a three-dimensional view of the stress distribution acting over the cross-sectional area.

**Prob. 188**

**189.** Determine the maximum bending stress in the handle of the cable cutter at section *a–a*. A force of 45 lb is applied to the handles. The cross-sectional area is shown in the figure.

**Prob. 189**

**190.** The curved beam is subjected to a bending moment of $M = 85$ N · m as shown. Determine the stress at points $A$ and $B$ and show the stress on a volume element located at these points.

**Prob. 190**

**191.** Determine the shear and moment in the beam as functions of $x$, where $0 \leq x < 6$ ft, then draw the shear and moment diagrams for the beam.

**Prob. 191**

**\*192.** A wooden beam has a square cross section as shown. Determine which orientation of the beam provides the greatest strength at resisting the moment **M**. What is the difference in the resulting maximum stress in both cases?

**Prob. 192**

**193.** Draw the shear and moment diagrams for the shaft if it is subjected to the vertical loadings of the belt, gear, and flywheel. The bearings at $A$ and $B$ exert only vertical reactions on the shaft.

**Prob. 193**

**194.** The strut has a square cross section $a$ by $a$ and is subjected to the bending moment **M** applied at an angle $\theta$ as shown. Determine the maximum bending stress in terms of $a$, $M$, and $\theta$. What angle $\theta$ will give the largest bending stress in the strut? Specify the orientation of the neutral axis for this case.

**Prob. 194**

# Solutions and Answers for Preliminary Problems

**P1a.**

**P1b.**

**P1c.**

**P1d.**

**P1e.**

**P1g.**

**P1f.**

**P1h.**

P2. $I = \left[ \dfrac{1}{12}(0.2\text{ m})(0.4\text{ m})^3 \right] - \left[ \dfrac{1}{12}(0.1\text{ m})(0.2\text{ m})^3 \right]$

$\qquad = 1.0\,(10^{-3})\text{ m}^4$

**P3.**

$$\bar{y} = \frac{\Sigma \tilde{y} A}{\Sigma A} = \frac{(0.05 \text{ m})(0.2 \text{ m})(0.1 \text{ m}) + (0.25 \text{ m})(0.1 \text{ m})(0.3 \text{ m})}{(0.2 \text{ m})(0.1 \text{ m}) + (0.1 \text{ m})(0.3 \text{ m})}$$

$$= 0.17 \text{ m}$$

$$I = \left[ \frac{1}{12} (0.2 \text{ m})(0.1 \text{ m})^3 + (0.2 \text{ m})(0.1 \text{ m})(0.17 \text{ m} - 0.05 \text{ m})^2 \right]$$

$$+ \left[ \frac{1}{12} (0.1 \text{ m})(0.3 \text{ m})^3 + (0.1 \text{ m})(0.3 \text{ m})(0.25 \text{ m} - 0.17 \text{ m})^2 \right]$$

$$= 0.722 \, (10^{-3}) \text{ m}^4$$

**P5a.**

**P4a.**

**P5b.**

**P4b.**

# Selected Answers

**1.** $T_1 = 250$ lb, $T_2 = 200$ lb

**2.**

**3.**

**5.**

**6.** For $0 \le x < \dfrac{L}{2}$: $V = \dfrac{w_0 L}{24}$, $M = \dfrac{w_0 L}{24}x$,

For $\dfrac{L}{2} < x \le L$: $V = \dfrac{w_0}{24L}\left[L^2 - 6(2x - L)^2\right]$,

$M = \dfrac{w_0}{24L}\left[L^2 x - (2x - L)^3\right]$

**7.**

**9.** For $0 \le x < 4$ m: $V = \{9 - 6x\}$ kN,
$M = \{9x - 3x^2\}$ kN·m,
For $4$ m $< x \le 6$ m: $V = \{6(6 - x)\}$ kN·m,
$M = -\{3(6 - x)^2\}$ kN·m

**10.**

**11.**

**13.**

**14.**

**17.** $V = \{-300 - 16.67x^2\}$ lb,
$M = \{-300x - 5.556x^3\}$ lb·ft

392

**18.** For $0 \le x < 6$ ft: $V = \{30.0 - 2x\}$ kip,
$M = \{-x^2 + 30.0x - 216\}$ kip·ft,
For 6 ft $< x \le 10$ ft: $V = 8.00$ kip,
$M = \{8.00x - 120\}$ kip·ft

**19.**

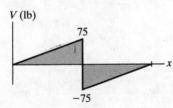

**21.** $M_{max} = 281$ lb·ft

**22.**

**23.**

**25.** $V = 1050 - 150x$
$M = -75x^2 + 1050x - 3200$

**27.**

**29.**

**30.**

**31.**

**33.**

**34.**

**35.** For $0 \le x < 3$ m: $V = 200$ N, $M = (200x)$ N·m,

For $3$ m $< x \le 6$ m: $V = \left\{ -\dfrac{100}{3}x^2 + 500 \right\}$ N,

$$M = \left\{ -\dfrac{100}{9}x^3 + 500x - 600 \right\} \text{N·m}$$

**37.**

**38.**

**39.**

**41.**

**42.**

395

**43.**

**45.**

**46.** $b = 0.207\,L$

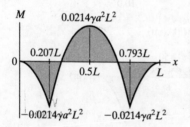

**47.** $r = 909$ mm, $M = 61.9$ N $\cdot$ m
**49.** $(\sigma_t)_{max} = 3.72$ ksi, $(\sigma_c)_{max} = 1.78$ ksi
**50.** $M = 2.50$ kip $\cdot$ ft
**51.** $(\sigma_{max})_t = 2.40$ ksi, $(\sigma_{max})_c = 4.80$ ksi
**53.** $F_R = 200$ kN
**54.** $(\sigma_{max})_c = 78.1$ MPa,
　　$(\sigma_{max})_t = 165$ MPa
**55.** $M = 50.3$ kN $\cdot$ m
**57.** $\sigma_{max} = 49.4$ MPa
**58.** $\sigma_B = 3.61$ MPa, $\sigma_C = 1.55$ MPa
**59.** $(\sigma_{max})_t = 6.71$ MPa, $(\sigma_{max})_c = 3.61$ MPa
**61.** % of moment carried by web = 22.6%
**62.** $\sigma_A = 6.21$ MPa (C), $\sigma_B = 5.17$ MPa (T)
**63.** $\sigma_A = 214$ psi (C), $\sigma_B = 33.0$ psi (T),
　　$\sigma_C = 115$ psi (T)
**65.** (a) $\sigma_{max} = 497$ kPa,
　　(b) $\sigma_{max} = 497$ kPa
**66.** (a) $\sigma_{max} = 249$ kPa,
　　(b) $\sigma_{max} = 249$ kPa
**67.** $\sigma_{max} = 158$ MPa
**69.** $\sigma_{min} = 74.7$ MPa
**70.** $\sigma_{max} = 22.1$ ksi
**71.** $\sigma_{max} = 21.1$ ksi
**73.** $d = 1.28$ in.
**74.** $\sigma_{max} = 45.1$ ksi
**75.** $\sigma_{max} = 52.8$ MPa
**77.** $(\sigma_{max})_c = 1.87$ ksi,
　　$(\sigma_{max})_t = 1.37$ ksi
**78.** $M = 2.92$ kip $\cdot$ ft
**79.** $F_R = 4.23$ kip
**81.** $M = 123$ kN $\cdot$ m
**82.** $\sigma_{max} = 24.4$ ksi
**83.** Use $d = 3\dfrac{1}{16}$ in.
**85.** $w = 18.75$ kN/m
**86.** $\sigma_{max} = 19.1$ ksi
**87.** $d = 2$ in.
**89.** $a = 66.9$ mm
**90.** $\sigma_{max} = \dfrac{23w_0 L^2}{36\,bh^2}$
**91.** $\sigma_{max} = 119$ MPa
**93.** $\sigma_{max} = 25.8$ ksi
**94.** $P = 10.4$ kN
**95.** $\sigma_{max} = 11.5$ MPa
**97.** $P = 114$ kip
**98.** $\sigma_{max} = 7.59$ ksi
**99.** $\sigma_{max} = 5.60$ ksi
**101.** $d = 410$ mm
**102.** $(\sigma_{max})_t = 2.77$ MPa, $(\sigma_{max})_c = 3.84$ MPa
**103.** $P = 2.60$ kN

**105.** $\sigma_A = -119$ kPa, $\sigma_B = 446$ kPa, $\sigma_D = -446$ kPa, $\sigma_E = 119$ kPa

**106.** $a = 0;\ b = -\left(\dfrac{M_z I_y + M_y I_{yz}}{I_y I_z - I_{yz}^2}\right);\ c = \dfrac{M_y I_z + M_z I_{yz}}{I_y I_z - I_{yz}^2}$

**107.** $\sigma_{max} = 5.66$ MPa (C), $\alpha = 79.8°$

**109.** $\sigma_{max} = 4.70$ MPa, $\alpha = -76.0°$

**110.** $M = 5.11$ kN $\cdot$ m

**111.** $\sigma_{max} = 131$ MPa (C), $\alpha = -66.5°$

**113.** When $\theta = 3°$: $\sigma_A = 925$ psi, $\alpha = -25.3°$, When $\theta = 0°$: $\sigma_A = 800$ psi

**114.** $\sigma_{max} = 3.33$ ksi (T), $\alpha = -63.1°$

**115.** $\sigma_{max} = 2.90$ MPa, $\alpha = -66.6°$

**117.** $\sigma_A = 2.60$ MPa

**118.** $\sigma_{max} = 151$ MPa, $\alpha = 72.5°$

**119.** $w = 4.37$ kN/m

**121.** $M = 128$ kN $\cdot$ m

**122.** $(\sigma_{max})_{st} = 22.6$ ksi, $(\sigma_{max})_{al} = 13.3$ ksi

**123.** $w = 0.875$ kip/ft

**125.** $M = 35.0$ kN $\cdot$ m

**126.** $(\sigma_{max})_{st} = 123$ MPa, $(\sigma_{max})_w = 5.14$ MPa

**127.** $\sigma_{max} = 20.1$ MPa

**129.** $(\sigma_{st})_{max} = 3.70$ MPa, $(\sigma_w)_{max} = 0.179$ MPa

**130.** $(\sigma_{pvc})_{max} = 1.53$ ksi

**131.** $d = 531$ mm, $M = 98.6$ kN $\cdot$ m

**133.** $M = 103$ kN $\cdot$ m

**134.** $(\sigma_{max})_{st} = 154$ MPa, $(\sigma_{max})_{al} = 171$ MPa

**135.** $(\sigma_{max})_{st} = 8.51$ ksi, $(\sigma_{max})_w = 0.558$ ksi

**137.** % of error $= 22.3\%$

**138.** $M = 51.8$ kN $\cdot$ m

**139.** $\sigma_{max} = 842$ psi (T)

**141.** $\sigma_A = 43.7$ MPa (T), $\sigma_B = 7.77$ MPa (T), $\sigma_C = 65.1$ MPa (C)

**142.** $P = 6.91$ kN

**143.** $(\sigma_{max})_t = 204$ psi, $(\sigma_{max})_c = 120$ psi

**145.** $(\sigma_{max})_c = 792$ kPa, $(\sigma_{max})_t = 1.02$ MPa

**146.** $(\sigma_{max})_t = 1.16$ ksi, $(\sigma_{max})_c = 0.994$ ksi

**147.** $\sigma_A = 10.1$ ksi (C), $\sigma_B = 0.955$ ksi (T), $\sigma_C = 5.94$ ksi (T)

**149.** $\sigma_{max} = \pm 1.39$ MPa

**150.** $r = 8.0$ mm

**151.** $\sigma_{max} = 14.6$ MPa

**153.** $\sigma_{max} = 54.4$ MPa

**154.** $P = 122$ lb

**155.** $\sigma_{max} = 29.5$ ksi

**157.** $M = 41.7$ N $\cdot$ m

**158.** $k = 1.17$

**159.** $\sigma_{top} = \sigma_{bottom} = 43.5$ Mpa

**161.** $\sigma_{top} = \sigma_{bottom} = 142$ MPa

**162.** $\sigma_{top} = \sigma_{bottom} = 67.1$ MPa

**163.** $M_p = 172$ kip $\cdot$ ft

**165.** $M_Y = 143$ kip $\cdot$ ft, $M_p = 243$ kip $\cdot$ ft

**166.** $k = 1.16$

**167.** Elastic: $P = 66.7$ kN, Plastic: $P = 100$ kN

**169.** $M_Y = 130.5$ kip $\cdot$ ft, $M_p = 223$ kip $\cdot$ ft

**170.** Elastic: $P = 37.3$ kip, Plastic: $P = 45.5$ kip

**171.** $k = \dfrac{16 r_o (r_o^3 - r_i^3)}{3\pi (r_o^4 - r_i^4)}$

**173.** $M_Y = 18$ kip $\cdot$ ft, $M_p = 36$ kip $\cdot$ ft

**174.** Elastic: $w = 4.27$ kip/ft, Plastic: $w = 6.40$ kip/ft

**175.** Elastic: $w_0 = 18.0$ kip/ft, Plastic: $w_0 = 22.8$ kip/ft

**177.** $P = 100$ lb

**178.** $M = 94.7$ N $\cdot$ m

**179.** Maximum elastic moment: $M = 35.0$ kip $\cdot$ ft, Ultimate moment: $M = 59.8$ kip $\cdot$ ft

**181.** $M = 73.5$ kip $\cdot$ ft

**182.** $M = 81.7$ kip $\cdot$ ft

**183.** $k = 1.22$

**186.** $M = 14.9$ kN $\cdot$ m

**187.** $M = 26.4$ kN $\cdot$ m

**189.** $\sigma_{max} = 8.41$ ksi

**190.** $\sigma_A = 225$ kPa (C), $\sigma_B = 265$ kPa (T)

**191.** $V = 20 - 2x$, $M = -x^2 + 20x - 166$

**194.** $\sigma_{max} = \dfrac{6M}{a^3}(\cos\theta + \sin\theta)$, $\theta = 45°$, $\alpha = 45°$

# Fundamental Problems Partial Solutions and Answers

**F1**    $\zeta + \Sigma M_B = 0; \quad A_y(6) - 30 = 0 \qquad A_y = 5 \text{ kN}$

       $+\uparrow \Sigma F_y = 0; \quad -V - 5 = 0 \qquad\qquad V = -5 \text{ kN}$

                                                     *Ans.*

       $\zeta + \Sigma M_O = 0; \quad M + 5x = 0 \quad M = \{-5x\} \text{ kN} \cdot \text{m}$

                                                     *Ans.*

**F2**    $+\uparrow \Sigma F_y = 0; \quad -V - 9 = 0 \qquad V = -9 \text{ kN} \qquad Ans.$

       $\zeta + \Sigma M_O = 0; \quad M + 9x = 0 \quad . \quad M = \{-9x\} \text{ kN} \cdot \text{m}$

                                                     *Ans.*

**F3**    $+\uparrow \Sigma F_y = 0; \quad -V - 2x = 0 \quad V = \{-2x\} \text{ kip} \qquad Ans.$

       $\zeta + \Sigma M_O = 0; \quad M + 2x\left(\dfrac{x}{2}\right) - 18 = 0$

                        $M = \{18 - x^2\} \text{ kip} \cdot \text{ft} \qquad Ans.$

**F4**    $+\uparrow \Sigma F_y = 0; \quad -V - \dfrac{1}{2}(4x)(x) = 0$

                          $V = \{-2x^2\} \text{ kN} \qquad Ans.$

       $\zeta + \Sigma M_O = 0; \, M + \left[\dfrac{1}{2}(4x)(x)\right]\left(\dfrac{x}{3}\right) = 0$

                        $M = \left\{-\dfrac{2}{3}x^3\right\} \text{ kN} \cdot \text{m} \qquad Ans.$

**F5**

**F6**

**F7**

**F8**

**F9**

$$I = 2\left[\frac{1}{12}(0.02)(0.2^3)\right] + \frac{1}{12}(0.26)(0.02^3)$$

$$= 26.84(10^{-6}) \text{ m}^4$$

$$\sigma_{max} = \frac{Mc}{I} = \frac{20(10^3)(0.1)}{26.84(10^{-6})} = 74.5 \text{ MPa} \qquad Ans.$$

**F10**

$$\bar{y} = \frac{0.3}{3} = 0.1 \text{ m}$$

$$I = \frac{1}{36}(0.3)(0.3^3) = 0.225(10^{-3}) \text{ m}^4$$

$$(\sigma_{max})_c = \frac{Mc}{I} = \frac{50(10^3)(0.3 - 0.1)}{0.225(10^{-3})}$$

$$= 44.4 \text{ MPa (C)} \qquad Ans.$$

$$(\sigma_{max})_t = \frac{My}{I} = \frac{50(10^3)(0.1)}{0.225(10^{-3})} = 22.2 \text{ MPa (T)} \; Ans.$$

**F11**

$$I = \frac{1}{12}(0.2)(0.3^3) - \frac{1}{12}(0.18)(0.26^3)$$

$$= 0.18636(10^{-3}) \text{ m}^4$$

$$\sigma_{max} = \frac{Mc}{I} = \frac{50(10^3)(0.15)}{0.18636(10^{-3})} = 40.2 \text{ MPa} \qquad Ans.$$

**F12**

$$I = 2\left[\frac{1}{12}(0.03)(0.4^3)\right] + 2\left[\frac{1}{12}(0.14)(0.03^3) + 0.14(0.03)(0.15^2)\right]$$

$$= 0.50963(10^{-3}) \text{ m}^4$$

$$\sigma_{max} = \frac{Mc}{I} = \frac{10(10^3)(0.2)}{0.50963(10^{-3})} = 3.92 \text{ MPa} \qquad Ans.$$

$$\sigma_A = 3.92 \text{ MPa (C)}$$

$$\sigma_B = 92 \text{ MPa (T)}$$

**F13**
$$I = \frac{1}{12}(0.05)(0.4)^3 + 2\left[\frac{1}{12}(0.025)(0.3)^3\right]$$
$$= 0.37917(10^{-3}) \ m^4$$
$$\sigma_A = \frac{My_A}{I} = \frac{5(10^3)(-0.15)}{0.37917(10^{-3})} = 1.98 \ MPa \ (T) \quad Ans.$$

**F14**
$$M_y = 50\left(\frac{4}{5}\right) = 40 \ kN \cdot m$$
$$M_z = 50\left(\frac{3}{5}\right) = 30 \ kN \cdot m$$
$$I_y = \frac{1}{12}(0.3)(0.2^3) = 0.2(10^{-3}) \ m^4$$
$$I_z = \frac{1}{12}(0.2)(0.3^3) = 0.45(10^{-3}) \ m^4$$
$$\sigma = -\frac{M_z y}{I_z} + \frac{M_y z}{I_y}$$
$$\sigma_A = -\frac{[30(10^3)](-0.15)}{0.45(10^{-3})} + \frac{[40(10^3)](0.1)}{0.2(10^{-3})}$$
$$= 30 \ MPa \ (T) \qquad Ans.$$

$$\sigma_B = -\frac{[30(10^3)](0.15)}{0.45(10^{-3})} + \frac{[40(10^3)](0.1)}{0.2(10^{-3})}$$
$$= 10 \ MPa \ (T) \qquad Ans.$$
$$\tan \alpha = \frac{I_z}{I_y} \tan \theta$$
$$\tan \alpha = \left[\frac{0.45(10^{-3})}{0.2(10^{-3})}\right]\left(\frac{4}{3}\right)$$
$$\alpha = 71.6° \qquad Ans.$$

**F15** Maximum stress occurs at $D$ or $A$.
$$(\sigma_{max})_D = \frac{(50\cos 30°)12(3)}{\frac{1}{12}(4)(6)^3} + \frac{(50\sin 30°)12(2)}{\frac{1}{12}(6)(4)^3}$$
$$= 40.4 \ psi \qquad Ans.$$

# Transverse Shear

From Chapter 7 of *Mechanics of Materials*, Ninth Edition. R. C. Hibbeler. Copyright © 2014 by Pearson Education, Inc. Published by Pearson Prentice Hall. All rights reserved.

Railroad ties act as beams that support very large transverse shear loadings. As a result, if they are made of wood they will tend to split at their ends, where the shear loads are the largest.

# Transverse Shear

## CHAPTER OBJECTIVES

■ In this chapter, we will develop a method for finding the shear stress in a beam having a prismatic cross section and made from homogeneous material that behaves in a linear-elastic manner. The method of analysis to be developed will be somewhat limited to special cases of cross-sectional geometry. Although this is the case, it has many wide-range applications in engineering design and analysis. The concept of shear flow, along with shear stress, will be discussed for beams and thin-walled members. The chapter ends with a discussion of the shear center.

## 1 Shear in Straight Members

In general, a beam will support both shear and moment. The shear **V** is the result of a transverse shear-stress distribution that acts over the beam's cross section. Due to the complementary property of shear, however, this stress will create corresponding longitudinal shear stresses which will act along longitudinal planes of the beam as shown in Fig. 1.

Transverse shear stress

Longitudinal shear stress

$\tau$

$\tau$

**V**

**Fig. 1**

Boards not bonded together
(a)

Boards bonded together
(b)

**Fig. 2**

Shear connectors are "tack welded" to this corrugated metal floor liner so that when the concrete floor is poured, the connectors will prevent the concrete slab from slipping on the liner surface. The two materials will thus act as a composite slab.

To illustrate this effect, consider the beam to be made from three boards, Fig. 2a. If the top and bottom surfaces of each board are smooth, and the boards are *not* bonded together, then application of the load **P** will cause the boards to *slide* relative to one another when the beam deflects. However, if the boards are bonded together, then the longitudinal shear stresses acting between the boards will prevent their relative sliding, and consequently the beam will act as a single unit, Fig. 2b.

As a result of the shear stress, shear strains will be developed and these will tend to distort the cross section in a rather complex manner. For example, consider the short bar in Fig. 3a made of a highly deformable material and marked with horizontal and vertical grid lines. When a shear **V** is applied, it tends to deform these lines into the pattern shown in Fig. 3b. This nonuniform shear-strain distribution will cause the cross section to *warp*.

(a) Before deformation

(b) After deformation

**Fig. 3**

404

As a result, when a beam is subjected to *both* bending and shear, the cross section will not remain plane as assumed in the development of the flexure formula. Although this is the case, we can generally assume the cross-sectional warping due to shear is small enough so that it can be *neglected*. This assumption is particularly true for the most common case of a *slender beam*; that is, one that has a small depth compared with its length.

## 2 The Shear Formula

Because the strain distribution for shear is not easily defined, as in the case of axial load, torsion, and bending, we will develop the shear formula in an indirect manner. To do this we will consider the *horizontal force equilibrium* of a portion of the element taken from the beam in Fig. 4a. A free-body diagram of this *element* is shown in Fig. 4b. This distribution is caused by the bending moments $M$ and $M + dM$. We have excluded the effects of $V$, $V + dV$, and $w(x)$ on the free-body diagram since these loadings are vertical and will therefore not be involved in a horizontal force summation. The element in Fig. 4b will indeed satisfy $\Sigma F_x = 0$ since the stress distribution on each side of the element forms only a couple moment and therefore a zero force resultant.

(a)

(b)

**Fig. 4**

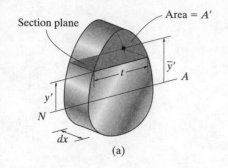

Section plane

Area = $A'$

$t$

$\bar{y}'$

$A$

$y'$

$N$

$dx$

(a)

Now consider the shaded top *portion* of the element that has been sectioned at $y'$ from the neutral axis, Fig. 4a. This segment has a width $t$ at the section, and the two cross-sectional sides each have an area $A'$. Because the resultant moments on each side of the element differ by $dM$, it can be seen in Fig. 4c that $\Sigma F_x = 0$ will not be satisfied *unless* a longitudinal shear stress $\tau$ acts over the bottom face of the segment. We will assume this shear stress is *constant* across the width $t$ of the bottom face. It acts on the area $t\,dx$. Applying the equation of horizontal force equilibrium, and using the flexure formula, Eq. 13, we have

$$\overset{+}{\leftarrow} \Sigma F_x = 0; \qquad \int_{A'} \sigma'\, dA' - \int_{A'} \sigma\, dA' - \tau(t\,dx) = 0$$

$$\int_{A'} \left(\frac{M + dM}{I}\right) y\, dA' - \int_{A'} \left(\frac{M}{I}\right) y\, dA' - \tau(t\,dx) = 0$$

$$\left(\frac{dM}{I}\right) \int_{A'} y\, dA' = \tau(t\,dx) \qquad (1)$$

Solving for $\tau$, we get

$$\tau = \frac{1}{It} \left(\frac{dM}{dx}\right) \int_{A'} y\, dA'$$

This equation can be simplified by noting that $V = dM/dx$ (Eq. 2). Also, the integral represents the moment of the area $A'$ about the neutral axis. We will denote this by the symbol $Q$. Since the location of the centroid of the area $A'$ is determined from $\bar{y}' = \int_{A'} y\, dA'/A'$, we can also write

$$Q = \int_{A'} y\, dA' = \bar{y}'A' \qquad (2)$$

$A'$

$\sigma$

$\tau$

$\sigma'$

$M$

$dx$

$t$

$M + dM$

$\sigma$

$\sigma'$

$M$

$\tau$

$y'$

$M + dM$

Three-dimensional view  (c)  Profile view

**Fig. 4 (cont.)**

406

The final result is therefore

$$\tau = \frac{VQ}{It} \tag{3}$$

Here, as shown in Fig. 5,

- $\tau$ = the shear stress in the member at the point located a distance $y'$ from the neutral axis. This stress is assumed to be constant and therefore *averaged* across the width $t$ of the member

- $V$ = the internal resultant shear force, determined from the method of sections and the equations of equilibrium

- $I$ = the moment of inertia of the *entire* cross-sectional area calculated about the neutral axis

- $t$ = the width of the member's cross-sectional area, measured at the point where $\tau$ is to be determined

- $Q$ = $\bar{y}'A'$, where $A'$ is the area of the top (or bottom) portion of the member's cross-sectional area, above (or below) the section plane where $t$ is measured, and $\bar{y}'$ is the distance from the neutral axis to the centroid of $A'$

The above equation is referred to as the *shear formula*. Although in the derivation we considered only the shear stresses acting on the beam's longitudinal plane, the formula applies as well for finding the transverse shear stress on the beam's cross-section. Recall that these stresses are complementary and numerically equal.

Also, because the flexure formula was used in the derivation, it is necessary that the material behave in a linear elastic manner and have a modulus of elasticity that is the *same* in tension as it is in compression.

**Fig. 5**

(a)

(b)

**Fig. 6**

## Limitations on the Use of the Shear Formula.

One of the major assumptions used in the development of the shear formula is that the shear stress is *uniformly* distributed over the *width t* at the section. In other words, the *average shear stress* is calculated across the width. We can test the accuracy of this assumption by comparing it with a more exact mathematical analysis based on the theory of elasticity. For example, if the beam's cross section is rectangular, the shear-stress distribution across the neutral axis as calculated from the theory of elasticity varies as shown in Fig. 6. The maximum value, $\tau'_{max}$, occurs at the *sides* of the cross section, and its magnitude depends on the ratio $b/h$ (width/depth). For sections having a $b/h = 0.5$, $\tau'_{max}$ is only about 3% greater than the shear stress calculated from the shear formula, Fig. 6a. However, for *flat sections*, say $b/h = 2$, $\tau'_{max}$ is about 40% greater than $\tau_{max}$, Fig. 6b. The error becomes even greater as the section becomes flatter, or as the $b/h$ ratio increases. Errors of this magnitude are certainly intolerable if one uses the shear formula to determine the shear stress in the *flange* of the wide-flange beam shown in Fig. 7.

It should also be pointed out that the shear formula will not give accurate results when used to determine the shear stress at the flange—web junction of a wide-flange beam, since this is a point of sudden cross-sectional change and therefore a *stress concentration* occurs here. Fortunately, these limitations for applying the shear formula to the flanges of a wide-flange beam are not important in engineering practice. Most often engineers must only calculate the *average maximum shear stress* in the beam, which occurs at the neutral axis, where the $b/h$ (width/depth) ratio for the web is *very small*, and therefore the calculated result is very close to the *actual* maximum shear stress as explained above.

**Fig. 7**

Another important limitation on the use of the shear formula can be illustrated with reference to Fig. 8a, which shows a member having a cross section with an irregular or nonrectangular boundary. If we apply the shear formula to determine the (average) shear stress $\tau$ along the line $AB$, it will be directed downward as shown in Fig. 8b. However, consider an element of material taken from the boundary point $B$, Fig. 8c. Here $\tau$ on the front face of the element is resolved into components, $\tau'$ and $\tau''$ acting perpendicular and parallel to the boundary. By inspection, $\tau'$ must be equal to zero since its corresponding longitudinal component $\tau'$, on the stress-free boundary surface, must be zero. To satisfy this boundary condition, therefore, the shear stress acting on this element must *actually be directed tangent to the boundary*. As a result, the shear-stress distribution across line $AB$ is directed as shown in Fig. 8d. Here specific values for the shear stress must be obtained using the theory of elasticity. Note, however, that we can apply the shear formula to obtain the shear stress acting across each of the colored lines in Fig. 8a. These lines intersect the tangents to the boundary at *right angles*, and as shown in Fig. 8e, the transverse shear stress is vertical and constant along each line.

To summarize the above points, the shear formula does not give accurate results when applied to members having cross sections that are *short or flat*, or at points where the cross section suddenly changes. Nor should it be applied across a section that intersects the boundary of the member at an angle other than 90°. Instead, for these cases the shear stress should be determined using more advanced methods based on the theory of elasticity.

Shear-stress distribution
from shear formula

Stress-free
outer surface

$\tau' = 0$

(a)          (b)          (c)          (d)

(e)

**Fig. 8**

## Important Points

- Shear forces in beams cause *nonlinear shear-strain* distributions over the cross section, causing it to *warp*.

- Due to the complementary property of shear stress, the shear stress developed in a beam acts over the cross section of the beam and along its longitudinal planes.

- The *shear formula* was derived by considering horizontal force equilibrium of the longitudinal shear-stress and bending-stress distributions acting on a portion of a differential segment of the beam.

- The shear formula is to be used on straight prismatic members made of homogeneous material that has linear elastic behavior. Also, the internal resultant shear force must be directed along an axis of symmetry for the cross-sectional area.

- The shear formula should not be used to determine the shear stress on cross sections that are short or flat, at points of sudden cross-sectional changes, or at a point on an inclined boundary.

## Procedure for Analysis

In order to apply the shear formula, the following procedure is suggested.

### Internal Shear.

- Section the member perpendicular to its axis at the point where the shear stress is to be determined, and obtain the internal shear $V$ at the section.

### Section Properties.

- Determine the location of the neutral axis, and determine the moment of inertia $I$ of the *entire cross-sectional area* about the neutral axis.

- Pass an imaginary horizontal section through the point where the shear stress is to be determined. Measure the width $t$ of the cross-sectional area at this section.

- The portion of the area lying either above or below this width is $A'$. Determine $Q$ by using $Q = \bar{y}'A'$. Here $\bar{y}'$ is the distance to the centroid of $A'$, measured from the neutral axis. It may be helpful to realize that $A'$ is the portion of the member's cross-sectional area that is being "held onto the member" by the longitudinal shear stresses. See Fig. 4c.

### Shear Stress.

- Using a consistent set of units, substitute the data into the shear formula and calculate the shear stress $\tau$.

- It is suggested that the direction of the transverse shear stress $\tau$ be established on a volume element of material located at the point where it is calculated. This can be done by realizing that $\tau$ acts on the cross section in the same direction as $V$. From this, the corresponding shear stresses acting on the other three planes of the element can then be established.

# EXAMPLE | 1

The beam shown in Fig. 9a is made from two boards. Determine the maximum shear stress in the glue necessary to hold the boards together along the seam where they are joined.

## SOLUTION

**Internal Shear.** The support reactions and the shear diagram for the beam are shown in Fig. 9b. It is seen that the maximum shear in the beam is 19.5 kN.

**Section Properties.** The centroid and therefore the neutral axis will be determined from the reference axis placed at the bottom of the cross-sectional area, Fig. 9a. Working in units of meters, we have

$$\bar{y} = \frac{\Sigma \tilde{y} A}{\Sigma A}$$

$$= \frac{[0.075 \text{ m}](0.150 \text{ m})(0.030 \text{ m}) + [0.165 \text{ m}](0.030 \text{ m})(0.150 \text{ m})}{(0.150 \text{ m})(0.030 \text{ m}) + (0.030 \text{ m})(0.150 \text{ m})} = 0.120 \text{ m}$$

The moment of inertia, about the neutral axis, Fig. 9a, is therefore

$$I = \left[ \frac{1}{12}(0.030 \text{ m})(0.150 \text{ m})^3 + (0.150 \text{ m})(0.030 \text{ m})(0.120 \text{ m} - 0.075 \text{ m})^2 \right]$$

$$+ \left[ \frac{1}{12}(0.150 \text{ m})(0.030 \text{ m})^3 + (0.030 \text{ m})(0.150 \text{ m})(0.165 \text{ m} - 0.120 \text{ m})^2 \right]$$

$$= 27.0(10^{-6}) \text{ m}^4$$

The top board (flange) is being held onto the bottom board (web) by the glue, which is applied over the thickness $t = 0.03$ m. Consequently $A'$ is defined as the area of the top board, Fig. 9a. We have

$$Q = \bar{y}'A' = [0.180 \text{ m} - 0.015 \text{ m} - 0.120 \text{ m}](0.03 \text{ m})(0.150 \text{ m})$$

$$= 0.2025(10^{-3}) \text{ m}^3$$

**Shear Stress.** Using the above data and applying the shear formula yields

$$\tau_{max} = \frac{VQ}{It} = \frac{19.5(10^3) \text{ N}(0.2025(10^{-3}) \text{ m}^3)}{27.0(10^{-6}) \text{ m}^4(0.030 \text{ m})} = 4.88 \text{ MPa} \qquad Ans.$$

The shear stress acting at the top of the bottom board is shown in Fig. 9c.

**NOTE:** It is the glue's resistance to this *longitudinal shear* stress that holds the boards from slipping at the right-hand support.

(a)

(b)

Plane containing glue

4.88 MPa

(c)

**Fig. 9**

# EXAMPLE | 2

Determine the distribution of the shear stress over the cross section of the beam shown in Fig. 10a.

(a)                              (b)

## SOLUTION

The distribution can be determined by finding the shear stress at an *arbitrary height y* from the neutral axis, Fig. 10b, and then plotting this function. Here, the dark colored area $A'$ will be used for $Q$.* Hence

$$Q = \bar{y}'A' = \left[ y + \frac{1}{2}\left(\frac{h}{2} - y\right)\right]\left(\frac{h}{2} - y\right)b = \frac{1}{2}\left(\frac{h^2}{4} - y^2\right)b$$

Applying the shear formula, we have

$$\tau = \frac{VQ}{It} = \frac{V\left(\frac{1}{2}\right)\left[(h^2/4) - y^2\right]b}{\left(\frac{1}{12}bh^3\right)b} = \frac{6V}{bh^3}\left(\frac{h^2}{4} - y^2\right) \qquad (1)$$

This result indicates that the shear-stress distribution over the cross section is **parabolic**. As shown in Fig. 10c, the intensity varies from zero at the top and bottom, $y = \pm h/2$, to a maximum value at the neutral axis, $y = 0$. Specifically, since the area of the cross section is $A = bh$, then at $y = 0$ we have

$$\boxed{\tau_{max} = 1.5\frac{V}{A}} \qquad (2)$$

This same value for $\tau_{max}$ can be obtained directly from the shear

Shear–stress distribution

(c)

**Fig. 10**

---

*The area below $y$ can also be used $\left[A' = b(h/2 + y)\right]$, but doing so involves a bit more algebraic manipulation.

(d)

**Fig. 10 (cont.)**

Typical shear failure of this wooden beam occurred at the support and through the approximate center of its cross section.

formula, $\tau = VQ/It$, by realizing that $\tau_{max}$ occurs where $Q$ is *largest*, since $V$, $I$, and $t$ are *constant*. By inspection, $Q$ will be a maximum when the entire area above (or below) the neutral axis is considered; that is, $A' = bh/2$ and $\bar{y}' = h/4$. Thus,

$$\tau_{max} = \frac{VQ}{It} = \frac{V(h/4)(bh/2)}{\left[\frac{1}{12}bh^3\right]b} = 1.5\frac{V}{A}$$

By comparison, $\tau_{max}$ is 50% greater than the *average* shear stress, that is, $\tau_{avg} = V/A$.

It is important to realize that $\tau_{max}$ also acts in the longitudinal direction of the beam, Fig. 10*d*. It is this stress that can cause a timber beam to fail as shown Fig. 10*e*. Here horizontal splitting of the wood starts to occur through the neutral axis at the beam's ends, since there the vertical reactions subject the beam to large shear stress and wood has a low resistance to shear along its grains, which are oriented in the longitudinal direction.

It is instructive to show that when the shear-stress distribution, Eq. 1, is integrated over the cross section it yields the resultant shear $V$. To do this, a differential strip of area $dA = b\,dy$ is chosen, Fig. 10*c*, and since $\tau$ acts uniformly over this strip, we have

$$\int_A \tau\,dA = \int_{-h/2}^{h/2} \frac{6V}{bh^3}\left(\frac{h^2}{4} - y^2\right)b\,dy$$

$$= \frac{6V}{h^3}\left[\frac{h^2}{4}y - \frac{1}{3}y^3\right]_{-h/2}^{h/2}$$

$$= \frac{6V}{h^3}\left[\frac{h^2}{4}\left(\frac{h}{2} + \frac{h}{2}\right) - \frac{1}{3}\left(\frac{h^3}{8} + \frac{h^3}{8}\right)\right] = V$$

(e)

## EXAMPLE | 3

A steel wide-flange beam has the dimensions shown in Fig. 11a. If it is subjected to a shear of $V = 80$ kN, plot the shear-stress distribution acting over the beam's cross-sectional area.

(a)

(b)

### SOLUTION

Since the flange and web are rectangular elements, then like the previous example, the shear-stress distribution will be parabolic and in this case it will vary in the manner shown in Fig. 11b. Due to symmetry, only the shear stresses at points $B'$, $B$, and $C$ have to be determined. To show how these values are obtained, we must first determine the moment of inertia of the cross-sectional area about the neutral axis. Working in meters, we have

$$I = \left[\frac{1}{12}(0.015 \text{ m})(0.200 \text{ m})^3\right]$$

$$+ 2\left[\frac{1}{12}(0.300 \text{ m})(0.02 \text{ m})^3 + (0.300 \text{ m})(0.02 \text{ m})(0.110 \text{ m})^2\right]$$

$$= 155.6(10^{-6}) \text{ m}^4$$

For point $B'$, $t_{B'} = 0.300$ m, and $A'$ is the dark shaded area shown in Fig. 11c. Thus,

$$Q_{B'} = \bar{y}'A' = [0.110 \text{ m}](0.300 \text{ m})(0.02 \text{ m}) = 0.660(10^{-3}) \text{ m}^3$$

so that

$$\tau_{B'} = \frac{VQ_{B'}}{It_{B'}} = \frac{80(10^3) \text{ N}(0.660(10^{-3}) \text{ m}^3)}{155.6(10^{-6}) \text{ m}^4(0.300 \text{ m})} = 1.13 \text{ MPa}$$

For point $B$, $t_B = 0.015$ m and $Q_B = Q_{B'}$, Fig. 11c. Hence

$$\tau_B = \frac{VQ_B}{It_B} = \frac{80(10^3) \text{ N}(0.660(10^{-3}) \text{ m}^3)}{155.6(10^{-6}) \text{ m}^4(0.015 \text{ m})} = 22.6 \text{ MPa}$$

Note from the discussion of "Limitations on the Use of the Shear Formula" that the calculated values for both $\tau_{B'}$ and $\tau_B$ will actually be very misleading. Why?

(c)

**Fig. 11**

(d)

**Fig. 11 (cont.)**

For point $C$, $t_C = 0.015$ m and $A'$ is the dark shaded area shown in Fig. 11d. Considering this area to be composed of two rectangles, we have

$$Q_C = \Sigma \bar{y}'A' = [0.110 \text{ m}](0.300 \text{ m})(0.02 \text{ m})$$

$$+ [0.05 \text{ m}](0.015 \text{ m})(0.100 \text{ m})$$

$$= 0.735(10^{-3}) \text{ m}^3$$

Thus,

$$\tau_C = \tau_{max} = \frac{VQ_C}{It_C} = \frac{80(10^3) \text{ N}[0.735(10^{-3}) \text{ m}^3]}{155.6(10^{-6}) \text{ m}^4(0.015 \text{ m})} = 25.2 \text{ MPa}$$

**NOTE:** From Fig. 11b, note that most of the shear stress occurs in the web and is almost uniform throughout its depth, varying from 22.6 MPa to 25.2 MPa. It is for this reason that for design, some codes permit the use of calculating the *average* shear stress on the cross section of the web rather than using the shear formula; that is,

$$\tau_{avg} = \frac{V}{A_w} = \frac{80(10^3) \text{ N}}{(0.015 \text{ m})(0.2 \text{ m})} = 26.7 \text{ MPa}$$

**415**

# PRELIMINARY PROBLEMS

**P1.** In each case, calculate the value of $Q$ and $t$ that are used in the shear formula for finding the shear stress at $A$. Also, show how the shear stress acts on a differential volume element located at point $A$.

(a)

(b)

(c)

(d)

(e)

(f)

# FUNDAMENTAL PROBLEMS

**F1.** If the beam is subjected to a shear force of $V = 100$ kN, determine the shear stress developed at point $A$. Represent the state of stress on a volume element at this point.

**F1**

**F2.** Determine the shear stress at points $A$ and $B$ on the beam if it is subjected to a shear force of $V = 600$ kN. Represent the state of stress on a volume element of these points.

**F2**

**F3.** Determine the absolute maximum shear stress developed in the beam.

**F3**

**F4.** If the beam is subjected to a shear force of $V = 20$ kN, determine the maximum shear stress developed in the beam.

**F4**

**F5.** If the beam is made from four plates and subjected to a shear force of $V = 20$ kN, determine the maximum shear stress developed in the beam at point $A$. Represent the state of stress on a volume element at this point.

**F5**

# PROBLEMS

**1.** If the wide-flange beam is subjected to a shear of $V = 20$ kN, determine the shear stress on the web at $A$. Indicate the shear-stress components on a volume element located at this point.

**2.** If the wide-flange beam is subjected to a shear of $V = 20$ kN, determine the maximum shear stress in the beam.

**3.** If the wide-flange beam is subjected to a shear of $V = 20$ kN, determine the shear force resisted by the web of the beam.

**Probs. 1/2/3**

**\*4.** If the T-beam is subjected to a vertical shear of $V = 12$ kip, determine the maximum shear stress in the beam. Also, compute the shear-stress jump at the flange-web junction $AB$. Sketch the variation of the shear-stress intensity over the entire cross section.

**5.** If the T-beam is subjected to a vertical shear of $V = 12$ kip, determine the vertical shear force resisted by the flange.

**Probs. 4/5**

**6.** The wood beam has an allowable shear stress of $\tau_{allow} = 7$ MPa. Determine the maximum shear force $V$ that can be applied to the cross section.

**Prob. 6**

**7.** The shaft is supported by a smooth thrust bearing at $A$ and a smooth journal bearing at $B$. If $P = 20$ kN, determine the absolute maximum shear stress in the shaft.

**\*8.** The shaft is supported by a smooth thrust bearing at $A$ and a smooth journal bearing at $B$. If the shaft is made from a material having an allowable shear stress of $\tau_{allow} = 75$ MPa, determine the maximum value for $P$.

**Probs. 7/8**

**9.** Determine the largest shear force $V$ that the member can sustain if the allowable shear stress is $\tau_{allow} = 8$ ksi.

**10.** If the applied shear force $V = 18$ kip, determine the maximum shear stress in the member.

**Probs. 9/10**

**11.** The overhang beam is subjected to the uniform distributed load having an intensity of $w = 50$ kN/m. Determine the maximum shear stress developed in the beam.

**Prob. 11**

**\*12.** The beam has a rectangular cross section and is made of wood having an allowable shear stress of $\tau_{allow} = 200$ psi. Determine the maximum shear force $V$ that can be developed in the cross section of the beam. Also, plot the shear-stress variation over the cross section.

**Prob. 12**

**13.** Determine the maximum shear stress in the strut if it is subjected to a shear force of $V = 20$ kN.

**14.** Determine the maximum shear force $V$ that the strut can support if the allowable shear stress for the material is $\tau_{allow} = 40$ MPa.

**Probs. 13/14**

**15.** The strut is subjected to a vertical shear of $V = 130$ kN. Plot the intensity of the shear-stress distribution acting over the cross-sectional area, and compute the resultant shear force developed in the vertical segment $AB$.

**Prob. 15**

**\*16.** The steel rod has a radius of 1.25 in. If it is subjected to a shear of $V = 5$ kip, determine the maximum shear stress.

**Prob. 16**

**17.** If the beam is subjected to a shear of $V = 15$ kN, determine the web's shear stress at $A$ and $B$. Indicate the shear-stress components on a volume element located at these points. Set $w = 125$ mm. Show that the neutral axis is located at $\bar{y} = 0.1747$ m from the bottom and $I_{NA} = 0.2182(10^{-3})$ m$^4$.

**18.** If the wide-flange beam is subjected to a shear of $V = 30$ kN, determine the maximum shear stress in the beam. Set $w = 200$ mm.

**19.** If the wide-flange beam is subjected to a shear of $V = 30$ kN, determine the shear force resisted by the web of the beam. Set $w = 200$ mm.

**Probs. 17/18/19**

**\*20.** The steel rod is subjected to a shear of 30 kip. Determine the maximum shear stress in the rod.

**Prob. 20**

**21.** If the beam is made from wood having an allowable shear stress $\tau_{allow} = 400$ psi, determine the maximum magnitude of **P**. Set $d = 4$ in.

**Prob. 21**

**22.** Determine the shear stress at point $B$ on the web of the cantilevered strut at section $a$–$a$.

**23.** Determine the maximum shear stress acting at section $a$–$a$ of the cantilevered strut.

**Probs. 22/23**

**\*24.** Determine the maximum shear stress in the T-beam at the critical section where the internal shear force is maximum.

**25.** Determine the maximum shear stress in the T-beam at section $C$. Show the result on a volume element at this point.

**Probs. 24/25**

**26.** The beam has a square cross section and is made of wood having an allowable shear stress of $\tau_{allow} = 1.4$ ksi. If it is subjected to a shear of $V = 1.5$ kip, determine the smallest dimension $a$ of its sides.

$V = 1.5$ kip

$a$

$a$

**Prob. 26**

**27.** The beam is slit longitudinally along both sides as shown. If it is subjected to an internal shear of $V = 250$ kN, compare the maximum shear stress developed in the beam before and after the cuts were made.

**\*28.** The beam is to be cut longitudinally along both sides as shown. If it is made from a material having an allowable shear stress of $\tau_{allow} = 75$ MPa, determine the maximum allowable internal shear force **V** that can be applied before and after the cut is made.

25 mm

200 mm

100 mm

25 mm

25 mm

**V**

25 mm

200 mm

25 mm

**Probs. 27/28**

**■29.** Write a computer program that can be used to determine the maximum shear stress in the beam that has the cross section shown, and is subjected to a specified constant distributed load $w$ and concentrated force $P$. Show an application of the program using the values $L = 4$ m, $a = 2$ m, $P = 1.5$ kN, $d_1 = 0$, $d_2 = 2$ m, $w = 400$ N/m, $t_1 = 15$ mm, $t_2 = 20$ mm, $b = 50$ mm, and $h = 150$ mm.

$d_2$

$d_1$

$w$

**P**

$A$

$B$

$a$

$L$

$t_1$

$t_2$

$h$

$b$

**Prob. 29**

**30.** The beam has a rectangular cross section and is subjected to a load $P$ that is just large enough to develop a fully plastic moment $M_p = PL$ at the fixed support. If the material is elastic-plastic, then at a distance $x < L$ the moment $M = Px$ creates a region of plastic yielding with an associated elastic core having a height $2y'$. Prove that the maximum shear stress developed in the beam is given by $\tau_{max} = \frac{3}{2}(P/A')$, where $A' = 2y'b$, the cross-sectional area of the elastic core.

**P**

$x$

Plastic region

$2y'$

$h$

$b$

Elastic region

$L$

**Prob. 30**

**31.** The beam is subjected to a fully plastic moment $\mathbf{M}_p$. Prove that the longitudinal and transverse shear stresses in the beam are zero. *Hint:* Consider an element of the beam as shown in Fig. 4c.

# 3  Shear Flow in Built-Up Members

**Fig. 12**

Occasionally in engineering practice, members are "built up" from several composite parts in order to achieve a greater resistance to loads. Examples are shown in Fig. 12. If the loads cause the members to bend, fasteners such as nails, bolts, welding material, or glue may be needed to keep the component parts from sliding relative to one another, Fig. 2. In order to design these fasteners or determine their spacing, it is necessary to know the shear force that must be resisted by the fastener. This loading, when measured as a force per unit length of beam, is referred to as *shear flow q.** 

The magnitude of the shear flow can be obtained using a development similar to that for finding the shear stress in the beam. To show this, we will consider finding the shear flow along the juncture where the segment in Fig. 13*a* is connected to the flange of the beam. As shown in Fig. 13*b*, three horizontal forces must act on this segment. Two of these forces, $F$ and $F + dF$, are developed by normal stresses caused by the moments $M$ and $M + dM$, respectively. The third force, which for equilibrium equals $dF$, acts at the juncture and it is to be supported by the fastener. Realizing that $dF$ is the result of $dM$, then, like Eq. 1, we have

$$dF = \frac{dM}{I} \int_{A'} y \, dA'$$

The integral represents $Q$, that is, the moment of the segment's area $A'$ in Fig. 13*b* about the neutral axis for the entire cross section. Since the segment has a length $dx$, the shear flow, or force per unit length along the beam, is $q = dF/dx$. Hence dividing both sides by $dx$ and noting that $V = dM/dx$, we can write

$$\boxed{q = \frac{VQ}{I}} \qquad (4)$$

Here

$q =$ the shear flow, measured as a force per unit length along the beam

$V =$ the internal resultant shear force, determined from the method of sections and the equations of equilibrium

$I =$ the moment of inertia of the *entire* cross-sectional area computed about the neutral axis

$Q = \bar{y}'A'$, where $A'$ is the cross-sectional area of the segment that is connected to the beam at the juncture where the shear flow is to be calculated, and $\bar{y}'$ is the distance from the neutral axis to the centroid of $A'$

---

*The use of the word "flow" in this terminology will become meaningful as it pertains to the discussion in Sec. 5.

(a)

(b)

**Fig. 13**

Application of this equation follows the same "procedure for analysis" as outlined in Sec. 2 for the shear formula. It is very important to identify $Q$ correctly when determining the shear flow at a particular junction on the cross section. A few examples should serve to illustrate how this is done. Consider the beam cross sections shown in Fig. 14. The shaded segments are connected to the beam by fasteners and at the planes of connection, identified by the thick black lines, the shear flow $q$ is determined by using a value of $Q$ calculated from $A'$ and $\bar{y}'$ indicated in each figure. This value of $q$ will be resisted by a *single* fastener in Fig. 14a, by *two* fasteners in Fig. 14b, and by *three* fasteners in Fig. 14c. In other words, the fastener in Fig. 14a supports the calculated value of $q$, and in Figs. 14b and 14c each fastener supports $q/2$ and $q/3$, respectively.

## Important Point

- *Shear flow* is a measure of the force per unit length along the axis of a beam. This value is found from the shear formula and is used to determine the shear force developed in fasteners and glue that holds the various segments of a composite beam together.

(a)

(b)

(c)

**Fig. 14**

## EXAMPLE | 4

The beam is constructed from three boards glued together as shown in Fig. 15a. If it is subjected to a shear of $V = 850$ kN, determine the shear flow at $B$ and $B'$ that must be resisted by the glue.

### SOLUTION

**Section Properties.** The neutral axis (centroid) will be located from the bottom of the beam, Fig. 15a. Working in units of meters, we have

$$\bar{y} = \frac{\Sigma \tilde{y} A}{\Sigma A} = \frac{2[0.15 \text{ m}](0.3 \text{ m})(0.01 \text{ m}) + [0.305 \text{ m}](0.250 \text{ m})(0.01 \text{ m})}{2(0.3 \text{ m})(0.01 \text{ m}) + 0.250 \text{ m}(0.01 \text{ m})}$$

$$= 0.1956 \text{ m}$$

The moment of inertia about the neutral axis is thus

$$I = 2\left[\frac{1}{12}(0.01 \text{ m})(0.3 \text{ m})^3 + (0.01 \text{ m})(0.3 \text{ m})(0.1956 \text{ m} - 0.150 \text{ m})^2\right]$$

$$+ \left[\frac{1}{12}(0.250 \text{ m})(0.01 \text{ m})^3 + (0.250 \text{ m})(0.01 \text{ m})(0.305 \text{ m} - 0.1956 \text{ m})^2\right]$$

$$= 87.42(10^{-6}) \text{ m}^4$$

Since the glue at $B$ and $B'$ in Fig. 15a "holds" the top board to the beam, we have

$$Q_B = \bar{y}'_B A'_B = [0.305 \text{ m} - 0.1956 \text{ m}](0.250 \text{ m})(0.01 \text{ m})$$

$$= 0.2735(10^{-3}) \text{ m}^3$$

**Shear Flow.** For $B$ and $B'$ we have

$$q'_B = \frac{V Q_B}{I} = \frac{850(10^3) \text{ N}(0.2735(10^{-3}) \text{ m}^3)}{87.42(10^{-6}) \text{ m}^4} = 2.66 \text{ MN/m}$$

Since *two seams* are used to secure the board, the glue per meter length of beam at the seam must be strong enough to resist *one-half* of the calculated value of $q'_B$. Thus,

$$q_B = q_B' = 1.33 \text{ MN/m} \qquad\qquad Ans.$$

If the board $CC'$ is added to the beam, Fig. 15b, then $\bar{y}$ and $I$ have to be recalculated, and the shear flow at $C$ and $C'$ determined from $q'_C = V\, y'_C A'_C / I$. Finally, this value is divided by one-half to obtain $q_C$ and $q'_C$.

10 mm

250 mm

$A'_B$

$B$     $B'$

$\bar{y}'_B$

N     A

300 mm

$V = 850$ kN

$\bar{y}$

10 mm — 125 mm — 10 mm

(a)

$C$     $C'$

$A'_C$

N     $\bar{y}'_C$     A

(b)

**Fig. 15**

## EXAMPLE 5

A box beam is constructed from four boards nailed together as shown in Fig. 16a. If each nail can support a shear force of 30 lb, determine the maximum spacing $s$ of the nails at $B$ and at $C$ so that the beam will support the force of 80 lb.

80 lb

### SOLUTION

**Internal Shear.** If the beam is sectioned at an *arbitrary point* along its length, the internal shear required for equilibrium is always $V = 80$ lb, and so the shear diagram is shown in Fig. 16b.

**Section Properties.** The moment of inertia of the cross-sectional area about the neutral axis can be determined by considering a 7.5-in. × 7.5-in square minus a 4.5-in. × 4.5-in. square.

$$I = \frac{1}{12}(7.5 \text{ in.})(7.5 \text{ in.})^3 - \frac{1}{12}(4.5 \text{ in.})(4.5 \text{ in.})^3 = 229.5 \text{ in}^4$$

(a)

The shear flow at $B$ is determined using $Q_B$ found from the darker shaded area shown in Fig. 16c. It is this "symmetric" portion of the beam that is to be "held" onto the rest of the beam by nails on the left side and by the fibers of the board on the right side. Thus,

$$Q_B = \bar{y}'A' = [3 \text{ in.}](7.5 \text{ in.})(1.5 \text{ in.}) = 33.75 \text{ in}^3$$

Likewise, the shear flow at $C$ can be determined using the "symmetric" shaded area shown in Fig. 16d. We have

$$Q_C = \bar{y}'A' = [3 \text{ in.}](4.5 \text{ in.})(1.5 \text{ in.}) = 20.25 \text{ in}^3$$

$V$ (lb)

80

$x$ (ft)

(b)

### Shear Flow.

$$q_B = \frac{VQ_B}{I} = \frac{80 \text{ lb}(33.75 \text{ in}^3)}{229.5 \text{ in}^4} = 11.76 \text{ lb/in.}$$

$$q_C = \frac{VQ_C}{I} = \frac{80 \text{ lb}(20.25 \text{ in}^3)}{229.5 \text{ in}^4} = 7.059 \text{ lb/in.}$$

These values represent the shear force per unit length of the beam that must be resisted by the nails at $B$ and the fibers at $B'$, Fig. 16c, and the nails at $C$ and the fibers at $C'$, Fig. 16d, respectively. Since in each case the shear flow is resisted at *two* surfaces and each nail can resist 30 lb, for $B$ the spacing is

(c)

$$s_B = \frac{30 \text{ lb}}{(11.76/2) \text{ lb/in.}} = 5.10 \text{ in.} \quad \text{Use } s_B = 5 \text{ in.} \qquad Ans.$$

And for $C$,

(d)

$$s_C = \frac{30 \text{ lb}}{(7.059/2) \text{ lb/in.}} = 8.50 \text{ in.} \quad \text{Use } s_C = 8.5 \text{ in.} \qquad Ans.$$

**Fig. 16**

# EXAMPLE | 6

Nails having a total shear strength of 40 lb are used in a beam that can be constructed either as in Case I or as in Case II, Fig. 17. If the nails are spaced at 9 in., determine the largest vertical shear that can be supported in each case so that the fasteners will not fail.

**Fig. 17**

## SOLUTION

Since the cross section is the same in both cases, the moment of inertia about the neutral axis is

$$I = \frac{1}{12}(3 \text{ in.})(5 \text{ in.})^3 - 2\left[\frac{1}{12}(1 \text{ in.})(4 \text{ in.})^3\right] = 20.58 \text{ in}^4$$

**Case I.** For this design a single row of nails holds the top or bottom flange onto the web. For one of these flanges,

$$Q = \bar{y}'A' = [2.25 \text{ in.}](3 \text{ in.}(0.5 \text{ in.})) = 3.375 \text{ in}^3$$

so that

$$q = \frac{VQ}{I}$$

$$\frac{40 \text{ lb}}{9 \text{ in.}} = \frac{V(3.375 \text{ in}^3)}{20.58 \text{ in}^4}$$

$$V = 27.1 \text{ lb} \qquad\qquad Ans.$$

**Case II.** Here a single row of nails holds one of the side boards onto the web. Thus,

$$Q = \bar{y}'A' = [2.25 \text{ in.}](1 \text{ in.}(0.5 \text{ in.})) = 1.125 \text{ in}^3$$

$$q = \frac{VQ}{I}$$

$$\frac{40 \text{ lb}}{9 \text{ in.}} = \frac{V(1.125 \text{ in}^3)}{20.58 \text{ in}^4}$$

$$V = 81.3 \text{ lb} \qquad\qquad Ans.$$

# FUNDAMENTAL PROBLEMS

**F6.** The two identical boards are bolted together to form the beam. Determine the maximum allowable spacing $s$ of the bolts to the nearest mm if each bolt has a shear strength of 15 kN. The beam is subjected to a shear force of $V = 50$ kN.

**F6**

**F7.** Two identical 20-mm thick plates are bolted to the top and bottom flange to form the built-up beam. If the beam is subjected to a shear force of $V = 300$ kN, determine the allowable maximum spacing $s$ of the bolts to the nearest mm. Each bolt has a shear strength of 30 kN.

**F7**

**F8.** The boards are bolted together to form the built-up beam. If the beam is subjected to a shear force of $V = 20$ kN, determine the allowable maximum spacing of the bolts to the nearest mm. Each bolt has a shear strength of 8 kN.

**F8**

**F9.** The boards are bolted together to form the built-up beam. If the beam is subjected to a shear force of $V = 15$ kip, determine the allowable maximum spacing of the bolts to the nearest $\frac{1}{8}$ in. Each bolt has a shear strength of 6 kip.

**F9**

## PROBLEMS

**\*32.** The beam is constructed from two boards fastened together at the top and bottom with two rows of nails spaced every 6 in. If each nail can support a 500-lb shear force, determine the maximum shear force $V$ that can be applied to beam.

**33.** The beam is construced from two boards fastened together at the top and bottom with two rows of nails spaced every 6 in. If an internal shear force of $V = 600$ lb is applied to the boards, determine the shear force resisted by each nail.

**Probs. 32/33**

**34.** The boards are glued together to form the built-up beam. If the wood has an allowable shear stress of $\tau_{allow} = 3$ MPa, and the glue seam at $B$ can withstand a maximum shear stress of 1.5 MPa, determine the maximum allowable internal shear $V$ that can be developed in the beam.

**35.** The boards are glued together to form the built-up beam. If the wood has an allowable shear stress of $\tau_{allow} = 3$ MPa, and the glue seam at $D$ can withstand a maximum shear stress of 1.5 MPa, determine the maximum allowable shear $V$ that can be developed in the beam.

**Probs. 34/35**

**\*36.** Three identical boards are bolted together to form the built-up beam. Each bolt has a shear strength of 1.5 kip and the bolts are spaced at a distance of $s = 6$ in. If the wood has an allowable shear stress of $\tau_{allow} = 450$ psi, determine the maximum allowable internal shear $V$ that can act on the beam.

**37.** Three identical boards are bolted together to form the built-up beam. If the wood has an allowable shear stress of $\tau_{allow} = 450$ psi, determine the maximum allowable internal shear $V$ that can act on the beam. Also, find the corresponding average shear stress in the $\frac{3}{8}$ in. diameter bolts which are spaced equally at $s = 6$ in.

**Probs. 36/37**

**38.** The beam is subjected to a shear of $V = 2$ kN. Determine the average shear stress developed in each nail if the nails are spaced 75 mm apart on each side of the beam. Each nail has a diameter of 4 mm.

**Prob. 38**

**39.** A beam is constructed from three boards bolted together as shown. Determine the shear force developed in each bolt if the bolts are spaced $s = 250$ mm apart and the applied shear is $V = 35$ kN.

**Prob. 39**

**\*40.** The simply-supported beam is built-up from three boards by nailing them together as shown. The wood has an allowable shear stress of $\tau_{allow} = 1.5$ MPa, and an allowable bending stress of $\sigma_{allow} = 9$ MPa. The nails are spaced at $s = 75$ mm, and each has a shear strength of 1.5 kN. Determine the maximum allowable force **P** that can be applied to the beam.

**41.** The simply-supported beam is built-up from three boards by nailing them together as shown. If $P = 12$ kN, determine the maximum allowable spacing $s$ of the nails to support that load, if each nail can resist a shear force of 1.5 kN.

**Probs. 40/41**

**42.** The T-beam is constructed as shown. If the nails can each support a shear force of 950 lb, determine the maximum shear force $V$ that the beam can support and the corresponding maximum nail spacing $s$ to the nearest $\frac{1}{8}$ in. The allowable shear stress for the wood is $\tau_{allow} = 450$ psi.

**Prob. P42**

**43.** The box beam is made from four pieces of plastic that are glued together as shown. If the glue has an allowable strength of 400 lb/in², determine the maximum shear the beam will support.

**\*44.** The box beam is made from four pieces of plastic that are glued together as shown. If $V = 2$ kip, determine the shear stress resisted by the seam at each of the glued joints.

**Probs. 43/44**

**45.** A beam is constructed from four boards which are nailed together. If the nails are on both sides of the beam and each can resist a shear of 3 kN, determine the maximum load $P$ that can be applied to the end of the beam.

Prob. 45

**46.** The beam is subjected to a shear of $V = 800$ N. Determine the average shear stress developed in the nails along the sides $A$ and $B$ if the nails are spaced $s = 100$ mm apart. Each nail has a diameter of 2 mm.

Prob. 46

**47.** The beam is made from four boards nailed together as shown. If the nails can each support a shear force of 100 lb., determine their required spacing $s'$ and $s$ if the beam is subjected to a shear of $V = 700$ lb.

Prob. 47

**\*48.** The beam is made from three polystyrene strips that are glued together as shown. If the glue has a shear strength of 80 kPa, determine the maximum load $P$ that can be applied without causing the glue to lose its bond.

Prob. 48

**■49.** The timber T-beam is subjected to a load consisting of $n$ concentrated forces, $P_n$. If the allowable shear $V_{nail}$ for each of the nails is known, write a computer program that will specify the nail spacing between each load. Show an application of the program using the values $L = 15$ ft, $a_1 = 4$ ft, $P_1 = 600$ lb, $a_2 = 8$ ft, $P_2 = 1500$ lb, $b_1 = 1.5$ in., $h_1 = 10$ in., $b_2 = 8$ in., $h_2 = 1$ in., and $V_{nail} = 200$ lb.

Prob. 49

# 4  Shear Flow in Thin-Walled Members

In this section we will show how to apply the shear flow equation $q = VQ/I$ to find the shear-flow *distribution* throughout a member's cross-sectional area. We will assume that the member has *thin walls*, that is, the wall thickness is small compared to its height or width. As will be shown in the next section, this analysis has important applications in structural and mechanical design.

Like the shear stress, the shear flow acts on both the longitudinal *and* transverse planes of the member. To show how to establish its direction on the cross section, consider the segment $dx$ of the wide-flange beam in Fig. 18a. Free-body diagrams of two segments $B$ and $C$ taken from the top flange are shown in Figs. 18b and 18c. The force $dF$ must act on the longitudinal section in order to balance the normal forces $F$ and $F + dF$ created by the moments $M$ and $M + dM$, respectively. Now, if the corner elements $B$ and $C$ of each segment are removed, then the transverse components $q$ act on the cross section as shown in Figs. 18b and 18c. Using this method, show that the shear flow at the corresponding points $B'$ and $C'$ on the bottom flange in Fig. 18d is directed as shown.

Although it is also true that $V + dV$ will create *vertical* shear-flow components on *this* element, here we will neglect its effects. This is because this component, like the shear stress, is approximately zero throughout the thickness of the element. Here, the flange is thin and the top and bottom surfaces of the element are free of stress, Fig. 18e. To summarize then, only the shear flow component that acts *parallel* to the sides of the flange will be considered.

(a)

(b)

(c)

(d)

$q'$ assumed to be zero throughout flange thickness since top and bottom of flange are stress free

$q$ assumed *constant* throughout flange thickness

(e)

**Fig. 18**

(a)

(b)                    (c)

**Fig. 19**

Having determined the direction of the shear flow in each flange, we can now find its distribution along the top right flange of the beam in Fig. 19a. To do this, consider the shear flow $q$, acting on the colored element $dx$, located an arbitrary distance $x$ from the centerline of the cross section, Fig. 19b. Here $Q = \bar{y}'A' = [d/2](b/2 - x)t$, so that

$$q = \frac{VQ}{I} = \frac{V[d/2](b/2 - x)t}{I} = \frac{Vtd}{2I}\left(\frac{b}{2} - x\right) \qquad (5)$$

By inspection, this distribution varies in a *linear* manner from $q = 0$ at $x = b/2$ to $(q_{max})_f = Vtdb/4I$ at $x = 0$. (The limitation of $x = 0$ is possible here since the member is assumed to have "thin walls" and so the thickness of the web is neglected.) Due to symmetry, a similar analysis yields the same distribution of shear flow for the other flange segments, so that the results are as shown in Fig. 19d.

The total force developed in each flange segment can be determined by integration. Since the force on the element $dx$ in Fig. 19b is $dF = q\,dx$, then

$$F_f = \int q\,dx = \int_0^{b/2} \frac{Vtd}{2I}\left(\frac{b}{2} - x\right) dx = \frac{Vtdb^2}{16I}$$

We can also determine this result by finding the area under the triangle in Fig. 19d. Hence,

$$F_f = \frac{1}{2}(q_{max})_f\left(\frac{b}{2}\right) = \frac{Vtdb^2}{16I}$$

All four of these forces are shown in Fig. 19e, and we can see from their direction that horizontal force equilibrium of the cross section is maintained.

432

(e)

Shear-flow distribution

(d)

**Fig. 19 (cont.)**

A similar analysis can be performed for the web, Fig. 19c. Here $q$ must act downward, and at element $dy$ we have $Q = \Sigma \bar{y}'A' = [d/2](bt) + [y + (1/2)(d/2 - y)]t(d/2 - y) = bt\,d/2 + (t/2)(d^2/4 - y^2)$, so that

$$q = \frac{VQ}{I} = \frac{Vt}{I}\left[\frac{db}{2} + \frac{1}{2}\left(\frac{d^2}{4} - y^2\right)\right] \qquad (6)$$

For the web, the shear flow varies in a *parabolic manner*, from $q = 2(q_{max})_f = Vt\,db/2I$ at $y = d/2$ to $(q_{max})_w = (Vt\,d/I)(b/2 + d/8)$ at $y = 0$, Fig. 19d.

Integrating to determine the force in the web, $F_w$, we have,

$$F_w = \int q\,dy = \int_{-d/2}^{d/2} \frac{Vt}{I}\left[\frac{db}{2} + \frac{1}{2}\left(\frac{d^2}{4} - y^2\right)\right] dy$$

$$= \frac{Vt}{I}\left[\frac{db}{2}y + \frac{1}{2}\left(\frac{d^2}{4}y - \frac{1}{3}y^3\right)\right]\Bigg|_{-d/2}^{d/2}$$

$$= \frac{Vt d^2}{4I}\left(2b + \frac{1}{3}d\right)$$

Simplification is possible by noting that the moment of inertia for the cross-sectional area is

$$I = 2\left[\frac{1}{12}bt^3 + bt\left(\frac{d}{2}\right)^2\right] + \frac{1}{12}td^3$$

Neglecting the first term, since the thickness of each flange is small, then

$$I = \frac{td^2}{4}\left(2b + \frac{1}{3}d\right)$$

Substituting this into the above equation, we see that $F_w = V$, which is to be expected, Fig. 19e.

433

From the foregoing analysis, three important points should be observed. First, the value of $q$ changes over the cross section, since $Q$ will be different for each area segment $A'$ for which it is determined. In particular, $q$ will vary *linearly* along segments (flanges) that are *perpendicular* to the direction of $\mathbf{V}$, and *parabolically* along segments (web) that are *inclined or parallel* to $\mathbf{V}$. Second, $q$ will *always act parallel to the walls* of the member, since the section on which $q$ is calculated is taken perpendicular to the walls. And third, the *directional sense* of $q$ is such that the shear appears to "*flow*" through the cross section, *inward* at the beam's top flange, "combining" and then "flowing" *downward* through the web, since it must contribute to the shear force $\mathbf{V}$, and then separating and "flowing" *outward* at the bottom flange. If one is able to "visualize" this "flow" it will provide an easy means for establishing not only the direction of $q$, but *also* the corresponding direction of $\tau$. Other examples of how $q$ is directed along the segments of thin-walled members are shown in Fig. 20. In all cases, symmetry prevails about an axis that is collinear with $\mathbf{V}$. As a result, $q$ "flows" in a direction such that it will provide the vertical force $\mathbf{V}$ and yet also satisfy horizontal force equilibrium for the cross section.

Shear flow $q$

**Fig. 20**

## Important Points

- The shear flow formula $q = VQ/I$ can be used to determine the distribution of the shear flow throughout a thin-walled member provided the shear $\mathbf{V}$ acts along an axis of symmetry or principal centroidal axis of inertia for the cross section.

- If a member is made from segments having thin walls, only the shear flow *parallel* to the walls of the member is important.

- The shear flow varies *linearly* along segments that are *perpendicular* to the direction of the shear $\mathbf{V}$.

- The shear flow varies *parabolically* along segments that are *inclined* or *parallel* to the direction of the shear $\mathbf{V}$.

- On the cross section, the shear "flows" along the segments so that it results in the vertical shear force $\mathbf{V}$ and yet satisfies horizontal force equilibrium.

## EXAMPLE | 7

The thin-walled box beam in Fig. 21a is subjected to a shear of 10 kip. Determine the variation of the shear flow throughout the cross section.

(a)

### SOLUTION

By symmetry, the neutral axis passes through the center of the cross section. For thin-walled members we use centerline dimensions for calculating the moment of inertia.

$$I = \frac{1}{12}(2 \text{ in.})(7 \text{ in.})^3 + 2\left[(5 \text{ in.})(1 \text{ in.})(3.5 \text{ in.})^2\right] = 179.7 \text{ in.}^4$$

(b)

Only the shear flow at points $B$, $C$, and $D$ has to be determined. For point $B$, the area $A' \approx 0$, Fig. 21b, since it can be thought of as being located entirely at point $B$. Alternatively, $A'$ can also represent the *entire* cross-sectional area, in which case $Q_B = \bar{y}'A' = 0$ since $\bar{y}' = 0$. Because $Q_B = 0$, then

$$q_B = 0$$

For point $C$, the area $A'$ is shown dark shaded in Fig. 21c. Here, we have used the mean dimensions since point $C$ is on the centerline of each segment. We have

(c)

$$Q_C = \bar{y}'A' = (3.5 \text{ in.})(5 \text{ in.})(1 \text{ in.}) = 17.5 \text{ in}^3$$

Since there are two points of attachment,

$$q_C = \frac{1}{2}\left(\frac{VQ_C}{I}\right) = \frac{1}{2}\left(\frac{10 \text{ kip}(17.5 \text{ in}^3))}{179.7 \text{ in}^4}\right) = 0.487 \text{ kip/in.}$$

The shear flow at $D$ is determined using the three dark-shaded rectangles shown in Fig. 21d. Again, using centerline dimensions

(d)

$$Q_D = \Sigma\bar{y}'A = 2\left[\frac{3.5 \text{ in.}}{2}\right](1 \text{ in.})(3.5 \text{ in.}) + [3.5 \text{ in.}](5 \text{ in.})(1 \text{ in.}) = 29.75 \text{ in}^3$$

Because there are two points of attachment,

$$q_D = \frac{1}{2}\left(\frac{VQ_D}{I}\right) = \frac{1}{2}\left(\frac{10 \text{ kip}(29.75 \text{ in}^3)}{179.7 \text{ in}^4}\right) = 0.828 \text{ kip/in.}$$

Using these results, and the symmetry of the cross section, the shear-flow distribution is plotted in Fig. 21e. The distribution is linear along the horizontal segments (perpendicular to $\mathbf{V}$) and parabolic along the vertical segments (parallel to $\mathbf{V}$).

(e)

**Fig. 21**

435

## *5 Shear Center for Open Thin-Walled Members

In the previous section, it was assumed that the internal shear **V** was applied along a principal centroidal axis of inertia that *also* represents an *axis of symmetry* for the cross section. In this section we will consider the effect of applying the shear along a principal centroidal axis that is *not* an axis of symmetry. As before, only open thin-walled members will be analyzed, so the dimensions to the centerline of the walls of the members will be used. A typical example of this case is the channel section shown in Fig. 22*a*. Here it is cantilevered from a fixed support and is subjected to the force **P**. If this force is applied along the once vertical, unsymmetrical axis that passes through the *centroid C* of the cross section, the channel will not only bend downward, *it will also twist* clockwise as shown.

Shear-flow distribution

(a)

(b)

(c)

(d)

(e)

**Fig. 22**

To understand why the member twists, it is necessary to show the shear-flow distribution along the channel's flanges and web, Fig. 22b. When this distribution is integrated over the flange and web areas, it will give resultant forces of $F_f$ in each flange and a force of $V = P$ in the web, Fig. 22c. If the moments of these forces are summed about point $A$, it can be seen that the couple or torque created by the flange forces is responsible for twisting the member. The actual twist is clockwise when viewed from the front of the beam as shown in Fig. 22a, since *reactive* internal "equilibrium" forces $F_f$ cause the twisting. In order to *prevent* this twisting it is therefore necessary to apply **P** at a point $O$ located an eccentric distance $e$ from the web of the channel, Fig. 22d. We require $\Sigma M_A = F_f d = Pe$, or

$$e = \frac{F_f d}{P}$$

Using the method discussed in the previous section, $F_f$ can be evaluated in terms of $P\,(=V)$ and the dimensions of the flanges and web. Once this is done, then $P$ will cancel upon substitution into the above equation, and it becomes possible to express $e$ simply as a function of the cross-sectional geometry (see Example 8). The point $O$ so located is called the **shear center** or **flexural center**. When **P** is applied at the shear center, the **beam will bend without twisting** as shown in Fig. 22e. Design handbooks often list the location of this point for a variety of beams having thin-walled cross sections that are commonly used in practice.

From this analysis, it should be noted that **the shear center will always lie on an axis of symmetry** of a member's cross-sectional area. For example, if the channel is rotated 90° and **P** is applied at $A$, Fig. 23a, no twisting will occur since the shear flow in the web and flanges for this case is *symmetrical*, and therefore the force resultants in these elements will create zero moments about $A$, Fig. 23b. Obviously, if a member has a cross section with *two* axes of symmetry, as in the case of a wide-flange beam, the shear center will then coincide with the intersection of these axes (the centroid).

Notice how this cantilever beam deflects when loaded through the centroid (above) and through the shear center (below).

(a)

$$V = \frac{P}{2} \qquad V = \frac{P}{2} \qquad = \qquad$$

(b)

**Fig. 23**

## Important Points

- The *shear center* is the point through which a force can be applied which will cause a beam to bend and yet not twist.
- The shear center will always lie on an axis of symmetry of the cross section.
- The location of the shear center is only a function of the geometry of the cross section, and does not depend upon the applied loading.

## Procedure for Analysis

The location of the shear center for an open thin-walled member for which the internal shear is in the *same direction* as a principal centroidal axis for the cross section may be determined by using the following procedure.

Shear-Flow Resultants.

- By observation, determine the direction of the shear flow through the various segments of the cross section, and sketch the force resultants on each segment of the cross section. (For example, see Fig. 22c.) Since the shear center is determined by taking the moments of these force resultants about a point (*A*), choose this point at a location that eliminates the moments of as many force resultants as possible.

- The magnitudes of the force resultants that create a moment about *A* must be calculated. For any segment this is done by determining the shear flow *q* at an arbitrary point on the segment and then integrating *q* along the segment's length. Realize that **V** will create a *linear* variation of shear flow in segments that are *perpendicular* to **V**, and a *parabolic* variation of shear flow in segments that are *parallel or inclined* to **V**.

Shear Center.

- Sum the moments of the shear-flow resultants about point *A* and set this moment equal to the moment of **V** about *A*. Solve this equation to determine the moment-arm or eccentric distance *e*, which locates the line of action of **V** from *A*.

- If an *axis of symmetry* for the cross section exists, the shear center lies at the point where this axis intersects the line of action of **V**.

# EXAMPLE | 8

Determine the location of the shear center for the thin-walled channel section having the dimensions shown in Fig. 24a.

(a)

## SOLUTION

**Shear-Flow Resultants.** A vertical downward shear **V** applied to the section causes the shear to flow through the flanges and web as shown in Fig. 24b. This causes force resultants $F_f$ and $V$ in the flanges and web as shown in Fig. 24c. We will take moments about point $A$ so that only the force $F_f$ on the lower flange has to be determined.

The cross-sectional area can be divided into three component rectangles—a web and two flanges. Since each component is assumed to be thin, the moment of inertia of the area about the neutral axis is

$$I = \frac{1}{12}th^3 + 2\left[ bt\left(\frac{h}{2}\right)^2 \right] = \frac{th^2}{2}\left(\frac{h}{6} + b\right)$$

$(q_{max})_w$

$(q_{max})_f$

Shear flow distribution

(b)

From Fig. 24d, $q$ at the arbitrary position $x$ is

$$q = \frac{VQ}{I} = \frac{V(h/2)[b - x]t}{(th^2/2)[(h/6) + b]} = \frac{V(b - x)}{h[(h/6) + b]}$$

Hence, the force $F_f$ is

$$F_f = \int_0^b q\, dx = \frac{V}{h[(h/6) + b]}\int_0^b (b - x)\, dx = \frac{Vb^2}{2h[(h/6) + b]}$$

This same result can also be determined by first finding $(q_{max})_f$, Fig. 24b, then determining the triangular area $\frac{1}{2}b(q_{max})_f = F_f$.

(c)

**Shear Center.** Summing moments about point $A$, Fig. 24c, we require

$$Ve = F_f h = \frac{Vb^2 h}{2h[(h/6) + b]}$$

Thus,

$$e = \frac{b^2}{[(h/3) + 2b]} \qquad Ans.$$

(d)

**Fig. 24**

As stated previously, $e$ depends only on the geometry of the cross section.

EXAMPLE | 9

Determine the location of the shear center for the angle having equal legs, Fig. 25a. Also, find the internal shear force resultant in each leg.

(a)

Shear-flow distribution

(b)

(c)

**Fig. 25**

SOLUTION

When a vertical downward shear **V** is applied at the section, the shear flow and shear-flow resultants are directed as shown in Figs. 25b and 25c, respectively. Note that the force $F$ in each leg must be equal, since for equilibrium the sum of their horizontal components must be equal to zero. Also, the lines of action of both forces intersect point $O$; therefore, this point *must be the shear center* since the sum of the moments of these forces and **V** about $O$ is zero, Fig. 25c.

The magnitude of **F** can be determined by first finding the shear flow at the arbitrary location $s$ along the top leg, Fig. 25d. Here

$$Q = \bar{y}'A' = \frac{1}{\sqrt{2}}\left((b-s) + \frac{s}{2}\right)ts = \frac{1}{\sqrt{2}}\left(b - \frac{s}{2}\right)st$$

(d)                    (e)

**Fig. 25 (cont.)**

The moment of inertia of the angle, about the neutral axis, must be determined from "first principles," since the legs are inclined with respect to the neutral axis. For the area element $dA = t\,ds$, Fig. 25e, we have

$$I = \int_A y^2\,dA = 2\int_0^b \left[\frac{1}{\sqrt{2}}(b - s)\right]^2 t\,ds = t\left(b^2 s - bs^2 + \frac{1}{3}s^3\right)\bigg|_0^b = \frac{tb^3}{3}$$

Thus, the shear flow is

$$q = \frac{VQ}{I} = \frac{V}{(tb^3/3)}\left[\frac{1}{\sqrt{2}}\left(b - \frac{s}{2}\right)st\right]$$

$$= \frac{3V}{\sqrt{2}b^3}s\left(b - \frac{s}{2}\right)$$

The variation of $q$ is parabolic, and it reaches a maximum value when $s = b$ as shown in Fig. 25b. The force $F$ is therefore

$$F = \int_0^b q\,ds = \frac{3V}{\sqrt{2}b^3}\int_0^b s\left(b - \frac{s}{2}\right)ds$$

$$= \frac{3V}{\sqrt{2}b^3}\left(b\frac{s^2}{2} - \frac{1}{6}s^3\right)\bigg|_0^b$$

$$= \frac{1}{\sqrt{2}}V \qquad\qquad\qquad \textit{Ans.}$$

**NOTE:** This result can be easily verified since the sum of the vertical components of the force $F$ in each leg must equal $V$ and, as stated previously, the sum of the horizontal components equals zero.

# PROBLEMS

**50.** A shear force of $V = 300$ kN is applied to the box girder. Determine the shear flow at points $A$ and $B$.

**51.** A shear force of $V = 450$ kN is applied to the box girder. Determine the shear flow at points $C$ and $D$.

**Probs. 50/51**

**\*52.** A shear force of $V = 18$ kN is applied to the symmetric box girder. Determine the shear flow at $A$ and $B$.

**53.** A shear force of $V = 18$ kN is applied to the box girder. Determine the shear flow at $C$.

**Probs. 52/53**

**54.** The aluminum strut is 10 mm thick and has the cross section shown. If it is subjected to a shear of, $V = 150$ N, determine the shear flow at points $A$ and $B$.

**55.** The aluminum strut is 10 mm thick and has the cross section shown. If it is subjected to a shear of $V = 150$ N, determine the maximum shear flow in the strut.

**Probs. 54/55**

**\*56.** The beam is subjected to a shear force of $V = 5$ kip. Determine the shear flow at points $A$ and $B$.

**57.** The beam is constructed from four plates and is subjected to a shear force of $V = 5$ kip. Determine the maximum shear flow in the cross section.

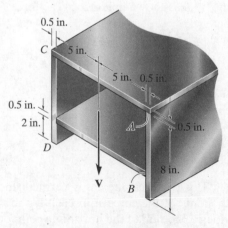

**Probs. 56/57**

**58.** The channel is subjected to a shear of $V = 75$ kN. Determine the shear flow developed at point $A$.

**59.** The channel is subjected to a shear of $V = 75$ kN. Determine the maximum shear flow in the channel.

**Probs. 58/59**

**\*60.** The built-up beam is formed by welding together the thin plates of thickness 5 mm. Determine the location of the shear center $O$.

**Prob. 60**

**61.** The assembly is subjected to a vertical shear of $V = 7$ kip. Determine the shear flow at points $A$ and $B$ and the maximum shear flow in the cross section.

**Prob. 61**

**62.** Determine the shear-stress variation over the cross section of the thin-walled tube as a function of elevation $y$ and show that $\tau_{max} = 2V/A$, where $A = 2\pi rt$. *Hint:* Choose a differential area element $dA = Rt\,d\theta$. Using $dQ = y\,dA$, formulate $Q$ for a circular section from $\theta$ to $(\pi - \theta)$ and show that $Q = 2R^2t\cos\theta$, where $\cos\theta = \sqrt{R^2 - y^2}/R$.

**Prob. 62**

**63.** Determine the location $e$ of the shear center, point $O$, for the thin-walled member having the cross section shown. The member segments have the same thickness $t$.

**Prob. 3**

**\*64.** Determine the location $e$ of the shear center, point $O$, for the thin-walled member having the cross section shown. The member segments have the same thickness $t$.

**Prob. 64**

**65.** The beam supports a vertical shear of $V = 7$ kip. Determine the resultant force developed in segment $AB$ of the beam.

**Prob. 65**

**66.** The built-up beam is fabricated from the three thin plates having a thickness $t$. Determine the location of the shear center $O$.

**Prob. 66**

**67.** Determine the location $e$ of the shear center, point $O$, for the thin-walled member having the cross section shown. The member segments have the same thickness $t$.

**Prob. 67**

**\*68.** A thin plate of thickness $t$ is bent to form the beam having the cross section shown. Determine the location of the shear center $O$.

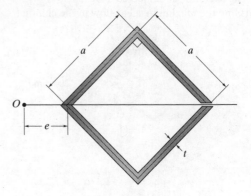

**Prob. 68**

**69.** A thin plate of thickness $t$ is bent to form the beam having the cross section shown. Determine the location of the shear center $O$.

**Prob. 69**

**70.** Determine the location $e$ of the shear center, point $O$, for the thin-walled member having the cross section shown.

**Prob. 70**

## CHAPTER REVIEW

Transverse shear stress in beams is determined indirectly by using the flexure formula and the relationship between moment and shear ($V = dM/dx$). The result is the shear formula

$$\tau = \frac{VQ}{It}$$

In particular, the value for $Q$ is the moment of the area $A'$ about the neutral axis, $Q = \bar{y}'A'$. This area is the portion of the cross-sectional area that is "held on" to the beam above (or below) the thickness $t$ where $\tau$ is to be determined.

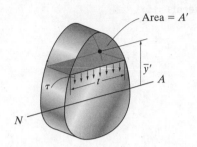

If the beam has a *rectangular* cross section, then the shear-stress distribution will be parabolic, having a maximum value at the neutral axis. The maximum shear stress can be determined using $\tau = 1.5\,\dfrac{V}{A}$.

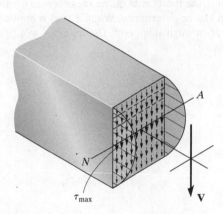

Shear–stress distribution

Fasteners, such as nails, bolts, glue, or welds, are used to connect the composite parts of a "built-up" section. The shear force resisted by these fasteners is determined from the shear flow, $q$, or force per unit length, that must be carried by the beam. The shear flow is

$$q = \frac{VQ}{I}$$

If the beam is made from thin-walled segments, then the shear-flow distribution along each segment can be determined. This distribution will vary linearly along horizontal segments, and parabolically along inclined or vertical segments.

Shear-flow distribution

Provided the shear-flow distribution in each element of an open thin-walled section is known, then using a balance of moments, the location $O$ of the shear center for the cross section can be determined. When a load is applied to the member through this point, the member will bend, and not twist.

# REVIEW PROBLEMS

**71.** The beam is fabricated from four boards nailed together as shown. Determine the shear force each nail along the sides $C$ and the top $D$ must resist if the nails are uniformly spaced at $s = 3$ in. The beam is subjected to a shear of $V = 4.5$ kip.

**Prob. 71**

**\*72.** The T-beam is subjected to a shear of $V = 150$ kN. Determine the amount of this force that is supported by the web $B$.

**Prob. 72**

**73.** The member is subject to a shear force of $V = 2$ kN. Determine the shear flow at points $A$, $B$, and $C$. The thickness of each thin-walled segment in 15 mm.

**Prob. 73**

**74.** Determine the shear stress at points $B$ and $C$ on the web of the beam located at section $a$–$a$.

**75.** Determine the maximum shear stress acting at section $a$–$a$ in the beam.

**Probs. 74/75**

# Solutions and Answers for Preliminary Problems

**P1a.**

$$Q = \bar{y}'A' = (0.1 \text{ m}) (0.1 \text{ m}) (0.4 \text{ m}) = 4(10^{-3}) \text{ m}^3$$
$$t = 0.4 \text{ m}$$

**P1b.**

$$Q = \bar{y}'A' = (0.15 \text{ m}) (0.3 \text{ m}) (0.1 \text{ m}) = 4.5(10^{-3}) \text{ m}^3$$
$$t = 0.3 \text{ m}$$

**P1c.**

$$Q = \bar{y}'A' = (0.2 \text{ m}) (0.1 \text{ m}) (0.5 \text{ m}) = 0.01 \text{ m}^3$$
$$t = 3 (0.1 \text{ m}) = 0.3 \text{ m}$$

**P1d.**

$$Q = \bar{y}'A' = (0.35 \text{ m}) (0.6 \text{ m}) (0.1 \text{ m}) = 0.021 \text{ m}^3$$
$$t = 0.6 \text{ m}$$

**P1e.**

$$Q = \bar{y}'A' = (0.25 \text{ m}) (0.2 \text{ m}) (0.1 \text{ m}) = 5(10^{-3}) \text{ m}^3$$
$$t = 0.2 \text{ m}$$

**P1f.**

$$Q = \Sigma\bar{y}'A' = (0.25 \text{ m}) (0.1 \text{ m}) (0.1 \text{ m})$$
$$+ (0.35 \text{ m}) (0.1 \text{ m}) (0.5 \text{ m}) = 0.02 \text{ m}^3$$
$$t = 0.1 \text{ m}$$

# Selected Answers

| | | | |
|---|---|---|---|
| **1.** | $\tau_A = 2.56$ MPa | **45.** | $P = 6.60$ kN |
| **2.** | $\tau_{max} = 3.46$ MPa | **46.** | $\tau_{avg} = 97.2$ MPa |
| **3.** | $V_w = 19.0$ kN | **47.** | $s = 8.66$ in., $s' = 1.21$ in. |
| **5.** | $V_f = 3.82$ kip | **50.** | $q_A = 228$ kN/m, $q_B = 462$ kN/m |
| **6.** | $V_{max} = 100$ kN | **51** | $q_C = 0, q_D = 601$ kN/m |
| **7.** | $\tau_{max} = 17.9$ MPa | **53.** | $q_C = 38.6$ kN/m |
| **9.** | $V = 32.1$ kip | **54.** | $q_A = 1.39$ kN/m, $q_B = 1.25$ kN/m |
| **10.** | $\tau_{max} = 4.48$ ksi | **55.** | $q_{max} = 1.63$ kN/m |
| **11.** | $\tau_{max} = 45.0$ MPa | **57.** | $q_{max} = 414$ lb/in. |
| **13.** | $\tau_{max} = 4.22$ MPa | **58.** | $q_A = 215$ kN/m |
| **14.** | $V = 190$ kN | **59.** | $q_{max} = 232$ kN/m |
| **15.** | $V_{AB} = 50.3$ kN | **61.** | $q_A = 196$ lb/in., $q_B = 452$ lb/in., |
| **17.** | $\tau_A = 1.99$ MPa, $\tau_B = 1.65$ MPa | | $q_{max} = 641$ lb/in. |
| **18.** | $\tau_{max} = 4.62$ MPa | **62.** | $\tau = \dfrac{V}{\pi R^2 t}\sqrt{R^2 - y^2}$ |
| **19.** | $V_w = 27.1$ kN | | |
| **21.** | $P = 1.28$ kip | **63.** | $e = 1.07$ in. |
| **22.** | $\tau_B = 4.41$ MPa | **65.** | $V_{AB} = 1.47$ kip |
| **23.** | $\tau_{max} = 4.85$ MPa | **66.** | $e = \dfrac{3}{14}a$ |
| **25.** | $\tau_{max} = 3.67$ MPa | | |
| **26.** | $a = 1.27$ in. | **67.** | $e = \dfrac{3\left[h^2 b^2 - (h - 2h_1)^2 b_1^2\right]}{h^3 + 6bh^2 + 6b_1(h - 2h_1)^2}$ |
| **27.** | $\tau_{max} = 22.0$ MPa, $(\tau_{max})_s = 66.0$ MPa | | |
| **33.** | $F = 675$ lb | | |
| **34.** | $V = 16.7$ kN | **69.** | $e = \left[\dfrac{3(\pi + 4)}{4 + 3\pi}\right]r$ |
| **35.** | $V = 28.2$ kN | | |
| **37.** | $V = 2571$ lb, $\tau_b = 14.0$ ksi | **70.** | $e = \dfrac{4r(\sin\alpha - \alpha\cos\alpha)}{2\alpha - \sin 2\alpha}$ |
| **38.** | $\tau = 35.2$ MPa | | |
| **39.** | $F = 12.5$ kN | **71.** | $F_C = 197$ lb, $F_D = 1.38$ kip |
| **41.** | $s = 71.3$ mm | **73.** | $q_A = 0, q_B = 1.21$ kN/m, $q_C = 3.78$ kN/m |
| **42.** | $V = 8.82$ kip, use $s = 1\dfrac{1}{8}$ in. | **74.** | $\tau_B = 795$ psi, $\tau_C = 596$ psi |
| | | **75.** | $\tau_{max} = 928$ psi |
| **43.** | $V = 1.24$ kip | | |

# Fundamental Problems Partial Solutions and Answers

**F1**
$$I = 2\left[\frac{1}{12}(0.02)(0.2^3)\right] + \frac{1}{12}(0.26)(0.02^3)$$
$$= 26.84(10^{-6})\ \text{m}^4$$
$$Q_A = 2[0.055(0.09)(0.02)] = 198(10^{-6})\ \text{m}^3$$
$$\tau_A = \frac{VQ_A}{It} = \frac{100(10^3)[198(10^{-6})]}{[26.84(10^{-6})]2(0.02)}$$
$$= 18.4\ \text{MPa} \qquad Ans.$$

**F2**
m$^4$
$$I = \frac{1}{12}(0.1)(0.3^3) + \frac{1}{12}(0.2)(0.1^3) = 0.24167(10^{-3})$$

$$Q_A = y'_1 A'_1 + y'_2 A'_2$$
$$= \left[\frac{1}{2}(0.05)\right](0.05)(0.3) + 0.1(0.1)(0.1)$$
$$= 1.375(10^{-3})\ \text{m}^3$$
$$Q_B = y'_2 A'_2 = 0.1(0.1)(0.1) = 1(10^{-3})\ \text{m}^3$$
$$\tau_A = \frac{VQ}{It} = \frac{600(10^3)[1.375(10^{-3})]}{[0.24167(10^{-3})](0.3)} = 11.4\ \text{MPa}\ Ans.$$
$$\tau_B = \frac{VQ}{It} = \frac{600(10^3)[1(10^{-3})]}{[0.24167(10^{-3})](0.1)} = 24.8\ \text{MPa} \qquad Ans.$$

**F3**    $V_{max} = 4.5$ kip

$I = \dfrac{1}{12}(3)(6^3) = 54$ in$^4$

$Q_{max} = y'A' = 1.5(3)(3) = 13.5$ in$^3$

$(\tau_{max})_{abs} = \dfrac{V_{max}Q_{max}}{It} = \dfrac{4.5(10^3)(13.5)}{54(3)} = 375$ psi

*Ans.*

**F4**    $I = 2\left[\dfrac{1}{12}(0.03)(0.4)^3\right] + 2\left[\dfrac{1}{12}(0.14)(0.03)^3\right.$

$\left. + 0.14(0.03)(0.15^2)\right] = 0.50963(10^{-3})$ m$^4$

$Q_{max} = 2y'_1 A'_1 + y'_2 A'_2 = 2(0.1)(0.2)(0.03)$
$+ (0.15)(0.14)(0.03) = 1.83(10^{-3})$ m$^3$

$\tau_{max} = \dfrac{VQ_{max}}{It} = \dfrac{20(10^3)[1.83(10^{-3})]}{0.50963(10^{-3})[2(0.03)]} = 1.20$ MPa

*Ans.*

**F5**    $I = \dfrac{1}{12}(0.05)(0.4)^3 + 2\left[\dfrac{1}{12}(0.025)(0.3)^3\right]$

$= 0.37917(10^{-3})$ m$^4$

$Q_{max} = 2y'_1 A'_1 + y'_2 A'_2 = 2(0.075)(0.025)(0.15)$

$+ (0.1)(0.05)(0.2) = 1.5625(10^{-3})$ m$^3$

$\tau_{max} = \dfrac{VQ_{max}}{It} = \dfrac{20(10^3)[1.5625(10^{-3})]}{[0.37917(10^{-3})][2(0.025)]}$

$= 1.65$ MPa          *Ans.*

**F6**    $I = \dfrac{1}{12}(0.3)(0.2^3) = 0.2(10^{-3})$ m$^4$

$Q = y'A' = 0.05(0.1)(0.3) = 1.5(10^{-3})$ m$^3$

$q_{allow} = 2\left(\dfrac{F}{s}\right) = \dfrac{2[15(10^3)]}{s} = \dfrac{30(10^3)}{s}$

$q_{allow} = \dfrac{VQ}{I};\quad \dfrac{30(10^3)}{s} = \dfrac{50(10^3)[1.5(10^{-3})]}{0.2(10^{-3})}$

$s = 0.08$ m $= 80$ mm    *Ans.*

**F7**    $I = \dfrac{1}{12}(0.2)(0.34^3) - \dfrac{1}{12}(0.19)(0.28^3)$

$= 0.3075(10^{-3})$ m$^4$

$Q = y'A' = 0.16(0.02)(0.2) = 0.64(10^{-3})$ m$^3$

$q_{allow} = 2\left(\dfrac{F}{s}\right) = \dfrac{2[30(10^3)]}{s} = \dfrac{60(10^3)}{s}$

$q_{allow} = \dfrac{VQ}{I};\quad \dfrac{60(10^3)}{s} = \dfrac{300(10^3)[0.64(10^{-3})]}{0.3075(10^{-3})}$

$s = 0.09609$ m $= 96.1$ mm

Use $s = 96$ mm                    *Ans.*

**F8**

$I = 2\left[\dfrac{1}{12}(0.025)(0.3^3)\right] + 2\left[\dfrac{1}{12}(0.05)(0.2^3) + 0.05(0.2)(0.15^2)\right]$

$= 0.62917(10^{-3})$ m$^4$

$Q = y'A' = 0.15(0.2)(0.05) = 1.5(10^{-3})$ m$^3$

$q_{allow} = 2\left(\dfrac{F}{s}\right) = \dfrac{2[8(10^3)]}{s} = \dfrac{16(10^3)}{s}$

$q_{allow} = \dfrac{VQ}{I};\quad \dfrac{16(10^3)}{s} = \dfrac{20(10^3)[1.5(10^{-3})]}{0.62917(10^{-3})}$

$s = 0.3356$ m $= 335.56$ mm

Use $s = 335$ mm                    *Ans.*

**F9**    $I = \dfrac{1}{12}(1)(6^3) + 4\left[\dfrac{1}{12}(0.5)(4^3) + 0.5(4)(3^2)\right]$

$= 100.67$ in$^4$

$Q = y'A' = 3(4)(0.5) = 6$ in$^3$

$q_{allow} = \dfrac{F}{s} = \dfrac{6}{s}$

$q_{allow} = \dfrac{VQ}{I};\quad \dfrac{6}{s} = \dfrac{15(6)}{100.67}$

$s = 6.711$ in.

Use $s = 6\dfrac{5}{8}$ in.                    *Ans.*

# Combined Loadings

From Chapter 8 of *Mechanics of Materials*, Ninth Edition. R. C. Hibbeler. Copyright © 2014 by Pearson Education, Inc.
Published by Pearson Prentice Hall. All rights reserved.

The offset hanger supporting this ski gondola is subjected to the combined loadings of axial force and bending moment.

# Combined Loadings

---

## 1  Thin-Walled Pressure Vessels

Cylindrical or spherical vessels are commonly used in industry to serve as boilers or tanks. When under pressure, the material of which they are made is subjected to a loading from all directions. Although this is the case, the vessel can be analyzed in a simple manner provided it has a thin wall. In general, "*thin wall*" refers to a vessel having an inner-radius-to-wall-thickness ratio of 10 or more ($r/t \geq 10$). Specifically, when $r/t = 10$ the results of a thin-wall analysis will predict a stress that is approximately 4% *less* than the actual maximum stress in the vessel. For larger $r/t$ ratios this error will be even smaller.

Provided the vessel wall is "thin," the stress distribution throughout its thickness will not vary significantly, and so we will assume that it is *uniform* or *constant*. Using this assumption, we will now analyze the state of stress in thin-walled cylindrical and spherical pressure vessels. In both cases, the pressure in the vessel is understood to be the *gauge pressure*, that is, it measures the pressure *above* atmospheric pressure, since atmospheric pressure is assumed to exist both inside and outside the vessel's wall before the vessel is pressurized.

Cylindrical pressure vessels, such as this gas tank, have semi-spherical end caps rather than flat ones in order to reduce the stress in the tank.

(a)

(b)

(c)

**Fig. 1**

**Cylindrical Vessels.** Consider the cylindrical vessel in Fig. 1a, having a wall thickness $t$, inner radius $r$, and subjected to a gauge pressure $p$ that developed within the vessel by a contained gas. Due to this loading, a small element of the vessel that is sufficiently removed from the ends and oriented as shown in Fig. 1a, is subjected to normal stresses $\sigma_1$ in the *circumferential or hoop direction* and $\sigma_2$ in the *longitudinal or axial direction*.

The hoop stress can be determined by considering the vessel to be sectioned by planes $a$, $b$, and $c$. A free-body diagram of the back segment along with the contained gas is shown in Fig. 1b. Here only the loadings in the $x$ direction are shown. These loadings are developed by the uniform hoop stress $\sigma_1$, acting on the vessel's wall, and the pressure acting on the vertical face of the gas. For equilibrium in the $x$ direction, we require

$$\Sigma F_x = 0; \qquad 2[\sigma_1(t\,dy)] - p(2r\,dy) = 0$$

$$\boxed{\sigma_1 = \frac{pr}{t}} \qquad (1)$$

The longitudinal stress can be determined by considering the left portion of section $b$ of the cylinder, Fig. 1a. As shown in Fig. 1c, $\sigma_2$ acts uniformly throughout the wall, and $p$ acts on the section of the contained gas. Since the mean radius is approximately equal to the vessel's inner radius, equilibrium in the $y$ direction requires

$$\Sigma F_y = 0; \qquad \sigma_2(2\pi r t) - p(\pi r^2) = 0$$

$$\boxed{\sigma_2 = \frac{pr}{2t}} \qquad (2)$$

In the above equations,

$\sigma_1, \sigma_2 =$ the normal stress in the hoop and longitudinal directions, respectively. Each is assumed to be *constant* throughout the wall of the cylinder, and each subjects the material to tension.
$p =$ the internal gauge pressure developed by the contained gas
$r =$ the inner radius of the cylinder
$t =$ the thickness of the wall ($r/t \geq 10$)

By comparison, note that the hoop or circumferential stress is twice as large as the longitudinal or axial stress. Consequently, when fabricating cylindrical pressure vessels from rolled-formed plates, the longitudinal joints must be designed to carry twice as much stress as the circumferential joints.

## Spherical Vessels.

We can analyze a spherical pressure vessel in a similar manner. To do this, consider the vessel to have a wall thickness $t$, inner radius $r$, and subjected to an internal gauge pressure $p$, Fig. 2a. If the vessel is sectioned in half, the resulting free-body diagram is shown in Fig. 2b. Like the cylinder, equilibrium in the $y$ direction requires

$$\Sigma F_y = 0; \qquad \sigma_2(2\pi rt) - p(\pi r^2) = 0$$

$$\boxed{\sigma_2 = \frac{pr}{2t}} \qquad (3)$$

This is the *same result* as that obtained for the longitudinal stress in the cylindrical pressure vessel. Furthermore, from the analysis, this stress will be the same *regardless* of the orientation of the hemispheric free-body diagram. Consequently, a small element of the material is subjected to the state of stress shown in Fig. 2a.

The above analysis indicates that an element of material taken from either a cylindrical or a spherical pressure vessel is subjected to **biaxial stress**, i.e., normal stress existing in only two directions. Actually, the pressure also subjects the material to a **radial stress**, $\sigma_3$, which acts along a radial line. This stress has a maximum value equal to the pressure $p$ at the interior wall and it decreases through the wall to zero at the exterior surface of the vessel, since the gauge pressure there is zero. For thin-walled vessels, however, we will *ignore* this radial-stress component, since our limiting assumption of $r/t = 10$ results in $\sigma_2$ and $\sigma_1$ being, respectively, 5 and 10 times *higher* than the maximum radial stress, $(\sigma_3)_{\max} = p$. Finally, if the vessel is subjected to an *external pressure*, the compressive stress developed within the thin wall may cause the vessel to become unstable, and collapse may occur by buckling rather than causing the material to fracture.

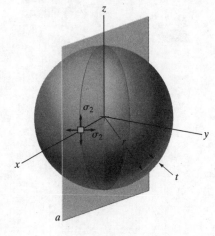

This thin-walled pipe was subjected to an excessive gas pressure that caused it to rupture in the circumferential or hoop direction. The stress in this direction is twice that in the axial direction as noted by Eqs. 1 and 2.

(a)

(b)

**Fig. 2**

# EXAMPLE 1

A cylindrical pressure vessel has an inner diameter of 4 ft and a thickness of $\frac{1}{2}$ in. Determine the maximum internal pressure it can sustain so that neither its circumferential nor its longitudinal stress component exceeds 20 ksi. Under the same conditions, what is the maximum internal pressure that a similar-size spherical vessel can sustain?

## SOLUTION

**Cylindrical Pressure Vessel.**  The maximum stress occurs in the circumferential direction. From Eq. 1 we have

$$\sigma_1 = \frac{pr}{t}; \qquad\qquad 20 \text{ kip/in}^2 = \frac{p(24 \text{ in.})}{\frac{1}{2} \text{ in.}}$$

$$p = 417 \text{ psi} \qquad\qquad Ans.$$

Note that when this pressure is reached, from Eq. 2, the stress in the longitudinal direction will be $\sigma_2 = \frac{1}{2}(20 \text{ ksi}) = 10 \text{ ksi}$. Furthermore, the *maximum stress* in the *radial direction* occurs on the material at the inner wall of the vessel and is $(\sigma_3)_{max} = p = 417 \text{ psi}$. This value is 48 times smaller than the circumferential stress (20 ksi), and as stated earlier, its effects will be neglected.

**Spherical Vessel.**  Here the maximum stress occurs in any two perpendicular directions on an element of the vessel, Fig. 2a. From Eq. 3, we have

$$\sigma_2 = \frac{pr}{2t}; \qquad\qquad 20 \text{ kip/in}^2 = \frac{p(24 \text{ in.})}{2\left(\frac{1}{2} \text{ in.}\right)}$$

$$p = 833 \text{ psi} \qquad\qquad Ans.$$

**NOTE:** Although it is more difficult to fabricate, the spherical pressure vessel will carry twice as much internal pressure as a cylindrical vessel.

## PROBLEMS

**1.** A spherical gas tank has an inner radius of $r = 1.5$ m. If it is subjected to an internal pressure of $p = 300$ kPa, determine its required thickness if the maximum normal stress is not to exceed 12 MPa.

**2.** A pressurized spherical tank is to be made of 0.5-in.-thick steel. If it is subjected to an internal pressure of $p = 200$ psi, determine its outer radius if the maximum normal stress is not to exceed 15 ksi.

**3.** The thin-walled cylinder can be supported in one of two ways as shown. Determine the state of stress in the wall of the cylinder for both cases if the piston $P$ causes the internal pressure to be 65 psi. The wall has a thickness of 0.25 in. and the inner diameter of the cylinder is 8 in.

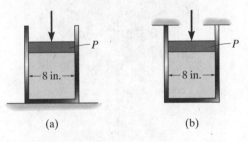

(a)                    (b)

**Prob. 3**

***4.** The tank of the air compressor is subjected to an internal pressure of 90 psi. If the internal diameter of the tank is 22 in., and the wall thickness is 0.25 in., determine the stress components acting at point $A$. Draw a volume element of the material at this point, and show the results on the element.

**Prob. 4**

**5.** The open-ended polyvinyl chloride pipe has an inner diameter of 4 in. and thickness of 0.2 in. If it carries flowing water at 60 psi pressure, determine the state of stress in the walls of the pipe.

**6.** If the flow of water within the pipe in Prob. 5 is stopped due to the closing of a valve, determine the state of stress in the walls of the pipe. Neglect the weight of the water. Assume the supports only exert vertical forces on the pipe.

**Probs. 5/6**

**7.** A boiler is constructed of 8-mm thick steel plates that are fastened together at their ends using a butt joint consisting of two 8-mm cover plates and rivets having a diameter of 10 mm and spaced 50 mm apart as shown. If the steam pressure in the boiler is 1.35 MPa, determine (a) the circumferential stress in the boiler's plate apart from the seam, (b) the circumferential stress in the outer cover plate along the rivet line $a$–$a$, and (c) the shear stress in the rivets.

**Prob. 7**

**\*8.** The steel water pipe has an inner diameter of 12 in. and wall thickness 0.25 in. If the valve $A$ is opened and the flowing water is under a gauge pressure of 250 psi, determine the longitudinal and hoop stress developed in the wall of the pipe.

**9.** The steel water pipe has an inner diameter of 12 in. and wall thickness 0.25 in. If the valve $A$ is closed and the water pressure is 300 psi, determine the longitudinal and hoop stress developed in the wall of the pipe. Draw the state of stress on a volume element located on the wall.

**11.** Two hemispheres having an inner radius of 2 ft and wall thickness of 0.25 in. are fitted together, and the inside gauge pressure is reduced to $-10$ psi. If the coefficient of static friction is $\mu_s = 0.5$ between the hemispheres, determine (a) the torque $T$ needed to initiate the rotation of the top hemisphere relative to the bottom one, (b) the vertical force needed to pull the top hemisphere off the bottom one, and (c) the horizontal force needed to slide the top hemisphere off the bottom one.

**Probs. 8/9**

**Prob. 11**

**10.** The A-36-steel band is 2 in. wide and is secured around the smooth rigid cylinder. If the bolts are tightened so that the tension in them is 400 lb, determine the normal stress in the band, the pressure exerted on the cylinder, and the distance half the band stretches.

**\*12.** A pressure-vessel head is fabricated by gluing the circular plate to the end of the vessel as shown. If the vessel sustains an internal pressure of 450 kPa, determine the average shear stress in the glue and the state of stress in the wall of the vessel.

**Prob. 10**

**Prob. 12**

458

**13.** An A-36-steel hoop has an inner diameter of 23.99 in., thickness of 0.25 in., and width of 1 in. If it and the 24-in.-diameter rigid cylinder have a temperature of 65° F, determine the temperature to which the hoop should be heated in order for it to just slip over the cylinder. What is the pressure the hoop exerts on the cylinder, and the tensile stress in the ring when it cools back down to 65° F?

**Prob. 13**

**14.** The ring, having the dimensions shown, is placed over a flexible membrane which is pumped up with a pressure $p$. Determine the change in the internal radius of the ring after this pressure is applied. The modulus of elasticity for the ring is $E$.

**Prob. 14**

**15.** The inner ring $A$ has an inner radius $r_1$ and outer radius $r_2$. Before heating, the outer ring $B$ has an inner radius $r_3$ and an outer radius $r_4$, and $r_2 > r_3$. If the outer ring is heated and then fitted over the inner ring, determine the pressure between the two rings when ring $B$ reaches the temperature of the inner ring. The material has a modulus of elasticity of $E$ and a coefficient of thermal expansion of $\alpha$.

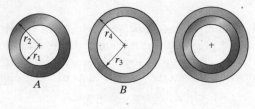

**Prob. 15**

**\*16.** A closed-ended pressure vessel is fabricated by cross winding glass filaments over a mandrel, so that the wall thickness $t$ of the vessel is composed entirely of filament and an expoxy binder as shown in the figure. Consider a segment of the vessel of width $w$ and wrapped at an angle $\theta$. If the vessel is subjected to an internal pressure $p$, show that the force in the segment is $F_\theta = \sigma_0 wt$, where $\sigma_0$ is the stress in the filaments. Also, show that the stresses in the hoop and longitudinal directions are $\sigma_h = \sigma_0 \sin^2\theta$ and $\sigma_1 = \sigma_0 \cos^2\theta$, respectively. At what angle $\theta$ (optimum winding angle) would the filaments have to be would so that the hoop and longitudinal stresses are equivalent?

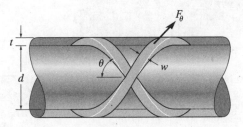

**Prob. 16**

**17.** In order to increase the strength of the pressure vessel, filament winding of the same material is wrapped around the circumference of the vessel as shown. If the pretension in the filament is $T$ and the vessel is subjected to an internal pressure $p$, determine the hoop stresses in the filament and in the wall of the vessel. Use the free-body diagram shown, and assume the filament winding has a thickness $t'$ and width $w$ for a corresponding length $L$ of the vessel.

**Prob. 17**

# 2 State of Stress Caused by Combined Loadings

Most often, the cross section of a member is subjected to *several* of these loadings *simultaneously*. When this occurs, the method of superposition can be used to determine the *resultant* stress distribution. The principle of superposition can be used for this purpose provided a *linear relationship* exists between the *stress* and the *loads*. Also, the geometry of the member should *not* undergo *significant change* when the loads are applied. These conditions are necessary in order to ensure that the stress produced by one load is not related to the stress produced by any other load.

This chimney is subjected to the combined loading of wind and weight. It is important to investigate the tensile stress in the chimney since masonry is weak in tension.

## Procedure for Analysis

The following procedure provides a general means for establishing the normal and shear stress components at a point in a member when the member is subjected to several different types of loadings simultaneously. It is assumed that the material is homogeneous and behaves in a linear elastic manner. Also, Saint-Venant's principle requires that the point where the stress is to be determined is far removed from any discontinuities in the cross section or points of applied load.

### Internal Loading.

- Section the member perpendicular to its axis at the point where the stress is to be determined and obtain the resultant internal normal and shear force components and the bending and torsional moment components.

- The force components should act through the *centroid* of the cross section, and the moment components should be computed about *centroidal axes*, which represent the principal axes of inertia for the cross section.

### Stress Components.

- Determine the stress component associated with *each* internal loading. For each case, represent the effect either as a distribution of stress acting over the entire cross-sectional area, or show the stress on an element of the material located at a specified point on the cross section.

### Normal Force.

- The internal normal force is developed by a uniform normal-stress distribution determined from $\sigma = P/A$.

### Shear Force.

- The internal shear force in a member is developed by a shear-stress distribution determined from the shear formula, $\tau = VQ/It$. Special care, however, must be exercised when applying this equation, as noted in Sec. 2.

### Bending Moment.

- For *straight members* the internal bending moment is developed by a normal-stress distribution that varies linearly from zero at the neutral axis to a maximum at the outer boundary of the member. This stress distribution is determined from the flexure formula, $\sigma = -My/I$. If the member is *curved*, the stress distribution is nonlinear and is determined from $\sigma = My/[A\,e(R - y)]$.

### Torsional Moment.

- For circular shafts and tubes the internal torsional moment is developed by a shear-stress distribution that varies linearly from zero at the central axis of the shaft to a maximum at the shaft's outer boundary. This stress distribution is determined from the torsional formula, $\tau = T\rho/J$.

### Thin-Walled Pressure Vessels.

- If the vessel is a thin-walled cylinder, the internal pressure $p$ will cause a biaxial state of stress in the material such that the hoop or circumferential stress component is $\sigma_1 = pr/t$ and the longitudinal stress component is $\sigma_2 = pr/2t$. If the vessel is a thin-walled sphere, then the biaxial state of stress is represented by two equivalent components, each having a magnitude of $\sigma_2 = pr/2t$.

### Superposition.

- Once the normal and shear stress components for each loading have been calculated, use the principle of superposition and determine the resultant normal and shear stress components.

- Represent the results on an element of material located at the point, or show the results as a distribution of stress acting over the member's cross-sectional area.

When a pretension force $F$ is developed in the blade of this coping saw, it will produce both a compressive force $F$ and bending moment $M$ in the region $AB$ of the frame. The material must therefore resist the normal stress produced by both of these loadings.

Problems in this section, which involve combined loadings, serve as a basic *review* of the application of the stress equations mentioned above. A thorough understanding of how these equations are applied is necessary if one is to successfully solve the problems at the end of this section. The following examples should be carefully studied before proceeding to solve the problems.

# EXAMPLE | 2

(a)

**Fig. 3**

(b)

A force of 150 lb is applied to the edge of the member shown in Fig. 3a. Neglect the weight of the member and determine the state of stress at points B and C.

## SOLUTION

**Internal Loadings.** The member is sectioned through B and C. For equilibrium at the section there must be an axial force of 150 lb acting through the *centroid* and a bending moment of 750 lb·in. about the centroidal principal axis, Fig. 3b.

**Stress Components.**

**Normal Force.** The uniform normal-stress distribution due to the normal force is shown in Fig. 3c. Here

$$\sigma = \frac{P}{A} = \frac{150 \text{ lb}}{(10 \text{ in.})(4 \text{ in})} = 3.75 \text{ psi}$$

**Bending Moment.** The normal-stress distribution due to the bending moment is shown in Fig. 3d. The maximum stress is

$$\sigma_{max} = \frac{Mc}{I} = \frac{750 \text{ lb} \cdot \text{in. (5 in.)}}{\frac{1}{12}(4 \text{ in.})(10 \text{ in.})^3} = 11.25 \text{ psi}$$

**Superposition.** If the above normal-stress distributions are added algebraically, the resultant stress distribution is shown in Fig. 3e.

Elements of material at B and C are subjected only to normal or *uniaxial stress* as shown in Fig. 3f and 3g. Hence,

$$\sigma_B = -\frac{P}{A} + \frac{Mc}{I} = -3.75 \text{ psi} + 11.25 \text{ psi} = 7.5 \text{ psi} \quad \text{(tension)} \quad Ans.$$

$$\sigma_C = -\frac{P}{A} - \frac{Mc}{I} = -3.75 \text{ psi} - 11.25 \text{ psi} = -15 \text{ psi} \quad \text{(compression)}$$
$$Ans.$$

Although it is not needed here, the location of the line of zero stress can be determined by proportional triangles; i.e.,

$$\frac{7.5 \text{ psi}}{x} = \frac{15 \text{ psi}}{10 \text{ in.} - x}; \quad x = 3.33 \text{ in.}$$

| Normal Force | | Bending Moment | | Combined Loading | | |
| (c) | + | (d) | = | (e) | (f) | (g) |

# EXAMPLE 3

The tank in Fig. 4a has an inner radius of 24 in. and a thickness of 0.5 in. It is filled to the top with water having a specific weight of $\gamma_w = 62.4\ \text{lb/ft}^3$. If it is made of steel having a specific weight of $\gamma_{st} = 490\ \text{lb/ft}^3$, determine the state of stress at point $A$. The tank is open at the top.

(a)

## SOLUTION

**Internal Loadings.** The free-body diagram of the section of both the tank and the water above point $A$ is shown in Fig. 4b. Notice that the weight of the water is supported by the water surface just *below* the section, *not* by the walls of the tank. In the vertical direction, the walls simply hold up the weight of the tank. This weight is

$$W_{st} = \gamma_{st}V_{st} = (490\ \text{lb/ft}^3)\left[\pi\left(\frac{24.5}{12}\ \text{ft}\right)^2 - \pi\left(\frac{24}{12}\ \text{ft}\right)^2\right](3\ \text{ft})$$

$$= 777.7\ \text{lb}$$

The stress in the circumferential direction is developed by the water pressure at level $A$. To obtain this (gauge) pressure we must use $p = \gamma_w z$, which gives the pressure at a point located a depth $z$ in the water. Consequently, the pressure on the tank at level $A$ is

$$p = \gamma_w z = (62.4\ \text{lb/ft}^3)(3\ \text{ft}) = 187.2\ \text{lb/ft}^2 = 1.30\ \text{psi}$$

(b)

**Stress Components.**

**Circumferential Stress.** Since $r/t = 24\ \text{in.}/0.5\ \text{in.} = 48 > 10$, the tank is a thin-walled vessel. Applying Eq. 1, using the inner radius $r = 24$ in., we have

$$\sigma_1 = \frac{pr}{t} = \frac{1.30\ \text{lb/in}^2(24\ \text{in.})}{0.5\ \text{in.}} = 62.4\ \text{psi} \qquad Ans.$$

**Longitudinal Stress.** Since the weight of the tank is supported uniformly by the walls, we have

$$\sigma_2 = \frac{W_{st}}{A_{st}} = \frac{777.7\ \text{lb}}{\pi[(24.5\ \text{in.})^2 - (24\ \text{in.})^2]} = 10.2\ \text{psi} \qquad Ans.$$

(c)

**Fig. 4**

**NOTE:** Eq. 2, $\sigma_2 = pr/2t$, does *not apply* here, since the tank is open at the top and therefore, as stated previously, the water cannot develop a loading on the walls in the longitudinal direction.

Point $A$ is therefore subjected to the biaxial stress shown in Fig. 4c.

EXAMPLE 4

The member shown in Fig. 5a has a rectangular cross section. Determine the state of stress that the loading produces at point C.

Fig. 5

SOLUTION

**Internal Loadings.** The support reactions on the member have been determined and are shown in Fig. 5b. If the left segment AC of the member is considered, Fig. 5c, the resultant internal loadings at the section consist of a normal force, a shear force, and a bending moment. Solving,

$$N = 16.45 \text{ kN} \qquad V = 21.93 \text{ kN} \qquad M = 32.89 \text{ kN} \cdot \text{m}$$

Normal Force

(d)

$+$

Shear Force

(e)

$+$

Bending Moment

(f)

**Fig. 5 (cont.)**

## Stress Components.

**Normal Force.** The uniform normal-stress distribution acting over the cross section is produced by the normal force, Fig. 5d. At point $C$,

$$\sigma_C = \frac{P}{A} = \frac{16.45(10^3) \text{ N}}{(0.050 \text{ m})(0.250 \text{ m})} = 1.32 \text{ MPa}$$

**Shear Force.** Here the area $A' = 0$, since point $C$ is located at the top of the member. Thus $Q = \bar{y}'A' = 0$ and for $C$, Fig. 5e, the shear stress

$$\tau_C = 0$$

**Bending Moment.** Point $C$ is located at $y = c = 0.125$ m from the neutral axis, so the normal stress at $C$, Fig. 5f, is

$$\sigma_C = \frac{Mc}{I} = \frac{(32.89(10^3) \text{ N} \cdot \text{m})(0.125 \text{ m})}{\left[\frac{1}{12}(0.050 \text{ m})(0.250 \text{ m}^3)\right]} = 63.16 \text{ MPa}$$

**Superposition.** The shear stress is zero. Adding the normal stresses determined above gives a compressive stress at $C$ having a value of

$$\sigma_C = 1.32 \text{ MPa} + 63.16 \text{ MPa} = 64.5 \text{ MPa} \qquad \textit{Ans.}$$

(g)

This result, acting on an element at $C$, is shown in Fig. 5g.

## EXAMPLE | 5

The solid rod shown in Fig. 6a has a radius of 0.75 in. If it is subjected to the force of 500 lb, determine the state of stress at point $A$.

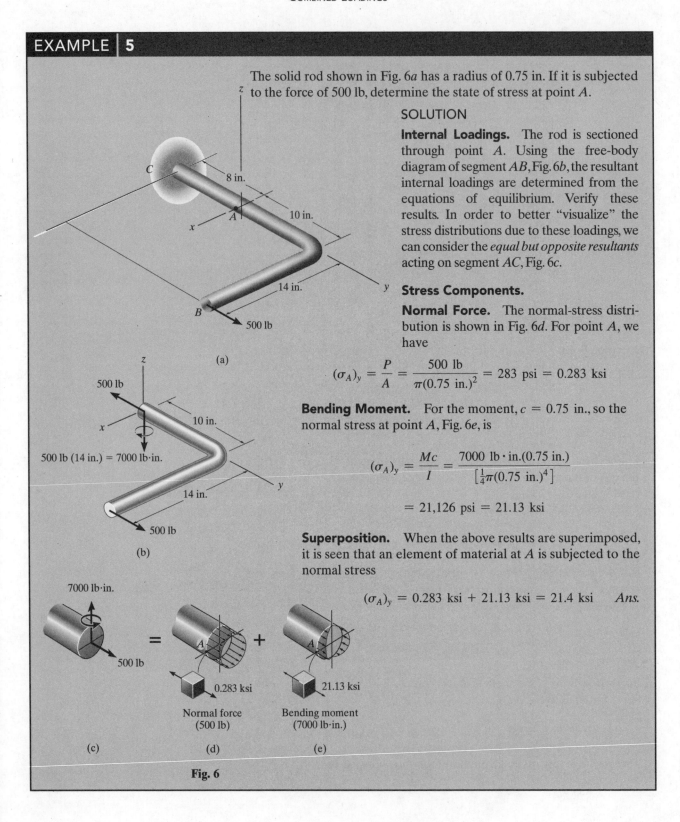

(a)

(b)

(c)          (d)          (e)

**Fig. 6**

### SOLUTION

**Internal Loadings.** The rod is sectioned through point $A$. Using the free-body diagram of segment $AB$, Fig. 6b, the resultant internal loadings are determined from the equations of equilibrium. Verify these results. In order to better "visualize" the stress distributions due to these loadings, we can consider the *equal but opposite resultants* acting on segment $AC$, Fig. 6c.

### Stress Components.

**Normal Force.** The normal-stress distribution is shown in Fig. 6d. For point $A$, we have

$$(\sigma_A)_y = \frac{P}{A} = \frac{500 \text{ lb}}{\pi(0.75 \text{ in.})^2} = 283 \text{ psi} = 0.283 \text{ ksi}$$

**Bending Moment.** For the moment, $c = 0.75$ in., so the normal stress at point $A$, Fig. 6e, is

$$(\sigma_A)_y = \frac{Mc}{I} = \frac{7000 \text{ lb} \cdot \text{in.}(0.75 \text{ in.})}{\left[\frac{1}{4}\pi(0.75 \text{ in.})^4\right]}$$

$$= 21,126 \text{ psi} = 21.13 \text{ ksi}$$

**Superposition.** When the above results are superimposed, it is seen that an element of material at $A$ is subjected to the normal stress

$$(\sigma_A)_y = 0.283 \text{ ksi} + 21.13 \text{ ksi} = 21.4 \text{ ksi} \qquad Ans.$$

Normal force (500 lb)

Bending moment (7000 lb·in.)

## EXAMPLE 6

The solid rod shown in Fig. 7a has a radius of 0.75 in. If it is subjected to the force of 800 lb, determine the state of stress at point A.

### SOLUTION

**Internal Loadings.** The rod is sectioned through point A. Using the free-body diagram of segment AB, Fig. 7b, the resultant internal loadings are determined from the six equations of equilibrium. Verify these results. The *equal but opposite resultants* are shown acting on segment AC, Fig. 7c.

### Stress Components.

**Shear Force.** The shear-stress distribution is shown in Fig. 7d. For point A, Q is determined from the shaded *semi-circular* area. Using the table on the inside front cover, we have

$$Q = \bar{y}'A' = \frac{4(0.75 \text{ in.})}{3\pi}\left[\frac{1}{2}\pi(0.75 \text{ in.})^2\right] = 0.2813 \text{ in}^3$$

so that

$$(\tau_{yz})_A = \frac{VQ}{It} = \frac{800 \text{ lb}(0.2813 \text{ in}^3)}{\left[\frac{1}{4}\pi(0.75 \text{ in.})^4\right]2(0.75 \text{ in.})}$$
$$= 604 \text{ psi} = 0.604 \text{ ksi}$$

**Bending Moment.** Since point A lies on the neutral axis, Fig. 7e, the normal stress is

$$\sigma_A = 0$$

**Torque.** At point A, $\rho_A = c = 0.75$ in., Fig. 7f. Thus the shear stress is

$$(\tau_{yz})_A = \frac{Tc}{J} = \frac{11\ 200 \text{ lb} \cdot \text{in.}(0.75 \text{ in.})}{\left[\frac{1}{2}\pi(0.75 \text{ in.})^4\right]} = 16\ 901 \text{ psi} = 16.90 \text{ ksi}$$

**Superposition.** Here the element of material at A is subjected only to a shear stress component, where

$$(\tau_{yz})_A = 0.604 \text{ ksi} + 16.90 \text{ ksi} = 17.5 \text{ ksi} \qquad Ans.$$

(a)

(b)

**Fig. 7**

(c)

(d) Shear force (800 lb) — 0.604 ksi

(e) Bending moment (8000 lb·in.)

(f) Torsional moment (11 200 lb·in.) — 16.90 ksi

## EXAMPLE 7

(a)

(b)

(c)

**Fig. 8**

Here is an example of where combined axial and bending stress can occur.

A rectangular block has a negligible weight and is subjected to a vertical force **P**, Fig. 8a. (a) Determine the range of values for the eccentricity $e_y$ of the load along the y axis so that it does not cause any tensile stress in the block. (b) Specify the region on the cross section where **P** may be applied without causing a tensile stress in the block.

### SOLUTION

**Part (a).** When **P** is moved to the centroid of the cross section, Fig. 8b, it is necessary to add a couple moment $M_x = Pe_y$ in order to maintain a statically equivalent loading. The combined normal stress at any coordinate location y on the cross section caused by these two loadings is

$$\sigma = -\frac{P}{A} - \frac{(Pe_y)y}{I_x} = -\frac{P}{A}\left(1 + \frac{Ae_yy}{I_x}\right)$$

Here the negative sign indicates compressive stress. For positive $e_y$, Fig. 7a, the *smallest* compressive stress will occur along edge AB, where $y = -h/2$, Fig. 8b. (By inspection, **P** causes compression there, but $\mathbf{M}_x$ causes tension.) Hence,

$$\sigma_{min} = -\frac{P}{A}\left(1 - \frac{Ae_yh}{2I_x}\right)$$

This stress will remain negative, i.e., compressive, provided the term in parentheses is positive; i.e.,

$$1 > \frac{Ae_yh}{2I_x}$$

Since $A = bh$ and $I_x = \frac{1}{12}bh^3$, then

$$1 > \frac{6e_y}{h} \quad \text{or} \quad e_y < \frac{1}{6}h \qquad \text{Ans.}$$

In other words, if $-\frac{1}{6}h \le e_y \le \frac{1}{6}h$, the stress in the block along edge AB or CD will be zero or remain *compressive*.

**NOTE:** This is sometimes referred to as the "*middle-third rule.*" It is very important to keep this rule in mind when loading columns or arches having a rectangular cross section and made of material such as stone or concrete, which can support little or no tensile stress. We can extend this analysis in the same way by placing **P** along the x axis in Fig. 8. The result will produce a shaded parallelogram shown in Fig. 8c. This region is referred to as the core or kern of the section. When **P** is applied within the kern, the normal stress at the corners of the cross section will be compressive.

## PRELIMINARY PROBLEMS

**P1.** In each case, determine the internal loadings that act on the indicated section. Show the results on the left segment.

(a)

(b)

(c)

(d)

**P1**

**P2.** The internal loadings act on the section. Show the stress that each of these loads produce on differential elements located at point $A$ and point $B$.

(a)

(b)

**P2**

# FUNDAMENTAL PROBLEMS

**F1.** Determine the normal stress developed at corners $A$ and $B$ of the column.

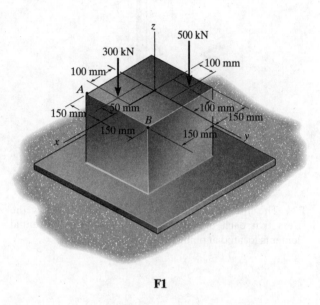

**F1**

**F3.** Determine the state of stress at point $A$ on the cross section of the beam at section $a$–$a$. Show the results in a differential element at the point.

Section $a$–$a$

**F3**

**F2.** Determine the state of stress at point $A$ on the cross section at section $a$–$a$ of the cantilever beam. Show the results in a differential element at the point.

Section $a$–$a$

**F2**

**F4.** Determine the magnitude of the load $P$ that will cause a maximum normal stress of $\sigma_{max} = 30$ ksi in the link along section $a$–$a$.

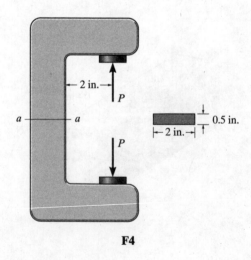

**F4**

**F5.** The beam has a rectangular cross section and is subjected to the loading shown. Determine the state of stress at point $B$. Show the results in a differential element at the point.

**F5**

**F7.** Determine the state of stress at point $A$ on the cross section of the pipe at section $a$–$a$. Show the results in a differential element at the point.

Section $a$–$a$

**F7**

**F6.** Determine the state of stress at point $A$ on the cross section of the pipe assembly at section $a$–$a$. Show the results in a differential element at the point.

Section $a$–$a$

**F6**

**F8.** Determine the state of stress at point $A$ on the cross section of the shaft at section $a$–$a$. Show the results in a differential element at the point.

Section $a$–$a$

**F8**

## PROBLEMS

**18.** The vertical force **P** acts on the bottom of the plate having a negligible weight. Determine the shortest distance $d$ to the edge of the plate at which it can be applied so that it produces no compressive stresses on the plate at section $a$–$a$. The plate has a thickness of 10 mm and **P** acts along the center line of this thickness.

300 mm

$a$      $a$

200 mm    500 mm

$d$

**P**

**Prob. 18**

**19.** Determine the maximum and minimum normal stress in the bracket at section $a$–$a$ when the load is applied at $x = 0$.

**\*20.** Determine the maximum and minimum normal stress in the bracket at section $a$–$a$ when the load is applied at $x = 300$ mm.

100 kN

15 mm

15 mm

$x$

200 mm

150 mm

$a$      $a$

**Probs. 19/20**

**21.** If the load has a weight of 600 lb, determine the maximum normal stress developed on the cross section of the supporting member at section $a$–$a$. Also, plot the normal stress distribution over the cross-section.

1.5 ft

$a$      $a$

1 in.

Section $a$ – $a$

**Prob. 21**

**22.** The clamp is made from members $AB$ and $AC$, which are pin connected at $A$. If it exerts a compressive force at $C$ and $B$ of 180 N, determine the maximum compressive stress in the clamp at section $a$–$a$. The screw $EF$ is subjected only to a tensile force along its axis.

**23.** The clamp is made from members $AB$ and $AC$, which are pin connected at $A$. If it exerts a compressive force at $C$ and $B$ of 180 N, sketch the stress distribution acting over section $a$–$a$. The screw $EF$ is subjected only to a tensile force along its axis.

30 mm   40 mm

$F$

$C$ — 180 N

15 mm

$a$ — $a$

15 mm

Section $a$–$a$

$B$ — 180 N

$A$

$E$

**Probs. 22/23**

**\*24.** The bearing pin supports the load of 700 lb. Determine the stress components in the support member at point $A$. The support is 0.5 in. thick.

**25.** The bearing pin supports the load of 700 lb. Determine the stress components in the support member at point $B$. The support is 0.5 in. thick.

**Probs. 24/25**

**26.** The column is built up by gluing the two identical boards together. Determine the maximum normal stress developed on the cross section when the eccentric force of $P = 50$ kN is applied.

**27.** The column is built up by gluing the two identical boards together. If the wood has an allowable normal stress of $\sigma_{allow} = 6$ MPa, determine the maximum allowable eccentric force **P** that can be applied to the column.

**Probs. 26/27**

**\*28.** The cylindrical post, having a diameter of 40 mm, is being pulled from the ground using a sling of negligible thickness. If the rope is subjected to a vertical force of $P = 500$ N, determine the normal stress at points $A$ and $B$. Show the results on a volume element located at each of these points.

**29.** Determine the maximum load $P$ that can be applied to the sling having a negligible thickness so that the normal stress in the post does not exceed $\sigma_{allow} = 30$ MPa. The post has a diameter of 50 mm.

**Probs. 28/29**

**30.** The rib-joint pliers are used to grip the smooth pipe $C$. If the force of 100 N is applied to the handles, determine the state of stress at points $A$ and $B$ on the cross section of the jaw at section $a$–$a$. Indicate the results on an element at each point.

Section $a$ – $a$

**Prob. 30**

**31.** Determine the smallest distance $d$ to the edge of the plate at which the force **P** can be applied so that it produces no compressive stresses in the plate at section $a$–$a$. The plate has a thickness of 20 mm and **P** acts along the centerline of this thickness.

**\*32.** The horizontal force of $P = 80$ kN acts at the end of the plate. The plate has a thickness of 10 mm and **P** acts along the centerline of this thickness such that $d = 50$ mm. Plot the distribution of normal stress acting along section $a$–$a$.

**Probs. 31/32**

**33.** The control lever is subjected to a horizontal force of 20 lb on the handle. Determine the state of stress at points $A$ and $B$. Sketch the results on differential elements located at each of these points. The assembly is pin-connected at $C$ and attached to a cable at $D$.

**34.** The control lever is subjected to a horizontal force of 20 lb on the handle. Determine the state of stress at points $E$ and $F$. Sketch the results on differential elements located at each of these points. The assembly is pin connected at $C$ and attached to a cable at $D$.

**Probs. 33/34**

**35.** The tubular shaft of the soil auger is subjected to the axial force and torque shown. If the auger is rotating at a constant rate, determine the state of stress at points $A$ and $B$ on the cross section of the shaft at section $a$–$a$.

**Prob. 35**

**\*36.** The drill is jammed in the wall and is subjected to the torque and force shown. Determine the state of stress at point $A$ on the cross section of drill bit at section $a$–$a$.

**37.** The drill is jammed in the wall and is subjected to the torque and force shown. Determine the state of stress at point $B$ on the cross section of drill bit, in back, at section $a$–$a$.

**Probs. 36/37**

**38.** The frame supports the distributed load shown. Determine the state of stress acting at point *D*. Show the results on a differential element at this point.

**39.** The frame supports the distributed load shown. Determine the state of stress acting at point *E*. Show the results on a differential element at this point.

**42.** Determine the state of stress at point *A* on the cross section of the post at section *a–a*. Indicate the results on a differential element at the point.

**43.** Determine the state of stress at point *B* on the cross section of the post at section *a–a*. Indicate the results on a differential element at the point.

**Probs. 38/39**

**Probs. 42/43**

**\*40.** The 500-kg engine is suspended from the jib crane at the position shown. Determine the state of stress at point *A* on the cross section of the boom at section *a–a*.

**41.** The 500-kg engine is suspended from the jib crane at the position shown. Determine the state of stress at point *B* on the cross section of the boom at section *a–a*. Point *B* is just above the bottom flange.

**\*44.** Determine the normal stress developed at points *A* and *B*. Neglect the weight of the block.

**45.** Sketch the normal stress distribution acting over the cross section at section *a–a*. Neglect the weight of the block.

**Probs. 40/41**

**Probs. 44/45**

**46.** The support is subjected to the compressive load **P**. Determine the absolute maximum possible and minimum possible normal stress acting in the material, for $x \geq 0$.

**Prob. 46**

**47.** The bent shaft is fixed in the wall at $A$. If a force **F** is applied at $B$, determine the stress components at points $D$ and $E$. Show the results on a differential element located at each of these points. Take $F = 12$ lb and $\theta = 0°$.

**\*48.** The bent shaft is fixed in the wall at $A$. If a force **F** is applied at $B$, determine the stress components at points $D$ and $E$. Show the results on a differential element located at each of these points. Take $F = 12$ lb and $\theta = 90°$.

**49.** The bent shaft is fixed in the wall at $A$. If a force **F** is applied at $B$, determine the stress components at points $D$ and $E$. Show the results on a volume element located at each of these points. Take $F = 12$ lb and $\theta = 45°$.

**Probs. 47/48/49**

**50.** The coiled spring is subjected to a force $P$. If we assume the shear stress caused by the shear force at any vertical section of the coil wire to be uniform, show that the maximum shear stress in the coil is $\tau_{max} = P/A + PRr/J$, where $J$ is the polar moment of inertia of the coil wire and $A$ is its cross-sectional area.

**Prob. 50**

**51.** A post having the dimensions shown is subjected to the bearing load **P**. Specify the region to which this load can be applied without causing tensile stress to be developed at points $A, B, C$, and $D$.

**Prob. 51**

**\*52.** The vertebra of the spinal column can support a maximum compressive stress of $\sigma_{max}$, before undergoing a compression fracture. Determine the smallest force $P$ that can be applied to a vertebra, if we assume this load is applied at an eccentric distance $e$ from the centerline of the bone, and the bone remains elastic. Model the vertebra as a hollow cylinder with an inner radius $r_i$ and outer radius $r_o$.

**55.** Determine the state of stress at point $A$ on the cross section of the post at section $a$–$a$. Indicate the results on a differential element at the point.

**\*56.** Determine the state of stress at point $B$ on the cross section of the post at section $a$–$a$. Indicate the results on a differential element at the point.

**Prob. 52**

**Probs. 55/56**

**53.** The 1-in.-diameter rod is subjected to the loads shown. Determine the state of stress at point $A$, and show the results on a differential element located at this point.

**54.** The 1-in.-diameter rod is subjected to the loads shown. Determine the state of stress at point $B$, and show the results on a differential element located at this point.

**57.** The sign is subjected to the uniform wind loading. Determine the stress components at points $A$ and $B$ on the 100-mm-diameter supporting post. Show the results on a volume element located at each of these points.

**58.** The sign is subjected to the uniform wind loading. Determine the stress components at points $C$ and $D$ on the 100-mm-diameter supporting post. Show the results on a volume element located at each of these points.

**Probs. 53/54**

**Probs. 57/58**

477

**59.** If $P = 60$ kN, determine the maximum normal stress developed on the cross section of the column.

**\*60.** Determine the maximum allowable force **P**, if the column is made from material having an allowable normal stress of $\sigma_{\text{allow}} = 100$ MPa.

**Probs. 59/60**

**61.** The C-frame is used in a riveting machine. If the force at the ram on the clamp at $D$ is $P = 8$ kN, sketch the stress distribution acting over the section $a$–$a$.

**62.** Determine the maximum ram force $P$ that can be applied to the clamp at $D$ if the allowable normal stress for the material is $\sigma_{\text{allow}} = 180$ MPa.

**Probs. 61/62**

**63.** The uniform sign has a weight of 1500 lb and is supported by the pipe $AB$, which has an inner radius of 2.75 in. and an outer radius of 3.00 in. If the face of the sign is subjected to a uniform wind pressure of $p = 150$ lb/ft², determine the state of stress at points $C$ and $D$. Show the results on a differential volume element located at each of these points. Neglect the thickness of the sign, and assume that it is supported along the outside edge of the pipe.

**\*64.** Solve Prob. 63 for points $E$ and $F$.

**Probs. 63/64**

**65.** Determine the state of stress at point $A$ on the cross section of the pipe at section $a$–$a$.

**66.** Determine the state of stress at point $B$ on the cross section of the pipe at section $a$–$a$.

**Probs. 65/66**

**67.** The metal link is subjected to the axial force of $P = 7$ kN. Its original cross section is to be altered by cutting a circular groove into one side. Determine the distance $a$ the groove can penetrate into the cross section so that the tensile stress does not exceed $\sigma_{allow} = 175$ MPa. Offer a better way to remove this depth of material from the cross section and calculate the tensile stress for this case. Neglect the effects of stress concentration.

**Prob. 67**

**\*68.** The bar has a diameter of 40 mm. If it is subjected to a force of 800 N as shown, determine the stress components that act at point $A$ and show the results on a volume element located at this point.

**69.** Solve Prob. 68 for point $B$.

**Probs. 68/69**

**70.** The $\frac{3}{4}$-in.-diameter shaft is subjected to the loading shown. Determine the stress components at point $A$. Sketch the results on a volume element located at this point. The journal bearing at $C$ can exert only force components $\mathbf{C}_y$ and $\mathbf{C}_z$ on the shaft, and the thrust bearing at $D$ can exert force components $\mathbf{D}_x$, $\mathbf{D}_y$, and $\mathbf{D}_z$ on the shaft.

**71.** Solve Prob. 70 for the stress components at point $B$.

**Probs. 70/71**

**\*72.** The hook is subjected to the force of 80 lb. Determine the state of stress at point $A$ at section $a$–$a$. The cross section is circular and has a diameter of 0.5 in. Use the curved-beam formula to compute the bending stress.

**73.** The hook is subjected to the force of 80 lb. Determine the state of stress at point $B$ at section $a$–$a$. The cross section has a diameter of 0.5 in. Use the curved-beam formula to compute the bending stress.

**Probs. 72/73**

# CHAPTER REVIEW

A pressure vessel is considered to have a thin wall provided $r/t \geq 10$. For a thin-walled cylindrical vessel, the circumferential or hoop stress is

$$\sigma_1 = \frac{pr}{t}$$

This stress is twice as great as the longitudinal stress,

$$\sigma_2 = \frac{pr}{2t}$$

Thin-walled spherical vessels have the same stress within their walls in all directions. It is

$$\sigma_1 = \sigma_2 = \frac{pr}{2t}$$

Superposition of stress components can be used to determine the normal and shear stress at a point in a member subjected to a combined loading. To do this, it is first necessary to determine the resultant axial and shear forces and the internal resultant torsional and bending moments at the section where the point is located. Then the normal and shear stress resultant components at the point are determined by algebraically adding the normal and shear stress components of each loading.

$$\sigma = \frac{P}{A}$$

$$\tau = \frac{VQ}{It}$$

$$\sigma = -\frac{My}{I}$$

$$\tau = \frac{T\rho}{J}$$

480

# CONCEPTUAL PROBLEMS

**C1.** Explain why failure of this garden hose occurred near its end and why the tear occurred along its length. Use numerical values to explain your result. Assume the water pressure is 30 psi.

C1

**C2.** This open-ended silo contains granular material. It is constructed from wood slats and held together with steel bands. Explain, using numerical values, why the bands are not spaced evenly along the height of the cylinder. Also, how would you find this spacing if each band is to be subjected to the same stress?

C2

**C3.** Unlike the turnbuckle at $B$, which is connected along the axis of the rod, the one at $A$ has been welded to the edges of the rod, and so it will be subjected to additional stress. Use the same numerical values for the tensile load in each rod and the rod's diameter, and compare the stress in each rod.

C3

**C4.** A constant wind blowing against the side of this chimney has caused creeping strains in the mortar joints, such that the chimney has a noticeable deformation. Explain how to obtain the stress distribution over a section at the base of the chimney, and sketch this distribution over the section.

C4

# REVIEW PROBLEMS

**74.** The eye hook has the dimensions shown. If it supports a cable loading of 80 kN, determine the maximum normal stress at section *a–a* and sketch the stress distribution acting over the cross section.

**Prob. 74**

**75.** The 20-kg drum is suspended from the hook mounted on the wooden frame. Determine the state of stress at point *E* on the cross section of the frame at section *a–a*. Indicate the results on an element.

***76.** The 20-kg drum is suspended from the hook mounted on the wooden frame. Determine the state of stress at point *F* on the cross section of the frame at section *b–b*. Indicate the results on an element.

**Probs. 75/76**

**77.** A bar having a square cross section of 30 mm by 30 mm is 2 m long and is held upward. If it has a mass of 5 kg/m, determine the largest angle $\theta$, measured from the vertical, at which it can be supported before it is subjected to a tensile stress along its axis near the grip.

**78.** Solve Prob. 77 if the bar has a circular cross section of 30-mm diameter.

**Probs. 77/78**

**79.** The gondola and passengers have a weight of 1500 lb and center of gravity at *G*. The suspender arm *AE* has a square cross-sectional area of 1.5 in. by 1.5 in., and is pin connected at its ends *A* and *E*. Determine the largest tensile stress developed in regions *AB* and *DC* of the arm.

**Prob. 79**

**\*80.** The hydraulic cylinder is required to support a force of $P = 100$ kN. If the cylinder has an inner diameter of 100 mm and is made from a material having an allowable normal stress of $\sigma_{allow} = 150$ MPa, determine the required minimum thickness $t$ of the wall of the cylinder.

**81.** The hydraulic cylinder has an inner diameter of 100 mm and wall thickness of $t = 4$ mm. If it is made from a material having an allowable normal stress of $\sigma_{allow} = 150$ MPa, determine the maximum allowable force **P**.

**Probs. 80/81**

**82.** If the cross section of the femur at section $a$–$a$ can be approximated as a circular tube as shown, determine the maximum normal stress developed on the cross section at section $a$–$a$ due to the load of 75 lb.

**Prob. 82**

**83.** Air pressure in the cylinder is increased by exerting forces $P = 2$ kN on the two pistons, each having a radius of 45 mm. If the cylinder has a wall thickness of 2 mm, determine the state of stress in the wall of the cylinder.

**\*84.** Determine the maximum force $P$ that can be exerted on each of the two pistons so that the circumferential stress component in the cylinder does not exceed 3 MPa. Each piston has a radius of 45 mm and the cylinder has a wall thickness of 2 mm.

**Probs. 83/84**

**85.** The wall hanger has a thickness of 0.25 in. and is used to support the vertical reactions of the beam that is loaded as shown. If the load is transferred uniformly to each strap of the hanger, determine the state of stress at points $C$ and $D$ on the strap at $A$. Assume the vertical reaction **F** at this end acts in the center and on the edge of the bracket as shown.

**86.** The wall hanger has a thickness of 0.25 in. and is used to support the vertical reactions of the beam that is loaded as shown. If the load is transferred uniformly to each strap of the hanger, determine the state of stress at points $C$ and $D$ on the strap at $B$. Assume the vertical reaction $F$ at this end acts in the center and on the edge of the bracket as shown.

**Probs. 85/86**

# Solutions and Answers for Preliminary Problems

**P1a.**

140 N·m

300 N

**P1b.**

600 N·m
200 N
300 N
100 N
400 N·m

**P1c.**

100 N·m
100 N
50 N·m

**P1d.**

300 N·m
1200 N
500 N
300 N
600 N·m
200 N

**P2a.**

Element *A*    P  +  M  +  V  +  T

Element *B*    P  +  M  +  V  +  T

**P2b.**

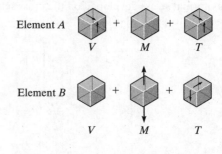

Element *A*    V  +  M  +  T

Element *B*    V  +  M  +  T

# Selected Answers

1.    $t = 18.8$ mm
2.    $r_o = 75.5$ in.
3.    (a) $\sigma_1 = 1.04$ ksi, $\sigma_2 = 0$,
       (b) $\sigma_1 = 1.04$ ksi, $\sigma_2 = 520$ psi
5.    $\sigma_1 = 600$ psi, $\sigma_2 = 0$
6.    $\sigma_1 = 600$ psi, $\sigma_2 = 300$ psi
7.    (a) $\sigma_1 = 127$ MPa,
       (b) $\sigma_1' = 79.1$ MPa, $(\tau_{avg})_b = 322$ MPa
9.    $\sigma_{hoop} = 7.20$ ksi, $\sigma_{long} = 3.60$ ksi
10.   $\sigma_1 = 1.60$ ksi, $p = 25$ psi, $\delta = 0.00140$ in.
11.   (a) $T = 18.2$ kip·ft,
       (b) $P = 18.1$ kip,
       (c) $F = 9.05$ kip
13.   $T_1 = 128°, \sigma_1 = 12.1$ ksi, $p = 252$ psi
14.   $\delta r_i = \dfrac{pr_i^2}{E(r_o - r_i)}$
15.   $p = \dfrac{E(r_2 - r_3)}{\dfrac{r_2^2}{r_2 - r_1} + \dfrac{r_3^2}{r_4 - r_3}}$
17.   $\sigma_{fil} = \dfrac{pr}{t + t'w/L} + \dfrac{T}{wt'}$,
       $\sigma_w = \dfrac{pr}{t + t'w/L} - \dfrac{T}{Lt}$
18.   $d = 66.7$ mm
19.   $\sigma_L = 66.7$ MPa (C), $\sigma_R = 33.3$ MPa (T)
21.   $\sigma_{max} = \sigma_L = 13.9$ ksi (T), $\sigma_R = 13.6$ ksi (C)
22.   $\sigma_{max} = 1.07$ MPa
23.   $\sigma_{const} = 1.07$ MPa
25.   $\sigma_B = 5.35$ ksi, $\tau_B = 0$
26.   $\sigma_{max} = 2.34$ MPa (C)
27.   $P = 128$ kN
29.   $P = 11.8$ kN
30.   $\sigma_A = 25$ MPa (C), $\sigma_B = 0$,
       $\tau_A = 0, \tau_B = 5$ MPa
31.   $d = 66.7$ mm
33.   $\sigma_B = 8.89$ ksi (C), $\tau_B = 0$,
       $\sigma_A = 720$ psi (T), $\tau_A = 0$
34.   $\sigma_E = 8.89$ ksi (T), $\tau_E = 0, \sigma_F = 0, \tau_F = 240$ psi
35.   $\sigma_A = \sigma_B = 306$ psi (C),
       $\tau_A = 8.46$ ksi, $\tau_B = 5.64$ ksi
37.   $\sigma_B = 1.53$ MPa (C), $\tau_B = 100$ MPa
38.   $\sigma_D = -88.0$ MPa, $\tau_D = 0$
39.   $\sigma_E = 57.8$ MPa, $\tau_E = 864$ kPa

41.   $\sigma_B = 3.26$ MPa (T), $\tau_B = 0.209$ MPa
42.   $\sigma_A = 3.31$ ksi (T), $\tau_A = 0.581$ ksi
43.   $\sigma_B = 1.99$ ksi (C), $\tau_B = 0.510$ ksi
45.   $\sigma_A = 1.00$ ksi (C), $\sigma_B = 3.00$ ksi (C)
46.   $\sigma_{max} = \dfrac{1.33P}{a^2}$ (C), $\sigma_{min} = \dfrac{P}{3a^2}$ (T)
47.   $\sigma_D = 0, \tau_D = 80.8$ psi,
       $\sigma_E = -501$ psi, $\tau_E = 93.9$ psi
49.   $\sigma_D = -126$ psi, $\tau_D = 57.2$ psi,
       $\sigma_E = -347$ psi, $\tau_E = 66.4$ psi
51.   $6e_y + 18e_z < 5a$
53.   $\sigma_A = 6.61$ ksi (T), $\tau_A = 1.39$ ksi
54.   $\sigma_B = 5.76$ ksi (C), $\tau_B = 1.36$ ksi
55.   $\sigma_A = 7.20$ MPa (T), $\tau_A = 0.6$ MPa
57.   $\sigma_A = 107$ MPa (T), $\tau_A = 15.3$ MPa,
       $\sigma_B = 0, \tau_B = 14.8$ MPa
58.   $\sigma_C = 107$ MPa (C), $\tau_C = 15.3$ MPa,
       $\sigma_D = 0, \tau_D = 15.8$ MPa
59.   $\sigma_{max} = 71.0$ MPa (C)
61.   $(\sigma_{max})_t = 106$ MPa, $(\sigma_{max})_c = -159$ MPa
62.   $P = 9.08$ kN
63.   $\sigma_C = 15.6$ ksi (T), $\sigma_D = 124$ ksi (T),
       $\tau_D = 62.4$ ksi, $\tau_C = 52.4$ ksi
65.   $\sigma_A = 605$ psi (T), $\tau_A = 327$ psi
66.   $\sigma_B = 466$ psi (C), $\tau_B = 422$ psi
67.   $a = 61.9$ mm. Remove material equally from
both sides, $\sigma = 15.5$ MPa.
69.   $\sigma_B = -21.7$ MPa, $\tau_B = 0$
70.   $\tau_A = 0, \sigma_A = 30.2$ ksi (C)
71.   $\sigma_B = 0, \tau_B = 0.377$ ksi
73.   $\sigma = 1.48$ psi (T), $\tau = 384$ psi
74.   $(\sigma_t)_{max} = 15.8$ ksi, $(\sigma_c)_{max} = -10.5$ ksi
75.   $\sigma_E = 802$ kPa, $\tau_E = 69.8$ kPa
77.   $\theta = 0.286°$
78.   $\theta = 0.215°$
79.   $(\sigma_{max})_{AB} = 667$ psi, $(\sigma_{max})_{CD} = 40.7$ ksi
81.   $P = 94.2$ kN
82.   $\sigma_{max} = 236$ psi (C)
83.   $\sigma_1 = 7.07$ MPa, $\sigma_2 = 0$
85.   $\sigma_C = 11.6$ ksi, $\tau_C = 0$,
       $\sigma_D = -23.2$ ksi, $\tau_D = 0$
86.   $\sigma_C = 10.4$ ksi, $\tau_C = 0$,
       $\sigma_D = -20.8$ ksi, $\tau_D = 0$

# Fundamental Problems Partial Solutions and Answers

**F1**  $+\uparrow \Sigma F_z = (F_R)_z;$  $-500 - 300 = P$

$P = -800$ kN

$\Sigma M_x = 0;$  $300(0.05) - 500(0.1) = M_x$

$M_x = -35$ kN $\cdot$ m

$\Sigma M_y = 0;$  $300(0.1) - 500(0.1) = M_y$

$M_y = -20$ kN $\cdot$ m

$A = 0.3(0.3) = 0.09$ m$^2$

$I_x = I_y = \dfrac{1}{12}(0.3)(0.3^3) = 0.675(10^{-3})$ m$^4$

$\sigma_A = \dfrac{-800(10^3)}{0.09} + \dfrac{[20(10^3)](0.15)}{0.675(10^{-3})} + \dfrac{[35(10^3)](0.15)}{0.675(10^{-3})}$

$= 3.3333$ MPa $= 3.33$ MPa (T)  *Ans.*

$\sigma_B = \dfrac{-800(10^3)}{0.09} + \dfrac{[20(10^3)](0.15)}{0.675(10^{-3})} - \dfrac{[35(10^3)](0.15)}{0.675(10^{-3})}$

$= -12.22$ MPa $= 12.2$ MPa (C)  *Ans.*

**F2**  $+\uparrow \Sigma F_y = 0;$  $V - 400 = 0$  $V = 400$ kN

$\zeta + \Sigma M_A = 0; -M - 400(0.5) = 0$  $M = -200$ kN $\cdot$ m

$I = \dfrac{1}{12}(0.1)(0.3^3) = 0.225(10^{-3})$ m$^4$

$Q_A = y'A' = 0.1(0.1)(0.1) = 1(10^{-3})$ m$^3$

$\sigma_A = \dfrac{My}{I} = \dfrac{[200(10^3)](-0.05)}{0.225(10^{-3})}$

$= -44.44$ MPa $= 44.4$ MPa (C)  *Ans.*

$\tau_A = \dfrac{VQ}{It} = \dfrac{400(10^3)[1(10^{-3})]}{0.225(10^{-3})(0.1)} = 17.8$ MPa  *Ans.*

**F3**  Left reaction is 20 kN.

Left segment:

$+\uparrow \Sigma F_y = 0;$  $20 - V = 0$  $V = 20$ kN

$\zeta + \Sigma M_s = 0;$  $M - 20(0.5) = 0$  $M = 10$ kN $\cdot$ m

$I = \dfrac{1}{12}(0.1)(0.2^3) - \dfrac{1}{12}(0.09)(0.18^3)$

$= 22.9267(10^{-6})$ m$^4$

$Q_A = y_1'A_1' + y_2'A_2' = 0.07(0.04)(0.01)$

$+ 0.095(0.1)(0.01) = 0.123(10^{-3})$ m$^3$

$\sigma_A = -\dfrac{My_A}{I} = -\dfrac{[10(10^3)](0.05)}{22.9267(10^{-6})}$

$= -21.81$ MPa $= 21.8$ MPa (C)  *Ans.*

$\tau_A = \dfrac{VQ_A}{It} = \dfrac{20(10^3)[0.123(10^{-3})]}{[22.9267(10^{-6})](0.01)}$

$= 10.7$ MPa  *Ans.*

**F4**  At the section through centroidal axis:

$N = P$

$V = 0$

$M = (2 + 1)P = 3P$

$\sigma = \dfrac{P}{A} + \dfrac{Mc}{I}$

$30 = \dfrac{P}{2(0.5)} + \dfrac{(3P)(1)}{\dfrac{1}{12}(0.5)(2)^3}$

$P = 3$ kip  *Ans.*

**F5**  At section through $B$:

$N = 500$ lb, $V = 400$ lb

$M = 400(10) = 4000$ lb $\cdot$ in.

Axial load:

$\sigma_x = \dfrac{P}{A} = \dfrac{500}{4(3)} = 41.667$ psi (T)

Shear load:

$\tau_{xy} = \dfrac{VQ}{It} = \dfrac{400[(1.5)(3)(1)]}{[\dfrac{1}{12}(3)(4)^3]3} = 37.5$ psi

Bending moment:

$\sigma_x = \dfrac{My}{I} = \dfrac{4000(1)}{\dfrac{1}{12}(3)(4)^3} = 250$ psi (C)

Thus

$\sigma_x = 41.667 - 250 = 208$ psi (C)  *Ans.*

$\sigma_y = 0$  *Ans.*

$\tau_{xy} = 37.5$ psi  *Ans.*

**F6**  Top segment:

$\Sigma F_y = 0;$  $V_y + 1000 = 0$  $V_y = -1000$ N

$\Sigma F_x = 0;$  $V_x - 1500 = 0$  $V_x = 1500$ N

$\Sigma M_z = 0;$  $T_z - 1500(0.4) = 0$  $T_z = 600$ N $\cdot$ m

$\Sigma M_y = 0;$  $M_y - 1500(0.2) = 0$  $M_y = 300$ N $\cdot$ m

$\Sigma M_x = 0;$  $M_x - 1000(0.2) = 0$  $M_x = 200$ N $\cdot$ m

$I_y = I_x = \dfrac{\pi}{4}(0.02^4) = 40(10^{-9})\pi$ m$^4$

$J = \dfrac{\pi}{2}(0.02^4) = 80(10^{-9})\pi$ m$^4$

$(Q_y)_A = \dfrac{4(0.02)}{3\pi}\left[\dfrac{\pi}{2}(0.02^2)\right] = 5.3333(10^{-6})$ m$^3$

$\sigma_A = \dfrac{M_x y}{I_x} = \dfrac{M_y x}{I_y} = \dfrac{200(0)}{40(10^{-9})\pi} + \dfrac{300(0.02)}{40(10^{-9})\pi}$

$= 47.7 \text{ MPa (T)}$ *Ans.*

$$[(\tau_{zy})_T]_A = \frac{T_z c}{J} = \frac{600(0.02)}{80(10^{-9})\pi} = 47.746 \text{ MPa}$$

$$[(\tau_{zy})_V]_A = \frac{V_y(Q_y)_A}{I_x t} = \frac{1000[5.3333(10^{-6})]}{[40(10^{-9})\pi](0.04)}$$

$$= 1.061 \text{ MPa}$$

Combining these two shear stress components,

$(\tau_{zy})_A = 47.746 + 1.061 = 48.8 \text{ MPa}$ *Ans.*

**F7**   Right Segment:

$\Sigma F_z = 0;$    $V_z - 6 = 0$      $V_z = 6 \text{ kN}$

$\Sigma M_y = 0;$    $T_y - 6(0.3) = 0$    $T_y = 1.8 \text{ kN} \cdot \text{m}$

$\Sigma M_x = 0;$    $M_x - 6(0.3) = 0$    $M_x = 1.8 \text{ kN} \cdot \text{m}$

$$I_x = \frac{\pi}{4}(0.05^4 - 0.04^4) = 0.9225(10^{-6})\pi \text{ m}^4$$

$$J = \frac{\pi}{2}(0.05^4 - 0.04^4) = 1.845(10^{-6})\pi \text{ m}^4$$

$(Q_z)_A = y_2' A_2' - y_1' A_1'$

$$= \frac{4(0.05)}{3\pi}\left[\frac{\pi}{2}(0.05^2)\right] - \frac{4(0.04)}{3\pi}\left[\frac{\pi}{2}(0.04^2)\right]$$

$$= 40.6667(10^{-6}) \text{ m}^3$$

$$\sigma_A = \frac{M_x z}{I_x} = \frac{1.8(10^3)(0)}{0.9225(10^{-6})\pi} = 0 \qquad Ans.$$

$$[(\tau_{yz})_T]_A = \frac{T_y c}{J} = \frac{[1.8(10^3)](0.05)}{1.845(10^{-6})\pi} = 15.53 \text{ MPa}$$

$$[(\tau_{yz})_V]_A = \frac{V_z(Q_z)_A}{I_x t} = \frac{6(10^3)[40.6667(10^{-6})]}{[0.9225(10^{-6})\pi](0.02)}$$

$$= 4.210 \text{ MPa}$$

Combining these two shear stress components,

$(\tau_{yz})_A = 15.53 - 4.210 = 11.3 \text{ MPa}$ *Ans.*

**F8**   Left Segment:

$\Sigma F_z = 0;$    $V_z - 900 - 300 = 0$    $V_z = 1200 \text{ N}$

$\Sigma M_y = 0;$    $T_y + 300(0.1) - 900(0.1) = 0$    $T_y = 60 \text{ N} \cdot \text{m}$

$\Sigma M_x = 0;$    $M_x + (900 + 300)0.3 = 0$    $M_x = -360 \text{ N} \cdot \text{m}$

$$I_x = \frac{\pi}{4}(0.025^4 - 0.02^4) = 57.65625(10^{-9})\pi \text{ m}^4$$

$$J = \frac{\pi}{2}(0.025^4 - 0.02^4) = 0.1153125(10^{-6})\pi \text{ m}^4$$

$(Q_y)_A = 0$

$$\sigma_A = \frac{M_x y}{I_x} = \frac{(360)(0.025)}{57.65625(10^{-9})\pi} = 49.7 \text{ MPa} \quad Ans.$$

$$[(\tau_{xy})_T]_A = \frac{T_y \rho_A}{J} = \frac{60(0.025)}{0.1153125(10^{-6})\pi} = 4.14 \text{ MPa } Ans.$$

$$[(\tau_{yz})_V]_A = \frac{V_z(Q_z)_A}{I_x t} = 0 \qquad\qquad Ans.$$

# Stress Transformation

From Chapter 9 of *Mechanics of Materials*, Ninth Edition. R. C. Hibbeler. Copyright © 2014 by Pearson Education, Inc. Published by Pearson Prentice Hall. All rights reserved.

These turbine blades are subjected to a complex pattern of stress. For design it is necessary to determine where and in what direction the maximum stress occurs.

# Stress Transformation

## CHAPTER OBJECTIVES

■ In this chapter, we will show how to transform the stress components that are associated with a particular coordinate system into components associated with a coordinate system having a different orientation. Once the necessary transformation equations are established, we will then be able to obtain the maximum normal and maximum shear stress at a point and find the orientation of elements upon which they act. Plane-stress transformation will be discussed in the first part of the chapter, since this condition is most common in engineering practice. At the end of the chapter we will discuss a method for finding the absolute maximum shear stress at a point when the material is subjected to both plane and three-dimensional states of stress.

## 1    Plane-Stress Transformation

The general state of stress at a point is characterized by *six* independent normal and shear stress components, which act on the faces of an element of material located at the point, Fig. 1*a*. This state of stress, however, is not often encountered in engineering practice. Instead, engineers frequently make approximations or simplifications of the loadings on a body in order that the stress produced in a structural member or mechanical element can be analyzed in a *single plane*. When this is the case, the material is said to be subjected to *plane stress*, Fig. 1*b*. For example, if there is no load on the surface of a body, then the normal and shear stress components will be zero on the face of an element that lies on this surface. Consequently, the corresponding stress components on the opposite face will also be zero, and so the material at the point will be subjected to plane stress.

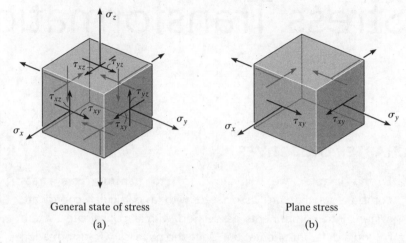

General state of stress

(a)

Plane stress

(b)

**Fig. 1**

(a)

‖

(b)

**Fig. 2**

The general state of *plane stress* at a point is therefore represented by a combination of two normal-stress components, $\sigma_x$, $\sigma_y$, and one shear-stress component, $\tau_{xy}$, which act on four faces of the element. For convenience, in this text we will view this state of stress in the $x$–$y$ plane, with the $x$, $y$ axes as shown in Fig. 2a. If this state of stress is defined on an element having a *different orientation* $\theta$ as in Fig. 2b, then it will be subjected to three *different* stress components defined as $\sigma_{x'}$, $\sigma_{y'}$, $\tau_{x'y'}$ relative to the $x'$, $y'$ axes. In other words, *the state of plane stress at the point is uniquely represented by two normal stress components and one shear stress component acting on an element. These three components will be different for each specific orientation $\theta$ of the element at the point*.

In this section, we will show how to *transform* the stress components from the orientation of an element in Fig. 2a to the orientation of the element in Fig. 2b. This is like knowing two force components, say, $\mathbf{F}_x$ and $\mathbf{F}_y$, directed along the $x$, $y$ axes, that produce a resultant force $\mathbf{F}_R$, and then trying to find the force components $\mathbf{F}_{x'}$ and $\mathbf{F}_{y'}$, directed along the $x'$, $y'$ axes, so they produce the *same* resultant. The transformation for force must only account for the force component's magnitude and direction. The transformation of stress components, however, is more difficult since it must account for the magnitude and direction of each stress component *and* the orientation of the area upon which each component acts.

## Procedure for Analysis

If the state of stress at a point is known for a given orientation of an element of material, Fig. 3a, then the state of stress in an element having some other orientation, $\theta$, Fig. 3b, can be determined using the following procedure.

- To determine the normal and shear stress components $\sigma_{x'}$, $\tau_{x'y'}$ acting on the $+x'$ face of the element, Fig. 3b, section the element in Fig. 3a as shown in Fig. 3c. If the sectioned area is $\Delta A$, then the adjacent areas of the segment will be $\Delta A \sin \theta$ and $\Delta A \cos \theta$.

- Draw the free-body diagram of the segment, which requires showing the *forces* that act on the segment, Fig. 3d. This is done by multiplying the stress components on each face by the area upon which they act.

- When $\Sigma F_{x'} = 0$ is applied to the free-body diagram the area $\Delta A$ will cancel out of each term and a *direct* solution for $\sigma_{x'}$ will be possible. Likewise, $\Sigma F_{y'} = 0$ will yield $\tau_{x'y'}$.

- If $\sigma_{y'}$, acting on the $+y'$ face of the element in Fig. 3b, is to be determined, then it is necessary to consider a segment of the element as shown in Fig. 3e and follow the same procedure just described. Here, however, the shear stress $\tau_{x'y'}$ does not have to be determined if it was previously calculated, since it is complementary, that is, it must have the same magnitude on each of the four faces of the element, Fig. 3b.

(a)

$\parallel$

(b)

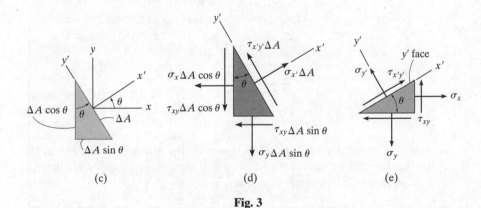

(c)   (d)   (e)

**Fig. 3**

# EXAMPLE | 1

The state of plane stress at a point on the surface of the airplane fuselage is represented on the element oriented as shown in Fig. 4a. Represent the state of stress at the point on an element that is oriented 30° clockwise from the position shown.

(a)

(b)

## SOLUTION

The rotated element is shown in Fig. 4d. To obtain the stress components on this element we will first section the element in Fig. 4a by the line a–a. The bottom segment is removed, and assuming the sectioned (inclined) plane has an area $\Delta A$, the horizontal and vertical planes have the areas shown in Fig. 4b. The free-body diagram of this segment is shown in Fig. 4c. Notice that the sectioned $x'$ face is defined by the *outward normal* $x'$ axis, and the $y'$ axis is *along* the face.

### Equilibrium.

Applying the equations of force equilibrium in the $x'$ and $y'$ directions, we have

$$+\nearrow\Sigma F_{x'} = 0; \qquad \sigma_{x'}\Delta A - (50\,\Delta A\cos 30°)\cos 30°$$
$$+ (25\,\Delta A\cos 30°)\sin 30° + (80\,\Delta A\,\sin 30°)\sin 30°$$
$$+ (25\,\Delta A\sin 30°)\cos 30° = 0$$
$$\sigma_{x'} = -4.15 \text{ MPa} \qquad\qquad Ans.$$

$$+\nwarrow\Sigma F_{y'} = 0; \qquad \tau_{x'y'}\Delta A - (50\,\Delta A\,\cos 30°)\sin 30°$$
$$- (25\,\Delta A\cos 30°)\cos 30° - (80\,\Delta A\,\sin 30°)\cos 30°$$
$$+ (25\,\Delta A\sin 30°)\sin 30° = 0$$
$$\tau_{x'y'} = 68.8 \text{ MPa} \qquad\qquad Ans.$$

Since $\sigma_{x'}$ is negative, it acts in the opposite direction of that shown in Fig. 4c. The results are shown on the *top* of the element in Fig. 4d, since this surface is the one considered in Fig. 4c.

(c)

**Fig. 4**

We must now repeat the procedure to obtain the stress on the *perpendicular* plane *b–b*. Sectioning the element in Fig. 4*a* along *b–b* results in a segment having sides with areas shown in Fig. 4*e*. Orienting the +$x'$ axis outward, perpendicular to the sectioned face, the associated free-body diagram is shown in Fig. 4*f*. Thus,

$+\searrow \Sigma F_{x'} = 0;$  $\sigma_{x'}\Delta A - (25\ \Delta A \cos 30°) \sin 30°$
$+ (80\ \Delta A \cos 30°) \cos 30° - (25\ \Delta A \sin 30°) \cos 30°$
$- (50\ \Delta A \sin 30°) \sin 30° = 0$
$\sigma_{x'} = -25.8\ \text{MPa}$  *Ans.*

$+\nearrow \Sigma F_{y'} = 0;$  $-\tau_{x'y'}\Delta A + (25\ \Delta A \cos 30°) \cos 30°$
$+ (80\ \Delta A \cos 30°) \sin 30° - (25\ \Delta A \sin 30°) \sin 30°$
$+ (50\ \Delta A \sin 30°) \cos 30° = 0$
$\tau_{x'y'} = 68.8\ \text{MPa}$  *Ans.*

Since $\sigma_{x'}$ is a negative quantity, it acts opposite to its direction shown in Fig. 4*f*. The stress components are shown acting on the *right side* of the element in Fig. 4*d*.

From this analysis we may therefore conclude that the state of stress at the point can be represented by choosing an element oriented as shown in Fig. 4*a*, or by choosing one oriented as shown in Fig. 4*d*. In other words, these states of stress are equivalent.

(d)

(e)

(f)

# 2 General Equations of Plane-Stress Transformation

The method of transforming the normal and shear stress components from the $x, y$ to the $x', y'$ coordinate axes, as discussed in the previous section, can be developed in a general manner and expressed as a set of stress-transformation equations.

**Sign Convention.**   First we must establish a sign convention for the stress components. To do this the $+x$ and $+x'$ axes are used to define the outward normal from a side of the element. Then $\sigma_x$ and $\sigma_{x'}$ are positive when they act in the positive $x$ and $x'$ directions, and $\tau_{xy}$ and $\tau_{x'y'}$ are positive when they act in the positive $y$ and $y'$ directions, Fig. 5.

The orientation of the plane on which the normal and shear stress components are to be determined will be defined by the angle $\theta$, which is measured from the $+x$ axis to the $+x'$ axis, Fig. 5b. Notice that the unprimed and primed sets of axes in this figure both form right-handed coordinate systems; that is, the positive $z$ (or $z'$) axis is established by the right-hand rule. Curling the fingers from $x$ (or $x'$) toward $y$ (or $y'$) gives the direction for the positive $z$ (or $z'$) axis that points outward, along the thumb. The *angle* $\theta$ will be *positive* provided it follows the curl of the right-hand fingers, i.e., counterclockwise as shown in Fig. 5b.

**Normal and Shear Stress Components.**   Using the established sign convention, the element in Fig. 6a is sectioned along the inclined plane and the segment shown in Fig. 6b is isolated. Assuming the sectioned area is $\Delta A$, then the horizontal and vertical faces of the segment have an area of $\Delta A \sin \theta$ and $\Delta A \cos \theta$, respectively.

(a)

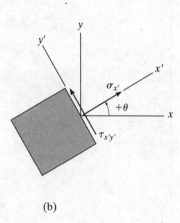

(b)

Positive Sign Convention

**Fig. 5**

(a)

The resulting *free-body diagram* of the segment is shown in Fig. 6c. Applying the equations of equilibrium to determine the unknown normal and shear stress components $\sigma_{x'}$ and $\tau_{x'y'}$, we have

$$+\nearrow\Sigma F_{x'} = 0; \quad \sigma_{x'}\Delta A - (\tau_{xy}\Delta A \sin\theta)\cos\theta - (\sigma_y\Delta A \sin\theta)\sin\theta$$
$$- (\tau_{xy}\Delta A \cos\theta)\sin\theta - (\sigma_x\Delta A \cos\theta)\cos\theta = 0$$
$$\sigma_{x'} = \sigma_x\cos^2\theta + \sigma_y\sin^2\theta + \tau_{xy}(2\sin\theta\cos\theta)$$

$$+\nwarrow\Sigma F_{y'} = 0; \quad \tau_{x'y'}\Delta A + (\tau_{xy}\Delta A \sin\theta)\sin\theta - (\sigma_y\Delta A \sin\theta)\cos\theta$$
$$- (\tau_{xy}\Delta A \cos\theta)\cos\theta + (\sigma_x\Delta A \cos\theta)\sin\theta = 0$$
$$\tau_{x'y'} = (\sigma_y - \sigma_x)\sin\theta\cos\theta + \tau_{xy}(\cos^2\theta - \sin^2\theta)$$

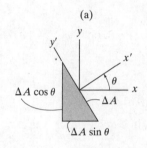

(b)

These two equations may be simplified by using the trigonometric identities $\sin 2\theta = 2\sin\theta\cos\theta$, $\sin^2\theta = (1 - \cos 2\theta)/2$, and $\cos^2\theta = (1 + \cos 2\theta)/2$, in which case,

$$\sigma_{x'} = \frac{\sigma_x + \sigma_y}{2} + \frac{\sigma_x - \sigma_y}{2}\cos 2\theta + \tau_{xy}\sin 2\theta \tag{1}$$

$$\tau_{x'y'} = -\frac{\sigma_x - \sigma_y}{2}\sin 2\theta + \tau_{xy}\cos 2\theta \tag{2}$$

If the normal stress acting in the $y'$ direction is needed, it can be obtained by simply substituting $\theta + 90°$ for $\theta$ into Eq. 1, Fig. 6d. This yields

$$\sigma_{y'} = \frac{\sigma_x + \sigma_y}{2} - \frac{\sigma_x - \sigma_y}{2}\cos 2\theta - \tau_{xy}\sin 2\theta \tag{3}$$

If $\sigma_{y'}$ is calculated as a positive quantity, it indicates that it acts in the positive $y'$ direction as shown in Fig. 6d.

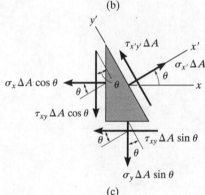

(c)

## Procedure for Analysis

To apply the stress transformation Eqs. 1 and 2, it is simply necessary to substitute in the known data for $\sigma_x$, $\sigma_y$, $\tau_{xy}$, and $\theta$ in accordance with the established sign convention, Fig. 5. Remember that the $x'$ axis is *always* directed *positive outward* from the plane upon which the normal stress is to be determined. The angle $\theta$ is *positive counterclockwise*, from the $x$ to the $x'$ axis. If $\sigma_{x'}$ and $\tau_{x'y'}$ are calculated as positive quantities, then these stresses act in the positive direction of the $x'$ and $y'$ axes.

For convenience, these equations can easily be programmed on a pocket calculator.

(d)

**Fig. 6**

## EXAMPLE | 2

(a)

(b)

(c)

(d)

**Fig. 7**

The state of plane stress at a point is represented by the element shown in Fig. 7a. Determine the state of stress at the point on another element oriented 30° clockwise from the position shown.

### SOLUTION

This problem was solved in Example 1 using basic principles. Here we will apply Eqs. 1 and 2. From the established sign convention, Fig. 5, it is seen that

$$\sigma_x = -80 \text{ MPa} \qquad \sigma_y = 50 \text{ MPa} \qquad \tau_{xy} = -25 \text{ MPa}$$

**Plane CD.** To obtain the stress components on plane $CD$, Fig. 7b, the positive $x'$ axis must be directed outward, perpendicular to $CD$, and the associated $y'$ axis is directed along $CD$. The angle measured from the $x$ to the $x'$ axis is $\theta = -30°$ (clockwise). Applying Eqs. 1 and 2 yields

$$\begin{aligned}
\sigma_{x'} &= \frac{\sigma_x + \sigma_y}{2} + \frac{\sigma_x - \sigma_y}{2} \cos 2\theta + \tau_{xy} \sin 2\theta \\
&= \frac{-80 + 50}{2} + \frac{-80 - 50}{2} \cos 2(-30°) + (-25) \sin 2(-30°) \\
&= -25.8 \text{ MPa} \qquad\qquad\qquad\qquad\qquad\qquad\qquad\qquad Ans.
\end{aligned}$$

$$\begin{aligned}
\tau_{x'y'} &= -\frac{\sigma_x - \sigma_y}{2} \sin 2\theta + \tau_{xy} \cos 2\theta \\
&= -\frac{-80 - 50}{2} \sin 2(-30°) + (-25) \cos 2(-30°) \\
&= -68.8 \text{ MPa} \qquad\qquad\qquad\qquad\qquad\qquad\qquad\qquad Ans.
\end{aligned}$$

The negative signs indicate that $\sigma_{x'}$ and $\tau_{x'y'}$ act in the negative $x'$ and $y'$ directions, respectively. The results are shown acting on the element in Fig. 7d.

**Plane BC.** Establishing the $x'$ axis outward from plane $BC$, Fig. 7c, then between the $x$ and $x'$ axes, $\theta = 60°$ (counterclockwise). Applying Eqs. 1 and 2,* we get

$$\begin{aligned}
\sigma_{x'} &= \frac{-80 + 50}{2} + \frac{-80 - 50}{2} \cos 2(60°) + (-25) \sin 2(60°) \\
&= -4.15 \text{ MPa} \qquad\qquad\qquad\qquad\qquad\qquad\qquad\qquad Ans.
\end{aligned}$$

$$\begin{aligned}
\tau_{x'y'} &= -\frac{-80 - 50}{2} \sin 2(60°) + (-25) \cos 2(60°) \\
&= 68.8 \text{ MPa} \qquad\qquad\qquad\qquad\qquad\qquad\qquad\qquad Ans.
\end{aligned}$$

Here $\tau_{x'y'}$ has been calculated twice in order to provide a check. The negative sign for $\sigma_{x'}$ indicates that this stress acts in the negative $x'$ direction, Fig. 7c. The results are shown on the element in Fig. 7d.

*Alternatively, we could apply Eq. 3 with $\theta = -30°$ rather than Eq. 1.

# 3 Principal Stresses and Maximum In-Plane Shear Stress

From Eqs. 1 and 2, it can be seen that the magnitudes of $\sigma_{x'}$ and $\tau_{x'y'}$ depend on the angle of inclination $\theta$ of the planes on which these stresses act. In engineering practice it is often important to determine the orientation of the element that causes the normal stress to be a maximum and a minimum and the orientation that causes the shear stress to be a maximum. In this section each of these problems will be considered.

**In-Plane Principal Stresses.**  To determine the maximum and minimum *normal stress*, we must differentiate Eq. 1 with respect to $\theta$ and set the result equal to zero. This gives

$$\frac{d\sigma_{x'}}{d\theta} = -\frac{\sigma_x - \sigma_y}{2}(2 \sin 2\theta) + 2\tau_{xy} \cos 2\theta = 0$$

Solving this equation we obtain the orientation $\theta = \theta_p$ of the planes of maximum and minimum normal stress.

$$\tan 2\theta_p = \frac{\tau_{xy}}{(\sigma_x - \sigma_y)/2} \qquad (4)$$

The solution has two roots, $\theta_{p_1}$, and $\theta_{p_2}$. Specifically, the values of $2\theta_{p_1}$ and $2\theta_{p_2}$ are 180° apart, so $\theta_{p_1}$ and $\theta_{p_2}$ will be 90° apart.

The values of $\theta_{p_1}$ and $\theta_{p_2}$ must be substituted into Eq. 1 if we are to obtain the required normal stresses. To do this we can obtain the necessary sine and cosine of $2\theta_{p_1}$ and $2\theta_{p_2}$ from the shaded triangles shown in Fig. 8. The construction of these triangles is based on Eq. 4, assuming that $\tau_{xy}$ and $(\sigma_x - \sigma_y)$ are both positive or both negative quantities.

**Fig. 8**

The cracks in this concrete beam were caused by tension stress, even though the beam was subjected to both an internal moment and shear. The stress-transformation equations can be used to predict the direction of the cracks, and the principal normal stresses that caused them.

Take a piece of blackboard chalk and twist it. Since it is brittle, it will fail in tension, caused by the principal normal stress. See Example 5.

Substituting these trigonometric values into Eq. 1 and simplifying, we obtain

$$\sigma_{1,2} = \frac{\sigma_x + \sigma_y}{2} \pm \sqrt{\left(\frac{\sigma_x - \sigma_y}{2}\right)^2 + \tau_{xy}^2} \tag{5}$$

Depending upon the sign chosen, this result gives the maximum or minimum in-plane normal stress acting at a point, where $\sigma_1 \geq \sigma_2$. This particular set of values are called the in-plane **principal stresses**, and the corresponding planes on which they act are called the **principal planes** of stress, Fig. 9. Furthermore, if the trigonometric relations for $\theta_{p_1}$ or $\theta_{p_2}$ are substituted into Eq. 2, it can be seen that $\tau_{x'y'} = 0$; in other words, **no shear stress acts on the principal planes**.

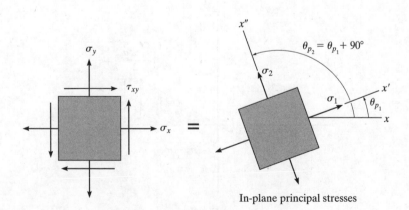

In-plane principal stresses

**Fig. 9**

500

## Maximum In-Plane Shear Stress.

The orientation of an element that is subjected to maximum shear stress on its sides can be determined by taking the derivative of Eq. 2 with respect to $\theta$ and setting the result equal to zero. This gives

$$\tan 2\theta_s = \frac{-(\sigma_x - \sigma_y)/2}{\tau_{xy}} \tag{6}$$

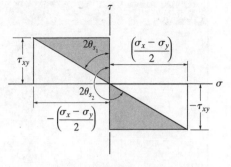

**Fig. 10**

The two roots of this equation, $\theta_{s_1}$ and $\theta_{s_2}$, can be determined from the shaded triangles shown in Fig. 10. By comparison with Eq. 4, $\tan 2\theta_s$ is the negative reciprocal of $\tan 2\theta_p$ and so each root $2\theta_s$ is $90°$ from $2\theta_p$, and the roots $\theta_s$ and $\theta_p$ are $45°$ apart. Therefore, an element subjected to *maximum shear stress will be $45°$ from the position of an element that is subjected to the principal stress*.

Using either one of the roots $\theta_{s_1}$ or $\theta_{s_2}$, the maximum shear stress can be found by taking the trigonometric values of $\sin 2\theta_s$ and $\cos 2\theta_s$ from Fig. 10 and substituting them into Eq. 2. The result is

$$\tau_{\substack{\max \\ \text{in-plane}}} = \sqrt{\left(\frac{\sigma_x - \sigma_y}{2}\right)^2 + \tau_{xy}^2} \tag{7}$$

The value of $\tau_{\substack{\max \\ \text{in-plane}}}$ as calculated from this equation is referred to as the *maximum in-plane shear stress* because it acts on the element in the $x$–$y$ plane.

Substituting the values for $\sin 2\theta_s$ and $\cos 2\theta_s$ into Eq. 1, we see that there is *also* an average normal stress on the planes of maximum in-plane shear stress. We get

$$\sigma_{\text{avg}} = \frac{\sigma_x + \sigma_y}{2} \tag{8}$$

Like the stress-transformation equations, it may be convenient to program Eqs. 4 through 8 for use on a pocket calculator.

---

## Important Points

- The *principal stresses* represent the maximum and minimum normal stress at the point.

- When the state of stress is represented by the principal stresses, *no shear stress* will act on the element.

- The state of stress at the point can also be represented in terms of the *maximum in-plane shear stress*. In this case an *average normal stress* will also act on the element.

- The element representing the maximum in-plane shear stress with the associated average normal stresses is *oriented* $45°$ from the element representing the principal stresses.

## EXAMPLE 3

Notice how the failure plane is at an angle (23.7°) due to tearing of the material, Fig. 11c.

(a)

(b)

(c)

**Fig. 11**

The state of plane stress at a failure point on the shaft is shown on the element in Fig. 11a. Represent this stress state in terms of the principal stresses.

SOLUTION

From the established sign convention, we have

$$\sigma_x = -20 \text{ MPa} \qquad \sigma_y = 90 \text{ MPa} \qquad \tau_{xy} = 60 \text{ MPa}$$

**Orientation of Element.**   Applying Eq. 4,

$$\tan 2\theta_p = \frac{\tau_{xy}}{(\sigma_x - \sigma_y)/2} = \frac{60}{(-20 - 90)/2}$$

Solving, and referring to this root as $\theta_{p_2}$, as will be shown below, yields

$$2\theta_{p_2} = -47.49° \qquad \theta_{p_2} = -23.7°$$

Since the difference between $2\theta_{p_1}$ and $2\theta_{p_2}$ is 180°, we have

$$2\theta_{p_1} = 180° + 2\theta_{p_2} = 132.51° \qquad \theta_{p_1} = 66.3°$$

Recall that $\theta$ must be measured positive *counterclockwise* from the $x$ axis to the outward normal ($x'$ axis) on the face of the element, and so the results are shown in Fig. 11b.

**Principal Stress.**   We have

$$\sigma_{1,2} = \frac{\sigma_x + \sigma_y}{2} \pm \sqrt{\left(\frac{\sigma_x - \sigma_y}{2}\right)^2 + \tau_{xy}^2}$$

$$= \frac{-20 + 90}{2} \pm \sqrt{\left(\frac{-20 - 90}{2}\right)^2 + (60)^2}$$

$$= 35.0 \pm 81.4$$

$$\sigma_1 = 116 \text{ MPa} \qquad\qquad\qquad\qquad Ans.$$

$$\sigma_2 = -46.4 \text{ MPa} \qquad\qquad\qquad\qquad Ans.$$

The principal plane on which each normal stress acts can be determined by applying Eq. 1 with, say, $\theta = \theta_{p_2} = -23.7°$. We have

$$\sigma_{x'} = \frac{\sigma_x + \sigma_y}{2} + \frac{\sigma_x - \sigma_y}{2} \cos 2\theta + \tau_{xy} \sin 2\theta$$

$$= \frac{-20 + 90}{2} + \frac{-20 - 90}{2} \cos 2(-23.7°) + 60 \sin 2(-23.7°)$$

$$= -46.4 \text{ MPa}$$

Hence, $\sigma_2 = -46.4$ MPa acts on the plane defined by $\theta_{p_2} = -23.7°$, whereas $\sigma_1 = 116$ MPa acts on the plane defined by $\theta_{p_1} = 66.3°$. The results are shown on the element in Fig. 11c. Recall that no shear stress acts on this element.

## EXAMPLE 4

The state of plane stress at a point on a body is represented on the element shown in Fig. 12a. Represent this stress state in terms of the maximum in-plane shear stress and associated average normal stress.

90 MPa

60 MPa

20 MPa

(a)

### SOLUTION

**Orientation of Element.** Since $\sigma_x = -20$ MPa, $\sigma_y = 90$ MPa, and $\tau_{xy} = 60$ MPa, applying Eq. 6, we have

$$\tan 2\theta_s = \frac{-(\sigma_x - \sigma_y)/2}{\tau_{xy}} = \frac{-(-20 - 90)/2}{60}$$

$$2\theta_{s_2} = 42.5° \qquad\qquad \theta_{s_2} = 21.3°$$

$$2\theta_{s_1} = 180° + 2\theta_{s_2} \qquad\qquad \theta_{s_1} = 111.3°$$

Note how these angles are formed between the $x$ and $x'$ axes, Fig. 12b. They happen to be 45° away from the principal planes of stress, which were determined in Example 3.

**Maximum In-Plane Shear Stress.** Applying Eq. 7,

$$\tau_{\substack{max \\ in\text{-plane}}} = \sqrt{\left(\frac{\sigma_x - \sigma_y}{2}\right)^2 + \tau_{xy}^2} = \sqrt{\left(\frac{-20 - 90}{2}\right)^2 + (60)^2}$$

$$= \pm 81.4 \text{ MPa} \qquad\qquad\qquad\qquad Ans.$$

(b)

The proper direction of $\tau_{\substack{max \\ in\text{-plane}}}$ on the element can be determined by substituting $\theta = \theta_{s_2} = 21.3°$ into Eq. 2. We have

$$\tau_{x'y'} = -\left(\frac{\sigma_x - \sigma_y}{2}\right)\sin 2\theta + \tau_{xy}\cos 2\theta$$

$$= -\left(\frac{-20 - 90}{2}\right)\sin 2(21.3°) + 60\cos 2(21.3°)$$

$$= 81.4 \text{ MPa}$$

This positive result indicates that $\tau_{\substack{max \\ in\text{-plane}}} = \tau_{x'y'}$ acts in the *positive* $y'$ direction on this face ($\theta = 21.3°$) Fig. 12b. The shear stresses on the other three faces are directed as shown in Fig. 12c.

(c)

**Fig. 12**

**Average Normal Stress.** Besides the maximum shear stress, as calculated above, the element is also subjected to an average normal stress determined from Eq. 8; that is,

$$\sigma_{avg} = \frac{\sigma_x + \sigma_y}{2} = \frac{-20 + 90}{2} = 35 \text{ MPa} \qquad\qquad Ans.$$

This is a tensile stress. The results are shown in Fig. 12c.

## EXAMPLE 5

(a)

When the torsional loading $T$ is applied to the bar in Fig. 13$a$, it produces a state of pure shear stress in the material. Determine (a) the maximum in-plane shear stress and the associated average normal stress, and (b) the principal stress.

### SOLUTION

From the established sign convention,

$$\sigma_x = 0 \qquad \sigma_y = 0 \qquad \tau_{xy} = -\tau$$

**Maximum In-Plane Shear Stress.** Applying Eqs. 7 and 8, we have

$$\tau_{\substack{max \\ in\text{-}plane}} = \sqrt{\left(\frac{\sigma_x - \sigma_y}{2}\right)^2 + \tau_{xy}^{\ 2}} = \sqrt{(0)^2 + (-\tau)^2} = \pm\tau \qquad Ans.$$

$$\sigma_{avg} = \frac{\sigma_x + \sigma_y}{2} = \frac{0 + 0}{2} = 0 \qquad Ans.$$

Thus, as expected, the maximum in-plane shear stress is represented by the element in Fig. 13$a$.

**NOTE:** Through experiment it has been found that materials that are *ductile* will *fail* due to *shear stress*. As a result, if the bar in Fig. 13$a$ is made of mild steel, the maximum in-plane shear stress will cause it to fail as shown in the adjacent photo.

(b)

**Fig. 13**

**Principal Stress.** Applying Eqs. 4 and 5 yields

$$\tan 2\theta_p = \frac{\tau_{xy}}{(\sigma_x - \sigma_y)/2} = \frac{-\tau}{(0 - 0)/2}, \theta_{p_2} = 45°, \theta_{p_1} = -45°$$

$$\sigma_{1,2} = \frac{\sigma_x + \sigma_y}{2} \pm \sqrt{\left(\frac{\sigma_x - \sigma_y}{2}\right)^2 + \tau_{xy}^{\ 2}} = 0 \pm \sqrt{(0)^2 + \tau^2} = \pm\tau \qquad Ans.$$

If we now apply Eq. 1 with $\theta_{p_2} = 45°$, then

$$\sigma_{x'} = \frac{\sigma_x + \sigma_y}{2} + \frac{\sigma_x - \sigma_y}{2}\cos 2\theta + \tau_{xy}\sin 2\theta$$

$$= 0 + 0 + (-\tau)\sin 90° = -\tau$$

Thus, $\sigma_2 = -\tau$ acts at $\theta_{p_2} = 45°$ as shown in Fig. 13$b$, and $\sigma_1 = \tau$ acts on the other face, $\theta_{p_1} = -45°$.

**NOTE:** Materials that are *brittle* fail due to *normal stress*. Therefore, if the bar in Fig. 13$a$ is made of cast iron it will fail in tension at a 45° inclination as seen in the adjacent photo.

## EXAMPLE 6

When the axial loading $P$ is applied to the bar in Fig. 14a, it produces a tensile stress in the material. Determine (a) the principal stress and (b) the maximum in-plane shear stress and associated average normal stress.

(a)

### SOLUTION

From the established sign convention,

$$\sigma_x = \sigma \qquad \sigma_y = 0 \qquad \tau_{xy} = 0$$

**Principal Stress.** By observation, the element oriented as shown in Fig. 14a illustrates a condition of principal stress since no shear stress acts on this element. This can also be shown by direct substitution of the above values into Eqs. 4 and 5. Thus,

$$\sigma_1 = \sigma \qquad \sigma_2 = 0 \qquad\qquad Ans.$$

**NOTE:** Experiments have shown that *brittle materials* will fail due to normal stress. Thus if the bar in Fig. 14a is made of cast iron, it will cause failure as shown in the adjacent photo.

**Maximum In-Plane Shear Stress.** Applying Eqs. 6, 7, and 8, we have

$$\tan 2\theta_s = \frac{-(\sigma_x - \sigma_y)/2}{\tau_{xy}} = \frac{-(\sigma - 0)/2}{0}; \theta_{s_1} = 45°, \theta_{s_2} = -45°$$

$$\tau_{\substack{max \\ in\text{-}plane}} = \sqrt{\left(\frac{\sigma_x - \sigma_y}{2}\right)^2 + \tau_{xy}^2} = \sqrt{\left(\frac{\sigma - 0}{2}\right)^2 + (0)^2} = \pm\frac{\sigma}{2} \quad Ans.$$

$$\sigma_{avg} = \frac{\sigma_x + \sigma_y}{2} = \frac{\sigma + 0}{2} = \frac{\sigma}{2} \qquad\qquad Ans.$$

To determine the proper orientation of the element, apply Eq. 2.

$$\tau_{x'y'} = -\frac{\sigma_x - \sigma_y}{2}\sin 2\theta + \tau_{xy}\cos 2\theta = -\frac{\sigma - 0}{2}\sin 90° + 0 = -\frac{\sigma}{2}$$

This negative shear stress acts on the $x'$ face, in the negative $y'$ direction as shown in Fig. 14b.

(b)

**Fig. 14**

**NOTE:** If the bar in Fig. 14a is made of a *ductile material* such as mild steel then *shear stress* will cause it to fail. This can be noted in the adjacent photo, where within the region of necking, shear stress has caused "slipping" along the steel's crystalline boundaries, resulting in a plane of failure that has formed a *cone* around the bar oriented at approximately 45° as calculated above.

# PRELIMINARY PROBLEMS

**P1.** In each case, the state of stress $\sigma_x$, $\sigma_y$, $\tau_{xy}$ produces normal and shear stress components along section $AB$ of the element that have values of $\sigma_{x'} = -5$ kPa and $\tau_{x'y'} = 8$ kPa when calculated using the stress transformation equations. Establish the $x'$ and $y'$ axes for each segment and specify the angle $\theta$, then show these results acting on each segment.

(c)

**P1**

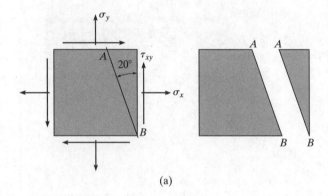

(a)

**P2.** Given the state of stress shown on the element, find $\sigma_{avg}$ and $\tau_{\substack{max \\ in\text{-}plane}}$ and show the results on a properly oriented element.

(b)

**P2**

# FUNDAMENTAL PROBLEMS

**F1.** Determine the normal stress and shear stress acting on the inclined plane $AB$. Sketch the result on the sectioned element.

**F1**

**F2.** Determine the equivalent state of stress on an element at the same point oriented 45° clockwise with respect to the element shown.

**F2**

**F3.** Determine the equivalent state of stress on an element at the same point that represents the principal stresses at the point. Also, find the corresponding orientation of the element with respect to the element shown.

**F3**

**F4.** Determine the equivalent state of stress on an element at the same point that represents the maximum in-plane shear stress at the point.

**F4**

**F5.** The beam is subjected to the load at its end. Determine the maximum principal stress at point $B$.

**F5**

**F6.** The beam is subjected to the loading shown. Determine the principal stress at point $C$.

**F6**

# PROBLEMS

**1.** Prove that the sum of the normal stresses $\sigma_x + \sigma_y = \sigma_{x'} + \sigma_{y'}$ is constant. See Figs. 2a and 2b.

**2.** The state of stress at a point in a member is shown on the element. Determine the stress components acting on the inclined plane $AB$. Solve the problem using the method of equilibrium described in Sec. 1.

**\*4.** Determine the normal stress and shear stress acting on the inclined plane $AB$. Solve the problem using the method of equilibrium described in Sec. 1.

**5.** Determine the normal stress and shear stress acting on the inclined plane $AB$. Solve the problem using the stress transformation equations. Show the results on the sectional element.

**Prob. 2**

**Probs. 4/5**

**3.** The state of stress at a point in a member is shown on the element. Determine the stress components acting on the inclined plane $AB$. Solve the problem using the method of equilibrium described in Sec. 1.

**6.** Determine the normal stress and shear stress acting on the inclined plane $AB$. Solve the problem using the method of equilibrium described in Sec. 1.

**7.** Determine the normal stress and shear stress acting on the inclined plane $AB$. Solve the problem using the stress transformation equations. Show the result on the sectioned element.

**Prob. 3**

**Probs. 6/7**

508

**\*8.** Determine the equivalent state of stress on an element at the same point oriented 30° clockwise with respect to the element shown. Sketch the results on the element.

**9.** Determine the equivalent state of stress on an element at the same point oriented 30° counterclockwise with respect to the element shown. Sketch the results on the element.

75 MPa

100 MPa

**Probs. 8/9**

**10.** Determine the equivalent state of stress on an element at the same point oriented 60° clockwise with respect to the element shown. Sketch the results on the element.

**11.** Determine the equivalent state of stress on an element at the same point oriented 60° counterclockwise with respect to the element shown. Sketch the results on the element.

100 MPa

75 MPa

150 MPa

**Probs. 10/11**

**\*12.** Determine the equivalent state of stress on an element if it is oriented 50° counterclockwise from the element shown. Use the stress-transformation equations.

10 ksi

16 ksi

**Prob. 12**

**13.** Determine the equivalent state of stress on an the element if it is oriented 30° clockwise from the element shown. Use the stress-transformation equations.

300 psi

950 psi

**Prob. 13**

**14.** The state of stress at a point is shown on the element. Determine (a) the principal stress and (b) the maximum in-plane shear stress and average normal stress at the point. Specify the orientation of the element in each case. Show the results on each element.

30 ksi

12 ksi

**Prob. 14**

**15.** The state of stress at a point is shown on the element. Determine (a) the principal stress and (b) the maximum in-plane shear stress and average normal stress at the point. Specify the orientation of the element in each case.

60 MPa

30 MPa

45 MPa

**Prob. 15**

**\*16.** Determine the equivalent state of stress on an element at the point which represents (a) the principal stresses and (b) the maximum in-plane shear stress and the associated average normal stress. Also, for each case, determine the corresponding orientation of the element with respect to the element shown and sketch the results on the element.

**Prob. 16**

**17.** Determine the equivalent state of stress on an element at the same point which represents (a) the principal stress, and (b) the maximum in-plane shear stress and the associated average normal stress. Also, for each case, determine the corresponding orientation of the element with respect to the element shown. Sketch the results on each element.

**Prob. 17**

**18.** A point on a thin plate is subjected to the two successive states of stress shown. Determine the resultant state of stress represented on the element oriented as shown on the right.

**Prob. 18**

**19.** Determine the equivalent state of stress on an element at the same point which represents (a) the principal stress, and (b) the maximum in-plane shear stress and the associated average normal stress. Also, for each case, determine the corresponding orientation of the element with respect to the element shown and sketch the results on the element.

**Prob. 19**

**\*20.** Planes $AB$ and $BC$ at a point are subjected to the stresses shown. Determine the principal stresses acting at this point and find $\sigma_{BC}$.

**Prob. 20**

**21.** The stress acting on two planes at a point is indicated. Determine the shear stress on plane $a$–$a$ and the principal stresses at the point.

**Prob. 21**

510

**22.** The grains of wood in the board make an angle of 20° with the horizontal as shown. Determine the normal and shear stress that act perpendicular and parallel to the grains if the board is subjected to an axial load of 250 N.

**Prob. 22**

**23.** The wood beam is subjected to a load of 12 kN. If a grain of wood in the beam at point $A$ makes an angle of 25° with the horizontal as shown, determine the normal and shear stress that act perpendicular and parallel to the grain due to the loading.

**Prob. 9–23**

**\*24.** The wood beam is subjected to a load of 12 kN. Determine the principal stress at point $A$ and specify the orientation of the element.

**Prob. 24**

**25.** The wooden block will fail if the shear stress acting along the grain is 550 psi. If the normal stress $\sigma_x = 400$ psi, determine the necessary compressive stress $\sigma_y$ that will cause failure.

**Prob. 25**

**26.** The bracket is subjected to the force of 3 kip. Determine the principal stress and maximum in-plane shear stress at point $A$ on the cross section at section $a$–$a$. Specify the orientation of this state of stress and show the results on elements.

**27.** The bracket is subjected to the force of 3 kip. Determine the principal stress and maximum in-plane shear stress at point $B$ on the cross section at section $a$–$a$. Specify the orientation of this state of stress and show the results on elements.

Section $a$ – $a$

**Probs. 26/27**

511

**\*28.** The 25-mm thick rectangular bar is subjected to the axial load of 10 kN. If the bar is joined by the weld, which makes an angle of 60° with the horizontal, determine the shear stress parallel to the weld and the normal stress perpendicular to the weld.

**Prob. 28**

**29.** The 3-in. diameter shaft is supported by a smooth thrust bearing at *A* and a smooth journal bearing at *B*. Determine the principal stresses and maximum in-plane shear stress at a point on the outer surface of the shaft at section *a–a*.

**Prob. 29**

**30.** The state of stress at a point in a member is shown on the element. Determine the stress components acting on the plane *AB*.

**Prob. 30**

**31.** Determine the principal stress at point *A* on the cross section of the arm at section *a–a*. Specify the orientation of this state of stress and indicate the results on an element at the point.

**\*32.** Determine the maximum in-plane shear stress developed at point *A* on the cross section of the arm at section *a–a*. Specify the orientation of this state of stress and indicate the results on an element at the point.

**Probs. 31/32**

512

**33.** The clamp bears down on the smooth surface at $E$ by tightening the bolt. If the tensile force in the bolt is 40 kN, determine the principal stress at points $A$ and $B$ and show the results on elements located at each of these points. The cross-sectional area at $A$ and $B$ is shown in the adjacent figure.

**Prob. 33**

**34.** Determine the principal stress and the maximum in-plane shear stress that are developed at point $A$ in the 2-in.-diameter shaft. Show the results on an element located at this point. The bearings only support vertical reactions.

**Prob. 34**

**35.** The square steel plate has a thickness of 10 mm and is subjected to the edge loading shown. Determine the maximum in-plane shear stress and the average normal stress developed in the steel.

**Prob. 35**

**\*36.** The square steel plate has a thickness of 0.5 in. and is subjected to the edge loading shown. Determine the principal stresses developed in the steel.

**Prob. 36**

**37.** The shaft has a diameter $d$ and is subjected to the loadings shown. Determine the principal stress and the maximum in-plane shear stress that is developed at point $A$. The bearings only support vertical reactions.

**Prob. 37**

**38.** A paper tube is formed by rolling a paper strip in a spiral and then gluing the edges together as shown. Determine the shear stress acting along the seam, which is at 30° from the vertical, when the tube is subjected to an axial force of 10 N. The paper is 1 mm thick and the tube has an outer diameter of 30 mm.

**39.** Solve Prob. 38 for the normal stress acting perpendicular to the seam.

**Probs. 38/39**

**42.** The drill pipe has an outer diameter of 3 in., a wall thickness of 0.25 in., and a weight of 50 lb/ft. If it is subjected to a torque and axial load as shown, determine (a) the principal stresses and (b) the maximum in-plane shear stress at a point on its surface at section *a*.

**Prob. 42**

**\*40.** The wide-flange beam is subjected to the 50-kN force. Determine the principal stresses in the beam at point *A* located on the *web* at the bottom of the upper flange. Although it is not very accurate, use the shear formula to calculate the shear stress.

**41.** Solve Prob. 40 for point *B* located on the *web* at the top of the bottom flange.

**43.** The nose wheel of the plane is subjected to a design load of 12 kN. Determine the principal stresses acting on the aluminum wheel support at point *A*.

**Probs. 40/41**

**Prob. 43**

# 4  Mohr's Circle—Plane Stress

In this section, we will show how to apply the equations for plane stress transformation using a graphical solution that is often convenient to use and easy to remember. Furthermore, this approach will allow us to "visualize" how the normal and shear stress components $\sigma_{x'}$ and $\tau_{x'y'}$ vary as the plane on which they act is oriented in different directions, Fig. 15a.

If we write Eqs. 1 and 2 in the form

$$\sigma_{x'} - \left(\frac{\sigma_x + \sigma_y}{2}\right) = \left(\frac{\sigma_x - \sigma_y}{2}\right)\cos 2\theta + \tau_{xy}\sin 2\theta \qquad (9)$$

$$\tau_{x'y'} = -\left(\frac{\sigma_x - \sigma_y}{2}\right)\sin 2\theta + \tau_{xy}\cos 2\theta \qquad (10)$$

then the parameter $\theta$ can be *eliminated* by squaring each equation and adding the equations together. The result is

$$\left[\sigma_{x'} - \left(\frac{\sigma_x + \sigma_y}{2}\right)\right]^2 + \tau_{x'y'}^2 = \left(\frac{\sigma_x - \sigma_y}{2}\right)^2 + \tau_{xy}^2$$

For a specific problem, $\sigma_x$, $\sigma_y$, $\tau_{xy}$ are *known constants*. Thus the above equation can be written in a more compact form as

$$(\sigma_{x'} - \sigma_{\text{avg}})^2 + \tau_{x'y'}^2 = R^2 \qquad (11)$$

where

$$\sigma_{\text{avg}} = \frac{\sigma_x + \sigma_y}{2}$$

$$R = \sqrt{\left(\frac{\sigma_x - \sigma_y}{2}\right)^2 + \tau_{xy}^2} \qquad (12)$$

If we establish coordinate axes, $\sigma$ *positive to the right* and $\tau$ *positive downward*, and then plot Eq. 11, it will be seen that this equation represents a *circle* having a radius $R$ and center on the $\sigma$ axis at point $C(\sigma_{\text{avg}}, 0)$, Fig. 15b. This circle is called *Mohr's circle*, because it was developed by the German engineer Otto Mohr.

(a)

**Fig. 15**

(b)

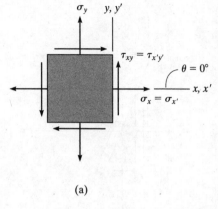

(a)

Each point on Mohr's circle represents the two stress components $\sigma_{x'}$ and $\tau_{x'y'}$ acting on the side of the element defined by the $x'$ axis, when the axis is in a specific direction $\theta$. For example, when $x'$ is coincident with the $x$ axis as shown in Fig. 16a, then $\theta = 0°$ and $\sigma_{x'} = \sigma_x$, $\tau_{x'y'} = \tau_{xy}$. We will refer to this as the "reference point" $A$ and plot its coordinates $A(\sigma_x, \tau_{xy})$, Fig. 16c.

Now consider rotating the $x'$ axis 90° counterclockwise, Fig. 16b. Then $\sigma_{x'} = \sigma_y$, $\tau_{x'y'} = -\tau_{xy}$. These values are the coordinates of point $G(\sigma_y, -\tau_{xy})$ on the circle, Fig. 16c. Hence, the radial line $CG$ is 180° counterclockwise from the "reference line" $CA$. In other words, a rotation $\theta$ of the $x'$ axis on the element will correspond to a rotation $2\theta$ on the circle in the *same direction*. (If instead the $\tau$ axis were constructed *positive upwards*, then the angle $2\theta$ on the circle would be measured in the *opposite direction* to the orientation $\theta$ of the $x'$ axis.)

Once constructed, Mohr's circle can be used to determine the principal stresses, the maximum in-plane shear stress and associated average normal stress, or the stress on any arbitrary plane.

(b)

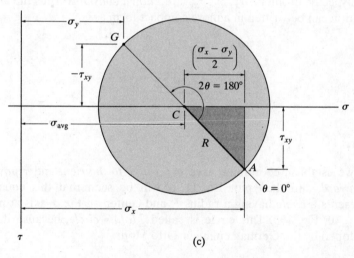

(c)

**Fig. 16**

## Procedure for Analysis

The following steps are required to draw and use Mohr's circle.

### Construction of the Circle.

- Establish a coordinate system such that the horizontal axis represents the normal stress $\sigma$, with *positive to the right*, and the vertical axis represents the shear stress $\tau$, with *positive downwards*, Fig. 17a.*

- Using the positive sign convention for $\sigma_x$, $\sigma_y$, $\tau_{xy}$, as shown in Fig. 17b, plot the center of the circle $C$, which is located on the $\sigma$ axis at a distance $\sigma_{avg} = (\sigma_x + \sigma_y)/2$ from the origin, Fig. 17a.

- Plot the "reference point" $A$ having coordinates $A(\sigma_x, \tau_{xy})$. This point represents the normal and shear stress components on the element's right-hand vertical face, and since the $x'$ axis coincides with the $x$ axis, this represents $\theta = 0°$, Fig. 17a.

- Connect point $A$ with the center $C$ of the circle and determine $CA$ by trigonometry. This distance represents the radius $R$ of the circle, Fig. 17a.

- Once $R$ has been determined, sketch the circle.

### Principal Stress.

- The principal stresses $\sigma_1$ and $\sigma_2$ ($\sigma_1 \geq \sigma_2$) are the coordinates of points $B$ and $D$ where the circle intersects the $\sigma$ axis, i.e., where $\tau = 0$, Fig. 17a.

- These stresses act on planes defined by angles $\theta_{p_1}$ and $\theta_{p_2}$, Fig. 17c. They are represented on the circle by angles $2\theta_{p_1}$ (shown) and $2\theta_{p_2}$ (not shown) and are measured *from* the radial reference line $CA$ *to* lines $CB$ and $CD$, respectively.

- Using trigonometry, only one of these angles needs to be calculated from the circle, since $\theta_{p_1}$ and $\theta_{p_2}$ are 90° apart. Remember that the direction of rotation $2\theta_p$ on the circle (here it happens to be counterclockwise) represents the *same* direction of rotation $\theta_p$ from the reference axis $(+x)$ to the principal plane $(+x')$, Fig. 17c.*

### Maximum In-Plane Shear Stress.

- The average normal stress and maximum in-plane shear stress components are determined from the circle as the coordinates of either point $E$ or $F$, Fig. 17a.

- In this case the angles $\theta_{s_1}$ and $\theta_{s_2}$ give the orientation of the planes that contain these components, Fig. 17d. The angle $2\theta_{s_1}$ is shown in Fig. 17a and can be determined using trigonometry. Here the rotation happens to be clockwise, from $CA$ to $CE$, and so $\theta_{s_1}$ must be clockwise on the element, Fig. 17d.*

## Procedure for Analysis (continued)

### Stresses on Arbitrary Plane.

- The normal and shear stress components $\sigma_{x'}$ and $\tau_{x'y'}$ acting on a specified plane or $x'$ axis, defined by the angle $\theta$, Fig. 17e, can be obtained from the circle using trigonometry to determine the coordinates of point $P$, Fig. 17a.

- To locate $P$, the known angle $\theta$ (in this case counterclockwise), Fig. 17e, must be measured on the circle in the *same direction* $2\theta$ (counterclockwise), *from* the radial reference line $CA$ *to* the radial line $CP$, Fig. 17a.*

*If the $\tau$ axis were constructed *positive upwards*, then the angle $2\theta$ on the circle would be measured in the *opposite direction* to the orientation $\theta$ of the $x'$ axis.

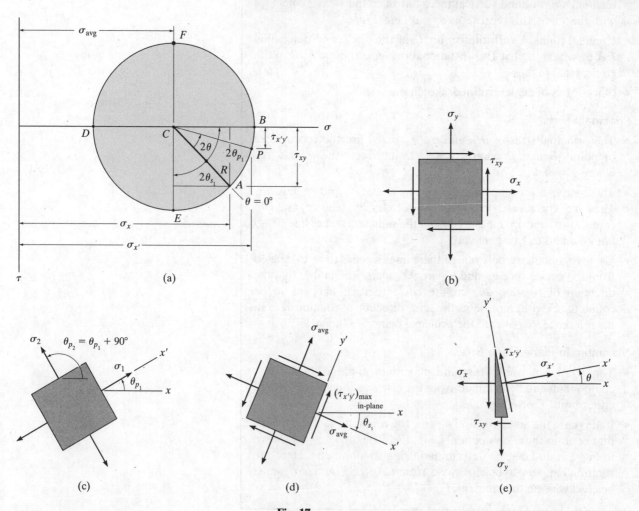

Fig. 17

## EXAMPLE 7

Due to the applied loading, the element at point $A$ on the solid shaft in Fig. 18$a$ is subjected to the state of stress shown. Determine the principal stresses acting at this point.

SOLUTION

**Construction of the Circle.** From Fig. 18$a$,

$$\sigma_x = -12 \text{ ksi} \qquad \sigma_y = 0 \qquad \tau_{xy} = -6 \text{ ksi}$$

The center of the circle is at

$$\sigma_{avg} = \frac{-12 + 0}{2} = -6 \text{ ksi}$$

The reference point $A(-12, -6)$ and the center $C(-6, 0)$ are plotted in Fig. 18$b$. The circle is constructed having a radius of

$$R = \sqrt{(12 - 6)^2 + (6)^2} = 8.49 \text{ ksi}$$

(a)

**Principal Stress.** The principal stresses are indicated by the coordinates of points $B$ and $D$. We have, for $\sigma_1 > \sigma_2$,

$$\sigma_1 = 8.49 - 6 = 2.49 \text{ ksi} \qquad\qquad Ans.$$
$$\sigma_2 = -6 - 8.49 = -14.5 \text{ ksi} \qquad\qquad Ans.$$

The orientation of the element can be determined by calculating the angle $2\theta_{p_2}$ in Fig. 18$b$, which here is measured *counterclockwise* from $CA$ to $CD$. It defines the direction $\theta_{p_2}$ of $\sigma_2$ and its associated principal plane. We have

$$2\theta_{p_2} = \tan^{-1}\frac{6}{12 - 6} = 45.0°$$

$$\theta_{p_2} = 22.5°$$

The element is oriented such that the $x'$ axis or $\sigma_2$ is directed 22.5° *counterclockwise* from the horizontal ($x$ axis) as shown in Fig. 18$c$.

(c)

(b)

**Fig. 18**

EXAMPLE | 8

90 MPa

60 MPa

20 MPa

(a)

The state of plane stress at a point is shown on the element in Fig. 19a. Determine the maximum in-plane shear stress at this point.

SOLUTION

**Construction of the Circle.** From the problem data,

$$\sigma_x = -20 \text{ MPa} \qquad \sigma_y = 90 \text{ MPa} \qquad \tau_{xy} = 60 \text{ MPa}$$

The $\sigma$, $\tau$ axes are established in Fig. 19b. The center of the circle C is located on the $\sigma$ axis, at the point

$$\sigma_{avg} = \frac{-20 + 90}{2} = 35 \text{ MPa}$$

Point C and the reference point $A(-20, 60)$ are plotted. Applying the Pythagorean theorem to the shaded triangle to determine the circle's radius CA, we have

$$R = \sqrt{(60)^2 + (55)^2} = 81.4 \text{ MPa}$$

F

35

C

$\sigma$ (MPa)

60

$R = 81.4$

$2\theta_{s_1}$

81.4

A

20

E

$\tau$ (MPa)

(b)

**Maximum In-Plane Shear Stress.** The maximum in-plane shear stress and the average normal stress are identified by point E (or F) on the circle. The coordinates of point $E(35, 81.4)$ give

$$\tau_{\substack{max \\ in\text{-}plane}} = 81.4 \text{ MPa} \qquad\qquad Ans.$$

$$\sigma_{avg} = 35 \text{ MPa} \qquad\qquad Ans.$$

The angle $\theta_{s_1}$, measured *counterclockwise* from CA to CE, can be found from the circle, identified as $2\theta_{s_1}$. We have

$$2\theta_{s_1} = \tan^{-1}\left(\frac{20 + 35}{60}\right) = 42.5°$$

$$\theta_{s_1} = 21.3° \qquad\qquad Ans.$$

$y'$

81.4 MPa

35 MPa

$x'$

21.3°

$x$

(c)

**Fig. 19**

This *counterclockwise* angle defines the direction of the $x'$ axis, Fig. 19c. Since point E has *positive* coordinates, then the average normal stress and the maximum in-plane shear stress both act in the *positive x'* and $y'$ directions as shown.

## EXAMPLE 9

The state of plane stress at a point is shown on the element in Fig. 20a. Represent this state of stress on an element oriented 30° counterclockwise from the position shown.

(a)

### SOLUTION

**Construction of the Circle.** From the problem data,

$$\sigma_x = -8 \text{ ksi} \qquad \sigma_y = 12 \text{ ksi} \qquad \tau_{xy} = -6 \text{ ksi}$$

The $\sigma$ and $\tau$ axes are established in Fig. 20b. The center of the circle $C$ is on the $\sigma$ axis at

$$\sigma_{\text{avg}} = \frac{-8 + 12}{2} = 2 \text{ ksi}$$

The reference point for $\theta = 0°$ has coordinates $A(-8, -6)$. Hence from the shaded triangle the radius $CA$ is

$$R = \sqrt{(10)^2 + (6)^2} = 11.66$$

**Stresses on 30° Element.** Since the element is to be rotated 30° *counterclockwise*, we must construct a radial line $CP$, $2(30°) = 60°$ *counterclockwise*, measured from $CA$ ($\theta = 0°$), Fig. 20b. The coordinates of point $P(\sigma_{x'}, \tau_{x'y'})$ must now be obtained. From the geometry of the circle,

$$\phi = \tan^{-1}\frac{6}{10} = 30.96° \qquad \psi = 60° - 30.96° = 29.04°$$

$$\sigma_{x'} = 2 - 11.66 \cos 29.04° = -8.20 \text{ ksi} \qquad \textit{Ans.}$$

$$\tau_{x'y'} = 11.66 \sin 29.04° = 5.66 \text{ ksi} \qquad \textit{Ans.}$$

(b)

These two stress components act on face $BD$ of the element shown in Fig. 20c since the $x'$ axis for this face is oriented 30° *counterclockwise* from the $x$ axis.

The stress components acting on the adjacent face $DE$ of the element, which is 60° *clockwise* from the positive $x$ axis, Fig. 20c, are represented by the coordinates of point $Q$ on the circle. This point lies on the radial line $CQ$, which is 180° from $CP$. The coordinates of point $Q$ are

$$\sigma_{x'} = 2 + 11.66 \cos 29.04° = 12.2 \text{ ksi} \qquad \textit{Ans.}$$

$$\tau_{x'y'} = -(11.66 \sin 29.04) = -5.66 \text{ ksi} \quad \text{(check)} \qquad \textit{Ans.}$$

**NOTE:** Here $\tau_{x'y'}$ acts in the $-y'$ direction.

(c)

**Fig. 20**

# FUNDAMENTAL PROBLEMS

**F7.** Using Mohr's circle, determine the normal stress and shear stress acting on the inclined plane $AB$. Sketch the result on the sectioned element.

**F7**

**F8.** Determine the equivalent state of stress on an element at the same point that represents the principal stresses at the point. Also, find the corresponding orientation of the element with respect to the element shown. Sketch the results on the element.

**F8**

**F9.** Draw Mohr's circle and determine the principal stresses.

**F9**

**F10.** The hollow circular shaft is subjected to the torque of $4 \ kN \cdot m$. Determine the principal stress developed at a point on the surface of the shaft.

**F10**

**F11.** Determine the principal stress developed at point $A$ on the cross section of the beam at section $a$–$a$.

**F11**

**F12.** Determine the maximum in-plane shear stress developed at point $A$ on the cross section of the beam at section $a$–$a$, which is located just to the left of the 60-kN force. Point $A$ is just below the flange.

**F12**

# PROBLEMS

**\*44.** Solve Prob. 3 using Mohr's circle.

**45.** Solve Prob. 6 using Mohr's circle.

**46.** Solve Prob. 14 using Mohr's circle.

**47.** Solve Prob. 10 using Mohr's circle.

**\*48.** Solve Prob. 12 using Mohr's circle.

**49.** Solve Prob. 16 using Mohr's circle.

**50.** Mohr's circle for the state of stress in Fig. 15a is shown in Fig. 15b. Show that finding the coordinates of point $P(\sigma_{x'}, \tau_{x'y'})$ on the circle gives the same value as the stress-transformation Eqs. 1 and 2.

**51.** Determine the equivalent state of stress if an element is oriented 45° clockwise from the element shown.

**Prob. 51**

**\*52.** Determine the equivalent state of stress if an element is oriented 20° clockwise from the element shown.

**Prob. 52**

**53.** Determine the equivalent state of stress if an element is oriented 30° clockwise from the element shown.

**Prob. 53**

**54.** Determine the equivalent state of stress which represents (a) the principal stress, and (b) the maximum in-plane shear stress and the associated average normal stress. For each case, determine the corresponding orientation of the element with respect to the element shown.

**Prob. 54**

**55.** Determine the equivalent state of stress which represents (a) the principal stress, and (b) the maximum in-plane shear stress and the associated average normal stress. For each case, determine the corresponding orientation of the element with respect to the element shown.

**Prob. 55**

**\*56.** Determine the principal stress, the maximum in-plane shear stress, and average normal stress. Specify the orientation of the element in each case.

**Prob. 56**

**57.** Determine (a) the principal stresses and (b) the maximum in-plane shear stress and average normal stress. Specify the orientation of the element in each case.

50 MPa

30 MPa

**Prob. 57**

**58.** Determine the equivalent state of stress if an element is oriented 25° counterclockwise from the element shown.

550 MPa

**Prob. 58**

**59.** Determine (a) the principal stresses and (b) the maximum in-plane shear stress and average normal stress. Specify the orientation of the element in each case.

8 ksi

4 ksi

12 ksi

**Prob. 59**

**\*60.** Determine the principal stresses, the maximum in-plane shear stress, and average normal stress. Specify the orientation of the element in each case.

200 MPa

500 MPa

350 MPa

**Prob. 60**

**61.** Draw Mohr's circle that describes each of the following states of stress.

5 MPa

5 MPa

20 ksi

20 ksi

(a)

(b)

18 MPa

(c)

**Prob. 61**

524

**62.** The grains of wood in the board make an angle of 20° with the horizontal as shown. Using Mohr's circle, determine the normal and shear stresses that act perpendicular and parallel to the grains if the board is subjected to an axial load of 250 N.

**Prob. 62**

**63.** The post has a square cross-sectional area. If it is fixed supported at its base and a horizontal force is applied at its end as shown, determine (a) the maximum in-plane shear stress developed at $A$ and (b) the principal stresses at $A$.

**Prob. 63**

**\*64.** Determine the principal stress, the maximum in-plane shear stress, and average normal stress. Specify the orientation of the element in each case.

**Prob. 64**

**65.** The thin-walled pipe has an inner diameter of 0.5 in. and a thickness of 0.025 in. If it is subjected to an internal pressure of 500 psi and the axial tension and torsional loadings shown, determine the principal stress at a point on the surface of the pipe.

**Prob. 65**

**66.** Determine the principal stress and maximum in-plane shear stress at point $A$ on the cross section of the pipe at section $a$–$a$.

**67.** Determine the principal stress and maximum in-plane shear stress at point $B$ on the cross section of the pipe at section $a$–$a$.

**Probs. 66/67**

**\*68.** The rotor shaft of the helicopter is subjected to the tensile force and torque shown when the rotor blades provide the lifting force to suspend the helicopter at midair. If the shaft has a diameter of 6 in., determine the principal stress and maximum in-plane shear stress at a point located on the surface of the shaft.

**Prob. 68**

**69.** The pedal crank for a bicycle has the cross section shown. If it is fixed to the gear at $B$ and does not rotate while subjected to a force of 75 lb, determine the principal stress in the material on the cross section at point $C$.

**Prob. 69**

**70.** A spherical pressure vessel has an inner radius of 5 ft and a wall thickness of 0.5 in. Draw Mohr's circle for the state of stress at a point on the vessel and explain the significance of the result. The vessel is subjected to an internal pressure of 80 psi.

**71.** The cylindrical pressure vessel has an inner radius of 1.25 m and a wall thickness of 15 mm. It is made from steel plates that are welded along the 45° seam. Determine the normal and shear stress components along this seam if the vessel is subjected to an internal pressure of 8 MPa.

**Probs. 70/71**

**\*72.** Determine the normal and shear stresses at point $D$ that act perpendicular and parallel, respectively, to the grains. The grains at this point make an angle of 30° with the horizontal as shown. Point $D$ is located just to the left of the 10-kN force.

**73.** Determine the principal stress at point $D$, which is located just to the left of the 10-kN force.

**Probs. 72/73**

**74.** If the box wrench is subjected to the 50 lb force, determine the principal stress and maximum in-plane shear stress at point $A$ on the cross section of the wrench at section $a$–$a$. Specify the orientation of these states of stress and indicate the results on elements at the point.

**75.** If the box wrench is subjected to the 50 lb force, determine the principal stress and maximum in-plane shear stress at point $B$ on the cross section of the wrench at section $a$–$a$. Specify the orientation of these states of stress and indicate the results on elements at the point.

**Probs. 74/75**

**\*76.** The ladder is supported on the rough surface at $A$ and by a smooth wall at $B$. If a man weighing 150 lb stands upright at $C$, determine the principal stresses in one of the legs at point $D$. Each leg is made from a 1-in.-thick board having a rectangular cross section. Assume that the total weight of the man is exerted vertically on the rung at $C$ and is shared equally by each of the ladder's two legs. Neglect the weight of the ladder and the forces developed by the man's arms.

**Prob. 76**

# 5 Absolute Maximum Shear Stress

When a point in a body is subjected to a general three-dimensional state of stress, an element of material has a normal-stress and two shear-stress components acting on each of its faces, Fig. 21a. As in case of plane stress, it is possible to develop stress-transformation equations that can be used to determine the normal and shear stress components $\sigma$ and $\tau$ acting on *any* skewed plane of the element, Fig. 21b. Furthermore, at the point it is also possible to determine the unique orientation of an element having only principal stresses acting on its faces. As shown in Fig. 21c, in general these principal stresses will have magnitudes of maximum, intermediate, and minimum intensity, i.e., $\sigma_{\max} \geq \sigma_{\text{int}} \geq \sigma_{\min}$. This is a condition known as ***triaxial stress***.

A discussion of the transformation of stress in three dimensions is beyond the scope of this text; however, it is discussed in books related to the theory of elasticity. For our purposes, we will confine our attention only to the case of plane stress. For example, consider the material to be

(a)

(b)

triaxial stress

(c)

**Fig. 21**

527

x–y plane stress

(a)

(b)

(c)

(d)

**Fig. 22**

subjected to the in-plane principal stresses $\sigma_1$ and $\sigma_2$ shown in Fig. 22a, where *both* of these stresses are tensile. If we view the element in two dimensions, that is, in the y–z, x–z, and x–y planes, Figs. 22b, 22c, and 22d, then we can use Mohr's circle to determine the maximum in-plane shear for each case and from this, determine the *absolute maximum shear stress* in the material. For example, the diameter of Mohr's circle extends between $0$ and $\sigma_2$ for the case shown in Fig. 22b. From this circle, Fig. 22e, the maximum in-plane shear stress is $\tau_{y'z'} = \sigma_2/2$. For all three circles, it is seen that although the maximum in-plane shear stress is $\tau_{x'y'} = (\sigma_1 - \sigma_2)/2$, this value is *not* the absolute maximum shear stress. Instead, from Fig. 22e,

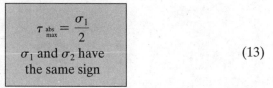

$$\tau_{\substack{abs \\ max}} = \frac{\sigma_1}{2}$$

$\sigma_1$ and $\sigma_2$ have the same sign

(13)

(e)

x–y plane stress

(a)

Maximum in-plane and
absolute maximum shear stress

(b)

**Fig. 23**

If one of the in-plane principal stresses has the *opposite sign* of that of the other, Fig. 23*a*, then the three Mohr's circles that describe the state of stress for element orientations about each coordinate axis are shown in Fig. 23*b*. Clearly, in this case

$$\tau_{\max}^{abs} = \frac{\sigma_1 - \sigma_2}{2}$$

$\sigma_1$ and $\sigma_2$ have opposite signs

(14)

Calculation of the absolute maximum shear stress as indicated here is important when designing members made of a ductile material, since the strength of the material depends on its ability to resist shear stress.

## Important Points

- The general three-dimensional state of stress at a point can be represented by an element oriented so that only three principal stresses $\sigma_{max}$, $\sigma_{int}$, $\sigma_{min}$ act on it.

- In the case of plane stress, if the in-plane principal stresses both have the *same sign*, the *absolute maximum shear stress* will occur *out of the plane* and has a value of $\tau_{\max}^{abs} = \sigma_{max}/2$. This value is greater than the in-plane shear stress.

- If the in-plane principal stresses are of *opposite signs*, then the *absolute maximum shear stress will equal the maximum in-plane shear stress*; that is, $\tau_{\max}^{abs} = (\sigma_{max} - \sigma_{min})/2$.

## EXAMPLE | 10

The point on the surface of the cylindrical pressure vessel in Fig. 24a is subjected to the state of plane stress. Determine the absolute maximum shear stress at this point.

32 MPa

16 MPa

(a)

### SOLUTION

The principal stresses are $\sigma_1 = 32$ MPa, $\sigma_2 = 16$ MPa. If these stresses are plotted along the $\sigma$ axis, the three Mohr's circles can be constructed that describe the stress state viewed in each of the three perpendicular planes, Fig. 24b. The largest circle has a radius of 16 MPa and describes the state of stress in the plane only containing $\sigma_1 = 32$ MPa, shown shaded in Fig. 24a. An orientation of an element 45° within this plane yields the state of absolute maximum shear stress and the associated average normal stress, namely,

$$\tau_{\max}^{abs} = 16 \text{ MPa} \qquad Ans.$$

$$\sigma_{avg} = 16 \text{ MPa}$$

This same result for $\tau_{\max}^{abs}$ can be obtained from direct application of Eq. 13.

$$\tau_{\max}^{abs} = \frac{\sigma_1}{2} = \frac{32}{2} = 16 \text{ MPa} \qquad Ans.$$

$$\sigma_{avg} = \frac{32 + 0}{2} = 16 \text{ MPa}$$

By comparison, the maximum in-plane shear stress can be determined from the Mohr's circle drawn between $\sigma_1 = 32$ MPa and $\sigma_2 = 16$ MPa, Fig. 24b. This gives a value of

$$\tau_{\substack{\max \\ \text{in-plane}}} = \frac{32 - 16}{2} = 8 \text{ MPa}$$

$$\sigma_{avg} = \frac{32 + 16}{2} = 24 \text{ MPa}$$

$\sigma_2$  $\sigma_1$  $\sigma$ (MPa)

8   8

16

16

32

$\tau$ (MPa)   (b)

**Fig. 24**

## EXAMPLE | 11

Due to an applied loading, an element at the point on a machine shaft is subjected to the state of plane stress shown in Fig. 25a. Determine the principal stresses and the absolute maximum shear stress at the point.

(a)

### SOLUTION

**Principal Stresses.** The in-plane principal stresses can be determined from Mohr's circle. The center of the circle is on the $\sigma$ axis at $\sigma_{avg} = (-20 + 0)/2 = -10$ psi. Plotting the reference point $A(-20, -40)$, the radius $CA$ is established and the circle is drawn as shown in Fig. 25b. The radius is

$$R = \sqrt{(20 - 10)^2 + (40)^2} = 41.2 \text{ psi}$$

The principal stresses are at the points where the circle intersects the $\sigma$ axis; i.e.,

$$\sigma_1 = -10 + 41.2 = 31.2 \text{ psi}$$
$$\sigma_2 = -10 - 41.2 = -51.2 \text{ psi}$$

(b)

From the circle, the *counterclockwise* angle $2\theta$, measured from $CA$ to the $-\sigma$ axis, is

$$2\theta = \tan^{-1}\left(\frac{40}{20 - 10}\right) = 76.0°$$

Thus,

$$\theta = 38.0°$$

This *counterclockwise* rotation defines the direction of the $x'$ axis and $\sigma_2$ and its associated principal plane, Fig. 25c. We have

$$\sigma_1 = 31.2 \text{ psi} \quad \sigma_2 = -51.2 \text{ psi} \qquad Ans.$$

(c)

**Absolute Maximum Shear Stress.** Since these stresses have opposite signs, applying Eq. 14 we have

$$\tau_{max}^{abs} = \frac{\sigma_1 - \sigma_2}{2} = \frac{31.2 - (-51.2)}{2} = 41.2 \text{ psi} \qquad Ans.$$

$$\sigma_{avg} = \frac{31.2 - 51.2}{2} = -10 \text{ psi}$$

(d)

**NOTE:** These same results can also be obtained by drawing Mohr's circle for each orientation of an element about the $x$, $y$, and $z$ axes, Fig. 25d. Since $\sigma_1$ and $\sigma_2$ are of *opposite signs*, then the absolute maximum shear stress equals the maximum in-plane shear stress.

**Fig. 25**

# PROBLEMS

**77.** Draw the three Mohr's circles that describe each of the following states of stress.

(a)

(b)

**Prob. 77**

**78.** Draw the three Mohr's circles that describe the following state of stress.

**Prob. 78**

**79.** The stress at a point is shown on the element. Determine the principal stresses and the absolute maximum shear stress.

**Prob. 79**

**\*80.** The stress at a point is shown on the element. Determine the principal stresses and the absolute maximum shear stress.

**Prob. 80**

**81.** The stress at a point is shown on the element. Determine the principal stresses and the absolute maximum shear stress.

**Prob. 81**

**82.** The stress at a point is shown on the element. Determine the principal stresses and the absolute maximum shear stress.

**Prob. 82**

**83.** The state of stress at a point is shown on the element. Determine the principal stresses and the absolute maximum shear stress.

2.5 ksi

4 ksi

5 ksi

**Prob. 83**

**■84.** Consider the general case of plane stress as shown. Write a computer program that will show a plot of the three Mohr's circles for the element, and will also calculate the maximum in-plane shear stress and the absolute maximum shear stress.

$\sigma_y$

$\tau_{xy}$

$\sigma_x$

**Prob. 84**

**85.** The solid cylinder having a radius $r$ is placed in a sealed container and subjected to a pressure $p$. Determine the stress components acting at point $A$ located on the center line of the cylinder. Draw Mohr's circles for the element at this point.

$A$

**Prob. 85**

**86.** The plate is subjected to a tensile force $P = 5$ kip. If it has the dimensions shown, determine the principal stresses and the absolute maximum shear stress. If the material is ductile it will fail in shear. Make a sketch of the plate showing how this failure would appear. If the material is brittle the plate will fail due to the principal stresses. Show how this failure occurs.

$P = 5$ kip

2 in.

2 in.  $P = 5$ kip

12 in.

0.5 in.

**Prob. 86**

**87.** Determine the principal stresses and absolute maximum shear stress developed at point $A$ on the cross section of the bracket at section $a$–$a$.

**\*88.** Determine the principal stresses and absolute maximum shear stress developed at point $B$ on the cross section of the bracket at section $a$–$a$.

12 in.

6 in.

$a$  $a$

3  5  4

500 lb

0.5 in.  0.25 in.

$A$

$B$

0.25 in.  0.25 in.

1.5 in. 1.5 in.

Section $a$ – $a$

**Probs. 87/88**

# CHAPTER REVIEW

Plane stress occurs when the material at a point is subjected to two normal stress components $\sigma_x$ and $\sigma_y$ and a shear stress $\tau_{xy}$. Provided these components are known, then the stress components acting on an element having a different orientation $\theta$ can be determined using the two force equations of equilibrium or the equations of stress transformation.

$$\sigma_{x'} = \frac{\sigma_x + \sigma_y}{2} + \frac{\sigma_x - \sigma_y}{2}\cos 2\theta + \tau_{xy}\sin 2\theta$$

$$\tau_{x'y'} = -\frac{\sigma_x - \sigma_y}{2}\sin 2\theta + \tau_{xy}\cos 2\theta$$

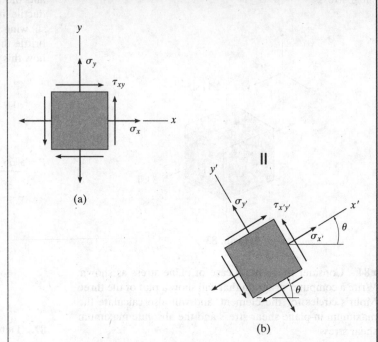

(a)

(b)

For design, it is important to determine the orientation of the element that produces the maximum principal normal stresses and the maximum in-plane shear stress. Using the stress transformation equations, it is found that no shear stress acts on the planes of principal stress. The principal stresses are

$$\sigma_{1,2} = \frac{\sigma_x + \sigma_y}{2} \pm \sqrt{\left(\frac{\sigma_x - \sigma_y}{2}\right)^2 + \tau_{xy}^2}$$

The planes of maximum in-plane shear stress are oriented 45° from this orientation, and on these shear planes there is an associated average normal stress.

$$\tau_{\substack{\max \\ \text{in-plane}}} = \sqrt{\left(\frac{\sigma_x - \sigma_y}{2}\right)^2 + \tau_{xy}^2}$$

$$\sigma_{\text{avg}} = \frac{\sigma_x + \sigma_y}{2}$$

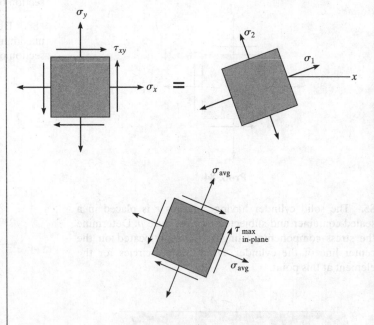

Mohr's circle provides a semi-graphical method for finding the stresses on any plane, the principal normal stresses, and the maximum in-plane shear stress. To draw the circle, the $\sigma$ and $\tau$ axes are established, the center of the circle $C[(\sigma_x + \sigma_y)/2, 0]$ and the reference point $A(\sigma_x, \tau_{xy})$ are plotted. The radius $R$ of the circle extends between these two points and is determined from trigonometry.

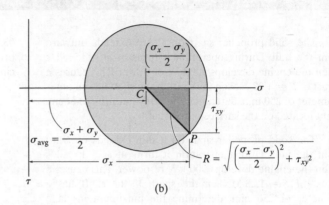

(b)

If $\sigma_1$ and $\sigma_2$ are of the same sign, then the absolute maximum shear stress will lie out of plane.

$$\tau_{\substack{abs \\ max}} = \frac{\sigma_1}{2}$$

In the case of plane stress, the absolute maximum shear stress will be equal to the maximum in-plane shear provided the principal stresses $\sigma_1$ and $\sigma_2$ have the opposite sign.

$$\tau_{\substack{abs \\ max}} = \frac{\sigma_1 - \sigma_2}{2}$$

x–y plane stress

x–y plane stress

# REVIEW PROBLEMS

**89.** The solid propeller shaft on a ship extends outward from the hull. During operation it turns at $\omega = 15$ rad/s when the engine develops 900 kW of power. This causes a thrust of $F = 1.23$ MN on the shaft. If the shaft has an outer diameter of 250 mm, determine the principal stresses at any point located on the surface of the shaft.

**90.** The solid propeller shaft on a ship extends outward from the hull. During operation it turns at $\omega = 15$ rad/s when the engine develops 900 kW of power. This causes a thrust of $F = 1.23$ MN on the shaft. If the shaft has a diameter of 250 mm, determine the maximum in-plane shear stress at any point located on the surface of the shaft.

**Probs. 89/90**

**91.** The steel pipe has an inner diameter of 2.75 in. and an outer diameter of 3 in. If it is fixed at $C$ and subjected to the horizontal 20-lb force acting on the handle of the pipe wrench at its end, determine the principal stresses in the pipe at point $A$, which is located on the surface of the pipe.

***92.** Solve Prob. 91 for point $B$, which is located on the surface of the pipe.

**Probs. 91/92**

**93.** Determine the equivalent state of stress if an element is oriented 40° clockwise from the element shown. Use Mohr's circle.

**Prob. 93**

**94.** The crane is used to support the 350-lb load. Determine the principal stresses acting in the boom at points $A$ and $B$. The cross section is rectangular and has a width of 6 in. and a thickness of 3 in. Use Mohr's circle.

**Prob. 94**

**95.** Determine the equivalent state of stress on an element at the same point which represents (a) the principal stresses, and (b) the maximum in-plane shear stress and the associated average normal stress. Also, for each case, determine the corresponding orientation of the element with respect to the element shown and sketch the results on the element.

**Prob. 95**

*96. The propeller shaft of the tugboat is subjected to the compressive force and torque shown. If the shaft has an inner diameter of 100 mm and an outer diameter of 150 mm, determine the principal stress at a point $A$ located on the outer surface.

**Prob. 96**

**97.** The box beam is subjected to the loading shown. Determine the principal stress in the beam at points $A$ and $B$.

**Prob. 97**

**98.** The state of stress at a point is shown on the element. Determine (a) the principal stresses and (b) the maximum in-plane shear stress and average normal stress at the point. Specify the orientation of the element in each case.

**Prob. 98**

**99.** The state of stress at a point in a member is shown on the element. Determine the stress components acting on the inclined plane $AB$. Solve the problem using the method of equilibrium described in Sec. 1.

**Prob. 99**

# Solutions and Answers for Preliminary Problems

**P1.**

**P1b.**

**P1c.**

**P2.**

$$\tau_{max} = \sqrt{\left(\frac{\sigma_x - \sigma_y}{2}\right)^2 + \tau_{xy}^2} = \sqrt{\left(\frac{4 - (-4)}{2}\right)^2 + (0)^2}$$

$$= 4 \text{ MPa}$$

$$\sigma_{avg} = \frac{\sigma_x + \sigma_y}{2} = \frac{4 - 4}{2} = 0$$

$$\tan 2\theta_s = -\frac{(\sigma_x - \sigma_y)/2}{\tau_{xy}} = \frac{[4 - (-4)]/2}{0} = -\infty$$

$$\theta_s = -45°$$

$$\tau_{x'y'} = -\frac{\sigma_x - \sigma_y}{2} \sin 2\theta + \tau_{xy} \cos 2\theta$$

$$= -\frac{4 - (-4)}{2} \sin 2(-45°) + 0 = 4 \text{ MPa}$$

# Selected Answers

**2.** $\sigma_{x'} = -4.05$ ksi, $\tau_{x'y'} = -0.404$ ksi

**3.** $\sigma_{x'} = -388$ psi, $\tau_{x'y'} = 455$ psi

**5.** $\sigma_{x'} = 1.45$ ksi, $\tau_{x'y'} = 3.50$ ksi

**6.** $\sigma_{x'} = -5$ MPa, $\tau_{x'y'} = 40$ MPa

**7.** $\sigma_{x'} = -5$ MPa, $\tau_{x'y'} = 40$ MPa

**9.** $\sigma_{x'} = 56.25$ MPa, $\sigma_{y'} = -31.25$ MPa, $\tau_{x'y'} = -75.8$ MPa

**10.** $\sigma_{x'} = 47.5$ MPa, $\sigma_{y'} = 202$ MPa, $\tau_{x'y'} = -15.8$ MPa

**11.** $\sigma_{x'} = 177$ MPa, $\sigma_{y'} = 72.5$ MPa, $\tau_{x'y'} = -59.2$ MPa

**13.** $\sigma_{x'} = -898$ psi, $\tau_{x'y'} = 605$ psi, $\sigma_{y'} = 598$ psi

**14.** $\sigma_1 = 4.21$ ksi, $\sigma_2 = -34.2$ ksi, $\theta_{p2} = 19.3°$ and $\theta_{p1} = -70.7°$, $\tau_{\max\text{ in-plane}} = 19.2$ ksi, $\sigma_{\text{avg}} = -15$ ksi, $\theta_s = -25.7°$ and $64.3°$

**15.** $\sigma_1 = 53.0$ MPa, $\sigma_2 = -68.0$ MPa, $\theta_{p1} = 14.9°$ and $\theta_{p2} = -75.1°$, $\sigma_{\text{avg}} = -7.50$ MPa, $\tau_{\max\text{ in-plane}} = 60.5$ MPa, $\theta_s = -30.1°$ and $59.9°$

**17.** $\sigma_1 = 137$ MPa, $\sigma_2 = -86.8$ MPa, $\theta_{p1} = -13.3°$, $\theta_{p2} = 76.7°$, $\tau_{\max\text{ in-plane}} = 112$ MPa, $\theta_s = 31.7°$ and $122°$, $\sigma_{\text{avg}} = 25$ MPa

**18.** $\sigma_x = 33.0$ MPa, $\sigma_y = 137$ MPa, $\tau_{xy} = -30$ MPa

**19.** $\sigma_1 = 5.90$ MPa, $\sigma_2 = -106$ MPa, $\theta_{p1} = 76.7°$ and $\theta_{p2} = -13.3°$, $\tau_{\max\text{ in-plane}} = 55.9$ MPa, $\sigma_{\text{avg}} = -50$ MPa, $\theta_s = 31.7°$ and $122°$

**21.** $\tau_a = -1.96$ ksi, $\sigma_1 = 80.1$ ksi, $\sigma_2 = 19.9$ ksi

**22.** $\sigma_{x'} = 19.5$ kPa, $\tau_{x'y'} = -53.6$ kPa

**23.** $\sigma_{x'} = 0.507$ MPa, $\tau_{x'y'} = 0.958$ MPa

**25.** $\sigma_y = -824$ psi

**26.** $\sigma_1 = 29.8$ ksi, $\sigma_2 = 0$, $\tau_{\max\text{ in-plane}} = 14.9$ ksi, $\theta_s = -45°$ and $45°$

**27.** $\sigma_1 = 0$, $\sigma_2 = -22.90$ ksi, $\tau_{\max\text{ in-plane}} = 11.5$ ksi, $\theta_s = 45°$ and $135°$

**29.** $\sigma_1 = 0.939$ ksi, $\sigma_2 = -1.36$ ksi, $\tau_{\max\text{ in-plane}} = 1.15$ ksi

**30.** $\sigma_{x'} = -63.3$ MPa, $\tau_{x'y'} = 35.7$ MPa

**31.** $\sigma_1 = 6.38$ MPa, $\sigma_2 = -0.360$ MPa, $\theta_{p1} = 13.4°$ and $\theta_{p2} = -76.6°$

**33.** Point $A$: $\sigma_1 = 0$, $\sigma_2 = -192$ MPa, $\theta_{p1} = 0$, $\theta_{p2} = 90°$, Point $B$: $\sigma_1 = 24.0$ MPa, $\sigma_2 = -24.0$ MPa, $\theta_{p1} = -45.0°$, $\theta_{p2} = 45.0°$

**34.** $\sigma_1 = 0$, $\sigma_2 = -1.34$ ksi, $\tau_{\max\text{ in-plane}} = 668$ psi, $\theta_s = 45°$ and $-45°$

**35.** $\tau_{\max\text{ in-plane}} = 5$ kPa, $\sigma_{\text{avg}} = 0$

**37.** $\sigma_1 = \dfrac{4}{\pi d^2}\left(\dfrac{2PL}{d} - F\right)$, $\sigma_2 = 0$, $\tau_{\max\text{ in-plane}} = \dfrac{2}{\pi d^2}\left(\dfrac{2PL}{d} - F\right)$

**38.** $\tau_{x'y'} = -47.5$ kPa

**39.** $\sigma_{x'} = 82.3$ kPa

**41.** $\sigma_1 = 1.37$ MPa, $\sigma_2 = -198$ MPa

**42.** $\sigma_1 = 2.97$ ksi, $\sigma_2 = -4.12$ ksi, $\tau_{\max\text{ in-plane}} = 3.55$ ksi

**43.** $\sigma_1 = 4.33$ MPa, $\sigma_2 = -13.0$ MPa

**45.** $\sigma_{x'} = -5$ MPa, $\tau_{x'y'} = 40$ MPa

**46.** $\sigma_1 = 4.21$ ksi, $\sigma_2 = -34.2$ ksi, $\theta_{p2} = 19.3°$ and $\theta_{p1} = -70.7°$, $\tau_{\max\text{ in-plane}} = 19.2$ ksi, $\sigma_{\text{avg}} = -15$ ksi, $\theta_s = 64.3°$

**47.** $\sigma_{x'} = 47.5$ MPa, $\tau_{x'y'} = -15.8$ MPa, $\sigma_{y'} = 202$ MPa

**49.** $\sigma_1 = 54.2$ MPa, $\sigma_2 = -4.15$ MPa, $\theta_p = -15.5°$, $\sigma_{\text{avg}} = 25$ MPa, $\tau_{\max\text{ in-plane}} = 29.2$ MPa, $\theta_s = 29.5°$

**51.** $\sigma_{x'} = 10$ ksi, $\tau_{x'y'} = -5$ ksi, $\sigma_{y'} = 0$

**53.** $\sigma_{x'} = 736$ MPa, $\sigma_{y'} = -156$ MPa, $\tau_{x'y'} = -188$ MPa

**54.** $\sigma_1 = 87.7$ MPa, $\sigma_2 = -128$ MPa, $(\theta_p)_1 = 10.9°$ (clockwise), $\sigma_{\text{avg}} = -20$ MPa, $\tau_{\max\text{ in-plane}} = -108$ MPa, $\theta_s = 34.1°$ (counterclockwise)

**55.** $\sigma_1 = 3.51$ ksi, $\sigma_2 = -28.5$ ksi, $(\theta_p)_1 = 19.3°$ (clockwise), $\tau_{\max\text{ in-plane}} = 16.0$ ksi, $\sigma_{\text{avg}} = -12.5$ ksi, $\theta_s = 25.7°$ (counterclockwise)

**57.** $\sigma_1 = 64.1$ MPa, $\sigma_2 = -14.1$ MPa, $\theta_{p2} = 25.1°$, $\sigma_{\text{avg}} = 25.0$ MPa, $\tau_{\max\text{ in-plane}} = 39.1$ MPa, $\theta_s = -19.9°$

**58.** $\sigma_{x'} = -421$ MPa, $\tau_{x'y'} = -354$ MPa, $\sigma_{y'} = 421$ MPa

**59.** (a) $\sigma_1 = -5.53$ ksi, $\sigma_2 = -14.5$ ksi, $\theta_p = -31.7°$
(b) $\tau_{\max\text{ in-plane}} = 4.47$ ksi, $\sigma_{\text{avg}} = -10$ ksi, $\theta_s = 13.3°$

**62.** $\sigma_{x'} = 19.5$ kPa, $\tau_{x'y'} = -53.6$ kPa

**63.** $\tau_{\max\text{ in-plane}} = 41.0$ psi, $\sigma_1 = 0.976$ psi, $\sigma_2 = -81.0$ psi

**65.** $\sigma_1 = 29.4$ ksi, $\sigma_2 = -17.0$ ksi

**66.** $\sigma_1 = 0.361$ MPa, $\sigma_2 = -5.36$ MPa, $\tau_{\max\text{ in-plane}} = 2.86$ MPa

**67.** $\sigma_1 = 0.942$ MPa, $\sigma_2 = -3.30$ MPa, $\tau_{\max\text{ in-plane}} = 2.12$ MPa

**69.** $\sigma_1 = 4.71$ ksi, $\sigma_2 = -0.0262$ ksi

**70.** Regardless of the orientation of the element, the shear stress is zero and the state of stress is represented by the same two normal stress components.

**71.** $\sigma_{x'} = 500$ MPa, $\tau_{x'y'} = -167$ MPa

**73.** $\sigma_1 = 1.15$ MPa, $\sigma_2 = -0.0428$ MPa

**74.** $\sigma_1 = 2.97$ ksi, $\sigma_2 = -2.97$ ksi, $\theta_{p1} = 45.0°$, $\theta_{p2} = -45.0°$, $\tau_{\substack{max \\ \text{in-plane}}} = 2.97$ ksi, $\theta_s = 0°$

**75.** $\sigma_1 = 2.59$ ksi, $\sigma_2 = -3.61$ ksi, $\theta_{p1} = -40.3°$, $\theta_{p2} = 49.7$, $\tau_{\substack{max \\ \text{in-plane}}} = 3.10$ ksi, $\theta_s = 4.73°$

**79.** $\sigma_1 = 100$ MPa, $\sigma_2 = 50$ MPa, $\sigma_3 = 0$, $\tau_{\substack{abs \\ max}} = 50$ MPa

**81.** $\sigma_2 = -0.807$ ksi, $\sigma_3 = -6.19$ ksi, $\sigma_1 = 0$, $\tau_{\substack{abs \\ max}} = -3.10$ ksi

**82.** $\sigma_1 = 222$ MPa, $\sigma_2 = 0$ MPa, $\sigma_3 = -102$ MPa, $\tau_{\substack{abs \\ max}} = 162$ MPa

**83.** $\sigma_1 = 6.73$ ksi, $\sigma_2 = 0$, $\sigma_3 = -4.23$ ksi, $\tau_{\substack{abs \\ max}} = 5.48$ ksi

**85.** The stress in every direction is
$\sigma_1 = \sigma_2 = \sigma_3 = -p$

**86.** $\sigma_1 = 2.50$ ksi, $\sigma_2 = \sigma_3 = 0$, $\tau_{\substack{abs \\ max}} = 1.25$ ksi

**87.** $\sigma_1 = 583$ psi, $\sigma_2 = 0$, $\sigma_3 = -926$ psi, $\tau_{\substack{abs \\ max}} = 755$ psi

**89.** $\sigma_1 = 10.7$ MPa, $\sigma_2 = -35.8$ MPa

**90.** $\tau_{\substack{max \\ \text{in-plane}}} = 23.2$ MPa

**91.** $\sigma_1 = 119$ psi, $\sigma_2 = -119$ psi

**93.** $\sigma_{x'} = -0.611$ ksi, $\tau_{x'y'} = 7.88$ ksi, $\sigma_{y'} = -3.39$ ksi

**94.** Point $A$: $\sigma_1 = 0$, $\sigma_2 = -1.20$ ksi,
Point $B$: $\sigma_1 = 9.88$ psi, $\sigma_2 = -43.1$ psi

**95.** $\sigma_1 = 3.03$ ksi, $\sigma_2 = -33.0$ ksi, $\theta_{p1} = -16.8°$ and $\theta_{p2} = 73.2°$, $\tau_{\substack{max \\ \text{in-plane}}} = 18.0$ ksi, $\sigma_{avg} = -15$ ksi, $\theta_s = 28.2°$

**97.** Point $A$: $\sigma_1 = 61.7$ psi, $\sigma_2 = 0$
Point $B$: $\sigma_1 = 0$, $\sigma_2 = -46.3$ psi

**98.** $\sigma_1 = 53.0$ MPa, $\sigma_2 = -68.0$ MPa, $\theta_{p1} = 14.9°$, $\theta_{p2} = -75.1°$, $\tau_{\substack{max \\ \text{in-plane}}} = 60.5$ MPa, $\sigma_{avg} = -7.50$ MPa, $\theta_s = -30.1°$ and $59.9°$

**99.** $\sigma_{x'} = -16.5$ ksi, $\tau_{x'y'} = 2.95$ ksi

# Fundamental Problems Partial Solutions and Answers

**F1**  $\theta = 120°$  $\sigma_x = 500$ kPa  $\sigma_y = 0$  $\tau_{xy} = 0$
Apply Eqs. 1, 2.
$\sigma_{x'} = 125$ kPa *Ans.*
$\tau_{x'y'} = 217$ kPa *Ans.*

**F2**  $\theta = -45°$  $\sigma_x = 0$  $\sigma_y = -400$ kPa
$\tau_{xy} = -300$ kPa
Apply Eqs. 1, 3, 2.
$\sigma_{x'} = 100$ kPa *Ans.*
$\sigma_{y'} = -500$ kPa *Ans.*
$\tau_{x'y'} = 200$ kPa *Ans.*

**F3**  $\sigma_x = 80$ MPa  $\sigma_y = 0$  $\tau_{xy} = 30$ MPa
Apply Eqs. 5, 4.
$\sigma_1 = 90$ MPa  $\sigma_2 = -10$ MPa *Ans.*
$\theta_p = 18.43°$ and $108.43°$
From Eq. 1,
$$\sigma_{x'} = \frac{80 + 0}{2} + \frac{80 - 0}{2}\cos 2(18.43°)$$
$$+ 30 \sin 2(18.43°)$$
$$= 90 \text{ MPa} = \sigma_1$$
Thus,
$(\theta_p)_1 = 18.4°$ and $(\theta_p)_2 = 108°$ *Ans.*

**F4**  $\sigma_x = 100$ kPa  $\sigma_y = 700$ kPa
$\tau_{xy} = -400$ kPa
Apply Eqs. 7, 8.
$\tau_{\max}^{\text{in-plane}} = 500$ kPa *Ans.*
$\sigma_{\text{avg}} = 400$ kPa *Ans.*

**F5**  At the cross section through $B$:
$N = 4$ kN  $V = 2$ kN
$M = 2(2) = 4$ kN·m
$$\sigma_B = \frac{P}{A} + \frac{Mc}{I} = \frac{4(10^3)}{0.03(0.06)} + \frac{4(10^3)(0.03)}{\frac{1}{12}(0.03)(0.06)^3}$$
$$= 224 \text{ MPa (T)}$$
Note $\tau_B = 0$ since $Q = 0$.
Thus,
$\sigma_1 = 224$ MPa *Ans.*
$\sigma_2 = 0$

**F6**  $A_y = B_y = 12$ kN
Segment $AC$:
$V_C = 0$  $M_C = 24$ kN·m
$\tau_C = 0$ (since $V_C = 0$)
$\sigma_C = 0$ (since $C$ is on neutral axis)
$\sigma_1 = \sigma_2 = 0$ *Ans.*

**F7**  $\sigma_{\text{avg}} = \dfrac{\sigma_x + \sigma_y}{2} = \dfrac{500 + 0}{2} = 250$ kPa
The coordinates of the center $C$ of the circle and the reference point $A$ are
$A(500, 0)$   $C(250, 0)$
$R = CA = 500 - 250 = 250$ kPa
$\theta = 120°$ (counterclockwise). Rotate the radial line $CA$ counterclockwise $2\theta = 240°$ to the coordinates of point $P(\sigma_{x'}, \tau_{x'y'})$.
$\alpha = 240° - 180° = 60°$
$\sigma_{x'} = 250 - 250 \cos 60° = 125$ kPa *Ans.*
$\tau_{x'y'} = 250 \sin 60° = 217$ kPa *Ans.*

**F8**  $\sigma_{\text{avg}} = \dfrac{\sigma_x + \sigma_y}{2} = \dfrac{80 + 0}{2} = 40$ kPa
The coordinates of the center $C$ of the circle and the reference point $A$ are
$A(80, 30)$   $C(40, 0)$
$R = CA = \sqrt{(80 - 40)^2 + 30^2} = 50$ MPa
$\sigma_1 = 40 + 50 = 90$ MPa *Ans.*
$\sigma_2 = 40 - 50 = -10$ MPa *Ans.*
$$\tan 2(\theta_p)_1 = \frac{30}{80 - 40} = 0.75$$
$(\theta_p)_1 = 18.4°$ (counterclockwise) *Ans.*

**F9**  The coordinates of the reference point $A$ and the center $C$ of the circle are
$A(30, 40)$   $C(0, 0)$
$R = CA = 50$ MPa
$\sigma_1 = 50$ MPa
$\sigma_2 = -50$ MPa

**F10**  $J = \dfrac{\pi}{2}(0.04^4 - 0.03^4) = 0.875(10^{-6})\pi$ m$^4$
$$\tau = \frac{Tc}{J} = \frac{4(10^3)(0.04)}{0.875(10^{-6})\pi} = 58.21 \text{ MPa}$$
$\sigma_x = \sigma_y = 0$ and $\tau_{xy} = -58.21$ MPa
$$\sigma_{\text{avg}} = \frac{\sigma_x + \sigma_y}{2} = 0$$
The coordinates of the reference point $A$ and the center $C$ of the circle are
$A(0, -58.21)$   $C(0, 0)$
$R = CA = 58.21$ MPa

$\sigma_1 = 0 + 58.21 = 58.2$ MPa *Ans.*

$\sigma_2 = 0 - 58.21 = -58.2$ MPa *Ans.*

F11

$+\uparrow \Sigma F_y = 0;$ $\quad V - 30 = 0$ $\quad\quad V = 30$ kN

$\zeta + \Sigma M_O = 0;$ $\quad -M - 30(0.3) = 0$ $\quad M = -9$ kN · m

$I = \dfrac{1}{12}(0.05)(0.15^3) = 14.0625(10^{-6})$ m$^4$

$Q_A = y'A' = 0.05(0.05)(0.05) = 0.125(10^{-3})$ m$^3$

$\sigma_A = -\dfrac{My_A}{I} = \dfrac{[-9(10^3)](0.025)}{14.0625(10^{-6})} = 16$ MPa (T)

$\tau_A = \dfrac{VQ_A}{It} = \dfrac{30(10^3)[0.125(10^{-3})]}{14.0625(10^{-6})(0.05)} = 5.333$ MPa

$\sigma_x = 16$ MPa, $\sigma_y = 0$, and $\tau_{xy} = -5.333$ MPa

$\sigma_{\text{avg}} = \dfrac{\sigma_x + \sigma_y}{2} = \dfrac{16 + 0}{2} = 8$ MPa

The coordinates of the reference point $A$ and the center $C$ of the circle are

$$A\,(16, -5.333) \quad\quad C(8, 0)$$

$R = CA = \sqrt{(16-8)^2 + (-5.333)^2} = 9.615$ MPa

$\sigma_1 = 8 + 9.615 = 17.6$ MPa *Ans.*

$\sigma_2 = 8 - 9.615 = -1.61$ MPa *Ans.*

F12

$\zeta + \Sigma M_B = 0;$ $\quad 60(1) - A_y(1.5) = 0$ $\quad A_y = 40$ kN

$+\uparrow \Sigma F_y = 0;$ $\quad 40 - V = 0$ $\quad\quad V = 40$ kN

$\zeta + \Sigma M_O = 0;$ $\quad M - 40(0.5) = 0$ $\quad M = 20$ kN · m

$I = \dfrac{1}{12}(0.1)(0.2^3) - \dfrac{1}{12}(0.09)(0.18^3) = 22.9267(10^{-6})$ m$^4$

$Q_A = y'A' = 0.095(0.01)(0.1) = 95(10^{-6})$ m$^3$

$\sigma_A = -\dfrac{My_A}{I} = -\dfrac{[20(10^3)](0.09)}{22.9267(10^{-6})} = -78.51$ MPa

$\quad\quad = 78.51$ MPa (C)

$\tau_A = \dfrac{VQ_A}{It} = \dfrac{40(10^3)[95(10^{-6})]}{[22.9267(10^{-6})](0.01)} = 16.57$ MPa

$\sigma_x = -78.51$ MPa, $\sigma_y = 0$, and $\tau_{xy} = -16.57$ MPa

$\sigma_{\text{avg}} = \dfrac{\sigma_x + \sigma_y}{2} = \dfrac{-78.51 + 0}{2} = -39.26$ MPa

The coordinates of the reference point $A$ and the center $C$ of the circle are

$$A(-78.51, -16.57) \quad C(-39.26, 0)$$

$R = CA = \sqrt{[-78.51 - (-39.26)]^2 + (-16.57)^2}$

$\quad\quad = 42.61$ MPa

$\tau_{\substack{\text{max} \\ \text{in-plane}}} = |R| = 42.6$ MPa $\quad\quad$ *Ans.*

# Strain Transformation

From Chapter 10 of *Mechanics of Materials*, Ninth Edition. R. C. Hibbeler. Copyright © 2014 by Pearson Education, Inc. Published by Pearson Prentice Hall. All rights reserved.

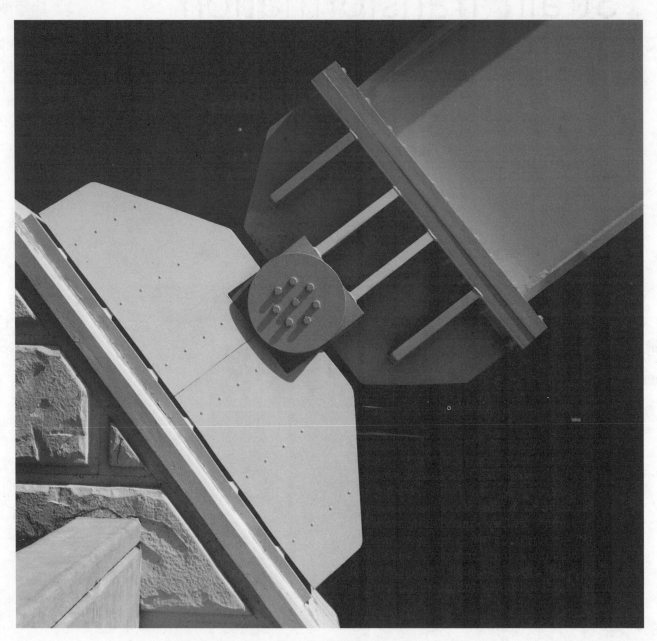

This pin support for a bridge has been tested with strain gages to ensure that the principle strains in the material do not exceed a failure criterion for the material.

# Strain Transformation

## CHAPTER OBJECTIVES

■ The transformation of strain at a point is similar to the transformation of stress. Here we will also discuss various ways for measuring strain and develop some important material-property relationships, including a generalized form of Hooke's law. At the end of the chapter, a few of the theories used to predict the failure of a material will be discussed.

## 1 Plane Strain

The general state of strain at a point in a body is represented by a combination of three components of normal strain, $\epsilon_x$, $\epsilon_y$, $\epsilon_z$, and three components of shear strain $\gamma_{xy}$, $\gamma_{xz}$, $\gamma_{yz}$. These six components tend to deform each face of an element of the material, and like stress, the normal and shear strain *components* at the point will vary according to the orientation of the element. The *strains* at a point are often determined by using strain gauges, which measure normal strain in *specified directions*. For both analysis and design, however, engineers must sometimes transform this data in order to obtain the strain in other directions.

To understand how this is done, we will first confine our attention to a study of **plane strain**. Specifically, we will not consider the effects of the components $\epsilon_z$, $\gamma_{xz}$, and $\gamma_{yz}$. In general, then, a plane-strained element is subjected to two components of normal strain, $\epsilon_x$, $\epsilon_y$, and one component of shear strain, $\gamma_{xy}$. Although plane strain and plane stress each have three components lying in the same plane, realize that plane stress *does not* necessarily cause plane strain or vice versa. The reason for this has to do with the Poisson effect discussed in Sec. 6. For example, if the element in Fig. 1 is subjected to plane stress $\sigma_x$ and $\sigma_y$, not only are normal strains $\epsilon_x$ and $\epsilon_y$ produced, but there is *also* an associated normal strain, $\epsilon_z$. This is obviously *not* a case of plane strain. In general, then, unless $\nu = 0$, the Poisson effect will *prevent* the simultaneous occurrence of plane strain and plane stress.

Plane stress, $\sigma_x$, $\sigma_y$, does not cause plane strain in the $x$–$y$ plane since $\epsilon_z \neq 0$.

**Fig. 1**

# 2  General Equations of Plane-Strain Transformation

It is important in plane-strain analysis to establish transformation equations that can be used to determine the $x'$, $y'$ components of normal and shear strain at a point, provided the $x$, $y$ components of strain are known. Essentially this problem is one of geometry and requires relating the deformations and rotations of line segments, which represent the sides of differential elements that are parallel to each set of axes.

(a)

(b)

Positive sign convention

**Fig. 2**

**Sign Convention.** Before the strain-transformation equations can be developed, we must first establish a sign convention for the strains. With reference to the differential element shown in Fig. 2a, *normal strains* $\epsilon_x$ and $\epsilon_y$ are *positive* if they cause *elongation* along the $x$ and $y$ axes, respectively, and the *shear strain* $\gamma_{xy}$ is *positive* if the interior angle $AOB$ *becomes smaller* than 90°. This sign convention also follows the corresponding one used for plane stress, that is, positive $\sigma_x$, $\sigma_y$, $\tau_{xy}$ will cause the element to *deform* in the positive $\epsilon_x$, $\epsilon_y$, $\gamma_{xy}$ directions, respectively.

The problem here will be to determine at a point the normal and shear strains $\epsilon_{x'}$, $\epsilon_{y'}$, $\gamma_{x'y'}$, measured relative to the $x'$, $y'$ axes, if we know $\epsilon_x$, $\epsilon_y$, $\gamma_{xy}$, measured relative to the $x$, $y$ axes. If the angle between the $x$ and $x'$ axes is $\theta$, then, like the case of plane stress, $\theta$ will be *positive* provided it follows the curl of the right-hand fingers, i.e., counterclockwise, as shown in Fig. 2b.

## Normal and Shear Strains.

In order to develop the strain-transformation equation for $\epsilon_{x'}$, we must determine the elongation of a line segment $dx'$ that lies along the $x'$ axis and is subjected to strain components $\epsilon_x$, $\epsilon_y$, $\gamma_{xy}$. As shown in Fig. 3a, the components of the line $dx'$ along the $x$ and $y$ axes are

$$dx = dx' \cos \theta$$
$$dy = dx' \sin \theta \qquad (1)$$

Before deformation

(a)

When the positive normal strain $\epsilon_x$ occurs, the line $dx$ is elongated $\epsilon_x \, dx$, Fig. 3b, which causes line $dx'$ to elongate $\epsilon_x \, dx \cos \theta$. Likewise, when $\epsilon_y$ occurs, line $dy$ elongates $\epsilon_y \, dy$, Fig. 3c, which causes line $dx'$ to elongate $\epsilon_y \, dy \sin \theta$. Finally, assuming that $dx$ remains fixed in position, the shear strain $\gamma_{xy}$, which is the change in angle between $dx$ and $dy$, causes the top of line $dy$ to be displaced $\gamma_{xy} \, dy$ to the right, as shown in Fig. 3d. This causes $dx'$ to elongate $\gamma_{xy} \, dy \cos \theta$. If all three of these elongations are added together, the resultant elongation of $dx'$ is then

Normal strain $\epsilon_x$

(b)

$$\delta x' = \epsilon_x \, dx \cos \theta + \epsilon_y \, dy \sin \theta + \gamma_{xy} \, dy \cos \theta$$

The normal strain along the line $dx'$ is $\epsilon_{x'} = \delta x' / dx'$. Using Eq. 1, we therefore have

$$\epsilon_{x'} = \epsilon_x \cos^2 \theta + \epsilon_y \sin^2 \theta + \gamma_{xy} \sin \theta \cos \theta \qquad (2)$$

Normal strain $\epsilon_y$

(c)

The rubber specimen is constrained between the two fixed supports, and so it will undergo plane strain when loads are applied to it in the horizontal plane.

Shear strain $\gamma_{xy}$

(d)

**Fig. 3**

547

Shear strain $\gamma_{xy}$

(d)

(e)

**Fig. 3 (cont.)**

The strain-transformation equation for $\gamma_{x'y'}$ can be developed by considering the amount of rotation each of the line segments $dx'$ and $dy'$ undergo when subjected to the strain components $\epsilon_x$, $\epsilon_y$, $\gamma_{xy}$. First we will consider the rotation of $dx'$, which is defined by the counterclockwise angle $\alpha$ shown in Fig. 3e. It can be determined by the displacement caused by $\delta y'$ using $\alpha = \delta y'/dx'$. To obtain $\delta y'$, consider the following three displacement components acting in the $y'$ direction: one from $\epsilon_x$, giving $-\epsilon_x\, dx \sin \theta$, Fig. 3b; another from $\epsilon_y$, giving $\epsilon_y\, dy \cos \theta$, Fig. 3c; and the last from $\gamma_{xy}$, giving $-\gamma_{xy}\, dy \sin \theta$, Fig. 3d. Thus, $\delta y'$, as caused by all three strain components, is

$$\delta y' = -\epsilon_x\, dx \sin \theta + \epsilon_y\, dy \cos \theta - \gamma_{xy}\, dy \sin \theta$$

Dividing each term by $dx'$ and using Eq. 1, with $\alpha = \delta y'/dx'$, we have

$$\alpha = (-\epsilon_x + \epsilon_y) \sin \theta \cos \theta - \gamma_{xy} \sin^2 \theta \tag{3}$$

As shown in Fig. 3e, the line $dy'$ rotates by an amount $\beta$. We can determine this angle by a similar analysis, or by simply substituting $\theta + 90°$ for $\theta$ into Eq. 3. Using the identities $\sin(\theta + 90°) = \cos \theta$, $\cos(\theta + 90°) = -\sin \theta$, we have

$$\beta = (-\epsilon_x + \epsilon_y) \sin(\theta + 90°) \cos(\theta + 90°) - \gamma_{xy} \sin^2(\theta + 90°)$$

$$= -(-\epsilon_x + \epsilon_y) \cos \theta \sin \theta - \gamma_{xy} \cos^2 \theta$$

Since $\alpha$ and $\beta$ represent the rotation of the sides $dx'$ and $dy'$ of a differential element whose sides were originally oriented along the $x'$ and $y'$ axes, Fig. 3e, the element is then subjected to a shear strain of

$$\gamma_{x'y'} = \alpha - \beta = -2(\epsilon_x - \epsilon_y) \sin \theta \cos \theta + \gamma_{xy}(\cos^2 \theta - \sin^2 \theta) \tag{4}$$

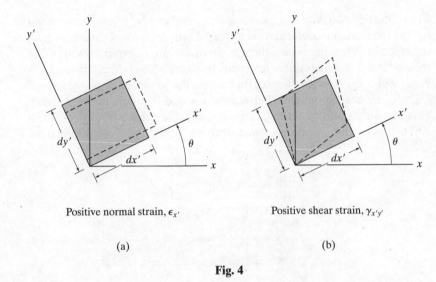

Positive normal strain, $\epsilon_{x'}$

Positive shear strain, $\gamma_{x'y'}$

(a)

(b)

**Fig. 4**

Using the trigonometric identities $\sin 2\theta = 2 \sin \theta \cos \theta$, $\cos^2 \theta = (1 + \cos 2\theta)/2$, and $\sin^2 \theta + \cos^2 \theta = 1$, we can rewrite Eqs. 2 and 4 in the final form

$$\epsilon_{x'} = \frac{\epsilon_x + \epsilon_y}{2} + \frac{\epsilon_x - \epsilon_y}{2} \cos 2\theta + \frac{\gamma_{xy}}{2} \sin 2\theta \qquad (5)$$

$$\frac{\gamma_{x'y'}}{2} = -\left(\frac{\epsilon_x - \epsilon_y}{2}\right) \sin 2\theta + \frac{\gamma_{xy}}{2} \cos 2\theta \qquad (6)$$

These strain-transformation equations give the normal strain $\epsilon_{x'}$ in the $x'$ direction and the shear strain $\gamma_{x'y'}$ of an element oriented at an angle $\theta$, as shown in Fig. 4. According to the established sign convention, if $\epsilon_{x'}$ is *positive*, the element *elongates* in the positive $x'$ direction, Fig. 4a, and if $\gamma_{x'y'}$ is positive, the element deforms as shown in Fig. 4b.

If the normal strain in the $y'$ direction is required, it can be obtained from Eq. 5 by simply substituting $(\theta + 90°)$ for $\theta$. The result is

$$\epsilon_{y'} = \frac{\epsilon_x + \epsilon_y}{2} - \frac{\epsilon_x - \epsilon_y}{2} \cos 2\theta - \frac{\gamma_{xy}}{2} \sin 2\theta \qquad (7)$$

The similarity between the above three equations and those for plane-stress transformation should be noted. By comparison, $\sigma_x$, $\sigma_y$, $\sigma_{x'}$, $\sigma_{y'}$ correspond to $\epsilon_x$, $\epsilon_y$, $\epsilon_{x'}$, $\epsilon_{y'}$; and $\tau_{xy}$, $\tau_{x'y'}$ correspond to $\gamma_{xy}/2$, $\gamma_{x'y'}/2$.

**Principal Strains.** Like stress, an element can be oriented at a point so that the element's deformation is caused only by normal strains, with *no* shear strain. When this occurs the normal strains are referred to as *principal strains*, and if the material is isotropic, the axes along which these strains occur will coincide with the axes that define the planes of principal stress.

From the correspondence between stress and strain mentioned above, between stress and strain mentioned above, the direction of the $x'$ axis and the two values of the principal strains $\epsilon_1$ and $\epsilon_2$ are determined from

Complex stresses are often developed at the joints where the cylindrical and hemispherical vessels are joined together. The stresses are determined by making measurements of strain.

$$\tan 2\theta_p = \frac{\gamma_{xy}}{\epsilon_x - \epsilon_y} \tag{8}$$

$$\epsilon_{1,2} = \frac{\epsilon_x + \epsilon_y}{2} \pm \sqrt{\left(\frac{\epsilon_x - \epsilon_y}{2}\right)^2 + \left(\frac{\gamma_{xy}}{2}\right)^2} \tag{9}$$

**Maximum In-Plane Shear Strain.** The direction of the $x'$ axis and the maximum in-plane shear strain and associated average normal strain are determined from the following equations: direction of the $x'$ axis, and the maximum in-plane shear strain and associated average normal strain are determined from the following equations:

$$\tan 2\theta_s = -\left(\frac{\epsilon_x - \epsilon_y}{\gamma_{xy}}\right) \tag{10}$$

$$\frac{\gamma_{\text{in-plane}}^{\text{max}}}{2} = \sqrt{\left(\frac{\epsilon_x - \epsilon_y}{2}\right)^2 + \left(\frac{\gamma_{xy}}{2}\right)^2} \tag{11}$$

$$\epsilon_{\text{avg}} = \frac{\epsilon_x + \epsilon_y}{2} \tag{12}$$

## Important Points

- In the case of plane stress, plane-strain analysis may be used within the plane of the stresses to analyze the data from strain gauges. Remember, though, there will be a normal strain that is perpendicular to the gauges due to the Poisson effect.

- When the state of strain is represented by the principal strains, no shear strain will act on the element.

- The state of strain at a point can also be represented in terms of the maximum in-plane shear strain. In this case an average normal strain will also act on the element.

- The element representing the maximum in-plane shear strain and its associated average normal strains is 45° from the orientation of an element representing the principal strains.

EXAMPLE | 1

A differential element of material at a point is subjected to a state of plane strain $\epsilon_x = 500(10^{-6})$, $\epsilon_y = -300(10^{-6})$, $\gamma_{xy} = 200(10^{-6})$, which tends to distort the element as shown in Fig. 5a. Determine the equivalent strains acting on an element of the material oriented at the point, *clockwise* 30° from the original position.

(a)

## SOLUTION

The strain-transformation Eqs. 5 and 6 will be used to solve the problem. Since $\theta$ is *positive counterclockwise*, then for this problem $\theta = -30°$. Thus,

$$\epsilon_{x'} = \frac{\epsilon_x + \epsilon_y}{2} + \frac{\epsilon_x - \epsilon_y}{2}\cos 2\theta + \frac{\gamma_{xy}}{2}\sin 2\theta$$

$$= \left[\frac{500 + (-300)}{2}\right](10^{-6}) + \left[\frac{500 - (-300)}{2}\right](10^{-6})\cos(2(-30°))$$

$$+ \left[\frac{200(10^{-6})}{2}\right]\sin(2(-30°))$$

$$\epsilon_{x'} = 213(10^{-6}) \qquad\qquad Ans.$$

$$\frac{\gamma_{x'y'}}{2} = -\left(\frac{\epsilon_x - \epsilon_y}{2}\right)\sin 2\theta + \frac{\gamma_{xy}}{2}\cos 2\theta$$

$$= -\left[\frac{500 - (-300)}{2}\right](10^{-6})\sin(2(-30°)) + \frac{200(10^{-6})}{2}\cos(2(-30°))$$

$$\gamma_{x'y'} = 793(10^{-6}) \qquad\qquad Ans.$$

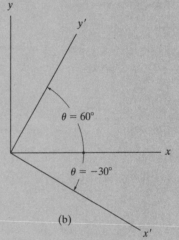

(b)

The strain in the $y'$ direction can be obtained from Eq. 7 with $\theta = -30°$. However, we can also obtain $\epsilon_{y'}$ using Eq. 5 with $\theta = 60°(\theta = -30° + 90°)$, Fig. 5b. We have with $\epsilon_{y'}$ replacing $\epsilon_{x'}$,

$$\epsilon_{y'} = \frac{\epsilon_x + \epsilon_y}{2} + \frac{\epsilon_x - \epsilon_y}{2}\cos 2\theta + \frac{\gamma_{xy}}{2}\sin 2\theta$$

$$= \left[\frac{500 + (-300)}{2}\right](10^{-6}) + \left[\frac{500 - (-300)}{2}\right](10^{-6})\cos(2(60°))$$

$$+ \frac{200(10^{-6})}{2}\sin(2(60°))$$

$$\epsilon_{y'} = -13.4(10^{-6}) \qquad\qquad Ans.$$

These results tend to distort the element as shown in Fig. 5c.

(c)

**Fig. 5**

## EXAMPLE 2

(a)

(b)

**Fig. 6**

A differential element of material at a point is subjected to a state of plane strain defined by $\epsilon_x = -350(10^{-6})$, $\epsilon_y = 200(10^{-6})$, $\gamma_{xy} = 80(10^{-6})$, which tends to distort the element as shown in Fig. 6a. Determine the principal strains at the point and the associated orientation of the element.

### SOLUTION

**Orientation of the Element.**   From Eq. 8 we have

$$\tan 2\theta_p = \frac{\gamma_{xy}}{\epsilon_x - \epsilon_y}$$

$$= \frac{80(10^{-6})}{(-350 - 200)(10^{-6})}$$

Thus, $2\theta_p = -8.28°$ and $-8.28° + 180° = 171.72°$, so that

$$\theta_p = -4.14° \text{ and } 85.9° \qquad Ans.$$

Each of these angles is measured *positive counterclockwise*, from the $x$ axis to the outward normals on each face of the element, Fig. 6b.

**Principal Strains.**   The principal strains are determined from Eq. 9. We have

$$\epsilon_{1,2} = \frac{\epsilon_x + \epsilon_y}{2} \pm \sqrt{\left(\frac{\epsilon_x - \epsilon_y}{2}\right)^2 + \left(\frac{\gamma_{xy}}{2}\right)^2}$$

$$= \frac{(-350 + 200)(10^{-6})}{2} \pm \left[\sqrt{\left(\frac{-350 - 200}{2}\right)^2 + \left(\frac{80}{2}\right)^2}\right](10^{-6})$$

$$= -75.0(10^{-6}) \pm 277.9(10^{-6})$$

$$\epsilon_1 = 203(10^{-6}) \qquad \epsilon_2 = -353(10^{-6}) \qquad Ans.$$

We can determine which of these two strains deforms the element in the $x'$ direction by applying Eq. 5 with $\theta = -4.14°$. Thus,

$$\epsilon_{x'} = \frac{\epsilon_x + \epsilon_y}{2} + \frac{\epsilon_x - \epsilon_y}{2}\cos 2\theta + \frac{\gamma_{xy}}{2}\sin 2\theta$$

$$= \left(\frac{-350 + 200}{2}\right)(10^{-6}) + \left(\frac{-350 - 200}{2}\right)(10^{-6})\cos 2(-4.14°)$$

$$+ \frac{80(10^{-6})}{2}\sin 2(-4.14°)$$

$$\epsilon_{x'} = -353(10^{-6})$$

Hence $\epsilon_{x'} = \epsilon_2$. When subjected to the principal strains, the element is distorted as shown in Fig. 6b.

## EXAMPLE | 3

A differential element of material at a point is subjected to a state of plane strain defined by $\epsilon_x = -350(10^{-6})$, $\epsilon_y = 200(10^{-6})$, $\gamma_{xy} = 80(10^{-6})$, which tends to distort the element as shown in Fig. 7a. Determine the maximum in-plane shear strain at the point and the associated orientation of the element.

(a)

### SOLUTION

**Orientation of the Element.** From Eq. 10 we have

$$\tan 2\theta_s = -\left(\frac{\epsilon_x - \epsilon_y}{\gamma_{xy}}\right) = -\frac{(-350 - 200)(10^{-6})}{80(10^{-6})}$$

Thus, $2\theta_s = 81.72°$ and $81.72° + 180° = 261.72°$, so that

$$\theta_s = 40.9° \text{ and } 131°$$

Note that this orientation is 45° from that shown in Fig. 6b in Example 2 as expected.

**Maximum In-Plane Shear Strain.** Applying Eq. 11 gives

$$\frac{\gamma_{\text{in-plane}}^{\max}}{2} = \sqrt{\left(\frac{\epsilon_x - \epsilon_y}{2}\right)^2 + \left(\frac{\gamma_{xy}}{2}\right)^2}$$

$$= \left[\sqrt{\left(\frac{-350 - 200}{2}\right)^2 + \left(\frac{80}{2}\right)^2}\right](10^{-6})$$

$$\gamma_{\text{in-plane}}^{\max} = 556(10^{-6}) \qquad\qquad Ans.$$

(b)

**Fig. 7**

Due to the square root, the proper sign of $\gamma_{\text{in-plane}}^{\max}$ can be obtained by applying Eq. 6 with $\theta_s = 40.9°$. We have

$$\frac{\gamma_{x'y'}}{2} = -\frac{\epsilon_x - \epsilon_y}{2} \sin 2\theta + \frac{\gamma_{xy}}{2}\cos 2\theta$$

$$= -\left(\frac{-350 - 200}{2}\right)(10^{-6})\sin 2(40.9°) + \frac{80(10^{-6})}{2}\cos 2(40.9°)$$

$$\gamma_{x'y'} = 556(10^{-6})$$

This result is positive and so $\gamma_{\text{in-plane}}^{\max}$ tends to distort the element so that the right angle between $dx'$ and $dy'$ is *decreased* (positive sign convention), Fig. 7b.

Also, there are associated average normal strains imposed on the element that are determined from Eq. 12:

$$\epsilon_{\text{avg}} = \frac{\epsilon_x + \epsilon_y}{2} = \frac{-350 + 200}{2}(10^{-6}) = -75(10^{-6})$$

These strains tend to cause the element to contract, Fig. 7b.

# *3  Mohr's Circle—Plane Strain

Since the equations of plane-strain transformation are mathematically similar to the equations of plane-stress transformation, we can also solve problems involving the transformation of strain using Mohr's circle.

Like the case for stress, the parameter $\theta$ in Eqs. 5 and 6 can be eliminated and the result rewritten in the form

$$(\epsilon_{x'} - \epsilon_{avg})^2 + \left(\frac{\gamma_{x'y'}}{2}\right)^2 = R^2 \tag{13}$$

where

$$\epsilon_{avg} = \frac{\epsilon_x + \epsilon_y}{2}$$

$$R = \sqrt{\left(\frac{\epsilon_x - \epsilon_y}{2}\right)^2 + \left(\frac{\gamma_{xy}}{2}\right)^2}$$

Equation 13 represents the equation of Mohr's circle for strain. It has a center on the $\epsilon$ axis at point $C(\epsilon_{avg}, 0)$ and a radius $R$.

$$R = \sqrt{\left(\frac{\epsilon_x - \epsilon_y}{2}\right)^2 + \left(\frac{\gamma_{xy}}{2}\right)^2}$$

**Fig. 8**

## Procedure for Analysis

The procedure for drawing Mohr's circle for strain follows the same one established for stress.

### Construction of the Circle.

- Establish a coordinate system such that the abscissa represents the normal strain $\epsilon$, with *positive to the right*, and the ordinate represents *half* the value of the shear strain, $\gamma/2$, with *positive downward*, Fig. 8.

- Using the positive sign convention for $\epsilon_x$, $\epsilon_y$, $\gamma_{xy}$, as shown in Fig. 2, determine the center of the circle $C$, which is located on the $\epsilon$ axis at a distance $\epsilon_{avg} = (\epsilon_x + \epsilon_y)/2$ from the origin, Fig. 8.

- Plot the reference point $A$ having coordinates $A(\epsilon_x, \gamma_{xy}/2)$. This point represents the case for which the $x'$ axis coincides with the $x$ axis. Hence $\theta = 0°$, Fig. 8.

- Connect point $A$ with the center $C$ of the circle and from the shaded triangle determine the radius $R$ of the circle, Fig. 8.

- Once $R$ has been determined, sketch the circle.

## Principal Strains.

- The principal strains $\epsilon_1$ and $\epsilon_2$ are determined from the circle as the coordinates of points $B$ and $D$, that is where $\gamma/2 = 0$, Fig. 9a.

- The orientation of the plane on which $\epsilon_1$ acts can be determined from the circle by calculating $2\theta_{p_1}$ using trigonometry. Here this angle happens to be counterclockwise *from* the radial reference line *CA to* line *CB*, Fig. 9a. Remember that the *rotation* of $\theta_{p_1}$ must be in this *same direction*, from the element's reference axis $x$ to the $x'$ axis, Fig. 9b.*

- When $\epsilon_1$ and $\epsilon_2$ are indicated as being positive as in Fig. 9a, the element in Fig. 9b will elongate in the $x'$ and $y'$ directions as shown by the dashed outline.

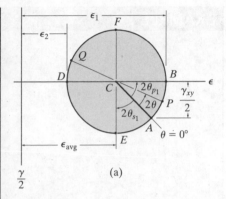

(a)

## Maximum In-Plane Shear Strain.

- The average normal strain and half the maximum in-plane shear strain are determined from the circle as the coordinates of point $E$ or $F$, Fig. 9a.

- The orientation of the plane on which $\gamma_{\text{in-plane}}^{\max}$ and $\epsilon_{\text{avg}}$ act can be determined from the circle by calculating $2\theta_{s_1}$ using trigonometry. Here this angle happens to be clockwise *from* the radial reference line *CA to* line *CE*, Fig. 9a. Remember that the *rotation* of $\theta_{s_1}$ must be in this *same direction*, from the element's reference axis $x$ to the $x'$ axis, Fig. 9c.*

(b)

## Strains on Arbitrary Plane.

- The normal and shear strain components $\epsilon_{x'}$ and $\gamma_{x'y'}$ for a plane oriented at an angle $\theta$, Fig. 9d, can be obtained from the circle using trigonometry to determine the coordinates of point $P$, Fig. 9a.

- To locate $P$, the known angle $\theta$ of the $x'$ axis is measured on the circle as $2\theta$. This measurement is made *from* the radial reference line *CA to* the radial line *CP*. Remember that measurements for $2\theta$ on the circle must be in the same direction as $\theta$ for the $x'$ axis.*

- If the value of $\epsilon_{y'}$ is required, it can be determined by calculating the $\epsilon$ coordinate of point $Q$ in Fig. 9a. The line $CQ$ lies $180°$ away from $CP$ and thus represents a $90°$ rotation of the $x'$ axis.

(c)

(d)

*If the $\gamma/2$ axis were constructed *positive upwards*, then the angle $2\theta$ on the circle would be measured in the *opposite direction* to the orientation $\theta$ of the plane.

**Fig. 9**

# EXAMPLE | 4

The state of plane strain at a point is represented by the components $\epsilon_x = 250(10^{-6})$, $\epsilon_y = -150(10^{-6})$, and $\gamma_{xy} = 120(10^{-6})$. Determine the principal strains and the orientation of the element.

## SOLUTION

**Construction of the Circle.** The $\epsilon$ and $\gamma/2$ axes are established in Fig. 10a. Remember that the *positive* $\gamma/2$ axis must be directed *downward* so that *counterclockwise* rotations of the element correspond to *counterclockwise* rotation around the circle, and vice versa. The center of the circle $C$ is located on the $\epsilon$ axis at

(a)

$$\epsilon_{avg} = \frac{250 + (-150)}{2}(10^{-6}) = 50(10^{-6})$$

Since $\gamma_{xy}/2 = 60(10^{-6})$, the reference point $A$ ($\theta = 0°$) has coordinates $A(250(10^{-6}), 60(10^{-6}))$. From the shaded triangle in Fig. 10a, the radius of the circle is $CA$; that is,

$$R = \left[\sqrt{(250 - 50)^2 + (60)^2}\right](10^{-6}) = 208.8(10^{-6})$$

**Principal Strains.** The $\epsilon$ coordinates of points $B$ and $D$ represent the principal strains. They are

$$\epsilon_1 = (50 + 208.8)(10^{-6}) = 259(10^{-6}) \qquad Ans.$$

$$\epsilon_2 = (50 - 208.8)(10^{-6}) = -159(10^{-6}) \qquad Ans.$$

The direction of the positive principal strain $\epsilon_1$ is defined by the *counterclockwise* angle $2\theta_{p_1}$, measured from the radial reference line $CA$ ($\theta = 0°$) to the line $CB$. We have

$$\tan 2\theta_{p_1} = \frac{60}{(250 - 50)}$$

$$\theta_{p_1} = 8.35° \qquad Ans.$$

(b)

**Fig. 10**

Hence, the side $dx'$ of the element is oriented *counterclockwise* 8.35° as shown in Fig. 10b. This also defines the direction of $\epsilon_1$. The deformation of the element is also shown in the figure.

## EXAMPLE 5

The state of plane strain at a point is represented by the components $\epsilon_x = 250(10^{-6})$, $\epsilon_y = -150(10^{-6})$, and $\gamma_{xy} = 120(10^{-6})$. Determine the maximum in-plane shear strains and the orientation of an element.

### SOLUTION

The circle has been established in the previous example and is shown in Fig. 11a.

**Maximum In-Plane Shear Strain.** Half the maximum in-plane shear strain and average normal strain are represented by the coordinates of point $E$ or $F$ on the circle. From the coordinates of point $E$,

$$\frac{(\gamma_{x'y'})^{\text{max}}_{\text{in-plane}}}{2} = 208.8(10^{-6})$$

$$(\gamma_{x'y'})^{\text{max}}_{\text{in-plane}} = 418(10^{-6}) \qquad \textit{Ans.}$$

$$\epsilon_{\text{avg}} = 50(10^{-6})$$

To orient the element, we can determine the clockwise angle $2\theta_{s_1}$ measured from $CA$ ($\theta = 0°$) to $CE$.

$$2\theta_{s_1} = 90° - 2(8.35°)$$

$$\theta_{s_1} = 36.7° \qquad \textit{Ans.}$$

This angle is shown in Fig. 11b. Since the shear strain defined from point $E$ on the circle has a positive value and the average normal strain is also positive, these strains deform the element into the dashed shape shown in the figure.

(b)

(a)

**Fig. 11**

# EXAMPLE | 6

The state of plane strain at a point is represented on an element having components $\epsilon_x = -300(10^{-6})$, $\epsilon_y = -100(10^{-6})$, and $\gamma_{xy} = 100(10^{-6})$. Determine the state of strain on an element oriented 20° clockwise from this reported position.

(a)

## SOLUTION

**Construction of the Circle.** The $\epsilon$ and $\gamma/2$ axes are established in Fig. 12a. The center of the circle is on the $\epsilon$ axis at

$$\epsilon_{avg} = \left(\frac{-300 - 100}{2}\right)(10^{-6}) = -200(10^{-6})$$

The reference point $A$ has coordinates $A(-300(10^{-6}), 50(10^{-6}))$. The radius $CA$ determined from the shaded triangle is therefore

$$R = \left[\sqrt{(300 - 200)^2 + (50)^2}\right](10^{-6}) = 111.8(10^{-6})$$

**Strains on Inclined Element.** Since the element is to be oriented 20° *clockwise*, we must establish a radial line $CP$, $2(20°) = 40°$ *clockwise*, measured from CA ($\theta = 0°$), Fig. 12a. The coordinates of point $P$ ($\epsilon_{x'}$, $\gamma_{x'y'}/2$) are obtained from the geometry of the circle. Note that

$$\phi = \tan^{-1}\left(\frac{50}{(300 - 200)}\right) = 26.57°, \qquad \psi = 40° - 26.57° = 13.43°$$

Thus,

$$\epsilon_{x'} = -(200 + 111.8 \cos 13.43°)(10^{-6})$$
$$= -309(10^{-6}) \qquad \qquad Ans.$$

$$\frac{\gamma_{x'y'}}{2} = -(111.8 \sin 13.43°)(10^{-6})$$

$$\gamma_{x'y'} = -52.0(10^{-6}) \qquad \qquad Ans.$$

The normal strain $\epsilon_{y'}$ can be determined from the $\epsilon$ coordinate of point $Q$ on the circle, Fig. 12a. Why?

$$\epsilon_{y'} = -(200 - 111.8 \cos 13.43°)(10^{-6}) = -91.3(10^{-6}) \qquad Ans.$$

As a result of these strains, the element deforms relative to the $x'$, $y'$ axes as shown in Fig. 12b.

(b)

**Fig. 12**

# PROBLEMS

**1.** Prove that the sum of the normal strains in perpendicular directions is constant.

**2.** The state of strain at the point has components of $\epsilon_x = 200(10^{-6})$, $\epsilon_y = -300(10^{-6})$, and $\gamma_{xy} = 400(10^{-6})$. Use the strain-transformation equations to determine the equivalent in-plane strains on an element oriented at an angle of $30°$ counterclockwise from the original position. Sketch the deformed element due to these strains within the $x$–$y$ plane.

**Prob. 2**

**3.** The state of strain at a point on a wrench has components $\epsilon_x = 120(10^{-6})$, $\epsilon_y = -180(10^{-6})$, $\gamma_{xy} = 150(10^{-6})$. Use the strain-transformation equations to determine (a) the in-plane principal strains and (b) the maximum in-plane shear strain and average normal strain. In each case specify the orientation of the element and show how the strains deform the element within $x$–$y$ plane.

**\*4.** The state of strain at the point on the gear tooth has components $\epsilon_x = 850(10^{-6})$, $\epsilon_y = 480(10^{-6})$, $\gamma_{xy} = 650(10^{-6})$. Use the strain-transformation equations to determine (a) the in-plane principal strains and (b) the maximum in-plane shear strain and average normal strain. In each case specify the orientation of the element and show how the strains deform the element within the $x$–$y$ plane.

**Prob. 4**

**5.** The state of strain at the point on the gear tooth has the components $\epsilon_x = 520(10^{-6})$, $\epsilon_y = -760(10^{-6})$, $\gamma_{xy} = -750(10^{-6})$. Use the strain-transformation equations to determine (a) the in-plane principal strains and (b) the maximum in-plane shear strain and average normal strain. In each case specify the orientation of the element and show how the strains deform the element within the $x$–$y$ plane.

**Prob. 5**

**6.** A differential elements on the bracket is subjected to plane strain that has the following components: $\epsilon_x = 150(10^{-6})$, $\epsilon_y = 200(10^{-6})$, $\gamma_{xy} = -700(10^{-6})$. Use the strain-transformation equations and determine the equivalent in plane strains on an element oriented at an angle of $\theta = 60°$ counterclockwise from the original position. Sketch the deformed element within the $x$–$y$ plane due to these strains.

**7.** Solve Prob. 6 for an element oriented $\theta = 30°$ clockwise.

**Probs. 6/7**

**\*8.** The state of strain at the point on the bracket has components $\epsilon_x = -200(10^{-6})$, $\epsilon_y = -650(10^{-6})$, $\gamma_{xy} = -175(10^{-6})$. Use the strain-transformation equations to determine the equivalent in-plane strains on an element oriented at an angle of $\theta = 20°$ counterclockwise from the original position. Sketch the deformed element due to these strains within the $x$–$y$ plane.

**10.** The state of strain at the point on the support has components of $\epsilon_x = 350(10^{-6})$, $\epsilon_y = 400(10^{-6})$, $\gamma_{xy} = -675(10^{-6})$. Use the strain-transformation equations to determine (a) the in-plane principal strains and (b) the maximum in-plane shear strain and average normal strain. In each case specify the orientation of the element and show how the strains deform the element within the $x$–$y$ plane.

**Prob. 8**

**Prob. 10**

**9.** The state of strain at the point has components of $\epsilon_x = 180(10^{-6})$, $\epsilon_y = -120(10^{-6})$, and $\gamma_{xy} = -100(10^{-6})$. Use the strain-transformation equations to determine (a) the in-plane principal strains and (b) the maximum in-plane shear strain and average normal strain. In each case specify the orientation of the element and show how the strains deform the element within the $x$–$y$ plane.

**11.** The state of strain on an element has components $\epsilon_x = -150(10^{-6})$, $\epsilon_y = 450(10^{-6})$, $\gamma_{xy} = 200(10^{-6})$. Determine the equivalent state of strain on an element at the same point oriented $30°$ counterclockwise with respect to the original element. Sketch the results on this element.

**Prob. 9**

**Prob. 11**

**\*12.** The state of strain on an element has components $\epsilon_x = -400(10^{-6})$, $\epsilon_y = 0$, $\gamma_{xy} = 150(10^{-6})$. Determine the equivalent state of strain on an element at the same point oriented 30° clockwise with respect to the original element. Sketch the results on this element.

**13.** The state of plane strain on an element is $\epsilon_x = -300(10^{-6})$, $\epsilon_y = 0$, and $\gamma_{xy} = 150(10^{-6})$. Determine the equivalent state of strain which represents (a) the principal strains, and (b) the maximum in-plane shear strain and the associated average normal strain. Specify the orientation of the corresponding elements for these states of strain with respect to the original element.

**Probs. 12/13**

**14.** The state of strain at the point on a boom of an hydraulic engine crane has components of $\epsilon_x = 250(10^{-6})$, $\epsilon_y = 300(10^{-6})$, and $\gamma_{xy} = -180(10^{-6})$. Use the strain-transformation equations to determine (a) the in-plane principal strains and (b) the maximum in-plane shear strain and average normal strain. In each case, specify the orientation of the element and show how the strains deform the element within the x–y plane.

**Prob. 14**

**■15.** Consider the general case of plane strain where $\epsilon_x$, $\epsilon_y$, and $\gamma_{xy}$ are known. Write a computer program that can be used to determine the normal and shear strain, $\epsilon_{x'}$ and $\gamma_{x'y'}$, on the plane of an element oriented $\theta$ from the horizontal. Also, include the principal strains and the element's orientation, and the maximum in-plane shear strain, the average normal strain, and the element's orientation.

**\*16.** The state of strain on an element has components $\epsilon_x = -300(10^{-6})$, $\epsilon_y = 100(10^{-6})$, $\gamma_{xy} = 150(10^{-6})$. Determine the equivalent state of strain, which represents (a) the principal strains, and (b) the maximum in-plane shear strain and the associated average normal strain. Specify the orientation of the corresponding elements for these states of strain with respect to the original element.

**Prob. 16**

**17.** Solve part (a) of Prob. 3 using Mohr's circle.

**18.** Solve part (b) of Prob. 3 using Mohr's circle.

**19.** Solve Prob. 4 using Mohr's circle.

**\*20.** Solve Prob. 5 using Mohr's circle.

**21.** Solve Prob. 7 using Mohr's circle.

# *4 Absolute Maximum Shear Strain

In the case of plane stress, the absolute maximum shear stress in an element of material will occur out of the plane when the principal stresses have the same sign, i.e., both are tensile or both are compressive. A similar result occurs for plane strain. For example, if the principal in-plane strains cause elongations, Fig. 13a, then the three Mohr's circles describing the normal and shear strain components for elements oriented about the $x'$, $y'$, and $z'$ axes are shown in Fig. 13b. By inspection, the largest circle has a radius $R = (\gamma_{x'z'})_{max}/2$. Hence,

x−y plane strain

(a)

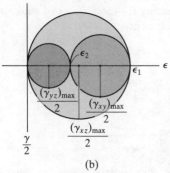

(b)

**Fig. 13**

$$\gamma_{max}^{abs} = (\gamma_{x'z'})_{max} = \epsilon_1$$
$\epsilon_1$ and $\epsilon_2$ have the same sign
(14)

This value gives the *absolute maximum shear strain* for the material. Note that it is *larger* than the maximum in-plane shear strain, which is $(\gamma_{x'y'})_{max} = \epsilon_1 - \epsilon_2$.

Now consider the case where one of the in-plane principal strains is of *opposite sign* to the other in-plane principal strain, so that $\epsilon_1$ causes elongation and $\epsilon_2$ causes contraction, Fig. 14a. Mohr's circles, which describe the strains on each element's orientation about the $x'$, $y'$, $z'$ axes, are shown in Fig. 14b. Here

$$\gamma_{max}^{abs} = (\gamma_{x'y'})_{max}^{in\text{-}plane} = \epsilon_1 - \epsilon_2$$
$\epsilon_1$ and $\epsilon_2$ have opposite signs
(15)

We may therefore summarize the above two cases as follows. If the in-plane principal strains both have the *same sign*, the *absolute maximum shear strain* will occur *out of plane* and has a value of $\gamma_{max}^{abs} = \epsilon_{max}$. However, if the in-plane principal strains are of *opposite signs*, then the absolute maximum shear strain *equals* the maximum in-plane shear strain.

x−y plane strain

(a)

(b)

**Fig. 14**

## Important Points

- The absolute maximum shear strain will be *larger* than the maximum in-plane shear strain whenever the in-plane principal strains have the *same sign*. When this occurs the absolute maximum shear strain will act out of the plane.

- If the in-plane principal strains are of opposite signs, then the absolute maximum shear strain will equal the maximum in-plane shear strain.

## EXAMPLE 7

The state of plane strain at a point is represented by the strain components $\epsilon_x = -400(10^{-6})$, $\epsilon_y = 200(10^{-6})$, $\gamma_{xy} = 150(10^{-6})$. Determine the maximum in-plane shear strain and the absolute maximum shear strain.

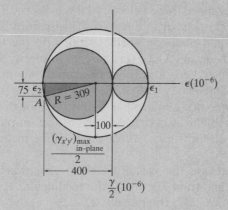

**Fig. 15**

## SOLUTION

**Maximum In-Plane Shear Strain.** We will solve this problem using Mohr's circle. From the strain components, the center of the circle is on the $\epsilon$ axis at

$$\epsilon_{\text{avg}} = \frac{-400 + 200}{2} (10^{-6}) = -100(10^{-6})$$

Since $\gamma_{xy}/2 = 75(10^{-6})$, the reference point $A$ has coordinates $(-400(10^{-6}), 75(10^{-6}))$. As shown in Fig. 15, the radius of the circle is therefore

$$R = \left[ \sqrt{(400 - 100)^2 + (75)^2} \right](10^{-6}) = 309(10^{-6})$$

Calculating the in-plane principal strains from the circle, we have

$$\epsilon_1 = (-100 + 309)(10^{-6}) = 209(10^{-6})$$
$$\epsilon_2 = (-100 - 309)(10^{-6}) = -409(10^{-6})$$

Also, the maximum in-plane shear strain is

$$\gamma_{\text{in-plane}}^{\text{max}} = \epsilon_1 - \epsilon_2 = [209 - (-409)](10^{-6}) = 618(10^{-6}) \qquad \textit{Ans.}$$

**Absolute Maximum Shear Strain.** From the above results, we have $\epsilon_1 = 209(10^{-6})$, $\epsilon_2 = -409(10^{-6})$. The three Mohr's circles, plotted for element orientations about each of the $x, y, z$ axes, are also shown in Fig. 15. It is seen that since the *principal in-plane strains have opposite signs*, the maximum in-plane shear strain is *also* the absolute maximum shear strain; i.e.,

$$\gamma_{\text{max}}^{\text{abs}} = 618(10^{-6}) \qquad \textit{Ans.}$$

# 5 Strain Rosettes

(a)

45° strain rosette

(b)

60° strain rosette

(c)

**Fig. 16**

When performing a tension test on a specimen, the normal strain in the material is measured using an ***electrical- resistance strain gauge***, which consists of a wire grid or piece of metal foil bonded to the specimen. For a general loading on a body, however, the strains at a point on its free surface are determined using a cluster of three electrical-resistance strain gauges, arranged in a specified pattern. This pattern is referred to as a ***strain rosette***, and once the normal strains on the three gauges are measured, the data can then be transformed to specify the state of strain at the point. Since these strains are measured *only* in the plane of the gauges, and since the body is stress-free on its surface, the gauges may be subjected to ***plane stress*** but *not* plane strain. Although the strain normal to the surface is not measured, realize that the out-of-plane displacement caused by this strain will *not* affect the in-plane measurements of the gauges.

In the general case, the axes of the three gauges are arranged at the angles $\theta_a$, $\theta_b$, $\theta_c$ shown in Fig. 16a. If the readings $\epsilon_a$, $\epsilon_b$, $\epsilon_c$ are taken, we can determine the strain components $\epsilon_x$, $\epsilon_y$, $\gamma_{xy}$ at the point by applying the strain-transformation equation, Eq. 2, for each gauge. We have

$$\begin{aligned}
\epsilon_a &= \epsilon_x \cos^2 \theta_a + \epsilon_y \sin^2 \theta_a + \gamma_{xy} \sin \theta_a \cos \theta_a \\
\epsilon_b &= \epsilon_x \cos^2 \theta_b + \epsilon_y \sin^2 \theta_b + \gamma_{xy} \sin \theta_b \cos \theta_b \\
\epsilon_c &= \epsilon_x \cos^2 \theta_c + \epsilon_y \sin^2 \theta_c + \gamma_{xy} \sin \theta_c \cos \theta_c
\end{aligned} \qquad (16)$$

The values of $\epsilon_x$, $\epsilon_y$, $\gamma_{xy}$ are determined by solving these three equations simultaneously.

Strain rosettes are often arranged in 45° or 60° patterns. In the case of the 45° or "rectangular" strain rosette shown in Fig. 16b, $\theta_a = 0°$, $\theta_b = 45°$, $\theta_c = 90°$, so that Eq. 16 gives

$$\begin{aligned}
\epsilon_x &= \epsilon_a \\
\epsilon_y &= \epsilon_c \\
\gamma_{xy} &= 2\epsilon_b - (\epsilon_a + \epsilon_c)
\end{aligned}$$

And for the 60° strain rosette in Fig. 16c, $\theta_a = 0°$, $\theta_b = 60°$, $\theta_c = 120°$. Here Eq. 16 gives

$$\begin{aligned}
\epsilon_x &= \epsilon_a \\
\epsilon_y &= \frac{1}{3} (2\epsilon_b + 2\epsilon_c - \epsilon_a) \\
\gamma_{xy} &= \frac{2}{\sqrt{3}} (\epsilon_b - \epsilon_c)
\end{aligned} \qquad (17)$$

Once $\epsilon_x$, $\epsilon_y$, $\gamma_{xy}$ are determined, the transformation equations of Sec. 2 or Mohr's circle can then be used to determine the principal in-plane strains and the maximum in-plane shear strain at the point.

Typical electrical resistance 45° strain rosette.

# EXAMPLE 8

The state of strain at point $A$ on the bracket in Fig. 17a is measured using the strain rosette shown in Fig. 17b. Due to the loadings, the readings from the gauges give $\epsilon_a = 60(10^{-6})$, $\epsilon_b = 135(10^{-6})$, and $\epsilon_c = 264(10^{-6})$. Determine the in-plane principal strains at the point and the directions in which they act.

(a)

## SOLUTION

We will use Eqs. 16 for the solution. Establishing an $x$ axis as shown in Fig. 17b and measuring the angles counterclockwise from the $+x$ axis to the centerlines of each gauge, we have $\theta_a = 0°$, $\theta_b = 60°$, and $\theta_c = 120°$. Substituting these results, along with the problem data, into the equations gives

$$60(10^{-6}) = \epsilon_x \cos^2 0° + \epsilon_y \sin^2 0° + \gamma_{xy} \sin 0° \cos 0°$$
$$= \epsilon_x \tag{1}$$
$$135(10^{-6}) = \epsilon_x \cos^2 60° + \epsilon_y \sin^2 60° + \gamma_{xy} \sin 60° \cos 60°$$
$$= 0.25\epsilon_x + 0.75\epsilon_y + 0.433\gamma_{xy} \tag{2}$$
$$264(10^{-6}) = \epsilon_x \cos^2 120° + \epsilon_y \sin^2 120° + \gamma_{xy} \sin 120° \cos 120°$$
$$= 0.25\epsilon_x + 0.75\epsilon_y - 0.433\gamma_{xy} \tag{3}$$

(b)

Using Eq. 1 and solving Eqs. 2 and 3 simultaneously, we get

$$\epsilon_x = 60(10^{-6}) \quad \epsilon_y = 246(10^{-6}) \quad \gamma_{xy} = -149(10^{-6})$$

These same results can also be obtained in a more direct manner from Eq. 17.

The in-plane principal strains can be determined using Mohr's circle. The reference point on the circle is at $A[60(10^{-6}), -74.5(10^{-6})]$ and the center of the circle, $C$, is on the $\epsilon$ axis at $\epsilon_{avg} = 153(10^{-6})$, Fig. 17c. From the shaded triangle, the radius is

$$R = \left[ \sqrt{(153 - 60)^2 + (74.5)^2} \right](10^{-6}) = 119.1(10^{-6})$$

(c)

The in-plane principal strains are thus

$$\epsilon_1 = 153(10^{-6}) + 119.1(10^{-6}) = 272(10^{-6}) \qquad Ans.$$
$$\epsilon_2 = 153(10^{-6}) - 119.1(10^{-6}) = 33.9(10^{-6}) \qquad Ans.$$
$$2\theta_{p_2} = \tan^{-1} \frac{74.5}{(153 - 60)} = 38.7°$$
$$\theta_{p_2} = 19.3° \qquad Ans.$$

**NOTE:** The deformed element is shown in the dashed position in Fig. 17d. Realize that, due to the Poisson effect, the element is *also* subjected to an out-of-plane strain, i.e., in the $z$ direction, although this value will not influence the calculated results.

(d)

**Fig. 17**

## PROBLEMS

**22.** The strain at point $A$ on the bracket has components $\epsilon_x = 300(10^{-6})$, $\epsilon_y = 550(10^{-6})$, $\gamma_{xy} = -650(10^{-6})$, $\epsilon_z = 0$. Determine (a) the principal strains at $A$ in the $x$–$y$ plane, (b) the maximum shear strain in the $x$–$y$ plane, and (c) the absolute maximum shear strain.

**Prob. 22**

**23.** The strain at point $A$ on a beam has components $\epsilon_x = 450(10^{-6})$, $\epsilon_y = 825(10^{-6})$, $\gamma_{xy} = 275(10^{-6})$, $\epsilon_z = 0$. Determine (a) the principal strains at $A$, (b) the maximum shear strain in the $x$–$y$ plane, and (c) the absolute maximum shear strain.

**Prob. 23**

**\*24.** The steel bar is subjected to the tensile load of 500 lb. If it is 0.5 in. thick determine the three principal strains. $E = 29(10^3)$ ksi, $\nu = 0.3$.

**Prob. 24**

**25.** The 45° strain rosette is mounted on a machine element. The following readings are obtained from each gauge: $\epsilon_a = 650(10^{-6})$, $\epsilon_b = -300(10^{-6})$, $\epsilon_c = 480(10^{-6})$. Determine (a) the in-plane principal strains and (b) the maximum in-plane shear strain and associated average normal strain. In each case show the deformed element due to these strains.

**Prob. 25**

**26.** The 60° strain rosette is attached to point $A$ on the surface of the support. Due to the loading the strain gauges give a reading of $\epsilon_a = 300(10^{-6})$, $\epsilon_b = -150(10^{-6})$, and $\epsilon_c = -450(10^{-6})$. Use Mohr's circle and determine (a) the in-plane principal strains and (b) the maximum in-plane shear strain and the associated average normal strain. Specify the orientation of each element that has these states of strain with respect to the $x$ axis.

**Prob. 26**

**27.** The strain rosette is attached at the point on the surface of the pump. Due to the loading, the strain gauges give a reading of $\epsilon_a = -250(10^{-6})$, $\epsilon_b = 300(10^{-6})$, and $\epsilon_c = -200(10^{-6})$. Determine (a) the in-plane principal strains, and (b) the maximum in-plane shear strain. Specify the orientation of each element that has these states of strain with respect to the $x$ axis.

**Prob. 27**

**\*28.** The 60° strain rosette is mounted on a beam. The following readings are obtained from each gauge: $\epsilon_a = 250(10^{-6})$, $\epsilon_b = -400(10^{-6})$, $\epsilon_c = 280(10^{-6})$. Determine (a) the in-plane principal strains and their orientation, and (b) the maximum in-plane shear strain and average normal strain. In each case show the deformed element due to these strains.

**Prob. 28**

**■29.** Consider the general orientation of three strain gauges at a point as shown. Write a computer program that can be used to determine the principal in-plane strains and the maximum in-plane shear strain at the point. Show an application of the program using the values $\theta_a = 40°$, $\epsilon_a = 160(10^{-6})$, $\theta_b = 125°$, $\epsilon_b = 100(10^{-6})$, $\theta_c = 220°$, $\epsilon_c = 80(10^{-6})$.

**Prob. 29**

# 6 Material-Property Relationships

In this section we will present some important relationships involving a material's properties that are used when the material is subjected to multiaxial stress and strain. To do so we will assume that the material is homogeneous and isotropic and behaves in a linear-elastic manner.

**Generalized Hooke's Law.**    If the material at a point is subjected to a state of triaxial stress, $\sigma_x, \sigma_y, \sigma_z$, Fig. 18a, associated normal strains $\epsilon_x$, $\epsilon_y, \epsilon_z$ will be developed in the material. The stresses can be related to these strains by using the principle of superposition, Poisson's ratio, $\epsilon_{\text{lat}} = -\nu\epsilon_{\text{long}}$, and Hooke's law, as it applies in the uniaxial direction, $\epsilon = \sigma/E$. For example, consider the normal strain of the element in the $x$ direction, caused by separate application of each normal stress. When $\sigma_x$ is applied, Fig. 18b, the element elongates in the $x$ direction and the strain $\epsilon_x'$ is

$$\epsilon_x' = \frac{\sigma_x}{E}$$

Application of $\sigma_y$ causes the element to contract with a strain $\epsilon_x''$, Fig. 18c. Here

$$\epsilon_x'' = -\nu\frac{\sigma_y}{E}$$

Likewise, application of $\sigma_z$, Fig. 18d, causes a contraction such that

$$\epsilon_x''' = -\nu\frac{\sigma_z}{E}$$

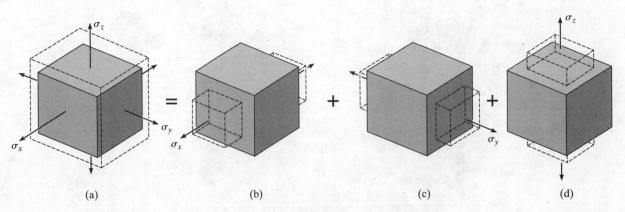

(a)                (b)                (c)                (d)

**Fig. 18**

When these three normal strains are superimposed, the normal strain $\epsilon_x$ is determined for the state of stress in Fig. 18a. Similar equations can be developed for the normal strains in the $y$ and $z$ directions. The final results can be written as

$$\epsilon_x = \frac{1}{E}[\sigma_x - \nu(\sigma_y + \sigma_z)]$$
$$\epsilon_y = \frac{1}{E}[\sigma_y - \nu(\sigma_x + \sigma_z)] \tag{18}$$
$$\epsilon_z = \frac{1}{E}[\sigma_z - \nu(\sigma_x + \sigma_y)]$$

These three equations express Hooke's law in a general form for a triaxial state of stress. For application tensile stresses are considered positive quantities, and compressive stresses are negative. If a resulting normal strain is *positive*, it indicates that the material *elongates*, whereas a *negative* normal strain indicates the material *contracts*.

If we now apply a shear stress $\tau_{xy}$ to the element, Fig. 19a, experimental observations indicate that the material will deform *only* due to a shear strain $\gamma_{xy}$; that is, $\tau_{xy}$ will not cause other strains in the material. Likewise, $\tau_{yz}$ and $\tau_{xz}$ will only cause shear strains $\gamma_{yz}$ and $\gamma_{xz}$, Figs. 19b and Fig. 19c, and so Hooke's law for shear stress and shear strain can be written as

$$\gamma_{xy} = \frac{1}{G}\tau_{xy} \qquad \gamma_{yz} = \frac{1}{G}\tau_{yz} \qquad \gamma_{xz} = \frac{1}{G}\tau_{xz} \tag{19}$$

(a)

(b)

(c)

**Fig. 19**

(a)

(b)

**Fig. 20**

(a)

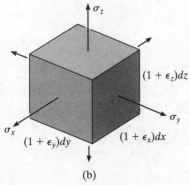

(b)

**Fig. 21**

## Relationship Involving *E*, *ν*, and *G*.

The modulus of elasticity *E* is related to the shear modulus *G* by

$$G = \frac{E}{2(1 + \nu)} \tag{20}$$

One way to derive this relationship is to consider an element of the material to be subjected to pure shear ($\sigma_x = \sigma_y = \sigma_z = 0$), Fig. 20a. The principal stresses are $\sigma_{max} = \tau_{xy}$ and $\sigma_{min} = -\tau_{xy}$. This element must be oriented $\theta_{p_1} = 45°$ counterclockwise from the *x* axis as shown in Fig. 20b. If the three principal stresses $\sigma_{max} = \tau_{xy}$, $\sigma_{int} = 0$, and $\sigma_{min} = -\tau_{xy}$ are substituted into the first of Eqs. 18, the principal strain $\epsilon_{max}$ can be related to the shear stress $\tau_{xy}$. The result is

$$\epsilon_{max} = \frac{\tau_{xy}}{E}(1 + \nu) \tag{21}$$

This strain, which deforms the element along the *x'* axis, can also be related to the shear strain $\gamma_{xy}$. To do this, first note that since $\sigma_x = \sigma_y = \sigma_z = 0$, then from the first and second Eqs. 18, $\epsilon_x = \epsilon_y = 0$. Substituting these results into the strain transformation Eq. 9, we get

$$\epsilon_1 = \epsilon_{max} = \frac{\gamma_{xy}}{2}$$

By Hooke's law, $\gamma_{xy} = \tau_{xy}/G$, so that $\epsilon_{max} = \tau_{xy}/2G$. Substituting into Eq. 21 and rearranging terms gives the final result, namely, Eq. 20.

## Dilatation and Bulk Modulus.

When an elastic material is subjected to normal stress, its volume will change. For example, consider a volume element which is subjected to the principal stresses $\sigma_x$, $\sigma_y$, $\sigma_z$. If the sides of the element are originally $dx$, $dy$, $dz$, Fig. 21a, then after application of the stress they become $(1 + \epsilon_x)\,dx$, $(1 + \epsilon_y)\,dy$, $(1 + \epsilon_z)\,dz$, Fig. 21b. The change in volume of the element is therefore

$$\delta V = (1 + \epsilon_x)(1 + \epsilon_y)(1 + \epsilon_z)\,dx\,dy\,dz - dx\,dy\,dz$$

Neglecting the products of the strains since the strains are very small, we have

$$\delta V = (\epsilon_x + \epsilon_y + \epsilon_z)\,dx\,dy\,dz$$

The change in volume per unit volume is called the "volumetric strain" or the **dilatation** *e*. It can be written as

$$e = \frac{\delta V}{dV} = \epsilon_x + \epsilon_y + \epsilon_z \tag{22}$$

By comparison, the shear strains will *not* change the volume of the element, rather they will only change its rectangular shape.

Also, if we use Hooke's law, as defined by Eq. 18, we can write the dilatation in terms of the applied stress. We have

$$e = \frac{1 - 2\nu}{E}(\sigma_x + \sigma_y + \sigma_z) \qquad (23)$$

When a volume element of material is subjected to the uniform pressure $p$ of a liquid, the pressure on the body is the same in all directions and is always normal to any surface on which it acts. Shear stresses are *not present*, since the shear resistance of a liquid is zero. This state of "hydrostatic" loading requires the normal stresses to be equal in any and all directions, and therefore an element of the body is subjected to principal stresses $\sigma_x = \sigma_y = \sigma_z = -p$, Fig. 22. Substituting into Eq. 23 and rearranging terms yields

$$\frac{p}{e} = -\frac{E}{3(1 - 2\nu)} \qquad (24)$$

Hydrostatic stress

**Fig. 22**

Since this ratio is *similar* to the ratio of linear elastic stress to strain, which defines $E$, i.e., $\sigma/\epsilon = E$, the term on the right is called the *volume modulus of elasticity* or the **bulk modulus**. It has the same units as stress and will be symbolized by the letter $k$; that is,

$$\boxed{k = \frac{E}{3(1 - 2\nu)}} \qquad (25)$$

Note that for most metals $\nu \approx \frac{1}{3}$ so $k \approx E$. If a material existed that did not change its volume then $\delta V = e = 0$, and $k$ would have to be infinite. From Eq. 25 the theoretical *maximum* value for Poisson's ratio is therefore $\nu = 0.5$. During yielding, no actual volume change of the material is observed, and so $\nu = 0.5$ is used when plastic yielding occurs.

## Important Points

- When a homogeneous isotropic material is subjected to a state of triaxial stress, the strain in each direction is influenced by the strains produced by *all* the stresses. This is the result of the Poisson effect, and results in the form of a generalized Hooke's law.

- Unlike normal stress, a shear stress applied to homogeneous isotropic material will only produce shear strain in the same plane.

- The material constants $E$, $G$, and $\nu$ are related mathematically.

- *Dilatation*, or *volumetric strain*, is caused only by normal strain, not shear strain.

- The *bulk modulus* is a measure of the stiffness of a volume of material. This material property provides an upper limit to Poisson's ratio of $\nu = 0.5$, which remains at this value while plastic yielding occurs.

EXAMPLE | 9

The bracket in Example 8, Fig. 23a, is made of steel for which $E_{st} = 200$ GPa, $\nu_{st} = 0.3$. Determine the principal stresses at point $A$.

(a)

**Fig. 23**

SOLUTION I
From Example 8 the principal strains have been determined as

$$\epsilon_1 = 272(10^{-6})$$

$$\epsilon_2 = 33.9(10^{-6})$$

Since point $A$ is on the *surface* of the bracket for which there is no loading, the stress on the surface is zero, and so point $A$ is subjected to plane stress. Applying Hooke's law with $\sigma_3 = 0$, we have

$$\epsilon_1 = \frac{\sigma_1}{E} - \frac{\nu}{E}\sigma_2; \quad 272(10^{-6}) = \frac{\sigma_1}{200(10^9)} - \frac{0.3}{200(10^9)}\sigma_2$$

$$54.4(10^6) = \sigma_1 - 0.3\sigma_2 \qquad (1)$$

$$\epsilon_2 = \frac{\sigma_2}{E} - \frac{\nu}{E}\sigma_1; \quad 33.9(10^{-6}) = \frac{\sigma_2}{200(10^9)} - \frac{0.3}{200(10^9)}\sigma_1$$

$$6.78(10^6) = \sigma_2 - 0.3\sigma_1 \qquad (2)$$

Solving Eqs. 1 and 2 simultaneously yields

$$\sigma_1 = 62.0 \text{ MPa} \qquad \qquad Ans.$$

$$\sigma_2 = 25.4 \text{ MPa} \qquad \qquad Ans.$$

(b)

**Fig. 23 (cont.)**

## SOLUTION II

It is also possible to solve the problem using the given state of strain,

$$\epsilon_x = 60(10^{-6}) \qquad \epsilon_y = 246(10^{-6}) \qquad \gamma_{xy} = -149(10^{-6})$$

as specified in Example 8. Applying Hooke's law in the $x$–$y$ plane, we have

$$\epsilon_x = \frac{\sigma_x}{E} - \frac{\nu}{E}\sigma_y; \quad 60(10^{-6}) = \frac{\sigma_x}{200(10^9)\,\text{Pa}} - \frac{0.3\sigma_y}{200(10^9)\,\text{Pa}}$$

$$\epsilon_y = \frac{\sigma_y}{E} - \frac{\nu}{E}\sigma_x; \quad 246(10^{-6}) = \frac{\sigma_y}{200(10^9)\,\text{Pa}} - \frac{0.3\sigma_x}{200(10^9)\,\text{Pa}}$$

$$\sigma_x = 29.4\ \text{MPa} \qquad \sigma_y = 58.0\ \text{MPa}$$

The shear stress is determined using Hooke's law for shear. First, however, we must calculate $G$.

$$G = \frac{E}{2(1 + \nu)} = \frac{200\ \text{GPa}}{2(1 + 0.3)} = 76.9\ \text{GPa}$$

Thus,

$$\tau_{xy} = G\gamma_{xy}; \qquad \tau_{xy} = 76.9(10^9)[-149(10^{-6})] = -11.46\ \text{MPa}$$

The Mohr's circle for this state of plane stress has a reference point $A$(29.4 MPa, $-11.46$ MPa) and center at $\sigma_{\text{avg}} = 43.7$ MPa, Fig. 23$b$. The radius is determined from the shaded triangle.

$$R = \sqrt{(43.7 - 29.4)^2 + (11.46)^2} = 18.3\ \text{MPa}$$

Therefore,

$$\sigma_1 = 43.7\ \text{MPa} + 18.3\ \text{MPa} = 62.0\ \text{MPa} \qquad \textit{Ans.}$$

$$\sigma_2 = 43.7\ \text{MPa} - 18.3\ \text{MPa} = 25.4\ \text{MPa} \qquad \textit{Ans.}$$

**NOTE:** Each of these solutions is valid provided the material is both linear elastic and isotropic, since then the principal planes of stress and strain coincide.

EXAMPLE | 10

The copper bar in Fig. 24 is subjected to a uniform loading along its edges as shown. If it has a length $a = 300$ mm, width $b = 50$ mm, and thickness $t = 20$ mm before the load is applied, determine its new length, width, and thickness after application of the load. Take $E_{cu} = 120$ GPa, $\nu_{cu} = 0.34$.

**Fig. 24**

SOLUTION

By inspection, the bar is subjected to a state of plane stress. From the loading we have

$$\sigma_x = 800 \text{ MPa} \qquad \sigma_y = -500 \text{ MPa} \qquad \tau_{xy} = 0 \qquad \sigma_z = 0$$

The associated normal strains are determined from the generalized Hooke's law, Eq. 18; that is,

$$\epsilon_x = \frac{\sigma_x}{E} - \frac{\nu}{E}(\sigma_y + \sigma_z)$$

$$= \frac{800 \text{ MPa}}{120(10^3) \text{ MPa}} - \frac{0.34}{120(10^3) \text{ MPa}}(-500 \text{ MPa} + 0) = 0.00808$$

$$\epsilon_y = \frac{\sigma_y}{E} - \frac{\nu}{E}(\sigma_x + \sigma_z)$$

$$= \frac{-500 \text{ MPa}}{120(10^3) \text{ MPa}} - \frac{0.34}{120(10^3) \text{ MPa}}(800 \text{ MPa} + 0) = -0.00643$$

$$\epsilon_z = \frac{\sigma_z}{E} - \frac{\nu}{E}(\sigma_x + \sigma_y)$$

$$= 0 - \frac{0.34}{120(10^3) \text{ MPa}}(800 \text{ MPa} - 500 \text{ MPa}) = -0.000850$$

The new bar length, width, and thickness are therefore

$$a' = 300 \text{ mm} + 0.00808(300 \text{ mm}) = 302.4 \text{ mm} \qquad \textit{Ans.}$$

$$b' = 50 \text{ mm} + (-0.00643)(50 \text{ mm}) = 49.68 \text{ mm} \qquad \textit{Ans.}$$

$$t' = 20 \text{ mm} + (-0.000850)(20 \text{ mm}) = 19.98 \text{ mm} \qquad \textit{Ans.}$$

## EXAMPLE | 11

If the rectangular block shown in Fig. 25 is subjected to a uniform pressure of $p = 20$ psi, determine the dilatation and the change in length of each side. Take $E = 600$ psi, $\nu = 0.45$.

**Fig. 25**

## SOLUTION

**Dilatation.** The dilatation can be determined using Eq. 23 with $\sigma_x = \sigma_y = \sigma_z = -20$ psi. We have

$$e = \frac{1 - 2\nu}{E}(\sigma_x + \sigma_y + \sigma_z)$$

$$= \frac{1 - 2(0.45)}{600 \text{ psi}}[3(-20 \text{ psi})]$$

$$= -0.01 \text{ in}^3/\text{in}^3 \qquad\qquad Ans.$$

**Change in Length.** The normal strain on each side can be determined from Hooke's law, Eq. 18; that is,

$$\epsilon = \frac{1}{E}[\sigma_x - \nu(\sigma_y + \sigma_z)]$$

$$= \frac{1}{600 \text{ psi}}[-20 \text{ psi} - (0.45)(-20 \text{ psi} - 20 \text{ psi})] = -0.00333 \text{ in./in.}$$

Thus, the change in length of each side is

$$\delta a = -0.00333(4 \text{ in.}) = -0.0133 \text{ in.} \qquad Ans.$$

$$\delta b = -0.00333(2 \text{ in.}) = -0.00667 \text{ in.} \qquad Ans.$$

$$\delta c = -0.00333(3 \text{ in.}) = -0.0100 \text{ in.} \qquad Ans.$$

The negative signs indicate that each dimension is decreased.

## PROBLEMS

**30.** For the case of plane stress, show that Hooke's law can be written as

$$\sigma_x = \frac{E}{(1 - \nu^2)}(\epsilon_x + \nu\epsilon_y), \quad \sigma_y = \frac{E}{(1 - \nu^2)}(\epsilon_y + \nu\epsilon_x)$$

**31.** Use Hooke's law, Eq. 18, to develop the strain-tranformation equations, Eqs. 5 and 6, from the stress-transformation equations

$$\sigma_{x'} = \frac{\sigma_x + \sigma_y}{2} + \frac{\sigma_x - \sigma_y}{2}\cos 2\theta + \tau_{xy}\sin 2\theta$$

$$\tau_{x'y'} = -\frac{\sigma_x - \sigma_y}{2}\sin 2\theta + \tau_{xy}\cos 2\theta$$

**\*32.** The principal plane stresses and associated strains in a plane at a point are $\sigma_1 = 36$ ksi, $\sigma_2 = 16$ ksi, $\epsilon_1 = 1.02(10^{-3})$, $\epsilon_2 = 0.180(10^{-3})$. Determine the modulus of elasticity and Poisson's ratio.

**33.** A rod has a radius of 10 mm. If it is subjected to an axial load of 15 N such that the axial strain in the rod is $\epsilon_x = 2.75(10^{-6})$, determine the modulus of elasticity $E$ and the change in its diameter. $\nu = 0.23$.

**34.** The polyvinyl chloride bar is subjected to an axial force of 900 lb. If it has the original dimensions shown determine the *change* in the angle $\theta$ after the load is applied. $E_{pvc} = 800(10^3)$ psi, $\nu_{pvc} = 0.20$.

**35.** The polyvinyl chloride bar is subjected to an axial force of 900 lb. If it has the original dimensions shown determine the value of Poisson's ratio if the angle $\theta$ decreases by $\Delta\theta = 0.01°$ after the load is applied. $E_{pvc} = 800(10^3)$ psi.

**Probs. 34/35**

**\*36.** The spherical pressure vessel has an inner diameter of 2 m and a thickness of 10 mm. A strain gauge having a length of 20 mm is attached to it, and it is observed to increase in length by 0.012 mm when the vessel is pressurized. Determine the pressure causing this deformation, and find the maximum in-plane shear stress, and the absolute maximum shear stress at a point on the outer surface of the vessel. The material is steel, for which $E_{st} = 200$ GPa and $\nu_{st} = 0.3$.

**Prob. 36**

**37.** Determine the bulk modulus for each of the following materials: (a) rubber, $E_r = 0.4$ ksi, $\nu_r = 0.48$, and (b) glass, $E_g = 8(10^3)$ ksi, $\nu_g = 0.24$.

**38.** The strain gauge is placed on the surface of a thin-walled steel boiler as shown. If it is 0.5 in. long, determine the pressure in the boiler when the gauge elongates $0.2(10^{-3})$ in. The boiler has a thickness of 0.5 in. and inner diameter of 60 in. Also, determine the maximum $x, y$ in-plane shear strain in the material. $E_{st} = 29(10^3)$ ksi, $\nu_{st} = 0.3$.

**Prob. 38**

**39.** The strain in the $x$ direction at point $A$ on the A-36 structural-steel beam is measured and found to be $\epsilon_x = 100(10^{-6})$. Determine the applied load $P$. What is the shear strain $\gamma_{xy}$ at point $A$?

**\*40.** The strain in the $x$ direction at point $A$ on the A-36 structural-steel beam is measured and found to be $\epsilon_x = 200(10^{-6})$. Determine the applied load $P$. What is the shear strain $\gamma_{xy}$ at point $A$?

**41.** If a load of $P = 3$ kip is applied to the A-36 structural-steel beam, determine the strain $\epsilon_x$ and $\gamma_{xy}$ at point $A$.

**43.** A strain gauge $a$ is attached in the longitudinal direction ($x$ axis) on the surface of the gas tank. When the tank is pressurized, the strain gauge gives a reading of $\epsilon_a = 100(10^{-6})$. Determine the pressure $p$ in the tank. The tank has an inner diameter of 1.5 m and wall thickness of 25 mm. It is made of steel having a modulus of elasticity $E = 200$ GPa and Poisson's ratio $\nu = \frac{1}{3}$.

**\*44.** Strain gauge $b$ is attached to the surface of the gas tank at an angle of $45°$ with $x$ axis as shown. When the tank is pressurized, the strain gauge gives a reading of $\epsilon_b = 250(10^{-6})$. Determine the pressure in the tank. The tank has an inner diameter of 1.5 m and wall thickness of 25 mm. It is made of steel having a modulus of elasticity $E = 200$ GPa and Poisson's ratio $\nu = \frac{1}{3}$.

**Probs. 39/40/41**

**Probs. 43/44**

**42.** The principal stresses at a point are shown in the figure. If the material is aluminum for which $E_{al} = 10(10^3)$ ksi and $\nu_{al} = 0.33$, determine the principal strains.

**45.** A material is subjected to principal stresses $\sigma_x$ and $\sigma_y$. Determine the orientation $\theta$ of a strain gauge placed at the point so that its reading of normal strain responds only to $\sigma_y$ and not $\sigma_x$. The material constants are $E$ and $\nu$.

**Prob. 42**

**Prob. 45**

**46.** The principal strains in a plane, measured experimentally at a point on the aluminum fuselage of a jet aircraft, are $\epsilon_1 = 630(10^{-6})$ and $\epsilon_2 = 350(10^{-6})$. If this is a case of plane stress, determine the associated principal stresses at the point in the same plane. $E_{al} = 10(10^3)$ ksi and $\nu_{al} = 0.33$.

**47.** The principal stresses at a point are shown in the figure. If the material is aluminum for which $E_{al} = 10(10^3)$ ksi and $\nu_{al} = 0.33$, determine the principal strains.

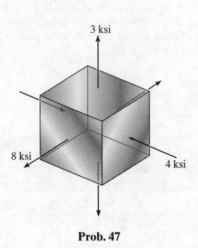

Prob. 47

**49.** Initially, gaps between the A-36 steel plate and the rigid constraint are as shown. Determine the normal stresses $\sigma_x$ and $\sigma_y$ developed in the plate if the temperature is increased by $\Delta T = 100°F$. To solve, add the thermal strain $\alpha \Delta T$ to the equations for Hooke's law.

Prob. 49

**\*48.** The 6061-T6 aluminum alloy plate fits snugly into the rigid constraint. Determine the normal stresses $\sigma_x$ and $\sigma_y$ developed in the plate if the temperature is increased by $\Delta T = 50°C$. To solve, add the thermal strain $\alpha \Delta T$ to the equations for Hooke's law.

**50.** The steel shaft has a radius of 15 mm. Determine the torque $T$ in the shaft if the two strain gauges, attached to the surface of the shaft, report strains of $\epsilon_{x'} = -80(10^{-6})$ and $\epsilon_{y'} = 80(10^{-6})$. Also, compute the strains acting in the $x$ and $y$ directions. $E_{st} = 200$ GPa, $\nu_{st} = 0.3$.

**51.** The shaft has a radius of 15 mm and is made of L2 tool steel. Determine the strains in the $x'$ and $y'$ direction if a torque $T = 2$ kN · m is applied to the shaft.

Prob. 48

Probs. 50/51

**\*52.** The metal block is fitted between the fixed supports. If the glued joint can resist a maximum shear stress of $\tau_{allow} = 2$ ksi, determine the temperature rise that will cause the joint to fail. Take $E = 10(10^3)$ ksi, $\nu = 0.2$, and $\alpha = 6.0(10^{-6})/°F$. *Hint:* Use Eq. 18 with an additional strain term of $\alpha \Delta T$ (Eq. 4).

**Prob. 52**

**53.** Air is pumped into the steel thin-walled pressure vessel at $C$. If the ends of the vessel are closed using two pistons connected by a rod $AB$, determine the increase in the diameter of the pressure vessel when the internal gauge pressure is 5 MPa. Also, what is the tensile stress in rod $AB$ if it has a diameter of 100 mm? The inner radius of the vessel is 400 mm, and its thickness is 10 mm. $E_{st} = 200$ GPa and $\nu_{st} = 0.3$.

**54.** Determine the increase in the diameter of the pressure vessel in Prob. 53 if the pistons are replaced by walls connected to the ends of the vessel.

**Probs. 53/54**

**55.** A thin-walled spherical pressure vessel having an inner radius $r$ and thickness $t$ is subjected to an internal pressure $p$. Show that the increase in the volume within the vessel is $\Delta V = (2p\pi r^4/Et)(1 - \nu)$. Use a small-strain analysis.

**\*56.** The thin-walled cylindrical pressure vessel of inner radius $r$ and thickness $t$ is subjected to an internal pressure $p$. If the material constants are $E$ and $\nu$, determine the strains in the circumferential and longitudinal directions. Using these results, compute the increase in both the diameter and the length of a steel pressure vessel filled with air and having an internal gauge pressure of 15 MPa. The vessel is 3 m long, and has an inner radius of 0.5 m and a thickness of 10 mm. $E_{st} = 200$ GPa, $\nu_{st} = 0.3$.

**57.** Estimate the increase in volume of the tank in Prob. 56.

**Prob. 57**

**58.** A soft material is placed within the confines of a rigid cylinder which rests on a rigid support. Assuming that $\epsilon_x = 0$ and $\epsilon_y = 0$, determine the factor by which the modulus of elasticity will be increased when a load is applied if $\nu = 0.3$ for the material.

**Prob. 58**

# *7 Theories of Failure

When an engineer is faced with the problem of design using a specific material, it becomes important to place an upper *limit* on the state of stress that defines the material's failure. If the material is *ductile*, failure is usually specified by the initiation of *yielding*, whereas if the material is *brittle*, it is specified by *fracture*. These modes of failure are readily defined if the member is subjected to a uniaxial state of stress, as in the case of simple tension; however, if the member is subjected to biaxial or triaxial stress, the criterion for failure becomes more difficult to establish.

In this section we will discuss four theories that are often used in engineering practice to predict the failure of a material subjected to a *multiaxial* state of stress. No single theory of failure, however, can be applied to a specific material at *all times*, because a material may behave in either a ductile or brittle manner depending on the temperature, rate of loading, chemical environment, or the way the material is shaped or formed. When using a particular theory of failure, it is first necessary to calculate the normal and shear stress at points where they are the largest in the member. Once this state of stress is established, the *principal stresses* at these critical points are then determined, since each of the following theories is based on knowing the principal stress.

## Ductile Materials

**Maximum-Shear-Stress Theory.** The most common type of *yielding of a ductile material* such as steel is caused by *slipping*, which occurs along the contact planes of randomly ordered crystals that make up the material. If we make a specimen into a highly polished thin strip and subject it to a simple tension test, we can actually see how this slipping causes the material to *yield*, Fig. 26. The edges of the planes of slipping as they appear on the surface of the strip are referred to as *Lüder's lines*. These lines clearly indicate the slip planes in the strip, which occur at approximately 45° with the axis of the strip.

The slipping that occurs is caused by shear stress. To show this, consider an element of the material taken from a tension specimen, when it is subjected to the yield stress $\sigma_Y$, Fig. 27a. The maximum shear stress can be determined by drawing Mohr's circle for the element, Fig. 27b. The results indicate that

$$\tau_{max} = \frac{\sigma_Y}{2} \tag{26}$$

45°

Lüder's lines on
mild steel strip

**Fig. 26**

Furthermore, this shear stress acts on planes that are 45° from the planes of principal stress, Fig. 27c, and these planes *coincide* with the direction of the Lüder lines shown on the specimen, indicating that indeed failure occurs by shear.

Using this idea, that ductile materials fail by shear, in 1868 Henri Tresca proposed the ***maximum-shear-stress theory*** or ***Tresca yield criterion***. This theory can be used to predict the failure stress of a ductile material subjected to any type of loading. The theory states that yielding of the material begins when the absolute maximum shear stress in the material reaches the shear stress that causes the same material to yield when it is subjected *only* to axial tension. Therefore, to avoid failure, it is required that $\tau_{\max}^{abs}$ in the material must be less than or equal to $\sigma_Y/2$, where $\sigma_Y$ is determined from a simple tension test.

For application we will express the absolute maximum shear stress in terms of the *principal stresses*. The procedure for doing this can be discussed with reference to a condition of plane stress, that is, where the out-of-plane principal stress is zero. If the two in-plane principal stresses have the *same sign*, i.e., they are both tensile or both compressive, then failure will occur out of the plane and,

$$\tau_{\max}^{abs} = \frac{\sigma_1}{2}$$

If instead the in-plane principal stresses are of *opposite signs*, the failure occurs in the plane and,

$$\tau_{\max}^{abs} = \frac{\sigma_1 - \sigma_2}{2}$$

Using these equations and Eq. 26, the maximum-shear-stress theory for *plane stress* can be expressed for any two in-plane principal stresses $\sigma_1$ and $\sigma_2$ by the following criteria:

$$\left.\begin{array}{r} |\sigma_1| = \sigma_Y \\ |\sigma_2| = \sigma_Y \end{array}\right\} \quad \sigma_1, \sigma_2 \text{ have same signs}$$

$$|\sigma_1 - \sigma_2| = \sigma_Y\} \quad \sigma_1, \sigma_2 \text{ have opposite signs}$$

(10–27)

A graph of these equations is given in Fig. 28. Clearly, if any point of the material is subjected to plane stress, and its in-plane principal stresses are represented by a coordinate $(\sigma_1, \sigma_2)$ plotted *on the boundary* or *outside* the shaded hexagonal area shown in this figure, the material will yield at the point and failure is said to occur.

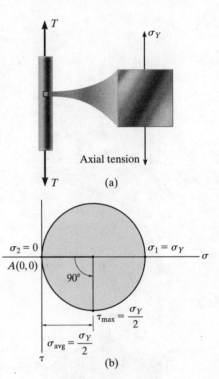

Axial tension

(a)

(b)

(c)

Fig. 27

Maximum-shear-stress theory

Fig. 28

## Maximum-Distortion-Energy Theory.

An external loading will deform a material, causing it to store energy *internally* throughout its volume. The energy per unit volume of material is called the **strain-energy density**, and if the material is subjected to a uniaxial stress the strain-energy density becomes

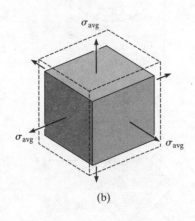

$$u = \frac{1}{2}\sigma\epsilon \tag{28}$$

If the material is subjected to triaxial stress, Fig. 29a, then each principal stress contributes a portion of the total strain-energy density, so that

$$u = \frac{1}{2}\sigma_1\epsilon_1 + \frac{1}{2}\sigma_2\epsilon_2 + \frac{1}{2}\sigma_3\epsilon_3$$

Furthermore, if the material behaves in a linear-elastic manner, then Hooke's law applies. Therefore, substituting Eq. 18 into the above equation and simplifying, we get

$$u = \frac{1}{2E}\left[\sigma_1^2 + \sigma_2^2 + \sigma_3^2 - 2\nu(\sigma_1\sigma_2 + \sigma_1\sigma_3 + \sigma_3\sigma_2)\right] \tag{29}$$

This strain-energy density can be considered as the sum of two parts, one part representing the energy needed to cause a *volume change* of the element with no change in shape, and the other part representing the energy needed to *distort* the element. Specifically, the energy stored in the element as a result of its volume being changed is caused by application of the average principal stress, $\sigma_{\text{avg}} = (\sigma_1 + \sigma_2 + \sigma_3)/3$, since this stress causes equal principal strains in the material, Fig. 29b. The remaining portion of the stress, $(\sigma_1 - \sigma_{\text{avg}})$, $(\sigma_2 - \sigma_{\text{avg}})$, $(\sigma_3 - \sigma_{\text{avg}})$, causes the energy of distortion, Fig. 29c.

Experimental evidence has shown that materials do not yield when subjected to a uniform (hydrostatic) stress, such as $\sigma_{\text{avg}}$ discussed above. As a result, in 1904, M. Huber proposed that yielding in a ductile material occurs when the *distortion energy* per unit volume of the material equals or exceeds the distortion energy per unit volume of the same material when it is subjected to yielding in a simple tension test. This theory is called the **maximum-distortion-energy theory**, and since it was later redefined independently by R. von Mises and H. Hencky, it sometimes also bears their names.

To obtain the distortion energy per unit volume, we will substitute the stresses $(\sigma_1 - \sigma_{\text{avg}})$, $(\sigma_2 - \sigma_{\text{avg}})$, and $(\sigma_3 - \sigma_{\text{avg}})$ for $\sigma_1$, $\sigma_2$, and $\sigma_3$, respectively, into Eq. 29, realizing that $\sigma_{\text{avg}} = (\sigma_1 + \sigma_2 + \sigma_3)/3$. Expanding and simplifying, we obtain

$$u_d = \frac{1 + \nu}{6E}\left[(\sigma_1 - \sigma_2)^2 + (\sigma_2 - \sigma_3)^2 + (\sigma_3 - \sigma_1)^2\right]$$

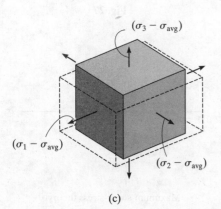

**Fig. 29**

In the case of *plane stress*, $\sigma_3 = 0$, and this equation reduces to

$$u_d = \frac{1 + \nu}{3E}\left(\sigma_1^2 - \sigma_1\sigma_2 + \sigma_2^2\right)$$

For a *uniaxial* tension test, $\sigma_1 = \sigma_Y, \sigma_2 = \sigma_3 = 0$, and so

$$(u_d)_Y = \frac{1 + \nu}{3E}\sigma_Y^2$$

Since the maximum-distortion-energy theory requires $u_d = (u_d)_Y$, then for the case of plane or biaxial stress, we have

$$\boxed{\sigma_1^2 - \sigma_1\sigma_2 + \sigma_2^2 = \sigma_Y^2} \tag{30}$$

This is the equation of an ellipse, Fig. 30. Thus, if a point in the material is stressed such that $(\sigma_1, \sigma_2)$ is plotted on the boundary or outside the shaded area, the material is said to fail.

A comparison of the above two failure criteria is shown in Fig. 31. Note that both theories give the same results when the principal stresses are equal, i.e., $\sigma_1 = \sigma_2 = \sigma_Y$, or when one of the principal stresses is zero and the other has a magnitude of $\sigma_Y$. If the material is subjected to pure shear, $\tau$, then the theories have the largest discrepancy in predicting failure. The stress coordinates of these points on the curves can be determined by considering the element shown in Fig. 32a. From the associated Mohr's circle for this state of stress, Fig. 32b, we obtain principal stresses $\sigma_1 = \tau$ and $\sigma_2 = -\tau$. Thus, with $\sigma_1 = -\sigma_2$, then from Eq. 27, the maximum-shear-stress theory gives $(\sigma_Y/2, -\sigma_Y/2)$, and from Eq. 30, the maximum-distortion-energy theory gives $(\sigma_Y/\sqrt{3}, -\sigma_Y/\sqrt{3})$, Fig. 31.

Actual torsion tests, used to develop a condition of pure shear in a ductile specimen, have shown that the maximum-distortion-energy theory gives more accurate results for pure-shear failure than the maximum-shear-stress theory. In fact, since $(\sigma_Y/\sqrt{3})/(\sigma_Y/2) = 1.15$, the shear stress for yielding of the material, as given by the maximum-distortion-energy theory, is 15% more accurate than that given by the maximum-shear-stress theory.

Maximum-distortion-energy theory

**Fig. 30**

**Fig. 31**

(a)

(b)

**Fig. 32**

Failure of a brittle material
in tension

(a)

45°

45°

Failure of a brittle material
in torsion

(b)

**Fig. 33**

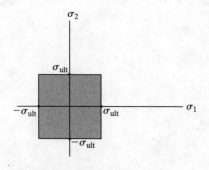

Maximum-normal-stress theory

**Fig. 34**

## Brittle Materials

### Maximum-Normal-Stress Theory.

It was previously stated that brittle materials, such as gray cast iron, tend to fail suddenly by *fracture* with no apparent yielding. In a *tension test*, the fracture occurs when the normal stress reaches the ultimate stress $\sigma_{ult}$, Fig. 33a. Also, brittle fracture occurs in a torsion test due to tension since the plane of fracture for an element is at 45° to the shear direction, Fig. 33b. The fracture surface is therefore helical as shown.* Experiments have further shown that during torsion the material's strength is somewhat *unaffected* by the presence of the associated principal compressive stress being at right angles to the principal tensile stress. Consequently, the tensile stress needed to fracture a specimen during a torsion test is approximately the same as that needed to fracture a specimen in simple tension. Because of this, the ***maximum-normal-stress theory*** states that a brittle material will fail when the maximum tensile stress, $\sigma_1$, in the material reaches a value that is equal to the ultimate normal stress the material can sustain when it is subjected to simple tension.

If the material is subjected to *plane stress*, we require that

$$|\sigma_1| = \sigma_{ult}$$
$$|\sigma_2| = \sigma_{ult}$$

(31)

These equations are shown graphically in Fig. 34. Therefore, if the stress coordinates $(\sigma_1, \sigma_2)$ at a point in the material fall on the boundary or outside the shaded area, the material is said to fracture. This theory is generally credited to W. Rankine, who proposed it in the mid-1800s. Experimentally it has been found to be in close agreement with the behavior of brittle materials that have stress–strain diagrams that are *similar* in both tension and compression.

### Mohr's Failure Criterion.

In some brittle materials tension and compression properties are *different*. When this occurs a criterion based on the use of Mohr's circle may be used to predict failure. This method was developed by Otto Mohr and is sometimes referred to as **Mohr's failure criterion**. To apply it, one first performs *three tests* on the material. A uniaxial tensile test and uniaxial compressive test are used to determine the ultimate tensile and compressive stresses $(\sigma_{ult})_t$ and $(\sigma_{ult})_c$, respectively. Also a torsion test is performed to determine the material's ultimate shear stress $\tau_{ult}$. Mohr's circle for each of these stress conditions is then plotted as shown in Fig. 35. These three circles are contained

*A stick of blackboard chalk fails in this way when its ends are twisted with the fingers.

in a "failure envelope" indicated by the extrapolated colored curve that is drawn tangent to all three circles. If a plane-stress condition at a point is represented by a circle that has a point of tangency with the envelope, or if it extends beyond the envelope's boundary, then failure is said to occur.

We may also represent this criterion on a graph of principal stresses $\sigma_1$ and $\sigma_2$. This is shown in Fig. 36. Here failure occurs when the absolute value of either one of the principal stresses reaches a value equal to or greater than $(\sigma_{ult})_t$ or $(\sigma_{ult})_c$ or in general, if the state of stress at a point defined by the stress coordinates $(\sigma_1, \sigma_2)$ is plotted on the boundary or outside the shaded area.

Either the maximum-normal-stress theory or Mohr's failure criterion can be used in practice to predict the failure of a brittle material. However, it should be realized that their usefulness is quite limited. A tensile fracture occurs very suddenly, and its initiation generally depends on stress concentrations developed at microscopic imperfections of the material such as inclusions or voids, surface indentations, and small cracks. Since each of these irregularities varies from specimen to specimen, it becomes difficult to specify fracture on the basis of a single test.

**Fig. 35**

Mohr's failure criterion

**Fig. 36**

## Important Points

- If a material is *ductile*, failure is specified by the initiation of *yielding*, whereas if it is *brittle*, it is specified by *fracture*.

- *Ductile failure* can be defined when *slipping* occurs between the crystals that compose the material. This slipping is due to *shear stress* and the *maximum-shear-stress theory* is based on this idea.

- *Strain energy* is stored in a material when it is subjected to normal stress. The *maximum-distortion-energy theory* depends on the *strain energy* that *distorts* the material, and not the part that increases its volume.

- The fracture of a *brittle material* is caused only by the *maximum tensile stress* in the material, and not the compressive stress. This is the basis of the *maximum-normal-stress theory*, and it is applicable if the stress-strain diagram is *similar* in tension and compression.

- If a *brittle material* has a stress-strain diagram that is *different* in tension and compression, then *Mohr's failure criterion* may be used to predict failure.

- Due to material imperfections, *tensile fracture* of a brittle material is *difficult to predict*, and so theories of failure for brittle materials should be used with caution.

# EXAMPLE | 12

The solid cast-iron shaft shown in Fig. 37$a$ is subjected to a torque of $T = 400$ lb·ft. Determine its smallest radius so that it does not fail according to the maximum-normal-stress theory. A specimen of cast iron, tested in tension, has an ultimate stress of $(\sigma_{ult})_t = 20$ ksi.

**Fig. 37**

## SOLUTION

The maximum or critical stress occurs at a point located on the surface of the shaft. Assuming the shaft to have a radius $r$, the shear stress is

$$\tau_{max} = \frac{Tc}{J} = \frac{(400 \text{ lb} \cdot \text{ft})(12 \text{ in./ft})r}{(\pi/2)r^4} = \frac{3055.8 \text{ lb} \cdot \text{in.}}{r^3}$$

Mohr's circle for this state of stress (pure shear) is shown in Fig. 37$b$. Since $R = \tau_{max}$, then

$$\sigma_1 = -\sigma_2 = \tau_{max} = \frac{3055.8 \text{ lb} \cdot \text{in.}}{r^3}$$

The maximum-normal-stress theory, Eq. 31, requires

$$|\sigma_1| \leq \sigma_{ult}$$

$$\frac{3055.8 \text{ lb} \cdot \text{in.}}{r^3} \leq 20\,000 \text{ lb/in}^2$$

Thus, the smallest radius of the shaft is determined from

$$\frac{3055.8 \text{ lb} \cdot \text{in.}}{r^3} = 20\,000 \text{ lb/in}^2$$

$$r = 0.535 \text{ in.} \qquad \qquad \textit{Ans.}$$

## EXAMPLE 13

The solid shaft shown in Fig. 38a has a radius of 0.5 in. and is made of steel having a yield stress of $\sigma_Y = 36$ ksi. Determine if the loadings cause the shaft to fail according to the maximum-shear-stress theory and the maximum-distortion-energy theory.

### SOLUTION

The state of stress in the shaft is caused by both the axial force and the torque. Since maximum shear stress caused by the torque occurs in the material at the outer surface, we have

$$\sigma_x = \frac{P}{A} = \frac{-15 \text{ kip}}{\pi(0.5 \text{ in.})^2} = -19.10 \text{ ksi}$$

$$\tau_{xy} = \frac{Tc}{J} = \frac{3.25 \text{ kip} \cdot \text{in. } (0.5 \text{ in.})}{\frac{\pi}{2}(0.5 \text{ in.})^4} = 16.55 \text{ ksi}$$

The stress components are shown acting on an element of material at point $A$ in Fig. 38b. Rather than using Mohr's circle, the principal stresses can also be obtained using the stress-transformation.

$$\sigma_{1,2} = \frac{\sigma_x + \sigma_y}{2} \pm \sqrt{\left(\frac{\sigma_x - \sigma_y}{2}\right)^2 + \tau_{xy}^2}$$

$$= \frac{-19.10 + 0}{2} \pm \sqrt{\left(\frac{-19.10 - 0}{2}\right)^2 + (16.55)^2}$$

$$= -9.55 \pm 19.11$$

$$\sigma_1 = 9.56 \text{ ksi}$$

$$\sigma_2 = -28.66 \text{ ksi}$$

(a)

(b)

**Fig. 38**

**Maximum-Shear-Stress Theory.** Since the principal stresses have opposite signs, then the absolute maximum shear stress will occur in the plane, and therefore, applying the second of Eqs. 27, we have

$$|\sigma_1 - \sigma_2| \le \sigma_Y$$

$$|9.56 - (-28.66)| \overset{?}{\le} 36$$

$$38.2 > 36$$

Thus, shear failure of the material will occur according to this theory.

**Maximum-Distortion-Energy Theory.** Applying Eq. 30, we have

$$(\sigma_1^2 - \sigma_1\sigma_2 + \sigma_2^2) \le \sigma_Y^2$$

$$\left[(9.56)^2 - (9.56)(-28.66) + (-28.66)^2\right] \overset{?}{\le} (36)^2$$

$$1187 \le 1296$$

Using this theory, failure will not occur.

# PROBLEMS

**59.** A material is subjected to plane stress. Express the distortion-energy theory of failure in terms of $\sigma_x, \sigma_y$, and $\tau_{xy}$.

**\*60.** A material is subjected to plane stress. Express the maximum-shear-stress theory of failure in terms of $\sigma_x, \sigma_y$, and $\tau_{xy}$. Assume that the principal stresses are of different algebraic signs.

**61.** The yield stress for a zirconium-magnesium alloy is $\sigma_Y = 15.3$ ksi. If a machine part is made of this material and a critical point in the material is subjected to in-plane principal stresses $\sigma_1$ and $\sigma_2 = -0.5\sigma_1$, determine the magnitude of $\sigma_1$ that will cause yielding according to the maximum-shear-stress theory.

**62.** Solve Prob. 61 using the maximum-distortion energy theory.

**63.** An aluminum alloy is to be used for a drive shaft such that it transmits 25 hp at 1500 rev/min. Using a factor of safety of 2.5 with respect to yielding, determine the smallest-diameter shaft that can be selected based on the maximum-distortion-energy theory. $\sigma_Y = 3.5$ ksi.

**\*64.** If a shaft is made of a material for which $\sigma_Y = 50$ ksi, determine the torsional shear stress required to cause yielding using the maximum-distortion-energy theory.

**65.** Solve Prob. 64 using the maximum-shear-stress theory.

**66.** Derive an expression for an equivalent torque $T_e$ that, if applied alone to a solid bar with a circular cross section, would cause the same energy of distortion as the combination of an applied bending moment $M$ and torque $T$.

**67.** Derive an expression for an equivalent bending moment $M_e$ that, if applied alone to a solid bar with a circular cross section, would cause the same energy of distortion as the combination of an applied bending moment $M$ and torque $T$.

**\*68.** The principal plane stresses acting on a differential element are shown. If the material is machine steel having a yield stress of $\sigma_Y = 700$ MPa, determine the factor of safety with respect to yielding if the maximum-shear-stress theory is considered.

**Prob. 68**

**69.** The short concrete cylinder having a diameter of 50 mm is subjected to a torque of 500 N · m and an axial compressive force of 2 kN. Determine if it fails according to the maximum-normal-stress theory. The ultimate stress of the concrete is $\sigma_{ult} = 28$ MPa.

**Prob. 69**

**70.** Derive an expression for an equivalent bending moment $M_e$ that, if applied alone to a solid bar with a circular cross section, would cause the same maximum shear stress as the combination of an applied moment $M$ and torque $T$. Assume that the principal stresses are of opposite algebraic signs.

**71.** The plate is made of hard copper, which yields at $\sigma_Y = 105$ ksi. Using the maximum-shear-stress theory, determine the tensile stress $\sigma_x$ that can be applied to the plate if a tensile stress $\sigma_y = 0.5\sigma_x$ is also applied.

**\*72.** Solve Prob. 71 using the maximum-distortion energy theory.

$\sigma_y = 0.5\sigma_x$

$\sigma_x$

**Probs. 71/72**

**73.** If the 2-in.-diameter shaft is made from brittle material having an ultimate strength of $\sigma_{ult} = 50$ ksi, for both tension and compression, determine if the shaft fails according to the maximum-normal-stress theory. Use a factor of safety of 1.5 against rupture.

**74.** If the 2-in.-diameter shaft is made from cast iron having tensile and compressive ultimate strengths of $(\sigma_{ult})_t = 50$ ksi and $(\sigma_{ult})_c = 75$ ksi, respectively, determine if the shaft fails in accordance with Mohr's failure criterion.

30 kip

4 kip · ft

**Probs. 73/74**

**75.** The components of plane stess at a critical point on an A-36 steel shell are shown. Determine if failure (yielding) has occurred on the basis of the maximum-shear-stress theory.

**\*76.** The components of plane stress at a critical point on an A-36 steel shell are shown. Determine if failure (yielding) has occurred on the basis of the maximum-distortion-energy theory.

60 MPa

40 MPa

70 MPa

**Probs. 75/76**

**77.** If the A-36 steel pipe has outer and inner diameters of 30 mm and 20 mm, respectively, determine the factor of safety against yielding of the material at point $A$ according to the maximum-shear-stress theory.

**78.** If the A-36 steel pipe has an outer and inner diameter of 30 mm and 20 mm, respectively, determine the factor of safety against yielding of the material at point $A$ according to the maximum-distortion-energy theory.

900 N

200 mm

150 mm

100 mm

$A$

200 mm

900 N

**Probs. 77/78**

**79.** The yield stress for heat-treated beryllium copper is $\sigma_Y = 130$ ksi. If this material is subjected to plane stress and elastic failure occurs when one principal stress is 145 ksi, what is the smallest magnitude of the other principal stress? Use the maximum-distortion-energy theory.

**\*80.** The yield stress for a uranium alloy is $\sigma_Y = 160$ MPa. If a machine part is made of this material and a critical point in the material is subjected to plane stress, such that the principal stresses are $\sigma_1$ and $\sigma_2 = 0.25\sigma_1$, determine the magnitude of $\sigma_1$ that will cause yielding according to the maximum-distortion energy theory.

**81.** Solve Prob. 80 using the maximum-shear-stress theory.

**82.** The state of stress acting at a critical point on the seat frame of an automobile during a crash is shown in the figure. Determine the smallest yield stress for a steel that can be selected for the member, based on the maximum-shear-stress theory.

**83.** Solve Prob. 82 using the maximum-distortion-energy theory.

**Probs. 82/83**

**\*84.** A bar with a circular cross-sectional area is made of SAE 1045 carbon steel having a yield stress of $\sigma_Y = 150$ ksi. If the bar is subjected to a torque of 30 kip · in. and a bending moment of 56 kip · in., determine the required diameter of the bar according to the maximum-distortion-energy theory. Use a factor of safety of 2 with respect to yielding.

**85.** The state of stress acting at a critical point on a machine element is shown in the figure. Determine the smallest yield stress for a steel that might be selected for the part, based on the maximum-shear-stress theory.

10 ksi

4 ksi

8 ksi

**Prob. 85**

**86.** The principal stresses acting at a point on a thin-walled cylindrical pressure vessel are $\sigma_1 = pr/t$, $\sigma_2 = pr/2t$, and $\sigma_3 = 0$. If the yield stress is $\sigma_Y$, determine the maximum value of $p$ based on (a) the maximum-shear-stress theory and (b) the maximum-distortion-energy theory.

**87.** If a solid shaft having a diameter $d$ is subjected to a torque **T** and moment **M**, show that by the maximum-shear-stress theory the maximum allowable shear stress is $\tau_{allow} = (16/\pi d^3)\sqrt{M^2 + T^2}$. Assume the principal stresses to be of opposite algebraic signs.

**\*88.** If a solid shaft having a diameter $d$ is subjected to a torque **T** and moment **M**, show that by the maximum-normal-stress theory the maximum allowable principal stress is $\sigma_{allow} = (16/\pi d^3)(M + \sqrt{M^2 + T^2})$.

$M$   $T$        $T$   $M$

**Probs. 87/88**

**89.** The gas tank has an inner diameter of 1.50 m and a wall thickness of 25 mm. If it is made from A-36 steel and the tank is pressured to 5 MPa, determine the factor of safety against yielding using (a) the maximum-shear-stress theory, and (b) the maximum-distortion-energy theory.

**91.** The internal loadings at a critical section along the steel drive shaft of a ship are calculated to be a torque of 2300 lb·ft, a bending moment of 1500 lb·ft, and an axial thrust of 2500 lb. If the yield points for tension and shear are $\sigma_Y = 100$ ksi and $\tau_Y = 50$ ksi, respectively, determine the required diameter of the shaft using the maximum-shear-stress theory.

Prob. 91

Prob. 89

**90.** The gas tank is made from A-36 steel and has an inner diameter of 1.50 m. If the tank is designed to withstand a pressure of 5 MPa, determine the required minimum wall thickness to the nearest millimeter using (a) the maximum-shear-stress theory, and (b) maximum-distortion-energy theory. Apply a factor of safety of 1.5 against yielding.

**\*92.** The shaft consists of a solid segment $AB$ and a hollow segment $BC$, which are rigidly joined by the coupling at $B$. If the shaft is made from A-36 steel, determine the maximum torque $T$ that can be applied according to the maximum-shear-stress theory. Use a factor of safety of 1.5 against yielding.

**93.** The shaft consists of a solid segment $AB$ and a hollow segment $BC$, which are rigidly joined by the coupling at $B$. If the shaft is made from A-36 steel, determine the maximum torque $T$ that can be applied according to the maximum-distortion-energy theory. Use a factor of safety of 1.5 against yielding.

Prob. 90

Probs. 92/93

# CHAPTER REVIEW

When an element of material is subjected to deformations that only occur in a single plane, then it undergoes plane strain. If the strain components $\epsilon_x$, $\epsilon_y$, and $\gamma_{xy}$ are known for a specified orientation of the element, then the strains acting for some other orientation of the element can be determined using the plane-strain transformation equations. Likewise, the principal normal strains and maximum in-plane shear strain can be determined using transformation equations.

$$\epsilon_{x'} = \frac{\epsilon_x + \epsilon_y}{2} + \frac{\epsilon_x - \epsilon_y}{2}\cos 2\theta + \frac{\gamma_{xy}}{2}\sin 2\theta$$

$$\epsilon_{y'} = \frac{\epsilon_x + \epsilon_y}{2} - \frac{\epsilon_x - \epsilon_y}{2}\cos 2\theta - \frac{\gamma_{xy}}{2}\sin 2\theta$$

$$\frac{\gamma_{x'y'}}{2} = -\left(\frac{\epsilon_x - \epsilon_y}{2}\right)\sin 2\theta + \frac{\gamma_{xy}}{2}\cos 2\theta$$

$$\epsilon_{1,2} = \frac{\epsilon_x + \epsilon_y}{2} \pm \sqrt{\left(\frac{\epsilon_x - \epsilon_y}{2}\right)^2 + \left(\frac{\gamma_{xy}}{2}\right)^2}$$

$$\frac{\gamma_{\substack{max \\ in\text{-}plane}}}{2} = \sqrt{\left(\frac{\epsilon_x - \epsilon_y}{2}\right)^2 + \left(\frac{\gamma_{xy}}{2}\right)^2}$$

$$\epsilon_{avg} = \frac{\epsilon_x + \epsilon_y}{2}$$

Strain transformation problems can also be solved in a semi-graphical manner using Mohr's circle. To draw the circle, the $\epsilon$ and $\gamma/2$ axes are established and the center of the circle $C\,[(\epsilon_x + \epsilon_y)/2, 0]$ and the "reference point" $A\,(\epsilon_x, \gamma_{xy}/2)$ are plotted. The radius of the circle extends between these two points and is determined from trigonometry.

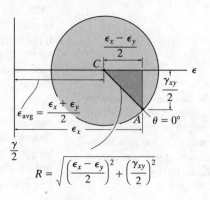

$$R = \sqrt{\left(\frac{\epsilon_x - \epsilon_y}{2}\right)^2 + \left(\frac{\gamma_{xy}}{2}\right)^2}$$

If $\epsilon_1$ and $\epsilon_2$ have the same sign then the absolute maximum shear strain will be out of plane.

$$\gamma_{\substack{abs \\ max}} = \epsilon_1$$

$$\gamma_{\substack{in\text{-}plane \\ max}} = \epsilon_1 - \epsilon_2$$

In the case of plane strain, the absolute maximum shear strain will be equal to the maximum in-plane shear strain provided the principal strains $\epsilon_1$ and $\epsilon_2$ have opposite signs.

$$\gamma_{\substack{abs \\ max}} = \epsilon_1 - \epsilon_2$$

| | |
|---|---|
| If the material is subjected to triaxial stress, then the strain in each direction is influenced by the strain produced by all three stresses. Hooke's law then involves the material properties $E$ and $\nu$. | $\epsilon_x = \dfrac{1}{E}[\sigma_x - \nu(\sigma_y + \sigma_z)]$ <br><br> $\epsilon_y = \dfrac{1}{E}[\sigma_y - \nu(\sigma_x + \sigma_z)]$ <br><br> $\epsilon_z = \dfrac{1}{E}[\sigma_z - \nu(\sigma_x + \sigma_y)]$ |
| If $E$ and $\nu$ are known, then $G$ can be determined. | $G = \dfrac{E}{2(1 + \nu)}$ |
| The dilatation is a measure of volumetric strain. <br><br> The bulk modulus is used to measure the stiffness of a volume of material. | $e = \dfrac{1 - 2\nu}{E}(\sigma_x + \sigma_y + \sigma_z)$ <br><br> $k = \dfrac{E}{3(1 - 2\nu)}$ |
| If the principal stresses at a critical point in the material are known, then a theory of failure can be used as a basis for design. <br><br> *Ductile materials fail in shear*, and here the maximum-shear-stress theory or the maximum-distortion-energy theory can be used to predict failure. Both of these theories make comparison to the yield stress of a specimen subjected to a uniaxial tensile stress. <br><br> *Brittle materials fail in tension*, and so the maximum-normal-stress theory or Mohr's failure criterion can be used to predict failure. Here comparisons are made with the ultimate tensile stress developed in a specimen. | |

# REVIEW PROBLEMS

**94.** In the case of plane stress, where the in-plane principal strains are given by $\epsilon_1$ and $\epsilon_2$, show that the third principal strain can be obtained from $\epsilon_3 = -[\nu/(1-\nu)](\epsilon_1 + \epsilon_2)$, where $\nu$ is Poisson's ratio for the material.

**95.** The plate is made of material having a modulus of elasticity $E = 200$ GPa and Poisson's ratio $\nu = \frac{1}{3}$. Determine the change in width $a$, height $b$, and thickness $t$ when it is subjected to the uniform distributed loading shown.

$a = 400$ mm

2 MN/m

$t = 20$ mm

3 MN/m

$b = 300$ mm

**Prob. 95**

**\*96.** The principal plane stresses acting at a point are shown in the figure. If the material is machine steel having a yield stress of $\sigma_Y = 500$ MPa, determine the factor of safety with respect to yielding if the maximum-shear-stress theory is considered.

100 MPa

150 MPa

**Prob. 96**

**97.** The components of plane stress at a critical point on a thin steel shell are shown. Determine if failure (yielding) has occurred on the basis of the maximum-distortion-energy theory. The yield stress for the steel is $\sigma_Y = 650$ MPa.

340 MPa

65 MPa

55 MPa

**Prob. 97**

**98.** The 60° strain rosette is mounted on a beam. The following readings are obtained for each gauge: $\epsilon_a = 600(10^{-6})$, $\epsilon_b = -700(10^{-6})$, and $\epsilon_c = 350(10^{-6})$. Determine (a) the in-plane principal strains and (b) the maximum in-plane shear strain and average normal strain. In each case show the deformed element due to these strains.

$a$

60°

60°

$b$

60°

$c$

**Prob. 98**

**99.** The state of strain at the point on the bracket has components $\epsilon_x = 350(10^{-6})$, $\epsilon_y = -860(10^{-6})$, $\gamma_{xy} = 250(10^{-6})$. Use the strain-transformation equations to determine the equivalent in-plane strains on an element oriented at an angle of $\theta = 45°$ clockwise from the original position. Sketch the deformed element within the $x$–$y$ plane due to these strains.

**Prob. 99**

**\*100.** The A-36 steel post is subjected to the forces shown. If the strain gauges $a$ and $b$ at point $A$ give readings of $\epsilon_a = 300(10^{-6})$ and $\epsilon_b = 175(10^{-6})$, determine the magnitudes of $\mathbf{P}_1$ and $\mathbf{P}_2$.

**Prob. 100**

**101.** A differential element is subjected to plane strain that has the following components; $\epsilon_x = 950(10^{-6})$, $\epsilon_y = 420(10^{-6})$, $\gamma_{xy} = -325(10^{-6})$. Use the strain-transformation equations and determine (a) the principal strains and (b) the maximum in plane shear strain and the associated average strain. In each case specify the orientation of the element and show how the strains deform the element.

**102.** The state of strain at the point on the bracket has components $\epsilon_x = -130(10^{-6})$, $\epsilon_y = 280(10^{-6})$, $\gamma_{xy} = 75(10^{-6})$. Use the strain-transformation equations to determine (a) the in-plane principal strains and (b) the maximum in-plane shear strain and average normal strain. In each case specify the orientation of the element and show how the strains deform the element within the $x$–$y$ plane.

**Prob. 102**

**103.** The state of plain strain on an element is $\epsilon_x = 400(10^{-6})$, $\epsilon_y = 200(10^{-6})$, and $\gamma_{xy} = -300(10^{-6})$. Determine the equivalent state of strain, which represents (a) the principal strains, and (b) the maximum in-plane shear strain and the associated average normal strain. Specify the orientation of the corresponding element at the point with respect to the original element. Sketch the results on the element.

**Prob. 103**

# Selected Answers

**2.** $\epsilon_{x'} = 248(10^{-6}), \gamma_{x'y'} = -233(10^{-6}),$
$\epsilon_{y'} = -348(10^{-6})$

**3.** $\epsilon_1 = 138(10^{-6}), \epsilon_2 = -198(10^{-6}),$
$\theta_{p1} = 13.3°, \theta_{p2} = -76.7°,$
$\gamma_{\max_{\text{in-plane}}} = 335(10^{-6}), \epsilon_{\text{avg}} = -30.0(10^{-6}),$
$\theta_s = -31.7°$ and $58.3°$

**5.** $\epsilon_1 = 622(10^{-6}), \epsilon_2 = -862(10^{-6}),$
$\theta_{p1} = -15.2°$ and $\theta_{p2} = 74.8°,$
$\gamma_{\max_{\text{in-plane}}} = -1484(10^{-6}), \epsilon_{\text{avg}} = -120(10^{-6}),$
$\theta_s = 29.8°$ and $-60.2°$

**6.** $\epsilon_{x'} = -116(10^{-6}), \epsilon_{y'} = 466(10^{-6}),$
$\gamma_{x'y'} = 393(10^{-6})$

**7.** $\epsilon_{x'} = 466(10^{-6}), \epsilon_{y'} = -116(10^{-6}),$
$\gamma_{x'y'} = -393(10^{-6})$

**9.** $\epsilon_1 = 188(10^{-6}), \epsilon_2 = -128(10^{-6}),$
$\theta_{p1} = -9.22°, \theta_{p2} = 80.8°,$
$\gamma_{\max_{\text{in-plane}}} = 316(10^{-6}), \theta_s = 35.8°$ and $-54.2°,$
$\epsilon_{\text{avg}} = 30(10^{-6})$

**10.** (a) $\epsilon_1 = 713(10^{-6}), \epsilon_2 = 36.6(10^{-6}), \theta_{p1} = 133°$
(b) $\gamma_{\max_{\text{in-plane}}} = 677(10^{-6}), \epsilon_{\text{avg}} = 375(10^{-6}),$
$\theta_s = -2.12°$

**11.** $\epsilon_{x'} = 86.6(10^{-6}), \gamma_{x'y'} = 620(10^{-6}),$
$\epsilon_{y'} = 213(10^{-6})$

**13.** $\epsilon_1 = 17.7(10^{-6}), \epsilon_2 = -318(10^{-6}),$
$\theta_{p1} = 76.7°$ and $\theta_{p2} = -13.3°,$
$\gamma_{\max_{\text{in-plane}}} = 335(10^{-6}), \theta_s = 31.7°$ and $122°,$
$\epsilon_{\text{avg}} = -150(10^{-6})$

**14.** $\epsilon_1 = 368(10^{-6}), \epsilon_2 = 182(10^{-6}),$
$\theta_{p1} = -52.8°$ and $\theta_{p2} = 37.2°,$
$\gamma_{\max_{\text{in-plane}}} = 187(10^{-6}), \theta_s = -7.76°$ and $82.2°,$
$\epsilon_{\text{avg}} = 275(10^{-6})$

**17.** $\epsilon_1 = 138(10^{-6}), \epsilon_2 = -198(10^{-6}), \theta_p = 13.3°$

**18.** $\gamma_{\max_{\text{in-plane}}} = 335(10^{-6}), \epsilon_{\text{avg}} = -30(10^{-6}),$
$\theta_s = -31.7°$

**19.** $\epsilon_1 = 1039(10^{-6}), \epsilon_2 = 291(10^{-6}), \theta_p = 30.2°,$
$\gamma_{\max_{\text{in-plane}}} = 748(10^{-9}), \epsilon_{\text{avg}} = 665(10^{-6}),$
$\theta_s = -14.8°$

**21.** $\epsilon_{x'} = 466(10^{-6}), \gamma_{x'y'} = -393(10^{-6}),$
$\epsilon_{y'} = -116(10^{-6})$

**22.** (a) $\epsilon_1 = 773(10^{-6}), \epsilon_2 = 76.8(10^{-6}),$
(b) $\gamma_{\max_{\text{in-plane}}} = 696(10^{-6}),$
(c) $\gamma_{\text{abs}_{\max}} = 773(10^{-6})$

**23.** (a) $\epsilon_1 = 870(10^{-6}), \epsilon_2 = 405(10^{-6}),$
(b) $\gamma_{\max_{\text{in-plane}}} = 465(10^{-6}),$
(c) $\gamma_{\text{abs}_{\max}} = 870(10^{-6})$

**25.** $\epsilon_1 = 1434(10^{-6}), \epsilon_2 = -304(10^{-6}),$
$\gamma_{\max_{\text{in-plane}}} = 1738(10^{-6}), \epsilon_{\text{avg}} = 565(10^{-6})$

**26.** $\epsilon_1 = 336(10^{-6}), \epsilon_2 = -536(10^{-6}),$
$\theta_{p1} = 11.7°$ (counterclockwise),
$\gamma_{\max_{\text{in-plane}}} = 872(10^{-6}), \epsilon_{\text{avg}} = -100(10^{-6}),$
$\theta_s = 33.3°$ (clockwise)

**27.** $\epsilon_1 = 301(10^{-6}), \epsilon_2 = -401(10^{-6}),$
$\theta_{p2} = 27.6°$ (clockwise),
$\gamma_{\max_{\text{in-plane}}} = 702(10^{-6}), \epsilon_{\text{avg}} = -50(10^{-6}),$
$\theta_s = 17.4°$ (counterclockwise)

**33.** $E = 17.4$ GPa, $\Delta d = -12.6(10^{-6})$ mm

**34.** $\Delta\theta = -0.0103°$

**35.** $\nu_{pvc} = 0.164$

**37.** (a) $k_r = 3.33$ ksi,
(b) $k_g = 5.13(10^3)$ ksi

**38.** $p = 0.967$ ksi, $\gamma_{\max_{\text{in-plane}}} = 1.30(10^{-3})$

**39.** $P = 13.0$ kip, $\gamma_{xy} = -13.7(10^{-6})$

**41.** $\epsilon_x = 23.0(10^{-6}), \gamma_{xy} = -3.16(10^{-6})$

**42.** $\epsilon_x = 2.35(10^{-3}), \epsilon_y = -0.972(10^{-3}),$
$\epsilon_z = -2.44(10^{-3})$

**43.** $p = 4$ MPa

**45.** $\theta = \tan^{-1}\left(\dfrac{1}{\sqrt{\nu}}\right)$

**46.** $\sigma_1 = 8.37$ ksi, $\sigma_2 = 6.26$ ksi

**47.** $\epsilon_1 = 833(10^{-6}), \epsilon_2 = 168(10^{-6}),$
$\epsilon_3 = -763(10^{-6})$

**49.** $\sigma_x = 15.5$ ksi (C), $\sigma_y = 16.8$ ksi (C)

**50.** $\epsilon_x = \epsilon_y = 0, \gamma_{xy} = -160(10^{-6}), T = 65.2$ N·m

**51.** $\epsilon_{x'} = -2.52(10^{-3}), \epsilon_{y'} = 2.52(10^{-3})$

**53.** $\Delta d = 0.800$ mm, $\sigma_{AB} = 315$ MPa

**54.** $\Delta d = 0.680$ mm

**57.** $\Delta V = 0.0168$ m³

**58.** $k = 1.35$

**59.** $\sigma_x^2 + \sigma_y^2 - \sigma_x\sigma_y + 3\tau_{xy}^2 = \sigma_y^2$

**61.** $\sigma_1 = 10.2$ ksi

**62.** $\sigma_1 = 11.6$ ksi

**63.** $d = 1.88$ in.

**65.** $\tau = 25$ ksi

**66.** $T_e = \sqrt{\dfrac{4}{3}M^2 + T^2}$

**67.** $M_e = \sqrt{M^2 + \dfrac{3}{4}T^2}$

**69.** No.

**70.** $M_e = \sqrt{M^2 + T^2}$

**71.** $\sigma_x = 105$ ksi

**73.** Yes.

**74.** No.

**75.** No.

**77.** F.S. = 1.43

**78.** F.S. = 1.64

**79.** $\sigma_2 = 38.9$ ksi

**81.** $\sigma_1 = 160$ MPa

**82.** $\sigma_Y = 94.3$ ksi

**83.** $\sigma_Y = 91.0$ ksi

**85.** $\sigma_Y = 19.7$ ksi

**86.** (a) $p = \dfrac{t}{r}\sigma_y$,

(b) $p = \dfrac{2t}{\sqrt{3}r}\sigma_y$

**89.** (a) F.S. = 1.67,

(b) F.S. = 1.92

**90.** (a) $t = 22.5$ mm,

(b) $t = 19.5$ mm

**91.** $d = 1.50$ in.

**93.** $T = 9.67$ kN·m

**95.** $\delta_a = 0.367$ mm, $\delta_b = -0.255$ mm,

$\delta_t = -0.00167$ mm

**97.** No.

**8.** $\epsilon_{\text{avg}} = 83.3(10^{-6})$, $\epsilon_1 = 880(10^{-6})$,

$\epsilon_2 = -713(10^{-6})$, $\theta_p = 54.8°$ (clockwise),

$\gamma_{\substack{\max \\ \text{in-plane}}} = -1593(10^{-6})$,

$\theta_s = 9.78°$ (clockwise)

**99.** $\epsilon_{x'} = -380(10^{-6})$, $\epsilon_{y'} = -130(10^{-6})$,

$\gamma_{x'y'} = 1.21(10^{-3})$

**101.** $\epsilon_1 = 996(10^{-6})$, $\epsilon_2 = 374(10^{-6})$, $\theta_{p1} = -15.8$,

$\theta_{p2} = 74.2$, $\gamma_{\substack{\max \\ \text{in-plane}}} = 622(10^{-6})$,

$\epsilon_{\text{avg}} = 685(10^{-6})$, $\theta_s = 29.2°$ and 119°

**102.** $\epsilon_1 = 283(10^{-6})$, $\epsilon_2 = -133(10^{-6})$,

$\theta_{p1} = 84.8°$, $\theta_{p2} = -5.18°$, $\gamma_{\substack{\max \\ \text{in-plane}}} = 417(10^{-6})$,

$\epsilon_{\text{avg}} = 75.0(10^{-6})$, $\theta_s = 39.8°$ and 130°

**103.** $\epsilon_1 = 480(10^{-6})$, $\epsilon_2 = 120(10^{-6})$,

$\theta_{p1} = -28.2°$ (clockwise),

$\gamma_{\substack{\max \\ \text{in-plane}}} = -361(10^{-6})$,

$\theta_s = 16.8°$ (counterclockwise),

$\epsilon_{\text{avg}} = 300(10^{-6})$

# Design of Beams
# and Shafts

From Chapter 11 of *Mechanics of Materials*, Ninth Edition. R. C. Hibbeler. Copyright © 2014 by Pearson Education, Inc. Published by Pearson Prentice Hall. All rights reserved.

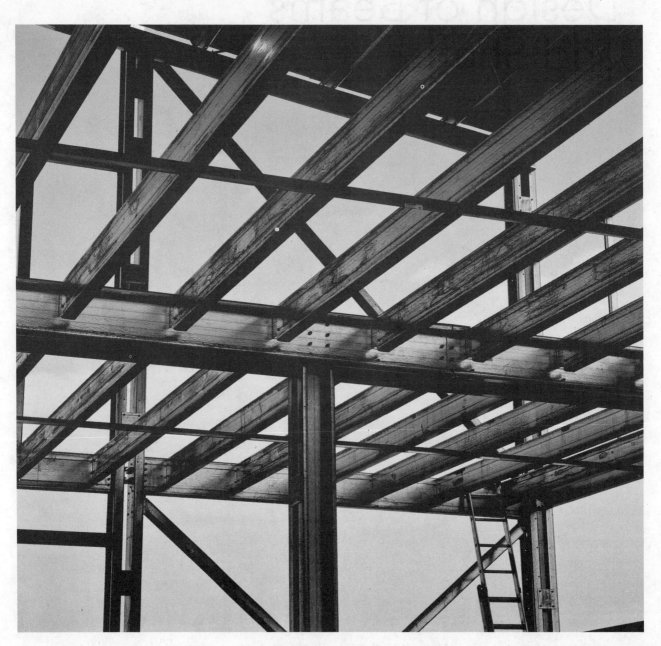

Beams are important structural members that are used to support roof and floor loadings.

# Design of Beams and Shafts

## 1 Basis for Beam Design

Beams are said to be designed on the basis of strength so that they can resist the internal shear and moment developed along their length. To design a beam in this way requires application of the shear and flexure formulas provided the material is homogeneous and has linear elastic behavior. Although some beams may also be subjected to an axial force, the effects of this force are often neglected in design since the axial stress is generally much smaller than the stress developed by shear and bending.

As shown in Fig. 1, the external loadings on a beam will create additional stresses in the beam *directly under the load*. Notably, a compressive stress $\sigma_y$ will be developed, in addition to the bending stress $\sigma_x$ and shear stress $\tau_{xy}$. Using advanced methods of analysis, as treated in the theory of elasticity, it can be shown that $\sigma_y$ diminishes rapidly throughout the beam's depth, and for *most* beam span-to-depth ratios used in engineering practice, the maximum value of $\sigma_y$ generally represents only a small percentage compared to the bending stress $\sigma_x$, that is, $\sigma_x \gg \sigma_y$. Furthermore, the direct application of concentrated loads is generally avoided in beam design. Instead, *bearing plates* are used to spread these loads more evenly onto the surface of the beam.

Although beams are designed mainly for strength, they must also be braced properly along their sides so that they do not buckle or suddenly become unstable. Furthermore, in some cases beams must be designed to resist a limited amount of *deflection*, as when they support ceilings made of brittle materials such as plaster. Limitations placed on beam buckling are often discussed in codes related to structural or mechanical design.

Since the shear and flexure formulas are used for beam design, we will discuss the general results obtained when these equations are applied to various points in a cantilevered beam that has a rectangular cross section and supports a load **P** at its end, Fig. 2a.

In general, at an arbitrary section *a–a* along the beam's axis, Fig. 2b, the internal shear **V** and moment **M** are developed from a *parabolic* shear-stress distribution, and a *linear* normal-stress distribution, Fig. 2c. As a result, the stresses acting on elements located at points 1 through 5 along the section will be as shown in Fig. 2d. Note that elements 1 and 5 are subjected only to the maximum normal stress, whereas element 3, which is on the neutral axis, is subjected only to the maximum shear stress. The intermediate elements 2 and 4 resist *both* normal and shear stress.

In each case the state of stress can be transformed into *principal stresses*, using either the stress-transformation equations or Mohr's circle. The results are shown in Fig. 2e. Here each successive element, 1 through 5, undergoes a counterclockwise orientation. Specifically, relative to element 1, considered to be at the 0° position, element 3 is oriented at 45° and element 5 is oriented at 90°.

**Fig. 1**

Whenever large shear loads occur on a beam it is important to use stiffeners such as at *A*, in order to prevent any localized failure such as crimping of the beam flanges.

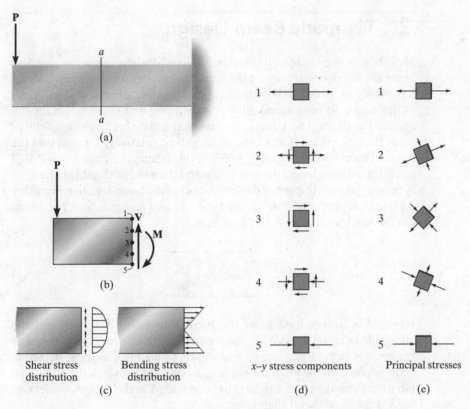

**Fig. 2**

P

| | x–y stress components | Principal stresses |
|---|---|---|
| 1 | | |

Shear stress
distribution

(c)

Bending stress
distribution

*x–y* stress components

(d)

Principal stresses

(e)

Stress trajectories for
cantilevered beam

**Fig. 3**

If this analysis is extended to many vertical sections along the beam other than *a–a*, a profile of the results can be represented by curves called *stress trajectories*. Each of these curves indicated the *direction* of a principal stress having a constant magnitude. Some of these trajectories are shown for the cantilevered beam in Fig. 3. Here the solid lines represent the direction of the tensile principal stresses and the dashed lines represent the direction of the compressive principal stresses. As expected, the lines intersect the neutral axis at 45° angles (like element 3) and the solid and dashed lines will intersect at 90° because the principal stresses are always 90° apart. Knowing the direction of these lines can help engineers decide where to reinforce a beam if it is made of brittle material so that it does not crack or become unstable.

## 2   Prismatic Beam Design

Most beams are made of ductile materials and when this is the case it is generally not necessary to plot the stress trajectories for the beam. Instead, it is simply necessary to be sure the actual bending stress and shear stress in the beam do not exceed allowable bending and shear stress for the material as defined by structural or mechanical codes. In the majority of cases the suspended span of the beam will be relatively long, so that the internal moments become large. When this occurs the engineer will first consider a design based upon bending and then check the shear strength. A bending design requires a determination of the beam's *section modulus*, a geometric property which is the ratio of $I$ and $c$, that is, $S = I/c$. Using the flexure formula, $\sigma = Mc/I$, we have

$$S_{\text{req'd}} = \frac{M_{\text{max}}}{\sigma_{\text{allow}}} \tag{1}$$

Here $M$ is determined from the beam's moment diagram, and the allowable bending stress, $\sigma_{\text{allow}}$, is specified in a design code. In many cases the beam's as yet unknown weight will be small and can be neglected in comparison with the loads the beam must carry. However, if the additional moment caused by the weight is to be included in the design, a selection for $S$ is made so that it slightly *exceeds* $S_{\text{req'd}}$.

Once $S_{\text{req'd}}$ is known, if the beam has a simple cross-sectional shape, such as a square, a circle, or a rectangle of known width-to-height proportions, its *dimensions* can be determined directly from $S_{\text{req'd}}$, since $S_{\text{req'd}} = I/c$. However, if the cross section is made from several elements, such as a wide-flange section, then an infinite number of web and flange dimensions can be determined that satisfy the value of $S_{\text{req'd}}$. In practice, however, engineers choose a particular beam meeting the requirement that $S > S_{\text{req'd}}$ from a handbook that lists the standard shapes available from manufacturers. Often several beams that have the same section modulus can be selected from these tables. If deflections are not restricted, usually the beam having the smallest cross-sectional area is chosen, since it is made of less material and is therefore both lighter and more economical than the others.

The two floor beams are connected to the beam $AB$, which transmits the load to the columns of this building frame. For design, all the connections can be considered to act as pins.

Once the beam has been selected, the shear formula $\tau_{allow} \geq VQ/It$ can then be used to check that the allowable shear stress is not exceeded. Often this requirement will not present a problem. However, if the beam is "short" and supports large concentrated loads, the shear-stress limitation may dictate the size of the beam. This limitation is particularly important in the design of wood beams, because wood tends to split along its grain due to shear.

**Fabricated Beams.** Since beams are often made of steel or wood, we will now discuss some of the tabulated properties of beams made from these materials.

**Steel Sections.** Most manufactured steel beams are produced by rolling a hot ingot of steel until the desired shape is formed. These so-called *rolled shapes* have properties that are tabulated in the American Institute of Steel Construction (AISC) manual. The wide-flange shapes are designated by their depth and weight per unit length; for example, W18 × 46 indicates a wide-flange cross section (W) having a depth of 18 in. and a weight of 46 lb/ft, Fig. 4. For any given section, the weight per length, dimensions, cross-sectional area, moment of inertia, and section modulus are reported. Also included is the radius of gyration $r$, which is a geometric property related to the section's buckling strength. The *AISC Manual* also lists data for other members such as channels and angles.

Typical profile view of a steel wide-flange beam

**Fig. 4**

The large shear force that occurs at the end reaction of this steel beam can cause localized buckling of the beam's flanges. To avoid this, a "stiffener" $A$ is placed along the web to keep the flanges straight.

**Wood Sections.** Most beams made of wood have rectangular cross sections because such beams are easy to manufacture and handle. Manuals, such as that of the National Forest Products Association, list the dimensions of lumber often used in the design of wood beams. Often, both the nominal and actual dimensions are reported. Lumber is identified by its *nominal* dimensions, such as 2 × 4 (2 in. by 4 in.); however, its actual or "dressed" dimensions are smaller, being 1.5 in. by 3.5 in. The reduction in the dimensions occurs in order to obtain a smooth surface from lumber that is rough sawn. Obviously, the *actual dimensions* must be used whenever stress calculations are performed on wood beams.

Welded          Bolted

Steel plate girders

**Fig. 5**

Wooden box beam

(a)

Glulam beam

(b)

**Fig. 6**

## Built-up Sections.

**Built-up Sections.** A *built-up section* is constructed from two or more parts joined together to form a single unit. Since $S_{req'd} = M/\sigma_{allow}$, the capacity of the beam to resist a moment will vary directly with its section modulus, and since $S_{req'd} = I/c$, then $S_{req'd}$ is *increased* if $I$ is *increased*. In order to increase I, *most of the material* should be placed as far *away* from the neutral axis as practical. This, of course, is what makes a deep wide-flange beam so efficient in resisting a moment. For a very large load, however, an available rolled-steel section may not have a section modulus great enough to support the load. Rather than using several available beams, instead engineers will usually "build up" a beam made from plates and angles. A deep I-shaped section having this form is called a *plate girder*. For example, the steel plate girder in Fig. 5 has two flange plates that are either welded or, using angles, bolted to the web plate.

Wood beams are also "built up," usually in the form of a box beam section, Fig. 6a. They may be made having plywood webs and larger boards for the flanges. For very large spans, *glulam beams* are used. These members are made from several boards glue-laminated together to form a single unit, Fig. 6b.

Just as in the case of rolled sections or beams made from a single piece, the design of built-up sections requires that the bending and shear stresses be checked. In addition, the shear stress in the fasteners, such as weld, glue, nails, etc., must be checked to be certain the beam acts as a single unit.

## Important Points

- Beams support loadings that are applied perpendicular to their axes. If they are designed on the basis of strength, they must resist allowable shear and bending stresses.

- The maximum bending stress in the beam is assumed to be much greater than the localized stresses caused by the application of loadings on the surface of the beam.

## Procedure for Analysis

Based on the previous discussion, the following procedure provides a rational method for the design of a beam on the basis of strength.

### Shear and Moment Diagrams.

- Determine the maximum shear and moment in the beam. Often this is done by constructing the beam's shear and moment diagrams.
- For built-up beams, shear and moment diagrams are useful for identifying *regions* where the shear and moment are excessively large and may require additional structural reinforcement or fasteners.

### Bending Stress.

- If the beam is relatively long, it is designed by finding its section modulus using the flexure formula, $S_{req'd} = M_{max}/\sigma_{allow}$.
- Once $S_{req'd}$ is determined, the cross-sectional dimensions for simple shapes can then be computed, since $S_{req'd} = I/c$.
- If rolled-steel sections are to be used, several possible values of $S$ may be selected. Of these, choose the one having the smallest
- Make sure that the selected section modulus, $S$, is *slightly greater* than $S_{req'd}$, so that the additional moment created by the beam's weight is considered.

### Shear Stress.

- Normally beams that are short and carry large loads, especially those made of wood, are first designed to resist shear and then later checked against the allowable-bending-stress requirements.
- Using the shear formula, check to see that the allowable shear stress is not exceeded; that is, use $\tau_{allow} \geq V_{max}\,Q/It$.
- If the beam has a solid *rectangular* cross section, the shear formula becomes $\tau_{allow} \geq 1.5\,(V_{max}/A)$ and if the cross section is a *wide flange*, it is generally appropriate to assume that the shear stress is *constant* over the cross-sectional area of the beam's web so that $\tau_{allow} \geq V_{max}/A_{web}$, where $A_{web}$ is determined from the product of the web's depth and its thickness.

### Adequacy of Fasteners.

- The adequacy of fasteners used on built-up beams depends upon the shear stress the fasteners can resist. Specifically, the required spacing of nails or bolts of a particular size is determined from the allowable shear flow, $q_{allow} = VQ/I$, calculated at points on the cross section where the fasteners are located.

## EXAMPLE | 1

(a)

(b)

**Fig. 7**

A beam is to be made of steel that has an allowable bending stress of $\sigma_{allow} = 24$ ksi and an allowable shear stress of $\tau_{allow} = 14.5$ ksi. Select an appropriate W shape that will carry the loading shown in Fig. 7a.

### SOLUTION

**Shear and Moment Diagrams.** The support reactions have been calculated, and the shear and moment diagrams are shown in Fig. 7b. From these diagrams, $V_{max} = 30$ kip and $M_{max} = 120$ kip·ft.

**Bending Stress.** The required section modulus for the beam is determined from the flexure formula,

$$S_{req'd} = \frac{M_{max}}{\sigma_{allow}} = \frac{120 \text{ kip} \cdot \text{ft} (12 \text{ in./ft})}{24 \text{ kip/in}^2} = 60 \text{ in}^3$$

The following beams are adequate:

| | |
|---|---|
| W18 × 40 | $S = 68.4 \text{ in}^3$ |
| W16 × 45 | $S = 72.7 \text{ in}^3$ |
| W14 × 43 | $S = 62.7 \text{ in}^3$ |
| W12 × 50 | $S = 64.7 \text{ in}^3$ |
| W10 × 54 | $S = 60.0 \text{ in}^3$ |
| W8 × 67 | $S = 60.4 \text{ in}^3$ |

The beam having the least weight per foot is chosen, i.e.,

$$\text{W18} \times 40$$

The *actual* maximum moment $M_{max}$, which includes the weight of the beam, can be calculated and the adequacy of the selected beam can be checked. In comparison with the applied loads, however, the beam's weight, $(0.040 \text{ kip/ft})(18 \text{ ft}) = 0.720$ kip, will only *slightly increase* $S_{req'd}$. In spite of this,

$$S_{req'd} = 60 \text{ in}^3 < 68.4 \text{ in}^3 \qquad \text{OK}$$

**Shear Stress.** Since the beam is a *wide-flange section*, the *average shear stress* within the web will be considered. Here the web is assumed to extend from the very top to the very bottom of the beam. For a W18 W18 × 40, $d = 17.90$ in., $t_w = 0.315$ in. Thus,

$$\tau_{avg} = \frac{V_{max}}{A_w} = \frac{30 \text{ kip}}{(17.90 \text{ in.})(0.315 \text{ in.})} = 5.32 \text{ ksi} < 14.5 \text{ ksi} \quad \text{OK}$$

Use a W18 × 40. *Ans.*

## EXAMPLE | 2

The laminated wooden beam shown in Fig. 8a supports a uniform distributed loading of 12 kN/m. If the beam is to have a height-to-width ratio of 1.5, determine its smallest width. The allowable bending stress is $\sigma_{\text{allow}} = 9$ MPa and the allowable shear stress is $\tau_{\text{allow}} = 0.6$ MPa. Neglect the weight of the beam.

(a)

### SOLUTION

**Shear and Moment Diagrams.** The support reactions at $A$ and $B$ have been calculated and the shear and moment diagrams are shown in Fig. 8b. Here $V_{\text{max}} = 20$ kN, $M_{\text{max}} = 10.67$ kN·m.

**Bending Stress.** Applying the flexure formula,

$$S_{\text{req'd}} = \frac{M_{\text{max}}}{\sigma_{\text{allow}}} = \frac{10.67(10^3) \text{ N} \cdot \text{m}}{9(10^6) \text{ N/m}^2} = 0.00119 \text{ m}^3$$

Assuming that the width is $a$, then the height is $1.5a$, Fig. 8a. Thus,

$$S_{\text{req'd}} = \frac{I}{c} = 0.00119 \text{ m}^3 = \frac{\frac{1}{12}(a)(1.5a)^3}{(0.75a)}$$

$$a^3 = 0.003160 \text{ m}^3$$

$$a = 0.147 \text{ m}$$

**Shear Stress.** Applying the shear formula for rectangular sections (which is a special case of $\tau_{\text{max}} = VQ/It$), we have

$$\tau_{\text{max}} = 1.5\frac{V_{\text{max}}}{A} = (1.5)\frac{20(10^3) \text{ N}}{(0.147 \text{ m})(1.5)(0.147 \text{ m})}$$

$$= 0.929 \text{ MPa} > 0.6 \text{ MPa}$$

**Fig. 8**

### EQUATION

Since the design fails the shear criterion, the beam must be redesigned on the basis of shear.

$$\tau_{\text{allow}} = 1.5\frac{V_{\text{max}}}{A}$$

$$600 \text{ kN/m}^2 = 1.5\frac{20(10^3) \text{ N}}{(a)(1.5a)}$$

$$a = 0.183 \text{ m} = 183 \text{ mm} \qquad \qquad \textit{Ans.}$$

This larger section will also adequately resist the normal stress.

## EXAMPLE 3

The wooden T-beam shown in Fig. 9a is made from two 200 mm × 30 mm boards. If the allowable bending stress is $\sigma_{allow}$ = 12 MPa and the allowable shear stress is $\tau_{allow}$ = 0.8 MPa, determine if the beam can safely support the loading shown. Also, specify the maximum spacing of nails needed to hold the two boards together if each nail can safely resist 1.50 kN in shear.

(a)

### SOLUTION

**Shear and Moment Diagrams.** The reactions on the beam are shown, and the shear and moment diagrams are drawn in Fig. 9b. Here $V_{max}$ = 1.5 kN, $M_{max}$ = 2 kN·m.

**Bending Stress.** The neutral axis (centroid) will be located from the bottom of the beam. Working in units of meters, we have

$$\bar{y} = \frac{\Sigma \bar{y} A}{\Sigma A}$$

$$= \frac{(0.1 \text{ m})(0.03 \text{ m})(0.2 \text{ m}) + 0.215 \text{ m}(0.03 \text{ m})(0.2 \text{ m})}{0.03 \text{ m}(0.2 \text{ m}) + 0.03 \text{ m}(0.2 \text{ m})} = 0.1575 \text{ m}$$

Thus,

$$I = \left[ \frac{1}{12}(0.03 \text{ m})(0.2 \text{ m})^3 + (0.03 \text{ m})(0.2 \text{ m})(0.1575 \text{ m} - 0.1 \text{ m})^2 \right]$$

$$+ \left[ \frac{1}{12}(0.2 \text{ m})(0.03 \text{ m})^3 + (0.03 \text{ m})(0.2 \text{ m})(0.215 \text{ m} - 0.1575 \text{ m})^2 \right]$$

$$= 60.125(10^{-6}) \text{ m}^4$$

Since $c$ = 0.1575 m (not 0.230 m − 0.1575 m = 0.0725 m), we require

$$\sigma_{allow} \geq \frac{M_{max} c}{I}$$

$$12(10^6) \text{ Pa} \geq \frac{2(10^3) \text{ N} \cdot \text{m}(0.1575 \text{ m})}{60.125(10^{-6}) \text{ m}^4} = 5.24(10^6) \text{ Pa} \qquad \text{OK}$$

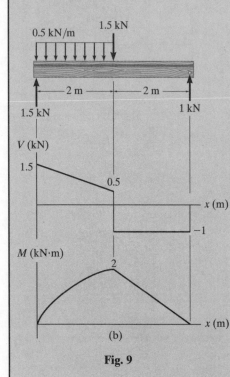

**Fig. 9**

**Shear Stress.** Maximum shear stress in the beam depends upon the magnitude of $Q$ and $t$. It occurs at the neutral axis, since $Q$ is a maximum there and the neutral axis is in the web, where the thickness $t = 0.03$ m is smallest for the cross section. For simplicity, we will use the rectangular area below the neutral axis to calculate $Q$, rather than a two-part composite area above this axis, Fig. 9c. We have

(c)

$$Q = \bar{y}'A' = \left(\frac{0.1575 \text{ m}}{2}\right)[(0.1575 \text{ m})(0.03 \text{ m})] = 0.372(10^{-3}) \text{ m}^3$$

so that

$$\tau_{allow} \geq \frac{V_{max}Q}{It}$$

$$800(10^3) \text{ Pa} \geq \frac{1.5(10^3) \text{ N}[0.372(10^{-3})] \text{ m}^3}{60.125(10^{-6}) \text{ m}^4(0.03 \text{ m})} = 309(10^3) \text{ Pa} \quad \text{OK}$$

**Nail Spacing.** From the shear diagram it is seen that the shear varies over the entire span. Since the nail spacing depends on the magnitude of shear in the beam, for simplicity (and to be conservative), we will design the spacing on the basis of $V = 1.5$ kN for region $BC$ and $V = 1$ kN for region $CD$. Since the nails join the flange to the web, Fig. 9d, we have

(d)

**Fig. 9 (cont.)**

$$Q = \bar{y}'A' = (0.0725 \text{ m} - 0.015 \text{ m})[(0.2 \text{ m})(0.03 \text{ m})] = 0.345(10^{-3}) \text{ m}^3$$

The shear flow for each region is therefore

$$q_{BC} = \frac{V_{BC}Q}{I} = \frac{1.5(10^3) \text{ N}[0.345(10^{-3}) \text{ m}^3]}{60.125(10^{-6}) \text{ m}^4} = 8.61 \text{ kN/m}$$

$$q_{CD} = \frac{V_{CD}Q}{I} = \frac{1(10^3) \text{ N}[0.345(10^{-3}) \text{ m}^3]}{60.125(10^{-6}) \text{ m}^4} = 5.74 \text{ kN/m}$$

One nail can resist 1.50 kN in shear, so the maximum spacing becomes

$$s_{BC} = \frac{1.50 \text{ kN}}{8.61 \text{ kN/m}} = 0.174 \text{ m}$$

$$s_{CD} = \frac{1.50 \text{ kN}}{5.74 \text{ kN/m}} = 0.261 \text{ m}$$

For ease of measuring, use

$$s_{BC} = 150 \text{ mm} \qquad \qquad Ans.$$

$$s_{CD} = 250 \text{ mm} \qquad \qquad Ans.$$

# FUNDAMENTAL PROBLEMS

**F1.** Determine the minimum dimension $a$ to the nearest mm of the beam's cross section to safely support the load. The wood has an allowable normal stress of $\sigma_{allow} = 10$ MPa and an allowable shear stress of $\tau_{allow} = 1$ MPa.

**F1**

**F2.** Determine the minimum diameter $d$ to the nearest $\frac{1}{8}$ in. of the rod to safely support the load. The rod is made of a material having an allowable normal stress of $\sigma_{allow} = 20$ ksi and an allowable shear stress of $\tau_{allow} = 10$ ksi.

**F2**

**F3.** Determine the minimum dimension $a$ to the nearest mm of the beam's cross section to safely support the load. The wood has an allowable normal stress of $\sigma_{allow} = 12$ MPa and an allowable shear stress of $\tau_{allow} = 1.5$ MPa.

**F3**

**F4.** Determine the minimum dimension $h$ to the nearest $\frac{1}{8}$ in. of the beam's cross section to safely support the load. The wood has an allowable normal stress of $\sigma_{allow} = 2$ ksi and an allowable shear stress of $\tau_{allow} = 200$ psi.

**F4**

**F5.** Determine the minimum dimension $b$ to the nearest mm of the beam's cross section to safely support the load. The wood has an allowable normal stress of $\sigma_{allow} = 12$ MPa and an allowable shear stress of $\tau_{allow} = 1.5$ MPa.

**F5**

**F6.** Select the lightest W410-shaped section that can safely support the load. The beam is made of steel having an allowable normal stress of $\sigma_{allow} = 150$ MPa and an allowable shear stress of $\tau_{allow} = 75$ MPa.

**F6**

# PROBLEMS

**1.** The simply supported beam is made of timber that has an allowable bending stress of $\sigma_{allow} = 6.5$ MPa and an allowable shear stress of $\tau_{allow} = 500$ kPa. Determine its dimensions if it is to be rectangular and have a height-to-width ratio of 1.25.

**Prob. 1**

**2.** Determine the minimum width of the beam to the nearest $\frac{1}{4}$ in. that will safely support the loading of $P = 8$ kip. The allowable bending stress is $\sigma_{allow} = 24$ ksi and the allowable shear stress is $\tau_{allow} = 15$ ksi.

**3.** Solve Prob. 2 if $P = 10$ kip.

**Probs. 2/3**

**\*4.** The brick wall exerts a uniform distributed load of 1.20 kip/ft on the beam. If the allowable bending stress is $\sigma_{allow} = 22$ ksi and the allowable shear stress is $\tau_{allow} = 12$ ksi, select the lightest wide-flange section with the shortest depth that will safely support the load. If there are several choices of equal weight, choose the one with the shortest height.

**Prob. 4**

**5.** Select the lightest-weight steel wide-flange beam that will safely support the machine loading shown. The allowable bending stress is $\sigma_{allow} = 24$ ksi and the allowable shear stress is $\tau_{allow} = 14$ ksi.

**Prob. 5**

**6.** The spreader beam $AB$ is used to slowly lift the 3000-lb pipe that is centrally located on the straps at $C$ and $D$. If the beam is a W12 × 45, determine if it can safely support the load. The allowable bending stress is $\sigma_{allow} = 22$ ksi and the allowable shear stress is $\tau_{allow} = 12$ ksi.

**Prob. 6**

**7.** Draw the shear and moment diagrams for the W12 × 14 beam and check if the beam will safely support the loading. Take $\sigma_{allow} = 22$ ksi and $\tau_{allow} = 12$ ksi.

**Prob. 7**

**\*8.** The simply supported beam is made of timber that has an allowable bending stress of $\sigma_{allow} = 1.20$ ksi and an allowable shear stress of $\tau_{allow} = 100$ psi. Determine its smallest dimensions to the nearest $\frac{1}{8}$ in. if it is rectangular and has a height-to-width ratio of 1.5.

**Prob. 8**

**9.** Select the lightest W 360 shape section that can safely support the loading acting on the overhanging beam. The beam is made from steel having an allowable normal stress of $\sigma_{allow} = 150$ MPa and an allowable shear stress of $\tau_{allow} = 80$ MPa.

**10.** Investigate if a W250 × 58 can safely support the loading acting on the overhanging beam. The beam is made from steel having an allowable normal stress of $\sigma_{allow} = 150$ MPa and an allowable shear stress of $\tau_{allow} = 80$ MPa.

**Probs. 9/10**

**11.** The timber beam is to be loaded as shown. If the ends support only vertical forces, determine the greatest magnitude of **P** that can be applied. $\sigma_{allow} = 25$ MPa, $\tau_{allow} = 700$ kPa.

**Prob. 11**

**\*12.** The joists of a floor in a warehouse are to be selected using square timber beams made of oak. If each beam is to be designed to carry 90 lb/ft over a simply supported span of 25 ft, determine the dimension $a$ of its square cross section to the nearest $\frac{1}{4}$ in. The allowable bending stress is $\sigma_{allow} = 4.5$ ksi and the allowable shear stress is $\tau_{allow} = 125$ psi.

**Prob. 12**

**13.** Select the shortest and lightest-weight steel wide-flange beam that will safely support the loading shown. The allowable bending stress is $\sigma_{allow} = 22$ ksi and the allowable shear stress is $\tau_{allow} = 12$ ksi. If there are several choices of equal weight, choose the one with the shortest height.

**Prob. 13**

**14.** Select the lightest-weight steel wide-flange beam that will safely support the loading shown. The allowable bending stress $\sigma_{allow} = 24$ ksi and the allowable shear stress of $\tau_{allow} = 14$ ksi.

**Prob. 14**

**15.** Two acetyl plastic members are to be glued together and used to support the loading shown. If the allowable bending stress for the plastic is $\sigma_{allow} = 13$ ksi and the allowable shear stress is $\tau_{allow} = 4$ ksi, determine the greatest load $P$ that can be supported and specify the required shear stress capacity of the glue.

**Prob. 15**

**\*16.** If the cable is subjected to a maximum force of $P = 50$ kN, select the lightest W310 shape that can safely support the load. The beam is made from steel having an allowable normal stress of $\sigma_{allow} = 150$ MPa and an allowable shear stress of $\tau_{allow} = 85$ MPa.

**17.** If the W360 $\times$ 45 beam is made from steel having an allowable normal stress of $\sigma_{allow} = 150$ MPa and an allowable shear stress of $\tau_{allow} = 85$ MPa, determine the maximum cable force **P** that can safely be supported by the beam.

**Probs. 16/17**

**18.** If $P = 800$ lb, determine the minimum dimension $a$ of the beam's cross section to the nearest $\frac{1}{8}$ in. to safely support the load. The wood species has an allowable normal stress of $\sigma_{allow} = 1.5$ ksi and an allowable shear stress of $\tau_{allow} = 150$ psi.

**19.** If $a = 3$ in. and the wood has an allowable normal stress of $\sigma_{allow} = 1.5$ ksi, and an allowable shear stress of $\tau_{allow} = 150$ psi, determine the maximum allowable value of $P$ acting on the beam.

**Probs. 18/19**

**\*20.** The shaft is supported by a smooth thrust bearing at $A$ and a smooth journal bearing at $B$. If $P = 5$ kN and the shaft is made from steel having an allowable normal stress of $\sigma_{allow} = 150$ MPa and an allowable shear stress of $\tau_{allow} = 85$ MPa, determine the required minimum wall thickness $t$ of the shaft to the nearest millimeter to safely support the load.

**21.** The shaft is supported by a smooth thrust bearing at $A$ and a smooth journal bearing at $B$. If the shaft is made from steel having an allowable normal stress of $\sigma_{allow} = 150$ MPa and allowable shear stress of $\tau_{allow} = 85$ MPa, determine the maximum allowable force **P** that can be applied to the shaft. The thickness of the shaft's wall is $t = 5$ mm.

**Probs. 20/21**

**22.** Determine the minimum depth $h$ of the beam to the nearest $\frac{1}{8}$ in. that will safely support the loading shown. The allowable bending stress is $\sigma_{allow} = 21$ ksi and the allowable shear stress is $\tau_{allow} = 10$ ksi. The beam has a uniform thickness of 3 in.

**Prob. 22**

**23.** The beam is constructed from three boards as shown. If each nail can support a shear force of 50 lb, determine the maximum spacing of the nails, $s, s', s''$, for regions $AB, BC$, and $CD$, respectively.

**Prob. 23**

**\*24.** The shaft is supported by a smooth thrust bearing at $A$ and smooth journal bearing at $B$. If $P = 10$ kN and the shaft is made from steel having an allowable normal stress of $\sigma_{allow} = 150$ MPa and an allowable shear stress of $\tau_{allow} = 85$ MPa, determine the required minimum wall thickness $t$ of the shaft to the nearest millimeter to safely support the load.

**25.** The circular hollow shaft is supported by a smooth thrust bearing at $A$ and smooth journal bearing at $B$. If the shaft is made from steel having an allowable normal stress of $\sigma_{allow} = 150$ MPa and allowable shear stress of $\tau_{allow} = 85$ MPa, determine the maximum allowable magnitude of the two forces **P** that can be applied to the shaft. The thickness of the shaft's wall is $t = 5$ mm.

**Probs. 24/25**

**26.** Select the lightest-weight steel wide-flange beam that will safely support the loading shown. The allowable bending stress is $\sigma_{allow} = 22$ ksi and the allowable shear stress is $\tau_{allow} = 12$ ksi.

**Prob. 26**

**27.** The steel cantilevered T-beam is made from two plates welded together as shown. Determine the maximum loads $P$ that can be safely supported on the beam if the allowable bending stress is $\sigma_{allow} = 170$ MPa and the allowable shear stress is $\tau_{allow} = 95$ MPa.

**Prob. 27**

***28.** The joist $AB$ used in housing construction is to be made from 8-in. by 1.5-in. Southern-pine boards. If the design loading on each board is placed as shown, determine the largest room width $L$ that the boards can span. The allowable bending stress for the wood is $\sigma_{allow} = 2$ ksi and the allowable shear stress is $\tau_{allow} = 180$ psi. Assume that the beam is simply supported from the walls at $A$ and $B$.

**Prob. 28**

**29.** The beam is to be used to support the machine, which exerts the forces of 6 kip and 8 kip as shown. If the maximum bending stress is not to exceed $\sigma_{allow} = 22$ ksi, determine the required width $b$ of the flanges.

**Prob. 29**

**30.** The simply supported beam supports a load of $P = 16$ kN. Determine the smallest dimension $a$ of each timber if the allowable bending stress for the wood is $\sigma_{allow} = 30$ MPa and the allowable shear stress is $\tau_{allow} = 800$ kPa. Also, if each bolt can sustain a shear of 2.5 kN, determine the spacing $s$ of the bolts at the calculated dimension $a$.

**Prob. 30**

## *3  Fully Stressed Beams

(a)

Haunched concrete beam

(b)

Wide-flange beam with cover plates

(c)

**Fig. 10**

Since the moment in a beam generally *varies* along its length, the choice of a prismatic beam is usually inefficient since it is never fully stressed at points where the internal moment is less than the maximum moment in the beam. In order to reduce the weight of the beam, engineers sometimes choose a beam having a *variable* cross-sectional area, such that at each cross section along the beam, the bending stress reaches its maximum allowable value. Beams having a variable cross-sectional area are called *nonprismatic beams*. They are often used in machines since they can be readily formed by casting. Examples are shown in Fig. 10a. In structures such beams may be "haunched" at their ends as shown in Fig. 10b. Also, beams may be "built up" or fabricated in a shop using plates. An example is a girder made from a rolled-shaped wide-flange beam and having cover plates welded to it in the region where the moment is a maximum, Fig. 10c.

The stress analysis of a nonprismatic beam is generally very difficult to perform and is beyond the scope of this text. Most often these shapes are analyzed by using a computer or the theory of elasticity. The results obtained from such an analysis, however, do indicate that the assumptions used in the derivation of the flexure formula are approximately correct for predicting the bending stresses in nonprismatic sections, provided the taper or slope of the upper or lower boundary of the beam is not too severe. On the other hand, the shear formula cannot be used for nonprismatic beam design, since the results obtained from it are very misleading.

Although caution is advised when applying the flexure formula to nonprismatic beam design, we will show here, in principle, how this formula can be used as an approximate means for obtaining the beam's general shape. In this regard, the *size* of the cross section of a nonprismatic beam that supports a given loading can be determined using the flexure formula written as

$$S = \frac{M}{\sigma_{\text{allow}}}$$

The beam for this bridge pier has a variable moment of inertia. This design will reduce material weight and save cost.

If we express the internal moment $M$ in terms of its position $x$ along the beam, then since $\sigma_{\text{allow}}$ is a known constant, the section modulus $S$ or the beam's dimensions become a function of $x$. A beam designed in this manner is called a ***fully stressed beam***. Although *only* bending stresses have been considered in approximating its final shape, attention must also be given to ensure that the beam will resist shear, especially at points where concentrated loads are applied.

## EXAMPLE | 4

Determine the shape of a fully stressed, simply supported beam that supports a concentrated force at its center, Fig. 11a. The beam has a rectangular cross section of constant width $b$, and the allowable stress is $\sigma_{\text{allow}}$.

(a)

(b)

**Fig. 11**

## SOLUTION

The internal moment in the beam, Fig. 11b, expressed as a function of position, $0 \leq x < L/2$, is

$$M = \frac{P}{2}x$$

Hence the required section modulus is

$$S = \frac{M}{\sigma_{\text{allow}}} = \frac{P}{2\sigma_{\text{allow}}}x$$

Since $S = I/c$, then for a cross-sectional area $h$ by $b$ we have

$$\frac{I}{c} = \frac{\frac{1}{12}bh^3}{h/2} = \frac{P}{2\sigma_{\text{allow}}}x$$

$$h^2 = \frac{3P}{\sigma_{\text{allow}}b}x$$

If $h = h_0$ at $x = L/2$, then

$$h_0{}^2 = \frac{3PL}{2\sigma_{\text{allow}}b}$$

so that

$$h^2 = \left(\frac{2h_0{}^2}{L}\right)x \qquad\qquad \textit{Ans.}$$

By inspection, the depth $h$ must therefore vary in a *parabolic* manner with the distance $x$.

**NOTE:** In practice this *shape* is the basis for the design of leaf springs used to support the rear-end axles of most heavy trucks or train cars as shown in the adjacent photo. Note that although this result indicates that $h = 0$ at $x = 0$, it is necessary that the beam resist shear stress at the supports, and so practically speaking, it must be required that $h > 0$ at the supports, Fig. 11a.

EXAMPLE 5

The cantilevered beam shown in Fig. 12a is formed into a trapezoidal shape having a depth $h_0$ at $A$ and a depth $3h_0$ at $B$. If it supports a load **P** at its end, determine the absolute maximum normal stress in the beam. The beam has a rectangular cross section of constant width $b$.

(a)

(b)

**Fig. 12**

### SOLUTION

At any cross section, the maximum normal stress occurs at the top and bottom surface of the beam. However, since $\sigma_{max} = M/S$ and the section modulus $S$ increases as $x$ increases, the absolute maximum normal stress does *not* necessarily occur at the wall $B$, where the moment is maximum. Using the flexure formula, we can express the maximum normal stress at an arbitrary section in terms of its position $x$, Fig. 12b. Here the internal moment has a magnitude of $M = Px$. Since the slope of the bottom of the beam is $2h_0/L$, Fig. 12a, the depth of the beam at position $x$ is

$$h = \frac{2h_0}{L}x + h_0 = \frac{h_0}{L}(2x + L)$$

Applying the flexure formula, we have

$$\sigma = \frac{Mc}{I} = \frac{Px(h/2)}{\left(\frac{1}{12}bh^3\right)} = \frac{6PL^2x}{bh_0^2(2x + L)^2} \tag{1}$$

To determine the position $x$ where the absolute maximum normal stress occurs, we must take the derivative of $\sigma$ with respect to $x$ and set it equal to zero. This gives

$$\frac{d\sigma}{dx} = \left(\frac{6PL^2}{bh_0^2}\right)\frac{1(2x + L)^2 - x(2)(2x + L)(2)}{(2x + L)^4} = 0$$

Thus,

$$4x^2 + 4xL + L^2 - 8x^2 - 4xL = 0$$

$$L^2 - 4x^2 = 0$$

$$x = \frac{1}{2}L$$

Substituting into Eq. 1 and simplifying, the absolute maximum normal stress is therefore

$$\sigma_{\substack{abs \\ max}} = \frac{3}{4}\frac{PL}{bh_0^2} \qquad\qquad Ans.$$

Note that at the wall, $B$, the maximum normal stress is

$$(\sigma_{max})_B = \frac{Mc}{I} = \frac{PL(1.5h_0)}{\left[\frac{1}{12}b(3h_0)^3\right]} = \frac{2}{3}\frac{PL}{bh_0^2}$$

which is 11.1% smaller than $\sigma_{\substack{abs \\ max}}$.

**NOTE:** Recall that the flexure formula was derived on the basis of assuming the beam to be *prismatic*. Since this is not the case here, some error is to be expected in this analysis and that of Example 4. A more exact mathematical analysis, using the theory of elasticity, reveals that application of the flexure formula as in the above example gives only small errors in the normal stress if the tapered angle of the beam is small. For example, if this angle is 15°, the stress calculated from the formula will be about 5% greater than that calculated by the more exact analysis. It may also be worth noting that the calculation of $(\sigma_{max})_B$ was done only for illustrative purposes, since, by Saint-Venant's principle, the actual stress distribution at the support (wall) is highly irregular.

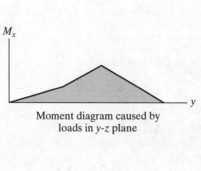

## *4 Shaft Design

Shafts that have circular cross sections are often used in the design of mechanical equipment and machinery. As a result, they can be subjected to cyclic or fatigue stress, which is caused by the combined bending and torsional loads they must transmit or resist. In addition to these loadings, stress concentrations may exist on a shaft due to keys, couplings, and sudden transitions in its cross-sectional area. In order to design a shaft properly, it is therefore necessary to take all of these effects into account.

Here we will discuss some of the important aspects of the design of shafts required to transmit power. These shafts are often subjected to loads applied to attached pulleys and gears, such as the one shown in Fig. 13a. Since the loads can be applied to the shaft at various angles, the internal bending and torsional moments at any cross section can be determined by first replacing the loads by their statically equivalent counterparts and then resolving these loads into components in two perpendicular planes, Fig. 13b. The bending-moment diagrams for the loads *in each plane* can then be drawn, and the resultant internal moment at any section along the shaft is then determined by vector addition, $M = \sqrt{M_x^2 + M_z^2}$, Fig. 13c. In addition to the moment, segments of the shaft are also subjected to different internal torques, Fig. 13b. To account for this general variation of torque along the shaft, a ***torque diagram*** may also be drawn, Fig. 13d.

(a)

(b)

Moment diagram caused by
loads in y-z plane

Moment diagram caused by
loads in x-y plane

(c)

Torque diagram caused by torques
applied about the shaft's axis

(d)

**Fig. 13**

Once the moment and torque diagrams have been established, it is then possible to investigate certain critical sections along the shaft where the *combination* of a resultant moment **M** and a torque **T** creates the worst stress situation. Since the moment of inertia of the shaft is the *same* about *any* diametrical axis, we can apply the flexure formula using the *resultant moment* to obtain the maximum bending stress. As shown in Fig. 13e, this stress will occur on two elements, C and D, each located on the outer boundary of the shaft. If a torque **T** is also resisted at this section, then a maximum shear stress is also developed on these elements, Fig. 13f. Furthermore, the external forces will also create shear stress in the shaft determined from $\tau = VQ/It$; however, this stress will generally contribute a much smaller stress distribution on the cross section compared with that developed by bending and torsion. In some cases, it must be investigated, but for simplicity, we will neglect its effect in the following analysis. In general, then, the critical element D (or C) on the shaft is subjected to *plane stress* as shown in Fig. 13g, where

(e)

$$\sigma = \frac{Mc}{I} \quad \text{and} \quad \tau = \frac{Tc}{J}$$

If the allowable normal or shear stress for the material is known, the size of the shaft is then based on the use of these equations and selection of an appropriate theory of failure. For example, if the material is known to be ductile, then the maximum-shear-stress theory may be appropriate. This theory requires the allowable shear stress, which is determined from the results of a simple tension test, to be equal to the maximum shear stress in the element. Using the stress-transformation equation for the stress state in Fig. 13g, we have

(f)

$$\tau_{\text{allow}} = \sqrt{\left(\frac{\sigma}{2}\right)^2 + \tau^2}$$

$$= \sqrt{\left(\frac{Mc}{2I}\right)^2 + \left(\frac{Tc}{J}\right)^2}$$

Since $I = \pi c^4/4$ and $J = \pi c^4/2$, this equation becomes

(g)

**Fig. 13 (cont.)**

$$\tau_{\text{allow}} = \frac{2}{\pi c^3} \sqrt{M^2 + T^2}$$

Solving for the radius of the shaft, we get

$$c = \left(\frac{2}{\pi \tau_{\text{allow}}} \sqrt{M^2 + T^2}\right)^{1/3} \tag{2}$$

Application of any other theory of failure will, of course, lead to a different formulation for c. However, in all cases it may be necessary to apply this formulation at various "critical sections" along the shaft in order to determine the particular combination of M and T that gives the largest value for c.

The following example illustrates the procedure numerically.

EXAMPLE 6

The shaft in Fig. 14a is supported by smooth journal bearings at A and B. Due to the transmission of power to and from the shaft, the belts on the pulleys are subjected to the tensions shown. Determine the smallest diameter of the shaft using the maximum-shear-stress theory, with $\tau_{\text{allow}} = 50$ MPa.

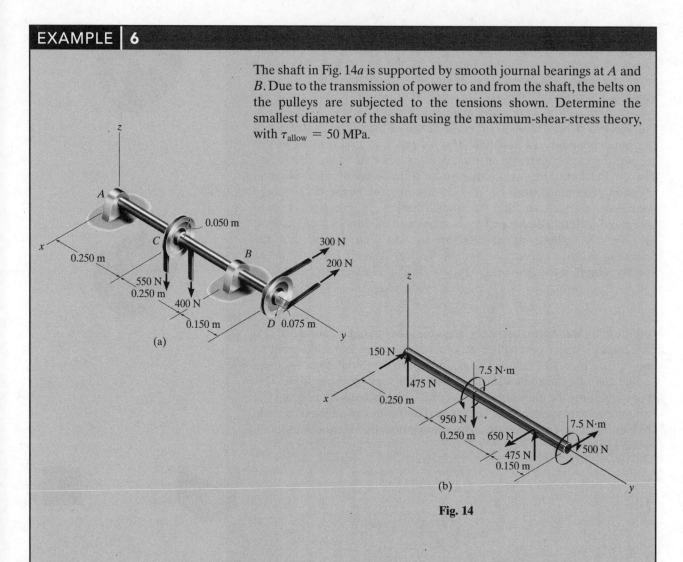

**Fig. 14**

## SOLUTION

The support reactions have been calculated and are shown on the free-body diagram of the shaft, Fig. 14b. Bending-moment diagrams for $M_x$ and $M_z$ are shown in Figs. 14c and 14d, respectively. The torque diagram is shown in Fig. 14e. By inspection, critical points for bending moment occur either at C or B. Also, just to the right of C *and* at B the torsional moment is 7.5 N·m. At C, the resultant moment is

$$M_C = \sqrt{(118.75\text{ N·m})^2 + (37.5\text{ N·m})^2} = 124.5\text{ N·m}$$

whereas at B it is smaller, namely

$$M_B = 75\text{ N·m}$$

Fig. 14 (cont.)

Since the design is based on the maximum-shear-stress theory, Eq. 2 applies. The radical $\sqrt{M^2 + T^2}$ will be the largest at a section just to the right of $C$. We have

$$c = \left( \frac{2}{\pi \tau_{\text{allow}}} \sqrt{M^2 + T^2} \right)^{1/3}$$

$$= \left( \frac{2}{\pi (50)(10^6) \ \text{N/m}^2} \sqrt{(124.5 \ \text{N} \cdot \text{m})^2 + (7.5 \ \text{N} \cdot \text{m})^2} \right)^{1/3}$$

$$= 0.0117 \ \text{m}$$

Thus, the smallest allowable diameter is

$$d = 2(0.0117 \ \text{m}) = 23.3 \ \text{mm} \qquad \qquad Ans.$$

# PROBLEMS

**31.** Determine the variation in the depth $w$ as a function of $x$ for the cantilevered beam that supports a concentrated force **P** at its end so that it has a maximum bending stress $\sigma_{\text{allow}}$ throughout its length. The beam has a constant thickness $t$.

**Prob. 31**

**\*32.** The beam is made from a plate that has a constant thickness $b$. If it is simply supported and carries a uniform load $w$, determine the variation of its depth as a function of $x$ so that it maintains a constant maximum bending stress $\sigma_{\text{allow}}$ throughout its length.

**Prob. 32**

**33.** The simply supported tapered rectangular beam with constant width $b$ supports the concentrated forces **P**. Determine the absolute maximum normal stress developed in the beam and specify its location.

**Prob. 33**

**34.** The beam is made from a plate that has a constant thickness $b$. If it is simply supported and carries the distributed loading shown, determine the variation of its depth as a function of $x$ so that it maintains a constant maximum bending stress $\sigma_{\text{allow}}$ throughout its length.

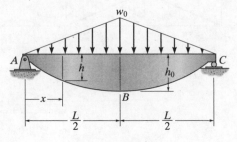

**Prob. 34**

**35.** Determine the variation in the depth $d$ of a cantilevered beam that supports a concentrated force **P** at its end so that it has a constant maximum bending stress $\sigma_{\text{allow}}$ throughout its length. The beam has a constant width $b_0$.

**Prob. 35**

**\*36.** Determine the variation of the radius $r$ of the cantilevered beam that supports the uniform distributed load so that it has a constant maximum bending stress $\sigma_{\text{max}}$ throughout its length.

**Prob. 36**

626

**37.** Determine the height $h$ of the rectangular cantilever beam of constant width $b$ in terms of $h_0$, $L$, and $x$ so that the maximum normal stress in the beam is constant throughout its length.

**39.** The tubular shaft has an inner diameter of 15 mm. Determine to the nearest millimeter its minimum outer diameter if it is subjected to the gear loading. The bearings at $A$ and $B$ exert force components only in the $y$ and $z$ directions on the shaft. Use an allowable shear stress of $\tau_{allow} = 70$ MPa, and base the design on the maximum-shear-stress theory of failure.

**\*40.** Determine to the nearest millimeter the minimum diameter of the solid shaft if it is subjected to the gear loading. The bearings at $A$ and $B$ exert force components only in the $y$ and $z$ directions on the shaft. Base the design on the maximum-distortion-energy theory of failure with $\sigma_{allow} = 150$ MPa.

**Prob. 37**

**Probs. 39/40**

**38.** Determine the variation in the width $b$ as a function of $x$ for the cantilevered beam that supports a uniform distributed load along its centerline so that it has the same maximum bending stress $\sigma_{allow}$ throughout its length. The beam has a constant depth $t$.

**41.** The 50-mm diameter shaft is supported by a smooth thrust bearing at $A$ and a smooth journal bearing at $B$. If the pulleys $C$ and $D$ are subjected to the vertical and horizontal loadings shown, determine the absolute maximum bending stress in the shaft.

**Prob. 38**

**Prob. 41**

**42.** The shaft is supported by a smooth thrust bearing at *A* and a smooth journal bearing at *B*. If shaft is made from material having an allowable bending stress of $\sigma_{allow} = 150$ MPa, determine the minimum diameter of the shaft to the nearest millimeter.

**Prob. 42**

**43.** The two pulleys attached to the shaft are loaded as shown. If the bearings at *A* and *B* exert only vertical forces on the shaft, determine the required diameter of the shaft to the nearest $\frac{1}{8}$ in. using the maximum-shear-stress theory. $\tau_{allow} = 12$ ksi.

**Prob. 43**

***44.** The two pulleys attached to the shaft are loaded as shown. If the bearings at *A* and *B* exert only vertical forces on the shaft, determine the required diameter of the shaft to the nearest $\frac{1}{8}$ in. using the maximum-distortion energy theory. $\sigma_{allow} = 67$ ksi.

**Prob. 44**

**45.** The bearings at *A* and *D* exert only *y* and *z* components of force on the shaft. If $\tau_{allow} = 60$ MPa, determine to the nearest millimeter the smallest-diameter shaft that will support the loading. Use the maximum-shear-stress theory of failure.

**Prob. 45**

**46.** The bearings at *A* and *D* exert only *y* and *z* components of force on the shaft. If $\sigma_{allow} = 130$ MPa, determine to the nearest millimeter the smallest-diameter shaft that will support the loading. Use the maximum-distortion-energy theory of failure.

**Prob. 46**

# CHAPTER REVIEW

Failure of a beam occurs when the internal shear or moment in the beam is a maximum. To resist these loadings, it is therefore important that the associated maximum shear and bending stress not exceed allowable values as stated in codes. Normally, the cross section of a beam is first designed to resist the allowable bending stress,

$$\sigma_{allow} = \frac{M_{max}\, c}{I}$$

Then the allowable shear stress is checked. For rectangular sections, $\tau_{allow} \geq 1.5(V_{max}/A)$ and for wide-flange sections it is appropriate to use $\tau_{allow} \geq V_{max}/A_{web}$. In general, use

$$\tau_{allow} = \frac{VQ}{It}$$

For built-up beams, the spacing of fasteners or the strength of glue or weld is determined using an allowable shear flow

$$q_{allow} = \frac{VQ}{I}$$

Fully stressed beams are nonprismatic and designed such that each cross section along the beam will resist the allowable bending stress. This will define the shape of the beam.

A mechanical shaft generally is designed to resist both torsion and bending stresses. Normally, the internal bending moment can be resolved into two planes, and so it is necessary to draw the moment diagrams for each bending-moment component and then select the maximum moment based on vector addition. Once the maximum bending and shear stresses are determined, then depending upon the type of material, an appropriate theory of failure is used to compare the allowable stress to what is required.

# REVIEW PROBLEMS

**47.** The cantilevered beam has a circular cross section. If it supports a force **P** at its end, determine its radius $y$ as a function of $x$ so that it is subjected to a constant maximum bending stress $\sigma_{allow}$ throughout its length.

**49.** The bearings at $A$ and $B$ exert only $x$ and $z$ components of force on the steel shaft. Determine the shaft's diameter to the nearest millimeter so that it can resist the loadings of the gears without exceeding an allowable shear stress of $\tau_{allow} = 80$ MPa. Use the maximum-shear-stress theory of failure.

**Prob. 47**

**Prob. 49**

***48.** Select the lightest-weight steel wide-flange beam that will safely support the loading. Assume the support at $A$ is a pin and the support at $B$ is a roller. The allowable bending stress is $\sigma_{allow} = 24$ ksi and the allowable shear stress is $\tau_{allow} = 14$ ksi.

**50.** The bearings at $A$ and $B$ exert only $x$ and $z$ components of force on the steel shaft. Determine the shaft's diameter to the nearest millimeter so that it can resist the loadings of the gears. Use the maximum-distortion-energy theory of failure with $\sigma_{allow} = 200$ MPa.

**Prob. 48**

**Prob. 50**

**51.** Select the lightest-weight steel wide-flange beam that will safely support the loading shown. The allowable bending stress is $\sigma_{allow} = 22$ ksi and the allowable shear stress is $\tau_{allow} = 22$ ksi.

**Prob. 51**

**53.** The simply supported joist is used in the construction of a floor for a building. In order to keep the floor low with respect to the sill beams $C$ and $D$, the ends of the joists are notched as shown. If the allowable shear stress for the wood is $\tau_{allow} = 350$ psi and the allowable bending stress is $\sigma_{allow} = 1700$ psi, determine the smallest height $h$ so that the beam will support a load of $P = 600$ lb. Also, will the entire joist safely support the load? Neglect the stress concentration at the notch.

**Prob. 53**

**\*52.** The simply supported joist is used in the construction of a floor for a building. In order to keep the floor low with respect to the sill beams $C$ and $D$, the ends of the joists are notched as shown. If the allowable shear stress for the wood is $\tau_{allow} = 350$ psi and the allowable bending stress is $\sigma_{allow} = 1500$ psi, determine the height $h$ that will cause the beam to reach both allowable stresses at the same time. Also, what load $P$ causes this to happen? Neglect the stress concentration at the notch.

**54.** The overhang beam is constructed using two 2-in. by 4-in. pieces of wood braced as shown. If the allowable bending stress is $\sigma_{allow} = 600$ psi, determine the largest load $P$ that can be applied. Also, determine the associated maximum spacing of nails, $s$, along the beam section $AC$ if each nail can resist a shear force of 800 lb. Assume the beam is pin-connected at $A$, $B$, and $D$. Neglect the axial force developed in the beam along $DA$.

**Prob. 52**

**Prob. 54**

# Selected Answers

**1.** $b = 211$ mm, $h = 264$ mm
**2.** Use $b = 4$ in.
**3.** Use $b = 5$ in.
**5.** Use W12 × 16
**6.** Yes.
**7.** No.
**9.** Use W360 × 45
**10.** Yes.
**11.** $P = 2.49$ kN
**13.** Use W12 × 26
**14.** Use W24 × 62
**15.** $P = 12.5$ kip, $\tau_{\text{req'd}} = 466$ psi
**17.** $P = 103$ kN
**18.** Use $a = 3\dfrac{1}{8}$ in.

**19.** $P = 750$ lb
**21.** $P = 6.24$ kN
**22.** Use $h = 9\dfrac{1}{8}$ in.
**23.** $s = 0.710$ in., $s' = 0.568$ in., $s'' = 2.84$ in.
**25.** $P = 13.7$ kN
**26.** Use W14 × 22
**27.** $P = 2.90$ kN
**29.** $b = 5.86$ in.
**30.** $a = 106$ mm, $s = 44.3$ mm
**31.** $w = \dfrac{w_0}{L}x$

**33.** $x = \dfrac{L}{3}, \dfrac{2L}{3}, \sigma_{\text{max}}^{\text{abs}} = \dfrac{18PL}{25bh_0^2}$
**34.** $h = \dfrac{h_0}{L^{3/2}}(3L^2x - 4x^3)^{1/2}$
**35.** $d = h\sqrt{\dfrac{x}{L}}$
**37.** $h = \dfrac{h_0}{L}x$
**38.** $b = \dfrac{b_0}{L^2}x^2$
**39.** Use $d = 21$ mm
**41.** $\sigma_{\text{max}} = 13.4$ MPa
**42.** Use $d = 23$ mm
**43.** Use $d = 1\dfrac{5}{8}$ in.
**45.** Use $d = 36$ mm
**46.** Use $d = 35$ mm
**47.** $y = \left[\dfrac{4P}{\pi\sigma_{\text{allow}}}x\right]^{\frac{1}{2}}$
**49.** Use $d = 44$ mm
**50.** Use $d = 41$ mm
**51.** Use W18 × 50
**53.** $h = 0.643$ in. Yes, the joist will support the load.
**54.** $P = 178$ lb, $s = 12.0$ in.

632

# Fundamental Problems Partial Solutions and Answers

## F1

$V_{max} = 12$ kN $\qquad M_{max} = 18$ kN $\cdot$ m

$$\sigma_{allow} = \frac{M_{max}c}{I}; \quad 10(10^6) = \frac{18(10^3)(a)}{\frac{2}{3}a^4}$$

$$a = 0.1392 \text{ m} = 139.2 \text{ mm}$$

Use $a = 140$ mm $\hspace{2cm}$ *Ans.*

$$I = \frac{2}{3}(0.14^4) = 0.2561(10^{-3}) \text{ m}^4$$

$$Q_{max} = \frac{0.14}{2}(0.14)(0.14) = 1.372(10^{-3}) \text{ m}^3$$

$$\tau_{max} = \frac{V_{max}Q_{max}}{It} = \frac{12(10^3)[1.372(10^{-3})]}{[0.2561(10^{-3})](0.14)}$$

$$= 0.459 \text{ MPa} < \tau_{allow} = 1 \text{ MPa (OK)}$$

## F2

$V_{max} = 3$ kip $\qquad M_{max} = 12$ kip $\cdot$ ft

$$I = \frac{\pi}{4}\left(\frac{d}{2}\right)^4 = \frac{\pi d^4}{64}$$

$$\sigma_{allow} = \frac{M_{max}c}{I}; \quad 20 = \frac{12(12)\left(\frac{d}{2}\right)}{\frac{\pi d^4}{64}}$$

$$d = 4.19 \text{ in.}$$

Use $d = 4\frac{1}{4}$ in. $\hspace{2cm}$ *Ans.*

$$I = \frac{\pi}{64}(4.25^4) = 16.015 \text{ in}^4$$

$$Q_{max} = \frac{4(4.25/2)}{3\pi}\left[\frac{1}{2}\left(\frac{\pi}{4}\right)(4.25^2)\right] = 6.397 \text{ in}^3$$

$$\tau_{max} = \frac{V_{max}Q_{max}}{It} = \frac{3(6.397)}{16.015(4.25)}$$

$$= 0.282 \text{ ksi} < \tau_{allow} = 10 \text{ ksi (OK)}$$

## F3

$V_{max} = 10$ kN $\qquad M_{max} = 5$ kN $\cdot$ m

$$I = \frac{1}{12}(a)(2a)^3 = \frac{2}{3}a^4$$

$$\sigma_{allow} = \frac{M_{max}c}{I}; \quad 12(10^6) = \frac{5(10^3)(a)}{\frac{2}{3}a^4}$$

$$a = 0.0855 \text{ m} = 85.5 \text{ mm}$$

Use $a = 86$ mm $\hspace{2cm}$ *Ans.*

$$I = \frac{2}{3}(0.086^4) = 36.4672(10^{-6}) \text{ m}^4$$

$$Q_{max} = \frac{0.086}{2}(0.086)(0.086)$$

$$= 0.318028(10^{-3}) \text{ m}^3$$

$$\tau_{max} = \frac{V_{max}Q_{max}}{It} = \frac{10(10^3)[0.318028(10^{-3})]}{[36.4672(10^{-6})](0.086)}$$

$$= 1.01 \text{ MPa} < \tau_{allow} = 1.5 \text{ MPa (OK)}$$

## F4

$V_{max} = 4.5$ kip $\qquad M_{max} = 6.75$ kip $\cdot$ ft

$$I = \frac{1}{12}(4)(h^3) = \frac{h^3}{3}$$

$$\sigma_{allow} = \frac{M_{max}c}{I}; \quad 2 = \frac{6.75(12)\left(\frac{h}{2}\right)}{\frac{h^3}{3}}$$

$$h = 7.794 \text{ in.}$$

$$Q_{max} = y'A' = \frac{h}{4}\left(\frac{h}{2}\right)(4) = \frac{h^2}{2}$$

$$\tau_{max} = \frac{V_{max}Q_{max}}{It}; \quad 0.2 = \frac{4.5\left(\frac{h^2}{2}\right)}{\frac{h^3}{3}(4)}$$

$$h = 8.4375 \text{ in. (controls)}$$

Use $h = 8\frac{1}{2}$ in. $\hspace{2cm}$ *Ans.*

## F5

$V_{max} = 25$ kN $\qquad M_{max} = 20$ kN $\cdot$ m

$$I = \frac{1}{12}(b)(3b)^3 = 2.25b^4$$

$$\sigma_{allow} = \frac{M_{max}c}{I}; \quad 12(10^6) = \frac{20(10^3)(1.5b)}{2.25b^4}$$

$$b = 0.1036 \text{ m} = 103.6 \text{ mm}$$

Use $b = 104$ mm $\hspace{2cm}$ *Ans.*

$$I = 2.25(0.104^4) = 0.2632(10^{-3}) \text{ m}^4$$

$$Q_{max} = 0.75(0.104)[1.5(0.104)(0.104)] = 1.2655(10^{-3}) \text{ m}^3$$

$$\tau_{max} = \frac{V_{max}Q_{max}}{It} = \frac{25(10^3)[1.2655(10^{-3})]}{[0.2632(10^{-3})](0.104)}$$

$$= 1.156 \text{ MPa} < \tau_{allow} = 1.5 \text{ MPa (OK)}.$$

**F6**

$V_{\text{max}} = 150 \text{ kN} \qquad M_{\text{max}} = 150 \text{ kN} \cdot \text{m}$

$S_{\text{req'd}} = \dfrac{M_{\text{max}}}{\sigma_{\text{allow}}} = \dfrac{150(10^3)}{150(10^6)} = 0.001 \text{ m}^3 = 1000(10^3) \text{ mm}^3$

Select W410 × 67 [$S_x = 1200(10^3)$ mm$^3$, $d = 410$ mm,

and $t_w = 8.76$ mm]. *Ans.*

$\tau_{\text{max}} = \dfrac{V}{t_w d} = \dfrac{150(10^3)}{0.00876(0.41)}$

$\qquad = 41.76 \text{ MPa} < \tau_{\text{allow}} = 75 \text{ MPa (OK)}$

# Deflection of Beams and Shafts

From Chapter 12 of *Mechanics of Materials*, Ninth Edition. R. C. Hibbeler. Copyright © 2014 by Pearson Education, Inc.
Published by Pearson Prentice Hall. All rights reserved.

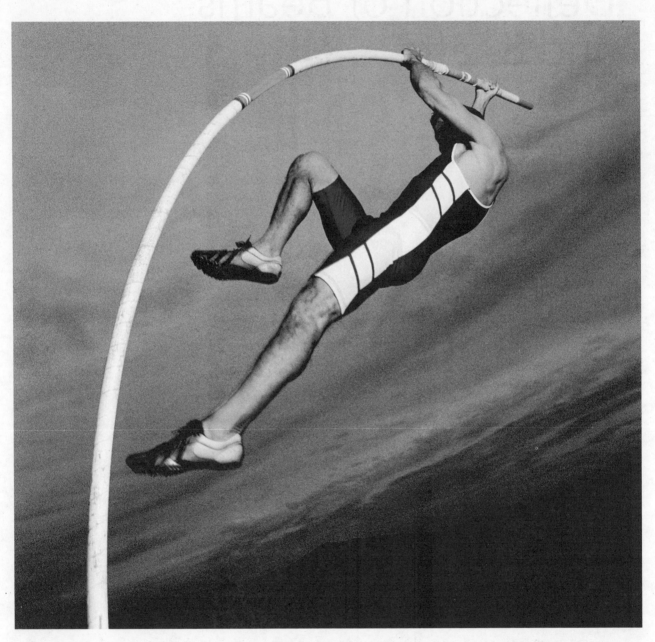

If the curvature of this pole is measured, it is then possible to determine the bending stress developed within it.

# Deflection of Beams and Shafts

## CHAPTER OBJECTIVES

■ Often limits must be placed on the amount of deflection a beam or shaft may undergo when it is subjected to a load, and so in this chapter we will discuss various methods for determining the deflection and slope at specific points on beams and shafts. The analytical methods include the integration method, the use of discontinuity functions, and the method of superposition. Also, a semigraphical technique, called the moment-area method, will be presented. At the end of the chapter, we will use these methods to solve for the support reactions on a beam or shaft that is statically indeterminate.

## 1  The Elastic Curve

The deflection of a beam or shaft must often be limited in order to provide integrity and stability of a structure or machine, and prevent the cracking of any attached brittle materials such as concrete or glass. Furthermore, code restrictions often require these members not vibrate or deflect severely in order to safely support their intended loading. Most important, though, deflections at specific points on a beam or shaft must be determined if one is to analyze those that are statically indeterminate.

Before the slope or the displacement at a point on a beam (or shaft) is determined, it is often helpful to sketch the deflected shape of the beam when it is loaded, in order to "visualize" any computed results and thereby partially check these results. The deflection curve of the longitudinal axis that passes through the centroid of each cross-sectional area of a beam is called the *elastic curve*. For most beams the elastic curve can be sketched without much difficulty. When doing so, however, it is necessary to know how the slope or displacement is restricted at various types of supports. In general, supports that resist a *force*, such as a pin, restrict *displacement*, and those that resist a *moment*, such as a fixed wall, restrict *rotation* or *slope* as well as displacement. With this in mind, two typical examples of the elastic curves for loaded beams (or shafts), sketched to an exaggerated scale, are shown in Fig. 1.

**Fig. 1**

Positive internal moment
concave upwards

(a)

Negative internal moment
concave downwards

(b)

**Fig. 2**

If the elastic curve for a beam seems difficult to establish, it is suggested that the moment diagram for the beam be drawn first. Using the beam sign convention, a positive a positive internal moment tends to bend the beam concave upward, Fig. 2a. Likewise, a negative moment tends to bend the beam concave downward, Fig. 2b. Therefore, if the moment diagram is *known*, it will be easy to construct the elastic curve. For example, consider the beam in Fig. 3a with its associated moment diagram shown in Fig. 3b. Due to the roller and pin supports, the displacement at $B$ and $D$ must be zero. Within the region of negative moment, $AC$, Fig. 3b, the elastic curve must be concave downward, and within the region of positive moment, $CD$, the elastic curve must be concave upward. Hence, there must be an *inflection point* at point $C$, where the curve changes from concave up to concave down, since this is a point of zero moment. Using these facts, the beam's elastic curve is sketched in Fig. 3c. It should also be noted that the displacements $\Delta_A$ and $\Delta_E$ are especially critical. At point $E$ the *slope* of the elastic curve is *zero*, and there the beam's *deflection* may be a *maximum*. Whether $\Delta_E$ is actually greater than $\Delta_A$ depends on the relative magnitudes of $\mathbf{P}_1$ and $\mathbf{P}_2$ and the location of the roller at $B$.

Following these same principles, note how the elastic curve in Fig. 4 was constructed. Here the beam is cantilevered from a fixed support at $A$ and therefore the elastic curve must have both zero displacement and zero slope at this point. Also, the largest displacement will occur either at $D$, where the slope is zero, or at $C$.

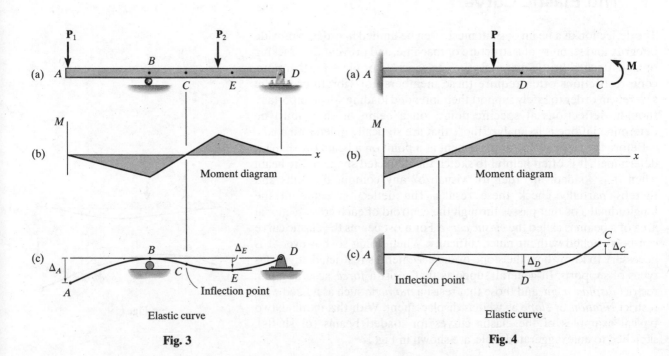

Moment diagram

Elastic curve

**Fig. 3**

Moment diagram

Inflection point

Elastic curve

**Fig. 4**

## Moment-Curvature Relationship.

**Moment-Curvature Relationship.** We will now develop an important relationship between the internal moment and the radius of curvature $\rho$ (rho) of the elastic curve at a point. The resulting equation will be used for establishing each of the methods presented in the chapter for finding the slope and displacement at points on the elastic curve.

The following analysis, here and in the next section, will require the use of three coordinates. As shown in Fig. 5a, the $x$ axis extends positive to the right, along the initially straight longitudinal axis of the beam. It is used to locate the differential element, having an undeformed width $dx$. The $v$ axis extends *positive upward* from the $x$ axis. It measures the *displacement* of the elastic curve. Lastly, a "localized" $y$ coordinate is used to specify the position of a fiber in the beam element. It is measured *positive upward* from the neutral axis (or elastic curve) as shown in Fig. 5b. Recall that this same sign convention for $x$ and $y$ was used in the derivation of the flexure formula.

To derive the relationship between the internal moment and $\rho$, we will limit the analysis to the most common case of an initially straight beam that is elastically deformed by loads applied perpendicular to the beam's $x$ axis and lying in the $x–v$ plane of symmetry for the beam's cross-sectional area. Due to the loading, the deformation of the beam is caused by both the internal shear force and bending moment. If the beam has a length that is much greater than its depth, the greatest deformation will be caused by bending, and therefore we will direct our attention to its effects.

(a)

Before deformation

After deformation

(b)

**Fig. 5**

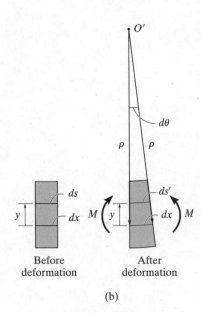

Before deformation   After deformation

(b)

**Fig 5 (cont.)**

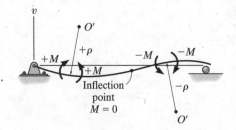

**Fig. 6**

When the internal moment $M$ deforms the element of the beam, the angle between the cross sections becomes $d\theta$, Fig. 5b. The arc $dx$ represents a portion of the elastic curve that intersects the neutral axis for each cross section. The *radius of curvature* for this arc is defined as the distance $\rho$, which is measured from the *center of curvature O'* to $dx$. Any arc on the element other than $dx$ is subjected to a normal strain. For example, the strain in arc $ds$, located at a position $y$ from the neutral axis, is $\epsilon = (ds' - ds)/ds$. However, $ds = dx = \rho\, d\theta$ and $ds' = (\rho - y)\, d\theta$, and so $\epsilon = [(\rho - y)\, d\theta - \rho\, d\theta]/\rho\, d\theta$ or

$$\frac{1}{\rho} = -\frac{\epsilon}{y} \tag{1}$$

If the material is homogeneous and behaves in a linear-elastic manner, then Hooke's law applies, $\epsilon = \sigma/E$. Also, since the flexure formula applies, $\sigma = -My/I$. Combining these two equations and substituting into the above equation, we have

$$\boxed{\frac{1}{\rho} = \frac{M}{EI}} \tag{2}$$

where

> $\rho$ = the radius of curvature at the point on the elastic curve ($1/\rho$ is referred to as the *curvature*)
>
> $M$ = the internal moment in the beam at the point
>
> $E$ = the material's modulus of elasticity
>
> $I$ = the beam's moment of inertia about the neutral axis

The product $EI$ in this equation is referred to as the *flexural rigidity*, and it is always a positive quantity. The sign for $\rho$ therefore depends on the direction of the moment. As shown in Fig. 6, when $M$ is *positive*, $\rho$ extends *above* the beam, i.e., in the positive $v$ direction; when $M$ is *negative*, $\rho$ extends *below* the beam, or in the negative $v$ direction.

Using the flexure formula, $\sigma = -My/I$, we can also express the curvature in terms of the stress in the beam, namely,

$$\frac{1}{\rho} = -\frac{\sigma}{Ey} \tag{3}$$

Both Eqs. 2 and 3 are valid for either small or large radii of curvature. However, the value of $\rho$ is almost always calculated as a *very large quantity*. For example, consider an A-36 steel beam made from a W14 × 53, where $E_{st} = 29(10^3)$ ksi and $\sigma_Y = 36$ ksi. When the material at the outer fibers, $y = \pm 7$ in., is about to *yield*, then, from Eq. 3, $\rho = \pm 5639$ in. Values of $\rho$ calculated at other points along the beam's elastic curve may be even *larger*, since $\sigma$ cannot exceed $\sigma_Y$ at the outer fibers.

## 2  Slope and Displacement by Integration

The equation of the elastic curve for a beam can be expressed mathematically as $v = f(x)$. To obtain this equation, we must first represent the curvature $(1/\rho)$ in terms of $v$ and $x$. In most calculus books it is shown that this relationship is

$$\frac{1}{\rho} = \frac{d^2v/dx^2}{[1 + (dv/dx)^2]^{3/2}}$$

Substituting into Eq. 2, we have

$$\frac{d^2v/dx^2}{[1 + (dv/dx)^2]^{3/2}} = \frac{M}{EI} \tag{4}$$

This equation represents a nonlinear second-order differential equation. Its solution, which is called the *elastica*, gives the exact shape of the elastic curve, assuming, of course, that beam deflections occur only due to bending. Through the use of higher mathematics, elastica solutions have been obtained only for simple cases of beam geometry and loading.

In order to facilitate the solution of a greater number of deflection problems, Eq. 4 can be modified. Most engineering design codes specify *limitations* on deflections for tolerance or esthetic purposes, and as a result the elastic deflections for the majority of beams and shafts form a shallow curve. Consequently, the *slope* of the elastic curve, which is determined from $dv/dx$, will be *very small*, and its square will be negligible compared with unity.* Therefore the curvature, as defined above, can be *approximated* by $1/\rho = d^2v/dx^2$. Using this simplification, Eq. 4 can now be written as

$$\frac{d^2v}{dx^2} = \frac{M}{EI} \tag{5}$$

It is also possible to write this equation in two alternative forms. If we differentiate each side with respect to $x$ and substitute $V = dM/dx$, we get

$$\frac{d}{dx}\left(EI\frac{d^2v}{dx^2}\right) = V(x) \tag{6}$$

Differentiating again, using $w = dV/dx$, yields

$$\frac{d^2}{dx^2}\left(EI\frac{d^2v}{dx^2}\right) = w(x) \tag{7}$$

*See Example 1.

For most problems the flexural rigidity ($EI$) will be constant along the length of the beam. Assuming this to be the case, the above results may be reordered into the following set of three equations:

$$EI\frac{d^4v}{dx^4} = w(x) \tag{8}$$

$$EI\frac{d^3v}{dx^3} = V(x) \tag{9}$$

$$EI\frac{d^2v}{dx^2} = M(x) \tag{10}$$

Solution of any of these equations requires successive integrations to obtain the deflection $v$ of the elastic curve. For each integration it is necessary to introduce a "constant of integration" and then solve for all the constants to obtain a unique solution for a particular problem. For example, if the distributed load $w$ is expressed as a function of $x$ and Eq. 8 is used, then four constants of integration must be evaluated; however, if the internal moment $M$ is determined and Eq. 10 is used, only two constants of integration must be found. The choice of which equation to start with depends on the problem. Generally, however, it is easier to determine the internal moment $M$ as a function of $x$, integrate twice, and evaluate only two integration constants.

If the loading on a beam is discontinuous, that is, consists of a series of several distributed and concentrated loads, then several functions must be written for the internal moment, each valid within the region between the discontinuities. Also, for convenience in writing each moment expression, *the origin* for each $x$ coordinate can be *selected arbitrarily*. For example, consider the beam shown in Fig. 7a. The internal moment in regions $AB$, $BC$, and $CD$ can be written in terms of the $x_1$, $x_2$, and $x_3$ coordinates selected, as shown in either Fig. 7b or Fig. 7c, or in fact in any manner that will yield $M = f(x)$ in as simple a form as possible. Once these functions are integrated twice through the use of Eq. 10 and the constants of integration determined, the functions will give the slope and deflection (elastic curve) for each region of the beam for which they are valid.

(a)

(b)

(c)

**Fig. 7**

**Sign Convention and Coordinates.** When applying Eqs. 8 through 10, it is important to use the proper signs for *M, V,* or *w* as established by the sign convention that was used in the derivation of these equations. For review, these terms are shown in their *positive directions* in Fig. 8*a*. Furthermore, recall that *positive deflection, v,* is *upward,* and as a result, the *positive slope angle* θ will be measured *counterclockwise* from the *x* axis when *x* is *positive to the right.* The reason for this is shown in Fig. 8*b*. Here positive increases *dx* and *dv* in *x* and *v* create an increased θ that is counterclockwise. If, however, *positive x* is directed to the *left,* then θ will be *positive clockwise,* Fig. 8*c*.

Realize that by assuming *dv/dx* to be very small, the original horizontal length of the beam's axis and the arc of its elastic curve will be about the same. In other words, *ds* in Figs. 8*b* and 8*c* is approximately equal to *dx,* since $ds = \sqrt{(dx)^2 + (dv)^2} = \sqrt{1 + (dv/dx)^2}\, dx \approx dx$. As a result, points on the elastic curve are assumed to be *displaced vertically,* and not horizontally. Also, since the *slope angle* θ will be *very small,* its value in radians can be determined *directly* from $\theta \approx \tan\theta = dv/dx$.

The design of a roof system requires a careful consideration of deflection. For example, rain can accumulate on areas of the roof, which then causes ponding, leading to further deflection, then further ponding, and finally possible failure of the roof.

Positive sign convention

(a)

Positive sign convention

(b)

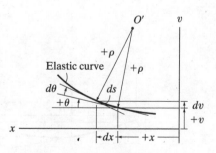

Positive sign convention

(c)

**Fig. 8**

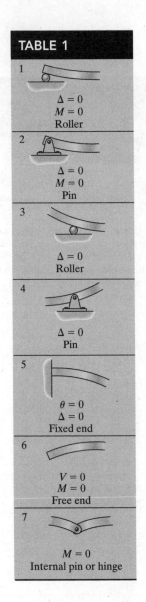

**TABLE 1**

1
$\Delta = 0$
$M = 0$
Roller

2
$\Delta = 0$
$M = 0$
Pin

3
$\Delta = 0$
Roller

4
$\Delta = 0$
Pin

5
$\theta = 0$
$\Delta = 0$
Fixed end

6
$V = 0$
$M = 0$
Free end

7
$M = 0$
Internal pin or hinge

**Boundary and Continuity Conditions.** When solving Eqs. 8, 9, or 10, the constants of integration are determined by evaluating the functions for shear, moment, slope, or displacement at a particular point on the beam where the value of the function is known. These values are called **boundary conditions**. Several possible boundary conditions that are often used to solve beam (or shaft) deflection problems are listed in Table 1. For example, if the beam is supported by a roller or pin (1, 2, 3, 4), then it is required that the displacement be *zero* at these points. Furthermore, if these supports are located at the *ends of the beam* (1, 2), the internal moment in the beam must also be zero. At the fixed support (5), the slope and displacement are both zero, whereas the free-ended beam (6) has both zero moment and zero shear. Lastly, if two segments of a beam are connected by an "internal" pin or hinge (7), the moment must be zero at this connection.

If the elastic curve cannot be expressed using a single coordinate, then **continuity conditions** must be used to evaluate some of the integration constants. For example, consider the beam in Fig. 9a. Here two $x$ coordinates are chosen with origins at $A$. Each is valid only within the regions $0 \leq x_1 \leq a$ and $a \leq x_2 \leq (a + b)$. Once the functions for the slope and deflection are obtained, they must give the *same values* for the slope and deflection at point $B$ so the elastic curve is physically *continuous*. Expressed mathematically, this requires that $\theta_1(a) = \theta_2(a)$ and $v_1(a) = v_2(a)$. These conditions can be used to evaluate two constants of integration. If instead the elastic curve is expressed in terms of the coordinates $0 \leq x_1 \leq a$ and $0 \leq x_2 \leq b$, shown in Fig. 9b, then the continuity of slope and deflection at $B$ requires $\theta_1(a) = -\theta_2(b)$ and $v_1(a) = v_2(b)$. In this particular case, a *negative* sign is necessary to match the slopes at $B$ since $x_1$ extends positive to the right, whereas $x_2$ extends positive to the left. Consequently, $\theta_1$ is positive counterclockwise, and $\theta_2$ is positive clockwise. See Figs. 8b and 8c.

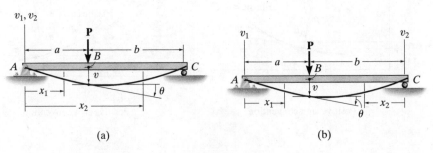

(a)    (b)

**Fig. 9**

# Procedure for Analysis

The following procedure provides a method for determining the slope and deflection of a beam (or shaft) using the method of integration.

## Elastic Curve.

- Draw an exaggerated view of the beam's elastic curve. Recall that zero slope and zero displacement occur at all fixed supports, and zero displacement occurs at all pin and roller supports.

- Establish the $x$ and $v$ coordinate axes. The $x$ axis must be parallel to the undeflected beam and can have an origin at any point along the beam, with a positive direction either to the right or to the left. In all cases, the associated positive $v$ axis should be directed upward.

- If several discontinuous loads are present, establish $x$ coordinates that are valid for each region of the beam between the discontinuities. Choose these coordinates so that they will simplify subsequent algebraic work.

## Load or Moment Function.

- For each region in which there is an $x$ coordinate, express the loading $w$ or the internal moment $M$ as a function of $x$. In particular, *always* assume that $M$ acts in the *positive direction* when applying the equation of moment equilibrium to determine $M = f(x)$.

## Slope and Elastic Curve.

- Provided $EI$ is constant, apply either the load equation $EI\, d^4v/dx^4 = w(x)$, which requires four integrations to get $v = v(x)$, or the moment equation $EI\, d^2v/dx^2 = M(x)$, which requires only two integrations. For each integration it is important to include a constant of integration.

- The constants are evaluated using the boundary conditions for the supports (Table 1) and the continuity conditions that apply to slope and displacement at points where two functions meet. Once the constants are evaluated and substituted back into the slope and deflection equations, the slope and displacement at *specific points* on the elastic curve can then be determined.

- The numerical values obtained can be checked graphically by comparing them with the sketch of the elastic curve. Realize that *positive* values for *slope* are *counterclockwise* if the $x$ axis extends *positive* to the *right*, and *clockwise* if the $x$ axis extends *positive* to the *left*. In either of these cases, *positive displacement* is *upward*.

## EXAMPLE | 1

The cantilevered beam shown in Fig. 10*a* is subjected to a vertical load **P** at its end. Determine the equation of the elastic curve. *EI* is constant.

### SOLUTION I

**Elastic Curve.** The load tends to deflect the beam as shown in Fig. 10*a*. By inspection, the internal moment can be represented throughout the beam using a single *x* coordinate.

**Moment Function.** From the free-body diagram, with **M** acting in the *positive direction*, Fig. 10*b*, we have

$$M = -Px$$

**Slope and Elastic Curve.** Applying Eq. 10 and integrating twice yields

$$EI\frac{d^2v}{dx^2} = -Px \qquad (1)$$

$$EI\frac{dv}{dx} = -\frac{Px^2}{2} + C_1 \qquad (2)$$

$$EIv = -\frac{Px^3}{6} + C_1 x + C_2 \qquad (3)$$

(a)

Using the boundary conditions $dv/dx = 0$ at $x = L$ and $v = 0$ at $x = L$, Eqs. 2 and 3 become

$$0 = -\frac{PL^2}{2} + C_1$$

$$0 = -\frac{PL^3}{6} + C_1 L + C_2$$

(b)

**Fig. 10**

Thus, $C_1 = PL^2/2$ and $C_2 = -PL^3/3$. Substituting these results into Eqs. 2 and 3 with $\theta = dv/dx$, we get

$$\theta = \frac{P}{2EI}(L^2 - x^2)$$

$$v = \frac{P}{6EI}(-x^3 + 3L^2 x - 2L^3) \qquad Ans.$$

Maximum slope and displacement occur at $A\,(x = 0)$, for which

$$\theta_A = \frac{PL^2}{2EI} \qquad (4)$$

$$v_A = -\frac{PL^3}{3EI} \qquad (5)$$

The *positive* result for $\theta_A$ indicates *counterclockwise* rotation and the *negative* result for $v_A$ indicates that $v_A$ is *downward*. This agrees with the results sketched in Fig. 10a.

In order to obtain some idea as to the actual *magnitude* of the slope and displacement at the end $A$, consider the beam in Fig. 10a to have a length of 15 ft, support a load of $P = 6$ kip, and be made of A-36 steel having $E_{st} = 29(10^3)$ ksi. If this beam was designed without a factor of safety by assuming the allowable normal stress is equal to the yield stress $\sigma_{allow} = 36$ ksi; then a W12 $\times$ 26 would be found to be adequate ($I = 204$ in$^4$). From Eqs. 4 and 5 we get

$$\theta_A = \frac{6 \text{ kip}(15 \text{ ft})^2(12 \text{ in./ft})^2}{2[29(10^3) \text{ kip/in}^2](204 \text{ in}^4)} = 0.0164 \text{ rad}$$

$$v_A = -\frac{6 \text{ kip}(15 \text{ ft})^3(12 \text{ in./ft})^3}{3[29(10^3) \text{ kip/in}^2](204 \text{ in}^4)} = -1.97 \text{ in.}$$

Since $\theta_A^2 = (dv/dx)^2 = 0.000270 \text{ rad}^2 \ll 1$, this justifies the use of Eq. 10, rather than applying the more exact Eq. 4, for computing the deflection of beams. Also, since this numerical application is for a *cantilevered beam*, we have obtained *larger values* for $\theta$ and $v$ than would have been obtained if the beam were supported using pins, rollers, or other fixed supports.

## SOLUTION II

This problem can also be solved using Eq. 8, $EI \, d^4v/dx^4 = w(x)$. Here $w(x) = 0$ for $0 \le x \le L$, Fig. 10a, so that upon integrating once we get the form of Eq. 9, i.e.,

$$EI\frac{d^4v}{dx^4} = 0$$

$$EI\frac{d^3v}{dx^3} = C_1' = V$$

The shear constant $C_1'$ can be evaluated at $x = 0$, since $V_A = -P$ (negative according to the beam sign convention, Fig. 8a). Thus, $C_1' = -P$. Integrating again yields the form of Eq. 10, i.e.,

$$EI\frac{d^3v}{dx^3} = -P$$

$$EI\frac{d^2v}{dx^2} = -Px + C_2' = M$$

Here $M = 0$ at $x = 0$, so $C_2' = 0$, and as a result one obtains Eq. 1 and the solution proceeds as before.

EXAMPLE | 2

The simply supported beam shown in Fig. 11a supports the triangular distributed loading. Determine its maximum deflection. $EI$ is constant.

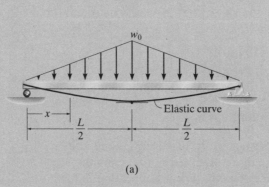

$$\frac{1}{2}\left(\frac{2w_0}{L}x\right)x = \frac{w_0 x^2}{L}$$

$$w = \frac{2w_0}{L}x$$

(a)

(b)

**Fig. 11**

## SOLUTION I

**Elastic Curve.** Due to symmetry, only one $x$ coordinate is needed for the solution, in this case $0 \leq x \leq L/2$. The beam deflects as shown in Fig. 11a. The maximum deflection occurs at the center since the slope is zero at this point.

**Moment Function.** A free-body diagram of the segment on the left is shown in Fig. 11b. The equation for the distributed loading is

$$w = \frac{2w_0}{L}x \qquad (1)$$

Hence,

$$\zeta + \Sigma M_{NA} = 0; \qquad M + \frac{w_0 x^2}{L}\left(\frac{x}{3}\right) - \frac{w_0 L}{4}(x) = 0$$

$$M = -\frac{w_0 x^3}{3L} + \frac{w_0 L}{4}x$$

**Slope and Elastic Curve.** Using Eq. 10 and integrating twice, we have

$$EI\frac{d^2v}{dx^2} = M = -\frac{w_0}{3L}x^3 + \frac{w_0L}{4}x \tag{2}$$

$$EI\frac{dv}{dx} = -\frac{w_0}{12L}x^4 + \frac{w_0L}{8}x^2 + C_1$$

$$EIv = -\frac{w_0}{60L}x^5 + \frac{w_0L}{24}x^3 + C_1x + C_2$$

The constants of integration are obtained by applying the boundary condition $v = 0$ at $x = 0$ and the symmetry condition that $dv/dx = 0$ at $x = L/2$. This leads to

$$C_1 = -\frac{5w_0L^3}{192} \qquad C_2 = 0$$

Hence,

$$EI\frac{dv}{dx} = -\frac{w_0}{12L}x^4 + \frac{w_0L}{8}x^2 - \frac{5w_0L^3}{192}$$

$$EIv = -\frac{w_0}{60L}x^5 + \frac{w_0L}{24}x^3 - \frac{5w_0L^3}{192}x$$

Determining the maximum deflection at $x = L/2$, we have

$$v_{\max} = -\frac{w_0L^4}{120EI} \qquad\qquad Ans.$$

## SOLUTION II

Since the distributed loading acts downward, it is negative according to our sign convention. Using Eq. 1 and applying Eq. 8, we have

$$EI\frac{d^4v}{dx^4} = -\frac{2w_0}{L}x$$

$$EI\frac{d^3v}{dx^3} = V = -\frac{w_0}{L}x^2 + C_1'$$

Since $V = +w_0L/4$ at $x = 0$, then $C_1' = w_0L/4$. Integrating again yields

$$EI\frac{d^3v}{dx^3} = V = -\frac{w_0}{L}x^2 + \frac{w_0L}{4}$$

$$EI\frac{d^2v}{dx^2} = M = -\frac{w_0}{3L}x^3 + \frac{w_0L}{4}x + C_2'$$

Here $M = 0$ at $x = 0$, so $C_2' = 0$. This yields Eq. 2. The solution now proceeds as before.

## EXAMPLE | 3

The simply supported beam shown in Fig. 12a is subjected to the concentrated force. Determine the maximum deflection of the beam. $EI$ is constant.

(a)

(b)

### SOLUTION

**Elastic Curve.** The beam deflects as shown in Fig. 12b. Two coordinates must be used, since the moment function will change at $B$. Here we will take $x_1$ and $x_2$, having the *same origin* at $A$.

**Moment Function.** From the free-body diagrams shown in Fig. 12c,

$$M_1 = 2x_1$$

$$M_2 = 2x_2 - 6(x_2 - 2) = 4(3 - x_2)$$

**Slope and Elastic Curve.** Applying Eq. 10 for $M_1$, for $0 \leq x_1 < 2$ m, and integrating twice yields

$$EI\frac{d^2v_1}{dx_1^2} = 2x_1$$

$$EI\frac{dv_1}{dx_1} = x_1^2 + C_1 \qquad (1)$$

$$EIv_1 = \frac{1}{3}x_1^3 + C_1x_1 + C_2 \qquad (2)$$

Likewise for $M_2$, for $2$ m $< x_2 \leq 3$ m,

$$EI\frac{d^2v_2}{dx_2^2} = 4(3 - x_2)$$

$$EI\frac{dv_2}{dx_2} = 4\left(3x_2 - \frac{x_2^2}{2}\right) + C_3 \qquad (3)$$

$$EIv_2 = 4\left(\frac{3}{2}x_2^2 - \frac{x_2^3}{6}\right) + C_3x_2 + C_4 \qquad (4)$$

(c)

**Fig. 12**

The four constants are evaluated using *two* boundary conditions, namely, $x_1 = 0$, $v_1 = 0$ and $x_2 = 3$ m, $v_2 = 0$. Also, *two* continuity conditions must be applied at $B$, that is, $dv_1/dx_1 = dv_2/dx_2$ at $x_1 = x_2 = 2$ m and $v_1 = v_2$ at $x_1 = x_2 = 2$ m. Substitution as specified results in the following four equations:

$$v_1 = 0 \text{ at } x_1 = 0; \qquad 0 = 0 + 0 + C_2$$

$$v_2 = 0 \text{ at } x_2 = 3 \text{ m}; \qquad 0 = 4\left(\frac{3}{2}(3)^2 - \frac{(3)^3}{6}\right) + C_3(3) + C_4$$

$$\left.\frac{dv_1}{dx_1}\right|_{x=2m} = \left.\frac{dv_2}{dx_2}\right|_{x=2m}; \quad (2)^2 + C_1 = 4\left(3(2) - \frac{(2)^2}{2}\right) + C_3$$

$$v_1(2 \text{ m}) = v_2(2 \text{ m}); \qquad \frac{1}{3}(2)^3 + C_1(2) + C_2 = 4\left(\frac{3}{2}(2)^2 - \frac{(2)^3}{6}\right) + C_3(2) + C_4$$

Solving, we get

$$C_1 = -\frac{8}{3} \qquad\qquad C_2 = 0$$

$$C_3 = -\frac{44}{3} \qquad\qquad C_4 = 8$$

Thus Eqs. 1-4 become

$$EI\frac{dv_1}{dx_1} = x_1{}^2 - \frac{8}{3} \qquad\qquad (5)$$

$$EIv_1 = \frac{1}{3}x_1{}^3 - \frac{8}{3}x_1 \qquad\qquad (6)$$

$$EI\frac{dv_2}{dx_2} = 12x_2 - 2x_2{}^2 - \frac{44}{3} \qquad\qquad (7)$$

$$EIv_2 = 6x_2{}^2 - \frac{2}{3}x_2{}^3 - \frac{44}{3}x_2 + 8 \qquad\qquad (8)$$

By inspection of the elastic curve, Fig. 12*b*, the maximum deflection occurs at $D$, somewhere within region $AB$. Here the slope must be zero. From Eq. 5,

$$x_1{}^2 - \frac{8}{3} = 0$$

$$x_1 = 1.633$$

Substituting into Eq. 6,

$$v_{\text{max}} = -\frac{2.90 \text{ kN} \cdot \text{m}^3}{EI} \qquad\qquad Ans.$$

The negative sign indicates that the deflection is downward.

## EXAMPLE | 4

The beam in Fig. 13a is subjected to a load at its end. Determine the displacement at C. EI is constant.

(a)

(b)

**Fig. 13**

### SOLUTION

**Elastic Curve.** The beam deflects into the shape shown in Fig. 13a. Due to the loading, two x coordinates will be considered, namely, $0 \leq x_1 < 2$ m and $0 \leq x_2 < 1$ m, where $x_2$ is directed to the left from C, since the internal moment is easy to formulate.

**Moment Functions.** Using the free-body diagrams shown in Fig. 13b, we have

$$M_1 = -2x_1 \qquad M_2 = -4x_2$$

**Slope and Elastic Curve.** Applying Eq. 10,

For $0 \leq x_1 \leq 2$: $\quad EI\dfrac{d^2v_1}{dx_1^2} = -2x_1$

$$EI\dfrac{dv_1}{dx_1} = -x_1^2 + C_1 \tag{1}$$

$$EIv_1 = -\dfrac{1}{3}x_1^3 + C_1x_1 + C_2 \tag{2}$$

For $0 \le x_2 \le 1$ m:
$$EI\frac{d^2v_2}{dx_2{}^2} = -4x_2$$

$$EI\frac{dv_2}{dx_2} = -2x_2{}^2 + C_3 \qquad (3)$$

$$EIv_2 = -\frac{2}{3}x_2{}^3 + C_3x_2 + C_4 \qquad (4)$$

The *four* constants of integration are determined using *three* boundary conditions, namely, $v_1 = 0$ at $x_1 = 0$, $v_1 = 0$ at $x_1 = 2$ m, and $v_2 = 0$ at $x_2 = 1$ m, and *one* continuity equation. Here the continuity of slope at the roller requires $dv_1/dx_1 = -dv_2/dx_2$ at $x_1 = 2$ m and $x_2 = 1$ m. Why is there a negative sign in this equation? (Note that continuity of displacement at $B$ has been indirectly considered in the boundary conditions, since $v_1 = v_2 = 0$ at $x_1 = 2$ m and $x_2 = 1$ m.) Applying these four conditions yields

$v_1 = 0$ at $x_1 = 0$; $\qquad 0 = 0 + 0 + C_2$

$v_1 = 0$ at $x_1 = 2$ m; $\qquad 0 = -\frac{1}{3}(2)^3 + C_1(2) + C_2$

$v_2 = 0$ at $x_2 = 1$ m; $\qquad 0 = -\frac{2}{3}(1)^3 + C_3(1) + C_4$

$\left.\dfrac{dv_1}{dx_1}\right|_{x=2\,\mathrm{m}} = \left.\dfrac{dv_2}{dx_2}\right|_{x=1\,\mathrm{m}}; \quad -(2)^2 + C_1 = -(-2(1)^2 + C_3)$

Solving, we obtain

$$C_1 = \frac{4}{3} \qquad C_2 = 0 \qquad C_3 = \frac{14}{3} \qquad C_4 = -4$$

Substituting $C_3$ and $C_4$ into Eq. 4 gives

$$EIv_2 = -\frac{2}{3}x_2{}^3 + \frac{14}{3}x_2 - 4$$

The displacement at $C$ is determined by setting $x_2 = 0$. We get

$$v_C = -\frac{4\,\mathrm{kN \cdot m^3}}{EI} \qquad\qquad Ans.$$

# PRELIMINARY PROBLEMS

**P1.** In each case, determine the internal bending moment as a function of $x$, and state the necessary boundary and/or continuity conditions used to determine the elastic curve for the beam.

(d)

(a)

(e)

(b)

(f)

(c)

**Prob. 1**

# FUNDAMENTAL PROBLEMS

**F1.** Determine the slope and deflection of end $A$ of the cantilevered beam. $E = 200$ GPa and $I = 65.0(10^6)$ mm$^4$.

**F1**

**F2.** Determine the slope and deflection of end $A$ of the cantilevered beam. $E = 200$ GPa and $I = 65.0(10^6)$ mm$^4$.

**F2**

**F3.** Determine the slope of end $A$ of the cantilevered beam. $E = 200$ GPa and $I = 65.0(10^6)$ mm$^4$.

**F3**

**F4.** Determine the maximum deflection of the simply supported beam. The beam is made of wood having a modulus of elasticity of $E_w = 1.5(10^3)$ ksi and a rectangular cross section of width $b = 3$ in. and height $h = 6$ in.

**F4**

**F5.** Determine the maximum deflection of the simply supported beam. $E = 200$ GPa and $I = 39.9(10^{-6})$ m$^4$.

**F5**

**F6.** Determine the slope of the simply supported beam at $A$. $E = 200$ GPa and $I = 39.9(10^{-6})$ m$^4$.

**F6**

## PROBLEMS

**1.** An L2 steel strap having a thickness of 0.125 in. and a width of 2 in. is bent into a circular arc of radius 600 in. Determine the maximum bending stress in the strap.

**2.** The L2 steel blade of the band saw wraps around the pulley having a radius of 12 in. Determine the maximum normal stress in the blade. The blade has a width of 0.75 in. and a thickness of 0.0625 in.

12 in.

**Prob. 2**

**3.** A picture is taken of a man performing a pole vault, and the minimum radius of curvature of the pole is estimated by measurement to be 4.5 m. If the pole is 40 mm in diameter and it is made of a glass-reinforced plastic for which $E_g$ = 131 GPa, determine the maximum bending stress in the pole.

$\rho$ = 4.5 m

**Prob. 3**

**\*4.** Determine the equations of the elastic curve using the $x_1$ and $x_2$ coordinates. $EI$ is constant.

P

$a$

$L$

$x_1$

$x_2$

**Prob. 4**

**5.** Determine the deflection of end $C$ of the 100-mm-diameter solid circular shaft. The shaft is made of steel having a modulus elasticity of $E$ = 200 GPa.

A

B

C

$x_1$

$x_2$

2 m

1 m

6 kN

**Prob. 5**

**6.** Determine the equations of the elastic curve for the beam using the $x_1$ and $x_3$ coordinates. Specify the beam's maximum deflection. $EI$ is constant.

P

A

B

$x_1$

$L$

$\dfrac{L}{2}$

$x_3$

**Prob. 6**

**7.** The beam is made of two rods and is subjected to the concentrated load **P**. Determine the maximum deflection of the beam if the moments of inertia of the rods are $I_{AB}$ and $I_{BC}$, and the modulus of elasticity is $E$.

**Prob. 7**

**\*8.** The shaft is supported at $A$ by a journal bearing that exerts only vertical reactions on the shaft, and at $C$ by a thrust bearing that exerts horizontal and vertical reactions on the shaft. Determine the equations of the elastic curve using the coordinates $x_1$ and $x_2$. $EI$ is constant.

**Prob. 8**

**9.** Determine the equations of the elastic curve for the beam using the $x_1$ and $x_2$ coordinates. $EI$ is constant.

**Prob. 9**

**10.** Determine the equations of the elastic curve for the beam using the $x$ coordinate. Specify the slope at $A$ and maximum deflection. $EI$ is constant.

**11.** Determine the deflection at the center of the beam and the slope at $B$. $EI$ is constant.

**Probs. 10/11**

**\*12.** Determine the equations of the elastic curve for the beam using the $x_1$ and $x_2$ coordinates. Specify the slope at $A$ and the maximum displacement of the beam. $EI$ is constant.

**Prob. 12**

**13.** Determine the maximum deflection of the beam and the slope at $A$. $EI$ is constant.

**Prob. 13**

**14.** The simply supported shaft has a moment of inertia of $2I$ for region $BC$ and a moment of inertia $I$ for regions $AB$ and $CD$. Determine the maximum deflection of the shaft due to the load **P**.

**Prob. 14**

**15.** The two wooden meter sticks are separated at their centers by a smooth rigid cylinder having a diameter of 50 mm. Determine the force $F$ that must be applied at each end in order to just make their ends touch. Each stick has a width of 20 mm and a thickness of 5 mm. $E_w = 11$ GPa.

**Prob. 15**

**\*16.** The pipe can be assumed roller supported at its ends and by a rigid saddle $C$ at its center. The saddle rests on a cable that is connected to the supports. Determine the force that should be developed in the cable if the saddle keeps the pipe from sagging or deflecting at its center. The pipe and fluid within it have a combined weight of 125 lb/ft. $EI$ is constant.

**Prob. 16**

**17.** Determine the elastic curve in terms of the $x_1$ and $x_2$ coordinates. What is the deflection of end $C$ of the shaft? $EI$ is constant.

**Prob. 17**

**18.** The bar is supported by a roller constraint at $B$, which allows vertical displacement but resists axial load and moment. If the bar is subjected to the loading shown, determine the slope at $A$ and the deflection at $C$. $EI$ is constant.

**19.** Determine the deflection at $B$ of the bar in Prob. 18.

**Probs. 18/19**

**\*20.** Determine the equations of the elastic curve using the $x_1$ and $x_2$ coordinates, and specify the slope at $A$ and the deflection at $C$. $EI$ is constant.

**Prob. 20**

**21.** Determine the maximum deflection of the solid circular shaft. The shaft is made of steel having $E = 200$ GPa. It has a diameter of 100 mm.

**Prob. 21**

**22.** Determine the elastic curve for the cantilevered W14 × 30 beam using the $x$ coordinate. Specify the maximum slope and maximum deflection. $E = 29(10^3)$ ksi.

**Prob. 22**

**23.** Determine the equations of the elastic curve using the coordinates $x_1$ and $x_2$, and specify the deflection and slope at $C$. $EI$ is constant.

**Probs. 12–23**

**\*24.** Determine the equations of the elastic curve using the coordinates $x_1$ and $x_2$, and specify the slope at $A$. $EI$ is constant.

**Probs. 24**

**25.** The floor beam of the airplane is subjected to the loading shown. Assuming that the fuselage exerts only vertical reactions on the ends of the beam, determine the maximum deflection of the beam. $EI$ is constant.

**Prob. 25**

**26.** Determine the maximum deflection of the rectangular simply supported beam. The beam is made of wood having a modulus of elasticity of $E = 1.5 (10^3)$ ksi.

Prob. 26

**27.** Determine the elastic curve and the maximum deflection of the cantilever beam.

Prob. 27

**\*28.** Determine the slope at end $B$ and the maximum deflection of the cantilever triangular plate of constant thickness $t$. The plate is made of material having a modulus of elasticity of $E$.

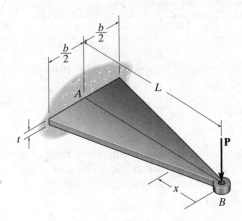

Prob. 28

**29.** Determine the equation of the elastic curve using the coordinates $x_1$ and $x_2$, and specify the slope and deflection at $B$. $EI$ is constant.

**30.** Determine the equations of the elastic curve using the coordinates $x_1$ and $x_3$, and specify the slope and deflection at point $B$. $EI$ is constant.

Probs. 29/30

## *3  Discontinuity Functions

The method of integration, used to find the equation of the elastic curve for a beam or shaft, is convenient if the load or internal moment can be expressed as a continuous function throughout the beam's entire length. If several different loadings act on the beam, however, the method becomes more tedious to apply, because separate loading or moment functions must be written for each region of the beam. Furthermore, integration of these functions requires the evaluation of integration constants using both boundary and continuity conditions. For example, the beam shown in Fig. 14 requires four moment functions to be written. They describe the moment in regions $AB$, $BC$, $CD$, and $DE$. When applying the moment-curvature relationship, $EI\,d^2v/dx^2 = M$, and integrating each moment equation twice, we must evaluate eight constants of integration. These involve two boundary conditions that require zero displacement at points $A$ and $E$, and six continuity conditions for both slope and displacement at points $B$, $C$, and $D$.

In this section, we will discuss a method for finding the equation of the elastic curve for a *multiply loaded beam* using a *single expression*, either formulated from the loading on the beam, $w = w(x)$, or from the beam's internal moment, $M = M(x)$. If the expression for $w$ is substituted into $EI\,d^4v/dx^4 = w(x)$ and integrated four times, or if the expression for $M$ is substituted into $EI\,d^2v/dx^2 = M(x)$ and integrated twice, the constants of integration will be determined only from the boundary conditions. Since the continuity equations will not be involved, the analysis will be greatly simplified.

For safety, the beams supporting these bags of cement must be designed for strength and a restricted amount of deflection.

**Discontinuity Functions.**   In order to express the load on the beam or the internal moment within it using a single expression, we will use two types of mathematical operators known as *discontinuity functions*.

**Fig. 14**

**TABLE 2**

| Loading | Loading Function $w = w(x)$ | Shear $V = \int w(x)dx$ | Moment $M = \int V dx$ |
|---|---|---|---|
| (1) $M_0$ | $w = M_0\langle x-a \rangle^{-2}$ | $V = M_0\langle x-a \rangle^{-1}$ | $M = M_0\langle x-a \rangle^{0}$ |
| (2) $P$ | $w = P\langle x-a \rangle^{-1}$ | $V = P\langle x-a \rangle^{0}$ | $M = P\langle x-a \rangle^{1}$ |
| (3) $w_0$ | $w = w_0\langle x-a \rangle^{0}$ | $V = w_0\langle x-a \rangle^{1}$ | $M = \dfrac{w_0}{2}\langle x-a \rangle^{2}$ |
| (4) slope $= m$ | $w = m\langle x-a \rangle^{1}$ | $V = \dfrac{m}{2}\langle x-a \rangle^{2}$ | $M = \dfrac{m}{6}\langle x-a \rangle^{3}$ |

**Macaulay Functions.** For purposes of beam or shaft deflection, Macaulay functions, named after the mathematician W. H. Macaulay, can be used to describe *distributed loadings*. These functions can be written in general form as

$$\langle x - a \rangle^n = \begin{cases} 0 & \text{for } x < a \\ (x - a)^n & \text{for } x \geq a \end{cases} \qquad (11)$$
$$n \geq 0$$

Here $x$ represents the coordinate position of a point along the beam, and $a$ is the location on the beam where a "discontinuity" occurs, namely the point where a distributed loading *begins*. Note that the Macaulay function $\langle x - a \rangle^n$ is written with angle (or Macaulay) brackets to distinguish it from the ordinary function $(x - a)^n$, written with parentheses. As stated by the equation, only when $x \geq a$ is $\langle x - a \rangle^n = (x - a)^n$, otherwise it is zero. Furthermore, these functions are valid only for exponential values $n \geq 0$. Integration of Macaulay functions follows the same rules as for ordinary functions, i.e.,

$$\int \langle x - a \rangle^n dx = = \frac{\langle x - a \rangle^{n+1}}{n + 1} + C \qquad (12)$$

Note how the Macaulay functions describe both the *uniform load* $w_0$ ($n = 0$) and *triangular load* ($n = 1$), shown in Table 2, items 3 and 4. This type of description can, of course, be extended to distributed loadings having other forms. Also, it is possible to use superposition with the uniform and triangular loadings to create the Macaulay function for a trapezoidal loading. Using integration, the Macaulay functions for shear, $V = \int w(x)\,dx$, and moment, $M = \int V\,dx$, are also shown in the table.

**Singularity Functions.** These functions are only used to describe the point location of concentrated forces or couple moments acting on a beam or shaft. Specifically, a concentrated force **P** can be considered as a special case of an infinitely large distributed loading, where the intensity of the loading is $w = P/\epsilon$ such that its length is $\epsilon$, where $\epsilon \to 0$, Fig. 15. The area under this loading diagram is equivalent to $P$, *positive upwards*, and has this value only when $x = a$. We will use a symbolic representation $w$ to express this result, namely

$$w = P\langle x - a\rangle^{-1} = \begin{cases} 0 & \text{for } x \neq a \\ P & \text{for } x = a \end{cases} \qquad (13)$$

This expression is referred to as a *singularity function* since it takes on the value $P$ only at the point $x = a$ where the load acts, otherwise it is zero.*

In a similar manner, a couple moment $\mathbf{M}_0$, considered *positive clockwise*, is a limit as $\epsilon \to 0$ of two distributed loadings as shown in Fig. 16. Here the following function describes its value.

**Fig. 15**

$$w = M_0\langle x - a\rangle^{-2} = \begin{cases} 0 & \text{for } x \neq a \\ M_0 & \text{for } x = a \end{cases} \qquad (14)$$

The exponent $n = -2$, in order to ensure that the units of $w$, force per length, are maintained.

Integration of the above two singularity functions follow the rules of operational calculus and yields results that are *different* from those of Macaulay functions. Specifically,

$$\int \langle x - a\rangle^n dx = \langle x - a\rangle^{n+1}, n = -1, -2 \qquad (15)$$

Using this formula, notice how $M_0$ and $P$, described in Table 2, items 1 and 2, are integrated once, then twice, to obtain the internal shear and moment in the beam.

Application of Eqs. 11 through 15 provides a rather direct means for expressing the loading or the internal moment in a beam as a function of $x$. When doing so, close attention must be paid to the signs of the external loadings. As stated above, and as shown in Table 2, *concentrated forces and distributed loads are positive upward, and couple moments are positive clockwise*. If this sign convention is followed, then the internal shear and moment are in accordance with the beam sign convention.

**Fig. 16**

---

*This function $\langle x - a\rangle^{-1}$ is also referred to as a unit impulse function or the Dirac delta.

As an example of how to apply discontinuity functions to describe the loading or internal moment consider the beam loaded as shown in Fig. 17a. Here the reactive 2.75-kN force created by the roller, Fig. 17b, is positive since it acts upward, and the 1.5-kN · m couple moment is also positive since it acts clockwise. Finally, the trapezoidal loading is negative and has been separated into triangular and uniform loadings. From Table 2, the loading at any point $x$ on the beam is therefore

$$w = 2.75\,\text{kN}\langle x - 0\rangle^{-1} + 1.5\,\text{kN}\cdot\text{m}\langle x - 3\,\text{m}\rangle^{-2} - 3\,\text{kN/m}\langle x - 3\,\text{m}\rangle^{0} - 1\,\text{kN/m}^2\langle x - 3\,\text{m}\rangle^{1}$$

The reactive force at $B$ is not included here since $x$ is never greater than 6 m, and furthermore, this value is of no consequence in calculating the slope or deflection. We can determine the moment expression directly from Table 2, rather than integrating this expression twice. In either case,

$$M = 2.75\,\text{kN}\langle x - 0\rangle^{1} + 1.5\,\text{kN}\cdot\text{m}\langle x - 3\,\text{m}\rangle^{0} - \frac{3\,\text{kN/m}}{2}\langle x - 3\,\text{m}\rangle^{2} - \frac{1\,\text{kN/m}^2}{6}\langle x - 3\,\text{m}\rangle^{3}$$

$$= 2.75x + 1.5\langle x - 3\rangle^{0} - 1.5\langle x - 3\rangle^{2} - \frac{1}{6}\langle x - 3\rangle^{3}$$

The deflection of the beam can now be determined after this equation is integrated two successive times and the constants of integration are evaluated using the boundary conditions of zero displacement at $A$ and $B$.

Fig. 17

## Procedure for Analysis

The following procedure provides a method for using discontinuity functions to determine a beam's elastic curve. This method is particularly advantageous for solving problems involving beams or shafts subjected to *several loadings*, since the constants of integration can be evaluated by using *only* the boundary conditions, while the compatibility conditions are automatically satisfied.

### Elastic Curve.

- Sketch the beam's elastic curve and identify the boundary conditions at the supports.

- Zero displacement occurs at all pin and roller supports, and zero slope and zero displacement occur at fixed supports.

- Establish the $x$ axis so that it extends to the right and has its origin at the beam's left end.

### Load or Moment Function.

- Calculate the support reactions and then use the discontinuity functions in Table 2 to express either the loading $w$ or the internal moment $M$ as a function of $x$. Make sure to follow the sign convention for each loading as it applies for this equation.

- Note that the distributed loadings must extend all the way to the beam's right end to be valid. If this does not occur, use the method of superposition, which is illustrated in Example 6.

### Slope and Elastic Curve.

- Substitute $w$ into $EI\,d^4v/dx^4 = w(x)$, or $M$ into the moment curvature relation $EI\,d^2v/dx^2 = M$, and integrate to obtain the equations for the beam's slope and deflection.

- Evaluate the constants of integration using the boundary conditions, and substitute these constants into the slope and deflection equations to obtain the final results.

- When the slope and deflection equations are evaluated at any point on the beam, a *positive slope* is *counterclockwise*, and a *positive displacement* is *upward*.

## EXAMPLE | 5

Determine the maximum deflection of the beam shown in Fig. 18a. *EI* is constant.

(a)

(b)

**Fig. 18**

## SOLUTION

**Elastic Curve.** The beam deflects as shown in Fig. 18a. The boundary conditions require zero displacement at *A* and *B*.

**Loading Function.** The reactions have been calculated and are shown on the free-body diagram in Fig. 18b. The loading function for the beam can be written as

$$w = -8 \text{ kip } \langle x - 0 \rangle^{-1} + 6 \text{ kip } \langle x - 10 \text{ ft} \rangle^{-1}$$

The couple moment and force at *B* are not included here, since they are located at the right end of the beam, and *x* cannot be greater than 30 ft. Integrating $dV/dx = w(x)$, we get

$$V = -8 \langle x - 0 \rangle^0 + 6 \langle x - 10 \rangle^0$$

In a similar manner, $dM/dx = V$ yields

$$M = -8 \langle x - 0 \rangle^1 + 6 \langle x - 10 \rangle^1$$
$$= (-8x + 6 \langle x - 10 \rangle^1) \text{ kip} \cdot \text{ft}$$

Notice how this equation can also be established *directly* using the results of Table 2 for moment.

**Slope and Elastic Curve.**   Integrating twice yields

$$EI\frac{d^2v}{dx^2} = -8x + 6\langle x - 10 \rangle^1$$

$$EI\frac{dv}{dx} = -4x^2 + 3\langle x - 10 \rangle^2 + C_1$$

$$EIv = -\frac{4}{3}x^3 + \langle x - 10 \rangle^3 + C_1 x + C_2 \qquad (1)$$

From Eq. 1, the boundary condition $v = 0$ at $x = 10$ ft and $v = 0$ at $x = 30$ ft gives

$$0 = -1333 + (10 - 10)^3 + C_1(10) + C_2$$
$$0 = -36\,000 + (30 - 10)^3 + C_1(30) + C_2$$

Solving these equations simultaneously for $C_1$ and $C_2$, we get $C_1 = 1333$ and $C_2 = -12\,000$. Thus,

$$EI\frac{dv}{dx} = -4x^2 + 3\langle x - 10 \rangle^2 + 1333 \qquad (2)$$

$$EIv = -\frac{4}{3}x^3 + \langle x - 10 \rangle^3 + 1333x - 12\,000 \qquad (3)$$

From Fig. 18a, maximum displacement may occur either at $C$, or at $D$, where the slope $dv/dx = 0$. To obtain the displacement of $C$, set $x = 0$ in Eq. 3. We get

$$v_C = -\frac{12\,000 \text{ kip} \cdot \text{ft}^3}{EI} \qquad \qquad Ans.$$

The *negative* sign indicates that the displacement is *downward* as shown in Fig. 18a. To locate point $D$, use Eq. 2 with $x > 10$ ft and $dv/dx = 0$. This gives

$$0 = -4x_D{}^2 + 3(x_D - 10)^2 + 1333$$

$$x_D{}^2 + 60x_D - 1633 = 0$$

Solving for the positive root,

$$x_D = 20.3 \text{ ft}$$

Hence, from Eq. 3,

$$EIv_D = -\frac{4}{3}(20.3)^3 + (20.3 - 10)^3 + 1333(20.3) - 12\,000$$

$$v_D = \frac{5006 \text{ kip} \cdot \text{ft}^3}{EI}$$

Comparing this value with $v_C$, we see that $v_{max} = v_C$.

# EXAMPLE | 6

(a)

(b)

**Fig. 19**

Determine the equation of the elastic curve for the cantilevered beam shown in Fig. 19a. EI is constant.

## SOLUTION

**Elastic Curve.** The loads cause the beam to deflect as shown in Fig. 19a. The boundary conditions require zero slope and displacement at $A$.

**Loading Function.** The support reactions at $A$ have been calculated and are shown on the free-body diagram in Fig. 19b. Since the distributed loading in Fig. 19a does not extend to $C$ as required, we can use the superposition of loadings shown in Fig. 19b to represent the same effect. By our sign convention, the beam's loading is therefore

$$w = 52 \text{ kN} \langle x - 0 \rangle^{-1} - 258 \text{ kN} \cdot \text{m} \langle x - 0 \rangle^{-2} - 8 \text{ kN/m} \langle x - 0 \rangle^{0}$$
$$+ 50 \text{ kN} \cdot \text{m} \langle x - 5 \text{ m} \rangle^{-2} + 8 \text{ kN/m} \langle x - 5 \text{ m} \rangle^{0}$$

The 12-kN load is *not included* here, since $x$ cannot be greater than 9 m. Because $dV/dx = w(x)$, then by integrating, neglecting the constant of integration since the reactions are included in the load function, we have

$$V = 52 \langle x - 0 \rangle^{0} - 258 \langle x - 0 \rangle^{-1} - 8 \langle x - 0 \rangle^{1} + 50 \langle x - 5 \rangle^{-1} + 8 \langle x - 5 \rangle^{1}$$

Furthermore, $dM/dx = V$, so that integrating again yields

$$M = -258 \langle x - 0 \rangle^{0} + 52 \langle x - 0 \rangle^{1} - \frac{1}{2}(8) \langle x - 0 \rangle^{2} + 50 \langle x - 5 \rangle^{0} + \frac{1}{2}(8) \langle x - 5 \rangle^{2}$$

$$= (-258 + 52x - 4x^{2} + 50 \langle x - 5 \rangle^{0} + 4 \langle x - 5 \rangle^{2}) \text{ kN} \cdot \text{m}$$

This same result can be obtained *directly* from Table 2.

**Slope and Elastic Curve.** Applying Eq. 10 and integrating twice, we have

$$EI\frac{d^{2}v}{dx^{2}} = -258 + 52x - 4x^{2} + 50 \langle x - 5 \rangle^{0} + 4 \langle x - 5 \rangle^{2}$$

$$EI\frac{dv}{dx} = -258x + 26x^{2} - \frac{4}{3}x^{3} + 50 \langle x - 5 \rangle^{1} + \frac{4}{3} \langle x - 5 \rangle^{3} + C_{1}$$

$$EIv = -129x^{2} + \frac{26}{3}x^{3} - \frac{1}{3}x^{4} + 25 \langle x - 5 \rangle^{2} + \frac{1}{3} \langle x - 5 \rangle^{4} + C_{1}x + C_{2}$$

Since $dv/dx = 0$ at $x = 0$, $C_{1} = 0$; and $v = 0$ at $x = 0$, so $C_{2} = 0$. Thus,

$$v = \frac{1}{EI} \left( -129x^{2} + \frac{26}{3}x^{3} - \frac{1}{3}x^{4} + 25 \langle x - 5 \rangle^{2} + \frac{1}{3} \langle x - 5 \rangle^{4} \right) \text{ m} \quad \textit{Ans.}$$

# PROBLEMS

**31.** The shaft is supported at $A$ by a journal bearing that exerts only vertical reactions on the shaft, and at $C$ by a thrust bearing that exerts horizontal and vertical reactions on the shaft. Determine the equation of the elastic curve. $EI$ is constant.

**Prob. 31**

**\*32.** The shaft supports the two pulley loads shown. Determine the equation of the elastic curve. The bearings at $A$ and $B$ exert only vertical reactions on the shaft. $EI$ is constant.

**Prob. 32**

**33.** Determine the equation of the elastic curve, the maximum deflection in region $BC$, and the deflection of end $A$ of the shaft. $EI$ is constant.

**Prob. 33**

**34.** Determine the equation of the elastic curve, the maximum deflection in region $AB$, and the deflection of end $C$ of the shaft. $EI$ is constant.

**Prob. 34**

**35.** The beam is subjected to the load shown. Determine the equation of the elastic curve. $EI$ is constant.

**Prob. 35**

**\*36.** Determine the equation of the elastic curve, the slope at $A$, and the deflection at $B$ of the simply supported beam. $EI$ is constant.

**37.** Determine the equation of the elastic curve and the maximum deflection of the simply supported beam. $EI$ is constant.

**Probs. 36/37**

**38.** The beam is subjected to the loads shown. Determine the equation of the elastic curve. *EI* constant.

**Prob. 38**

**39.** Determine the maximum deflection of the cantilevered beam. The beam is made of material having an $E = 200$ GPa and $I = 65.0(10^6)$ mm$^4$.

**Prob. 39**

**\*40.** Determine the slope at *A* and the deflection of end *C* of the overhang beam. $E = 29(10^3)$ ksi and $I = 204$ in$^4$.

**41.** Determine the maximum deflection in region *AB* of the overhang beam. $E = 29(10^3)$ ksi and $I = 204$ in$^4$.

**Probs. 40/41**

**42.** The beam is subjected to the load shown. Determine the equation of the elastic curve. *EI* is constant.

**Prob. 42**

**43.** Determine the equation of the elastic curve. *EI* is constant.

**Prob. 43**

**\*44.** The beam is subjected to the load shown. Determine the equation of the elastic curve. *EI* is constant.

**Prob. 44**

**45.** Determine the deflection at each of the pulleys $C$, $D$, and $E$. The shaft is made of steel and has a diameter of 30 mm. The bearings at $A$ and $B$ exert only vertical reactions on the shaft. $E_{st} = 200$ GPa.

250 mm — 250 mm — 250 mm — 250 mm

150 N · · · 60 N · · · 150 N

**Prob. 45**

**46.** Determine the slope of the shaft at the bearings at $A$ and $B$. The shaft is made of steel and has a diameter of 30 mm. The bearings at $A$ and $B$ exert only vertical reactions on the shaft. $E_{st} = 200$ GPa.

250 mm — 250 mm — 250 mm — 250 mm

150 N · · · 60 N · · · 150 N

**Prob. 46**

**47.** The shaft is made of steel and has a diameter of 15 mm. Determine its maximum deflection. The bearings at $A$ and $B$ exert only vertical reactions on the shaft. $E_{st} = 200$ GPa.

15 mm

200 mm — 300 mm — 200 mm

250 N · · · 80 N

**Prob. 47**

**\*48.** The wooden beam is subjected to the load shown. Determine the equation of the elastic curve. Specify the deflection at the end $C$. $E_w = 1.6(10^3)$ ksi.

0.8 kip/ft · · · 1.5 kip

12 in.

6 in.

9 ft — 9 ft

**Prob. 48**

**49.** Determine the displacement $C$ and the slope at $A$ of the beam. $EI$ is constant.

8 kip/ft

6 ft — 9 ft

**Prob. 49**

**50.** The beam is subjected to the load shown. Determine the equations of the slope and elastic curve. $EI$ is constant.

3 kN/m

15 kN·m

5 m — 3 m

**Prob. 50**

# *4  Slope and Displacement by the Moment-Area Method

The moment-area method provides a semigraphical technique for finding the slope and displacement at specific points on the elastic curve of a beam or shaft. Application of the method requires calculating areas associated with the beam's moment diagram; and so if this diagram consists of simple shapes, the method is very convenient to use. Normally this is the case when the beam is loaded with concentrated forces and couple moments.

To develop the moment-area method we will make the same assumptions we used for the method of integration: The beam is initially straight, it is elastically deformed by the loads, such that the slope and deflection of the elastic curve are very small, and the deformations are only caused by bending. The moment-area method is based on two theorems, one used to determine the slope and the other to determine the displacement at a point on the elastic curve.

**Theorem 1.**   Consider the simply supported beam with its associated elastic curve, shown in Fig. 20a. A differential segment $dx$ of the beam is isolated in Fig. 20b. Here the beam's internal moment $M$ deforms the element such that the *tangents* to the elastic curve at each side of the element intersect at an angle $d\theta$. This angle can be determined from Eq. 10, written as

$$EI\frac{d^2v}{dx^2} = EI\frac{d}{dx}\left(\frac{dv}{dx}\right) = M$$

Since the *slope* is *small*, $\theta = dv/dx$, and therefore

$$d\theta = \frac{M}{EI}dx \tag{16}$$

If the moment diagram for the beam is constructed and divided by the flexural rigidity, $EI$, Fig. 20c, then this equation indicates that $d\theta$ is equal to the *area* under the "$M/EI$ diagram" for the beam segment $dx$. Integrating from a selected point $A$ on the elastic curve to another point $B$, we have

$$\theta_{B/A} = \int_A^B \frac{M}{EI}dx \tag{17}$$

This equation forms the basis for the first moment-area theorem.

**Theorem 1:**   *The angle between the tangents at any two points on the elastic curve equals the area under the M/EI diagram between these two points.*

The notation $\theta_{B/A}$ is referred to as the angle of the tangent at $B$ measured *with respect to* the tangent at $A$. From the proof it should be evident that this angle is measured *counterclockwise*, from tangent $A$ to

tan B          tan A

Elastic curve

(a)

(b)

$\frac{M}{EI}$ Diagram

(c)

**Fig. 20**

672

tangent $B$, if the area under the $M/EI$ diagram is *positive*. Conversely, if the area is *negative*, or lies below the $x$ axis, the angle $\theta_{B/A}$ is measured clockwise from tangent $A$ to tangent $B$. Furthermore, from the dimensions of Eq. 17, $\theta_{B/A}$ will be in *radians*.

**Theorem 2.** The second moment-area theorem is based on the relative deviation of tangents to the elastic curve. Shown in Fig. 21*a* is a greatly exaggerated view of the vertical deviation $dt$ of the tangents on each side of the differential element $dx$. This deviation is caused by the curvature of the element and has been measured along a vertical line passing through point $A$ on the elastic curve. Since the slope of the elastic curve and its deflection are assumed to be very small, it is satisfactory to approximate the length of each tangent line by $x$ and the arc $ds'$ by $dt$. Using the circular-arc formula $s = \theta r$, where $r$ is the length $x$ and $s$ is $dt$, we can write $dt = x\,d\theta$. Substituting Eq. 16 into this equation and integrating from $A$ to $B$, the vertical deviation of the tangent at $A$ *with respect to* the tangent at $B$ can then be determined; that is,

(a)

$$t_{A/B} = \int_A^B x\frac{M}{EI}dx \qquad (18)$$

Since the centroid of an area is found from $\bar{x}\int dA = \int x\,dA$, and $\int (M/EI)\,dx$ represents the area under the $M/EI$ diagram, we can also write

$$t_{A/B} = \bar{x}\int_A^B \frac{M}{EI}dx \qquad (19)$$

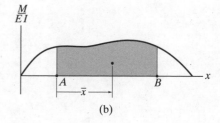

(b)

Here $\bar{x}$ is the distance from $A$ to the *centroid* of the area under the $M/EI$ diagram between $A$ and $B$, Fig. 21*b*.

The second moment-area theorem can now be stated in reference to Fig. 21*a* as follows:

**Theorem 2:** *The vertical distance between the tangent at a point $(A)$ on the elastic curve and the tangent extended from another point $(B)$ equals the moment of the area under the $M/EI$ diagram between these two points $(A$ and $B)$. This moment is calculated about the point $(A)$ where the vertical distance $(t_{A/B})$ is to be determined.*

Note that $t_{A/B}$ is *not* equal to $t_{B/A}$, which is shown in Fig. 21*c*. Specifically, the moment of the area under the $M/EI$ diagram between $A$ and $B$ is calculated about point $A$ to determine $t_{A/B}$, Fig. 21*b*, and it is calculated about point $B$ to determine $t_{B/A}$, Fig. 21*c*.

If the moment of a *positive $M/EI$* area between $A$ and $B$ is found for $t_{A/B}$, it indicates that point $A$ is *above* the tangent extended from point $B$, Fig. 21*a*. Similarly, *negative $M/EI$* areas indicate that point $A$ is *below* the tangent extended from point $B$. This same rule applies for $t_{B/A}$.

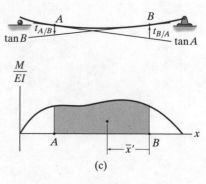

(c)

**Fig. 21**

# Procedure for Analysis

The following procedure provides a method that may be used to apply the two moment-area theorems.

## M/EI Diagram.

- Determine the support reactions and draw the beam's $M/EI$ diagram. If the beam is loaded with concentrated forces, the $M/EI$ diagram will consist of a series of straight line segments, and the areas and their moments required for the moment-area theorems will be relatively easy to calculate. If the loading consists of a series of distributed loads, the $M/EI$ diagram will consist of parabolic or perhaps higher-order curves, and it is suggested that the table on the inside front cover be used to locate the area and centroid under each curve.

## Elastic Curve.

- Draw an exaggerated view of the beam's elastic curve. Recall that points of zero slope and zero displacement always occur at a fixed support, and zero displacement occurs at all pin and roller supports.

- If it becomes difficult to draw the general shape of the elastic curve, use the moment (or $M/EI$) diagram. Realize that when the beam is subjected to a *positive moment*, the beam bends *concave up*, whereas *negative moment* bends the beam *concave down*. Furthermore, an inflection point or change in curvature occurs where the moment in the beam (or $M/EI$) is zero.

- The unknown displacement and slope to be determined should be indicated on the curve.

- Since the moment-area theorems apply *only between two tangents*, attention should be given as to which tangents should be constructed so that the angles or vertical distance between them will lead to the solution of the problem. In this regard, *the tangents at the supports should be considered*, since the beam has zero displacement and/or zero slope at the supports.

## Moment-Area Theorems.

- Apply Theorem 1 to determine the *angle* between any two tangents on the elastic curve and Theorem 2 to determine the vertical distance between the tangents.

- The algebraic sign of the answer can be checked from the angle or vertical distance indicated on the elastic curve.

- A *positive* $\theta_{B/A}$ represents a *counterclockwise* rotation of the tangent at $B$ with respect to the tangent at $A$, and a *positive* $t_{B/A}$ indicates that point $B$ on the elastic curve lies *above* the extended tangent from point $A$.

## EXAMPLE 7

Determine the slope of the beam shown in Fig. 22a at point B. EI is constant.

(a)

(b)

(c)

**Fig. 22**

## SOLUTION

**M/EI Diagram.** See Fig. 22b.

**Elastic Curve.** The force **P** causes the beam to deflect as shown in Fig. 22c. (The elastic curve is concave downward, since M/EI is negative.) The tangent at B is indicated since we are required to find $\theta_B$. Also, the tangent at the support (A) is shown. This tangent has a *known* zero slope. By the construction, the angle between tan A and tan B, that is, $\theta_{B/A}$, is equivalent to $\theta_B$, or

$$\theta_B = \theta_{B/A}$$

**Moment-Area Theorem.** Applying Theorem 1, $\theta_{B/A}$ is equal to the area under the M/EI diagram between points A and B; that is,

$$\theta_B = \theta_{B/A} = \frac{1}{2}\left(-\frac{PL}{EI}\right)L$$

$$= -\frac{PL^2}{2EI} \qquad\qquad Ans.$$

The *negative sign* indicates that the angle measured from the tangent at A to the tangent at B is *clockwise*. This checks, since the beam slopes downward at B.

## EXAMPLE | 8

Determine the displacement of points $B$ and $C$ of the beam shown in Fig. 23a. $EI$ is constant.

(a)

(c)

(b)

**Fig. 23**

### SOLUTION

**M/EI Diagram.** See Fig. 23b.

**Elastic Curve.** The couple moment at $C$ causes the beam to deflect as shown in Fig. 23c. The tangents at $B$ and $C$ are indicated since we are required to find $\Delta_B$ and $\Delta_C$. Also, the tangent at the support ($A$) is shown since it is horizontal. The required displacements can now be related directly to the vertical distance between the tangents at $B$ and $A$ and $C$ and $A$. Specifically,

$$\Delta_B = t_{B/A}$$
$$\Delta_C = t_{C/A}$$

**Moment-Area Theorem.** Applying Theorem 2, $t_{B/A}$ is equal to the moment of the shaded area under the $M/EI$ diagram between $A$ and $B$ calculated about point $B$ (the point on the elastic curve), since this is the point where the vertical distance is to be determined. Hence, from Fig. 23b,

$$\Delta_B = t_{B/A} = \left(\frac{L}{4}\right)\left[\left(-\frac{M_0}{EI}\right)\left(\frac{L}{2}\right)\right] = -\frac{M_0L^2}{8EI} \qquad Ans.$$

Likewise, for $t_{C/A}$ we must determine the moment of the area under the *entire* $M/EI$ diagram from $A$ to $C$ about point $C$ (the point on the elastic curve). We have

$$\Delta_C = t_{C/A} = \left(\frac{L}{2}\right)\left[\left(-\frac{M_0}{EI}\right)(L)\right] = -\frac{M_0L^2}{2EI} \qquad Ans.$$

**NOTE:** Since both answers are *negative*, they indicate that points $B$ and $C$ lie *below* the tangent at $A$. This checks with Fig. 23c.

## EXAMPLE | 9

Determine the slope at point $C$ of the shaft in Fig. 24a. $EI$ is constant.

(a)

(b)

(c)

**Fig. 24**

## SOLUTION

**M/EI Diagram.** See Fig. 24b.

**Elastic Curve.** Since the loading is applied symmetrically to the shaft, the elastic curve is symmetric, and the tangent at $D$ is horizontal, Fig. 24c. Also the tangent at $C$ is drawn, since we must find the slope $\theta_C$. By the construction, the angle $\theta_{C/D}$ between the tangents at tan $D$ and $C$ is equal to $\theta_C$; that is,

$$\theta_C = \theta_{C/D}$$

**Moment-Area Theorem.** Using Theorem 1, $\theta_{C/D}$ is equal to the shaded area under the $M/EI$ diagram between points $D$ and $C$. We have

$$\theta_C = \theta_{C/D} = \left(\frac{PL}{8EI}\right)\left(\frac{L}{4}\right) + \frac{1}{2}\left(\frac{PL}{4EI} - \frac{PL}{8EI}\right)\left(\frac{L}{4}\right) = \frac{3PL^2}{64EI} \quad Ans.$$

What does the positive result indicate?

EXAMPLE | 10

(a)

(b)

(c)

**Fig. 25**

Determine the slope at point $C$ for the steel beam in Fig. 25$a$. Take $E_{st} = 200$ GPa, $I = 17(10^6)$ mm$^4$.

## SOLUTION

**M/EI Diagram.**  See Fig. 25$b$.

**Elastic Curve.**  The elastic curve is shown in Fig. 25$c$. The tangent at $C$ is shown since we are required to find $\theta_C$. Tangents at the *supports*, $A$ and $B$, are also constructed as shown. Angle $\theta_{C/A}$ is the angle between the tangents at $A$ and $C$. The slope at $A$, $\theta_A$, in Fig. 25$c$ can be found using $|\theta_A| = |t_{B/A}|/L_{AB}$. This equation is valid since $t_{B/A}$ is actually very small, so that $t_{B/A}$ in meters can be approximated by the length of a circular arc defined by a radius of $L_{AB} = 8$ m and a sweep of $\theta_A$ in radians. (Recall that $s = \theta r$.) From the geometry of Fig. 25$c$, we have

$$|\theta_C| = |\theta_A| - |\theta_{C/A}| = \left|\frac{t_{B/A}}{8}\right| - |\theta_{C/A}| \qquad (1)$$

Note that Example 9 could also be solved using this method.

**Moment-Area Theorems.**  Using Theorem 1, $\theta_{C/A}$ is equivalent to the area under the $M/EI$ diagram between points $A$ and $C$; that is,

$$\theta_{C/A} = \frac{1}{2}(2 \text{ m})\left(\frac{8 \text{ kN} \cdot \text{m}}{EI}\right) = \frac{8 \text{ kN} \cdot \text{m}^2}{EI}$$

Applying Theorem 2, $t_{B/A}$ is equivalent to the moment of the area under the $M/EI$ diagram between $B$ and $A$ about point $B$ (the point on the elastic curve), since this is the point where the vertical distance is to be determined. We have

$$t_{B/A} = \left(2 \text{ m} + \frac{1}{3}(6 \text{ m})\right)\left[\frac{1}{2}(6 \text{ m})\left(\frac{24 \text{ kN} \cdot \text{m}}{EI}\right)\right]$$

$$+ \left(\frac{2}{3}(2 \text{ m})\right)\left[\frac{1}{2}(2 \text{ m})\left(\frac{24 \text{ kN} \cdot \text{m}}{EI}\right)\right]$$

$$= \frac{320 \text{ kN} \cdot \text{m}^3}{EI}$$

Substituting these results into Eq. 1, we get

$$\theta_C = \frac{320 \text{ kN} \cdot \text{m}^2}{(8 \text{ m})EI} - \frac{8 \text{ kN} \cdot \text{m}^2}{EI} = \frac{32 \text{ kN} \cdot \text{m}^2}{EI} \;\curvearrowright$$

We have calculated this result in units of kN and m, so converting $EI$ into these units, we have

$$\theta_C = \frac{32 \text{ kN} \cdot \text{m}^2}{[200(10^6) \text{ kN/m}^2][17(10^{-6}) \text{ m}^4]} = 0.00941 \text{ rad} \;\curvearrowright \qquad Ans.$$

## EXAMPLE | 11

Determine the displacement at $C$ for the beam shown in Fig. 26a. $EI$ is constant.

Fig. 26

### SOLUTION

**M/EI Diagram.** See Fig. 26b.

**Elastic Curve.** The tangent at $C$ is drawn on the elastic curve since we are required to find $\Delta_C$, Fig. 26c. (Note that $C$ is *not* the location of the maximum deflection of the beam, because the loading and hence the elastic curve are *not symmetric*.) Also indicated in Fig. 26c are the tangents at the supports $A$ and $B$. It is seen that $\Delta_C = \Delta' - t_{C/B}$. If $t_{A/B}$ is determined, then $\Delta'$ can be found from proportional triangles, that is, $\Delta'/(L/2) = t_{A/B}/L$ or $\Delta' = t_{A/B}/2$. Hence,

$$\Delta_C = \frac{t_{A/B}}{2} - t_{C/B} \qquad (1)$$

**Moment-Area Theorem.** Applying Theorem 2 to determine $t_{A/B}$ and $t_{C/B}$, we have

$$t_{A/B} = \left(\frac{1}{3}(L)\right)\left[\frac{1}{2}(L)\left(\frac{M_0}{EI}\right)\right] = \frac{M_0 L^2}{6EI}$$

$$t_{C/B} = \left(\frac{1}{3}\left(\frac{L}{2}\right)\right)\left[\frac{1}{2}\left(\frac{L}{2}\right)\left(\frac{M_0}{2EI}\right)\right] = \frac{M_0 L^2}{48EI}$$

Substituting these results into Eq. 1 gives

$$\Delta_C = \frac{1}{2}\left(\frac{M_0 L^2}{6EI}\right) - \left(\frac{M_0 L^2}{48EI}\right)$$

$$= \frac{M_0 L^2}{16EI} \downarrow \qquad\qquad Ans.$$

# EXAMPLE | 12

Determine the displacement at point $C$ for the steel overhanging beam shown in Fig. 27$a$. Take $E_{st} = 29(10^3)$ ksi, $I = 125$ in$^4$.

(a)

(b)

## SOLUTION

**M/EI Diagram.** See Fig. 27$b$.

**Elastic Curve.** The loading causes the beam to deflect as shown in Fig. 27$c$. We are required to find $\Delta_C$. By constructing tangents at $C$ and at the supports $A$ and $B$, it is seen that $\Delta_C = |t_{C/A}| - \Delta'$. However, $\Delta'$ can be related to $t_{B/A}$ by proportional triangles; that is, $\Delta'/24 = |t_{B/A}|/12$ or $\Delta' = 2|t_{B/A}|$. Hence

$$\Delta_C = |t_{C/A}| - 2|t_{B/A}| \qquad (1)$$

(c)

**Fig. 27**

**Moment-Area Theorem.** Applying Theorem 2 to determine $t_{C/A}$ and $t_{B/A}$, we have

$$t_{C/A} = (12 \text{ ft})\left(\frac{1}{2}(24 \text{ ft})\left(-\frac{60 \text{ kip} \cdot \text{ft}}{EI}\right)\right)$$

$$= -\frac{8640 \text{ kip} \cdot \text{ft}^3}{EI}$$

$$t_{B/A} = \left(\frac{1}{3}(12 \text{ ft})\right)\left[\frac{1}{2}(12 \text{ ft})\left(-\frac{60 \text{ kip} \cdot \text{ft}}{EI}\right)\right] = -\frac{1440 \text{ kip} \cdot \text{ft}^3}{EI}$$

Why are these terms negative? Substituting the results into Eq. 1 yields

$$\Delta_C = \frac{8640 \text{ kip} \cdot \text{ft}^3}{EI} - 2\left(\frac{1440 \text{ kip} \cdot \text{ft}^3}{EI}\right) = \frac{5760 \text{ kip} \cdot \text{ft}^3}{EI} \downarrow$$

Realizing that the calculations were made in units of kip and ft, we have

$$\Delta_C = \frac{5760 \text{ kip} \cdot \text{ft}^3(1728 \text{ in}^3/\text{ft}^3)}{[29(10^3) \text{ kip/in}^2](125 \text{ in}^4)} = 2.75 \text{ in.} \downarrow \qquad Ans.$$

# FUNDAMENTAL PROBLEMS

**F7.** Determine the slope and deflection of end $A$ of the cantilevered beam. $E = 200$ GPa and $I = 65.0(10^{-6})$ m$^4$.

**F7**

**F8.** Determine the slope and deflection of end $A$ of the cantilevered beam. $E = 200$ GPa and $I = 126(10^{-6})$ m$^4$.

**F8**

**F9.** Determine the slope and deflection of end $A$ of the cantilevered beam. $E = 200$ GPa and $I = 121(10^{-6})$ m$^4$.

**F9**

**F10.** Determine the slope and deflection at $A$ of the cantilevered beam. $E = 29(10^3)$ ksi, $I = 245$ in$^4$.

**F10**

**F11.** Determine the maximum deflection of the simply supported beam. $E = 200$ GPa and $I = 42.8(10^{-6})$ m$^4$.

**F11**

**F12.** Determine the maximum deflection of the simply supported beam. $E = 200$ GPa and $I = 39.9(10^{-6})$ m$^4$.

**F12**

681

# PROBLEMS

**51.** Determine the slope and deflection at C. EI is constant.

**Prob. 51**

**\*52.** Determine the slope and deflection at C. EI is constant.

**Prob. 52**

**53.** Determine the deflection of end B of the cantilever beam. EI is constant.

**Prob. 53**

**54.** If the bearings at A and B exert only vertical reactions on the shaft, determine the slope at B and the deflection at C. EI is constant.

**Prob. 54**

**55.** The composite simply supported steel shaft is subjected to a force of 10 kN at its center. Determine its maximum deflection. $E_{st} = 200$ GPa.

**Prob. 55**

**\*56.** If the bearings at A and B exert only vertical reactions on the shaft, determine the slope at A and the maximum deflection of the shaft. EI is constant.

**Prob. 56**

**57.** Determine the maximum deflection of the shaft. $EI$ is constant. The bearings exert only vertical reactions on the shaft.

**Prob. 57**

**58.** Determine the deflection at $C$ and the slope of the beam at $A, B,$ and $C$. $EI$ is constant.

**Prob. 58**

**59.** Determine the slope at $A$ of the solid circular shaft of diameter 100 mm. The shaft is made of steel having a modulus elasticity of $E = 200$ GPa.

**\*60.** Determine the deflection at $C$ of the solid circular shaft of diameter 100 mm. The shaft is made of steel having a modulus elasticity of $E = 200$ GPa.

**Probs. 59/60**

**61.** Determine the position $a$ of roller support $B$ in terms of $L$ so that the deflection at end $C$ is the same as the maximum deflection of region $AB$ of the overhang beam. $EI$ is constant.

**Prob. 61**

**62.** The flat spring is made of A-36 steel and has a rectangular cross section as shown. Determine the maximum elastic load $P$ that can be applied. What is the deflection at $B$ when $P$ reaches its maximum value? Assume that the spring is fixed supported at $A$.

**Prob. 62**

**63.** Determine the slope and the deflection of end $B$ of the cantilever beam. $EI$ is constant.

**Prob. 63**

**\*64.** The beam is subjected to the loading shown. Determine the slope at $B$ and deflection at $C$. $EI$ is constant.

**Prob. 64**

**65.** The beam is subjected to the loading shown. Determine the slope at $A$ and the displacement at $C$. Assume the support at $A$ is a pin and $B$ is a roller. $EI$ is constant.

**Prob. 65**

**66.** The shaft supports the gear at its end $C$. Determine the deflection at $C$ and the slopes at the bearings $A$ and $B$. $EI$ is constant. The bearings exert only vertical reactions on the shaft.

**67.** The shaft supports the gear at its end $C$. Determine its maximum deflection within region $AB$. $EI$ is constant. The bearings exert only vertical reactions on the shaft.

**Probs. 66/67**

**\*68.** Determine the slope at $A$ and the maximum deflection of the simply supported beam. $EI$ is constant.

**Prob. 68**

**69.** Determine the slope at $C$ and the deflection at $B$. $EI$ is constant.

**Prob. 69**

**70.** Determine the slope at $A$ and the maximum deflection in the beam. $EI$ is constant.

**Prob. 70**

**71.** The beam is made of a ceramic material. In order to obtain its modulus of elasticity, it is subjected to the loading shown. If the moment of inertia is $I$ and the beam has a measured maximum deflection $\Delta$, determine $E$. The supports at $A$ and $D$ exert only vertical reactions on the beam.

**Prob. 71**

*72. A beam having a constant $EI$ is supported as shown. Attached to the beam at $A$ is a pointer, free of load. Both the beam and pointer are originally horizontal when no load is applied to the beam. Determine the distance between the end of the beam and the pointer after each has been displaced by the loading shown.

**Prob. 72**

73. Determine the slope at $A$ and the maximum deflection of the shaft. $EI$ is constant.

**Prob. 73**

74. The rod is constructed from two shafts for which the moment of inertia of $AB$ is $I$ and of $BC$ is $2I$. Determine the maximum slope and deflection of the rod due to the loading. The modulus of elasticity is $E$.

**Prob. 74**

75. Determine the slope at $B$ and the deflection at $C$ of the beam. $E = 200$ GPa and $I = 65.0(10^6)$ mm$^4$.

**Prob. 75**

*76. Determine the slope at point $A$ and the maximum deflection of the simply supported beam. The beam is made of material having a modulus of elasticity $E$. The moment of inertia of segments $AB$ and $CD$ of the beam is $I$, while the moment of inertia of segment $BC$ is $2I$.

**Prob. 76**

77. Determine the position $a$ of roller support $B$ in terms of $L$ so that deflection at end $C$ is the same as the maximum deflection of region $AB$ of the overhang beam. $EI$ is constant.

**Prob. 77**

**78.** The beam is subjected to the loading shown. Determine the slope at *B* and deflection at *C*. *EI* is constant.

**Prob. 78**

**79.** The cantilevered beam is subjected to the loading shown. Determine the slope and displacement at *C*. *EI* is constant.

**Prob. 79**

***80.** Determine the slope at *C* and deflection at *B*. *EI* is constant.

**Prob. 80**

**81.** The two bars are pin connected at *D*. Determine the slope at *A* and the deflection at *D*. *EI* is constant.

**Prob. 81**

**82.** Determine the maximum deflection of the beam. *EI* is constant.

**Prob. 82**

# 5   Method of Superposition

The differential equation $EI\, d^4v/dx^4 = w(x)$ satisfies the two necessary requirements for applying the principle of superposition; i.e., the load $w(x)$ is linearly related to the deflection $v(x)$, and the load is assumed not to change significantly the original geometry of the beam or shaft. As a result, the deflections for a series of separate loadings acting on a beam may be superimposed. For example, if $v_1$ is the deflection for one load and $v_2$ is the deflection for another load, the total deflection for both loads acting together is the algebraic sum $v_1 + v_2$. Using tabulated results for various beam loadings, such as the ones listed in Appendix: Slopes and Deflections of Beams, or those found in various engineering handbooks, it is therefore possible to find the slope and displacement at a point on a beam subjected to several different loadings by algebraically adding the effects of its various component parts.

The following examples illustrate how to use the method of superposition to solve deflection problems, where the deflection is caused not only by beam deformations, but also by rigid-body displacements, such as those that occur when the beam is supported by springs.

The resultant deflection at any point on this beam can be determined from the superposition of the deflections caused by each of the separate loadings acting on the beam.

## EXAMPLE | 13

Determine the displacement at point $C$ and the slope at the support $A$ of the beam shown in Fig. 28a. $EI$ is constant.

**Fig. 28**

### SOLUTION

The loading can be separated into two component parts as shown in Figs. 28b and 28c. The displacement at $C$ and slope at $A$ are found. For the distributed loading,

$$(\theta_A)_1 = \frac{3wL^3}{128EI} = \frac{3(2 \text{ kN/m})(8 \text{ m})^3}{128EI} = \frac{24 \text{ kN} \cdot \text{m}^2}{EI} \circlearrowright$$

$$(v_C)_1 = \frac{5wL^4}{768EI} = \frac{5(2 \text{ kN/m})(8 \text{ m})^4}{768EI} = \frac{53.33 \text{ kN} \cdot \text{m}^3}{EI} \downarrow$$

For the 8-kN concentrated force,

$$(\theta_A)_2 = \frac{PL^2}{16EI} = \frac{8 \text{ kN}(8 \text{ m})^2}{16EI} = \frac{32 \text{ kN} \cdot \text{m}^2}{EI} \circlearrowright$$

$$(v_C)_2 = \frac{PL^3}{48EI} = \frac{8 \text{ kN}(8 \text{ m})^3}{48EI} = \frac{85.33 \text{ kN} \cdot \text{m}^3}{EI} \downarrow$$

The displacement at $C$ and the slope at $A$ are the algebraic sums of these components. Hence,

$$(+\circlearrowright) \qquad \theta_A = (\theta_A)_1 + (\theta_A)_2 = \frac{56 \text{ kN} \cdot \text{m}^2}{EI} \circlearrowright \qquad \textit{Ans.}$$

$$(+\downarrow) \qquad v_C = (v_C)_1 + (v_C)_2 = \frac{139 \text{ kN} \cdot \text{m}^3}{EI} \downarrow \qquad \textit{Ans.}$$

EXAMPLE | 14

Determine the displacement at the end $C$ of the overhanging beam shown in Fig. 29a. $EI$ is constant.

(a)

**SOLUTION**

The beam will be separated will be separated into a simply supported and a cantilevered portion. First we will calculate the slope at $B$, as caused by the distributed load acting on the simply supported span, Fig. 29b.

$$(\theta_B)_1 = \frac{wL^3}{24EI} = \frac{5 \text{ kN/m}(4 \text{ m})^3}{24EI} = \frac{13.33 \text{ kN} \cdot \text{m}^2}{EI} \;\rotatebox{0}{$\curvearrowright$}$$

(b)

Since this angle is *small*, $(\theta_B)_1 \approx \tan(\theta_B)_1$, and the vertical displacement at point $C$ is

$$(v_C)_1 = (2 \text{ m})\left(\frac{13.33 \text{ kN} \cdot \text{m}^2}{EI}\right) = \frac{26.67 \text{ kN} \cdot \text{m}^3}{EI}\uparrow$$

(c)

Next, the 10-kN load on the overhang causes a statically equivalent force of 10 kN and couple moment of 20 kN $\cdot$ m at the support $B$ of the simply supported span, Fig. 29c. The 10-kN force does not cause a displacement or slope at $B$; however, the 20-kN $\cdot$ m couple moment does cause a slope. The slope at $B$ due to this moment is

$$(\theta_B)_2 = \frac{M_0 L}{3EI} = \frac{20 \text{ kN} \cdot \text{m}(4 \text{ m})}{3EI} = \frac{26.67 \text{ kN} \cdot \text{m}^2}{EI}\;\rotatebox{0}{$\curvearrowright$}$$

(d)

**Fig. 29**

so that the extended point $C$ is displaced

$$(v_C)_2 = (2 \text{ m})\left(\frac{26.7 \text{ kN} \cdot \text{m}^2}{EI}\right) = \frac{53.33 \text{ kN} \cdot \text{m}^3}{EI}\downarrow$$

Finally, the cantilevered portion $BC$ is displaced by the 10-kN force, Fig. 29d. We have

$$(v_C)_3 = \frac{PL^3}{3EI} = \frac{10 \text{ kN}(2 \text{ m})^3}{3EI} = \frac{26.67 \text{ kN} \cdot \text{m}^3}{EI}\downarrow$$

Summing these results algebraically, we obtain the displacement of point $C$,

$$(+\downarrow) \qquad v_C = -\frac{26.7}{EI} + \frac{53.3}{EI} + \frac{26.7}{EI} = \frac{53.3 \text{ kN} \cdot \text{m}^3}{EI}\downarrow \qquad\qquad Ans.$$

EXAMPLE | 15

Determine the displacement at the end $C$ of the cantilever beam shown in Fig. 30. $EI$ is constant.

**Fig. 30**

SOLUTION
The slope and displacement and displacement at point $B$ are

$$\theta_B = \frac{w_0 L^3}{24EI} = \frac{4 \text{ kN/m}(6 \text{ m})^3}{24EI} = \frac{36 \text{ kN} \cdot \text{m}^2}{EI}$$

$$v_B = \frac{w_0 L^4}{30EI} = \frac{4 \text{ kN/m}(6 \text{ m})^4}{30EI} = \frac{172.8 \text{ kN} \cdot \text{m}^3}{EI}$$

The unloaded region $BC$ of the beam remains straight, as shown in Fig. 30. Since $\theta_B$ is small, the displacement at $C$ becomes

$$(+\downarrow) \qquad\qquad v_C = v_B + \theta_B(L_{BC})$$

$$= \frac{172.8 \text{ kN} \cdot \text{m}^3}{EI} + \frac{36 \text{ kN} \cdot \text{m}^2}{EI}(2 \text{ m})$$

$$= \frac{244.8 \text{ kN} \cdot \text{m}^3}{EI}\downarrow \qquad\qquad\qquad Ans.$$

## EXAMPLE | 16

The steel bar shown in Fig. 31$a$ is supported by two springs at its ends $A$ and $B$. Each spring has a stiffness of $k = 15$ kip/ft and is originally unstretched. If the bar is loaded with a force of 3 kip at point $C$, determine the vertical displacement of the force. Neglect the weight of the bar and take $E_{st} = 29(10^3)$ ksi, $I = 12$ in$^4$.

## SOLUTION

The end reactions at $A$ and $B$ are calculated and shown in Fig. 31$b$. Each spring deflects by an amount

$$(v_A)_1 = \frac{2 \text{ kip}}{15 \text{ kip/ft}} = 0.1333 \text{ ft}$$

$$(v_B)_1 = \frac{1 \text{ kip}}{15 \text{ kip/ft}} = 0.0667 \text{ ft}$$

If the bar is considered to be *rigid*, these displacements cause it to move into the position shown in Fig. 31$b$. For this case, the vertical displacement at $C$ is

$$(v_C)_1 = (v_B)_1 + \frac{6 \text{ ft}}{9 \text{ ft}}[(v_A)_1 - (v_B)_1]$$

$$= 0.0667 \text{ ft} + \frac{2}{3}[0.1333 \text{ ft} - 0.0667 \text{ ft}] = 0.1111 \text{ ft} \downarrow$$

We can find the displacement at $C$ caused by the deformation of the bar, Fig. 31$c$. We have

Deformable body displacement

(c)

**Fig. 31**

$$(v_C)_2 = \frac{Pab}{6EIL}(L^2 - b^2 - a^2)$$

$$= \frac{3 \text{ kip}(3 \text{ ft})(6 \text{ ft})[(9 \text{ ft})^2 - (6 \text{ ft})^2 - (3 \text{ ft})^2]}{6[29(10^3)\text{kip/in}^2](144 \text{ in}^2/1 \text{ ft}^2)(12 \text{ in}^4)(1 \text{ ft}^4/20\ 736 \text{ in}^4)(9 \text{ ft})}$$

$$= 0.0149 \text{ ft} \downarrow$$

Adding the two displacement components, we get

$$(+\downarrow) \quad v_C = 0.1111 \text{ ft} + 0.0149 \text{ ft} = 0.126 \text{ ft} = 1.51 \text{ in}. \downarrow \qquad Ans.$$

# PROBLEMS

**83.** The W10 × 15 cantilevered beam is made of A-36 steel and is subjected to the loading shown. Determine the slope and displacement at its end $B$.

**Prob. 83**

**\*84.** The W10 × 15 cantilevered beam is made of A-36 steel and is subjected to the loading shown. Determine the displacement at $B$ and the slope at $B$.

**Prob. 84**

**85.** Determine the slope and deflection at end $C$ of the overhang beam. $EI$ is constant.

**86.** Determine the slope at $A$ and the deflection at point $D$ of the overhang beam. $EI$ is constant.

**Probs. 85/86**

**87.** The W12 × 45 simply supported beam is made of A-36 steel and is subjected to the loading shown. Determine the deflection at its center $C$.

**Prob. 87**

**\*88.** Determine the slope at $A$ and the deflection at point $C$ of the simply supported beam. The modulus of elasticity of the wood is $E = 10$ GPa.

**Prob. 88**

**89.** The W8 × 24 simply supported beam is made of A-36 steel and is subjected to the loading shown. Determine the deflection at its center $C$.

**Prob. 89**

**90.** The simply supported beam carries a uniform load of 2 kip/ft. Code restrictions, due to a plaster ceiling, require the maximum deflection not to exceed 1/360 of the span length. Select the lightest-weight A-36 steel wide-flange beam that will satisfy this requirement and safely support the load. The allowable bending stress is $\sigma_{allow} = 24$ ksi and the allowable shear stress is $\tau_{allow} = 14$ ksi. Assume $A$ is a pin and $B$ a roller support.

**\*92.** The W10 × 30 cantilevered beam is made of A-36 steel and is subjected to unsymmetrical bending caused by the applied moment. Determine the deflection of the centroid at its end $A$ due to the loading. *Hint:* Resolve the moment into components and use superposition

**Prob. 92**

**Prob. 90**

**93.** The rod is pinned at its end $A$ and attached to a torsional spring having a stiffness $k$, which measures the torque per radian of rotation of the spring. If a force **P** is always applied perpendicular to the end of the rod, determine the displacement of the force. $EI$ is constant.

**Prob. 93**

**94.** Determine the vertical deflection and slope at the end $A$ of the bracket. Assume that the bracket is fixed supported at its base, and neglect the axial deformation of segment $AB$. $EI$ is constant.

**91.** The simply supported beam is made of A-36 steel and is subjected to the loading shown. Determine the deflection at its center $C$. $I = 0.1457(10^{-3})$ m$^4$.

**Prob. 91**

**Prob. 94**

**95.** The pipe assembly consists of three equal-sized pipes with flexibility stiffness $EI$ and torsional stiffness $GJ$. Determine the vertical deflection at point $A$.

**97.** The wide-flange beam acts as a cantilever. Due to an error it is installed at an angle $\theta$ with the vertical. Determine the ratio of its deflection in the $x$ direction to its deflection in the $y$ direction at $A$ when a load **P** is applied at this point. The moments of inertia are $I_x$ and $I_y$. For the solution, resolve **P** into components and use the method of superposition. *Note:* The result indicates that large lateral deflections ($x$ direction) can occur in narrow beams, $I_y \ll I_x$, when they are improperly installed in this manner. To show this numerically, compute the deflections in the $x$ and $y$ directions for an A992 steel W10 × 15, with $P = 1.5$ kip, $\theta = 10°$, and $L = 12$ ft.

**Prob. 95**

**Prob. 97**

**\*96.** The framework consists of two A992 steel cantilevered beams $CD$ and $BA$ and a simply supported beam $CB$. If each beam is made of steel and has a moment of inertia about its principal axis $I_x = 118$ in$^4$, determine the deflection at the center $G$ of beam $CB$.

**98.** Determine the vertical deflection at the end $A$ of the bracket. Assume that the bracket is fixed supported at its base $B$ and neglect axial deflection. $EI$ is constant.

**Prob. 96**

**Prob. 12–98**

# 6    Statically Indeterminate Beams and Shafts

In this section we will illustrate a general method for determining the reactions on statically indeterminate beams and shafts. Specifically, a member of any type is classified as *statically indeterminate* if the number of unknown reactions *exceeds* the available number of equilibrium equations.

The additional support reactions on the beam or shaft that are *not needed* to keep it in stable equilibrium are called *redundants*. The number of these redundants is referred to as the *degree of indeterminacy*. For example, consider the beam shown in Fig. 32$a$. If the free-body diagram is drawn, Fig. 32$b$, there will be four unknown support reactions, and since three equilibrium equations are available for solution, the beam is classified as being indeterminate to the first degree. Either $A_y$, $B_y$, or $M_A$ can be classified as the redundant, for if any one of these reactions is removed, the beam remains stable and in equilibrium ($A_x$ cannot be classified as the redundant, for if it were removed, $\Sigma F_x = 0$ would not be satisfied.) In a similar manner, the *continuous beam* in Fig. 33$a$ is indeterminate to the second degree, since there are five unknown reactions and only three available equilibrium equations, Fig. 33$b$. Here the two redundant support reactions can be chosen among $A_y$, $B_y$, $C_y$, and $D_y$.

Fig. 32

Fig. 33

695

To determine the reactions on a beam (or shaft) that is statically indeterminate, it is first necessary to specify the redundant reactions. We can determine these redundants from the load-displacement relationship and the conditions of geometry known as *compatibility conditions*. Once determined, the redundants are then applied to the beam, and the remaining reactions are determined from the equations of equilibrium.

In the following sections we will illustrate this procedure for solution using the method of integration, Sec. 7; the moment-area method, Sec. 8; and the method of superposition, Sec. 9.

# 7 Statically Indeterminate Beams and Shafts—Method of Integration

The method of integration, discussed in Sec. 2, requires applying the load-displacement relationship, represented by the differential equation $d^2v/dx^2 = M/EI$. If the beam is statically indeterminate, $M$ will be expressed in terms of position $x$ and in terms of the *unknown* redundants. After integrating this equation twice, there will be two constants of integration along with the redundants to be determined. Although this is the case, these unknowns can always be found from the equilibrium equations and the boundary and/or continuity conditions for the problem.

The following example problems illustrate specific applications of this method using the procedure for analysis outlined in Sec. 2.

An example of a statically indeterminate beam used to support a bridge deck.

## EXAMPLE | 17

The beam is subjected to the distributed loading shown in Fig. 34a. Determine the reaction at $A$. $EI$ is constant.

(a)

### SOLUTION

**Elastic Curve.** The beam deflects as shown in Fig. 34a. Only one coordinate $x$ is needed. For convenience we will take it directed to the right, since the internal moment is easy to formulate.

**Moment Function.** The beam is indeterminate to the first degree as indicated from the free-body diagram, Fig. 34b. We can express the internal moment $M$ in terms of the redundant force at $A$ using the segment shown in Fig. 34c. Here

$$M = A_y x - \frac{1}{6} w_0 \frac{x^3}{L}$$

(b)

**Slope and Elastic Curve.** Applying Eq. 10, we have

$$EI \frac{d^2v}{dx^2} = A_y x - \frac{1}{6} w_0 \frac{x^3}{L}$$

$$EI \frac{dv}{dx} = \frac{1}{2} A_y x^2 - \frac{1}{24} w_0 \frac{x^4}{L} + C_1$$

$$EIv = \frac{1}{6} A_y x^3 - \frac{1}{120} w_0 \frac{x^5}{L} + C_1 x + C_2$$

(c)

**Fig. 34**

The three unknowns $A_y$, $C_1$, and $C_2$ are determined from the boundary conditions $x = 0$, $v = 0$; $x = L$, $dv/dx = 0$; and $x = L$, $v = 0$. Applying these conditions yields

$$x = 0, v = 0; \qquad 0 = 0 - 0 + 0 + C_2$$

$$x = L, \frac{dv}{dx} = 0; \qquad 0 = \frac{1}{2} A_y L^2 - \frac{1}{24} w_0 L^3 + C_1$$

$$x = L, v = 0; \qquad 0 = \frac{1}{6} A_y L^3 - \frac{1}{120} w_0 L^4 + C_1 L + C_2$$

Solving,

$$A_y = \frac{1}{10} w_0 L \qquad\qquad Ans.$$

$$C_1 = -\frac{1}{120} w_0 L^3 \qquad C_2 = 0$$

**NOTE:** Using the result for $A_y$, the reactions at $B$ can be determined from the equations of equilibrium, Fig. 34b. Show that $B_x = 0$, $B_y = 2w_0 L/5$, and $M_B = w_0 L^2/15$.

# EXAMPLE | 18

(a)

(b)

(c)

Fig. 35

The beam in Fig. 35a is fixed supported at both ends and is subjected to the uniform loading shown. Determine the reactions at the supports. Neglect the effect of axial load.

## SOLUTION

**Elastic Curve.** The beam deflects as shown in Fig. 35a. As in the previous problem, only one $x$ coordinate is necessary for the solution since the loading is continuous across the span.

**Moment Function.** From the free-body diagram, Fig. 35b, the respective shear and moment reactions at $A$ and $B$ must be equal, since there is symmetry of both loading and geometry. Because of this, the equation of equilibrium, $\Sigma F_y = 0$, requires

$$V_A = V_B = \frac{wL}{2} \qquad\qquad Ans.$$

The beam is indeterminate to the second degree, with $M'$ the redundant at each end. Using the beam segment shown in Fig. 35c, the internal moment $\mathbf{M}$ can be expressed in terms of $M'$ as follows:

$$M = \frac{wL}{2} x - \frac{w}{2} x^2 - M'$$

**Slope and Elastic Curve.** Applying Eq. 10, we have

$$EI\frac{d^2v}{dx} = \frac{wL}{2} x - \frac{w}{2} x^2 - M'$$

$$EI\frac{dv}{dx} = \frac{wL}{4} x^2 - \frac{w}{6} x^3 - M'x + C_1$$

$$EIv = \frac{wL}{12} x^3 - \frac{w}{24} x^4 - \frac{M'}{2} x^2 + C_1 x + C_2$$

The three unknowns, $M'$, $C_1$, and $C_2$, can be determined from the *three* boundary conditions $v = 0$ at $x = 0$, which yields $C_2 = 0$; $dv/dx = 0$ at $x = 0$, which yields $C_1 = 0$; and $v = 0$ at $x = L$, which yields

$$M' = \frac{wL^2}{12} \qquad\qquad Ans.$$

Using these results, notice that because of symmetry the remaining boundary condition $dv/dx = 0$ at $x = L$ is automatically satisfied.

**NOTE:** It should be realized that this method of solution is generally suitable when only one $x$ coordinate is needed to describe the elastic curve. If several $x$ coordinates are needed, equations of continuity must be written, thus complicating the solution process.

## PROBLEMS

**99.** Determine the reactions at the supports $A$ and $B$, then draw the shear and moment diagram. $EI$ is constant. Neglect the effect of axial load.

**Prob. 99**

**\*100.** Determine the value of $a$ for which the maximum positive moment has the same magnitude as the maximum negative moment. $EI$ is constant.

**Prob. 100**

**101.** Determine the reactions at the supports $A$, $B$, and $C$; then draw the shear and moment diagrams. $EI$ is constant.

**Prob. 101**

**102.** Determine the reactions at the supports $A$ and $B$, then draw the shear and moment diagrams. Use discontinuity functions. $EI$ is constant.

**Prob. 102**

**103.** Determine the reactions at the supports $A$ and $B$, then draw the shear and moment diagrams. $EI$ is constant.

**Prob. 103**

**\*104.** The loading on a floor beam used in the airplane is shown. Use discontinuity functions and determine the rections at the supports $A$ and $B$, and then draw the moment diagram for the beam.

**Prob. 104**

**105.** Use discontinuity functions and determine the reactions at the supports, then draw the shear and moment diagrams. $EI$ is constant.

**Prob. 105**

**106.** Determine the reactions at the support $A$ and $B$. $EI$ is constant.

**Prob. 106**

**107.** Determine the reactions at pin support $A$ and roller supports $B$ and $C$. $EI$ is constant.

**Prob. 107**

**\*108.** Determine the moment reactions at the supports $A$ and $B$, then draw the shear and moment diagrams. Solve by expressing the internal moment in the beam in terms of $A_y$ and $M_A$. $EI$ is constant.

**Prob. 108**

**109.** The beam has a constant $E_1 I_1$ and is supported by the fixed wall at $B$ and the rod $AC$. If the rod has a cross-sectional area $A_2$ and the material has a modulus of elasticity $E_2$, determine the force in the rod.

**Prob. 109**

**110.** The beam is supported by a pin at $A$, a roller at $B$, and a post having a diameter of 50 mm at $C$. Determine the support reactions at $A$, $B$, and $C$. The post and the beam are made of the same material having a modulus of elasticity $E = 200$ GPa, and the beam has a constant moment of inertia $I = 255(10^6)$ mm$^4$.

**Prob. 110**

700

# *8 Statically Indeterminate Beams and Shafts—Moment-Area Method

If the moment-area method is used to determine the unknown redundants of a statically indeterminate beam or shaft, then the $M/EI$ diagram must be drawn such that the redundants are represented as unknowns on this diagram. Once the $M/EI$ diagram is established, the two moment-area theorems can then be applied to obtain the proper relationships between the tangents on the elastic curve in order to meet the conditions of displacement and/or slope at the supports of the beam. In all cases the number of these compatibility conditions will be equivalent to the number of redundants, and so a solution for the redundants can be obtained.

## Moment Diagrams Constructed by the Method of Superposition.

Since application of the moment-area theorems requires calculation of both the area under the $M/EI$ diagram and the centroidal location of this area, it is often convenient to use *separate* $M/EI$ diagrams for *each* of the known loads and redundants rather than using the *resultant diagram* to calculate these geometric quantities. This is especially true if the resultant moment diagram has a complicated shape. The method for drawing the moment diagram in parts is based on the principle of superposition.

Most loadings on cantilevered *beams or shafts* will be a combination of the four loadings shown in Fig. 36. We will now show how to use the method of superposition to represent the resultant moment diagram by a series of separate moment diagrams for the cantilevered beam shown in Fig. 37a. To do this, we will first replace the loads by a system of statically equivalent loads. For example, the three cantilevered beams shown in Fig. 37a are statically equivalent to the

(a)

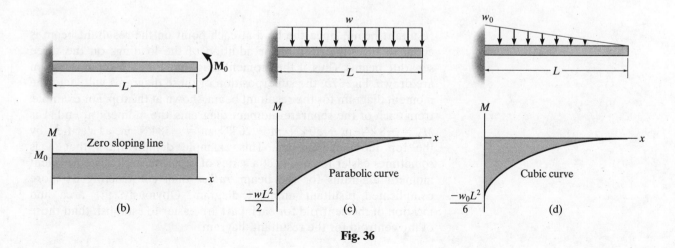

(b)

(c)

(d)

Fig. 36

Superposition of loadings

(a)

Superposition of moment diagrams

(b)

**Fig. 37**

resultant beam, since the load at each point on the resultant beam is equal to the superposition or addition of the loadings on the three separate beams. Thus, if the moment diagrams for each separate beam are drawn, Fig. 37b, the superposition of these diagrams will yield the moment diagram for the resultant beam, shown at the top. For example, from each of the separate moment diagrams, the moment at end $A$ is $M_A = -8 \text{ kN} \cdot \text{m} - 30 \text{ kN} \cdot \text{m} - 20 \text{ kN} \cdot \text{m} = -58 \text{ kN} \cdot \text{m}$, as verified by the top moment diagram. This example demonstrates that it is sometimes easier to construct a series of separate statically equivalent moment diagrams for the beam, *rather* than constructing its more complicated resultant moment diagram. Obviously, the area and location of the centroid for each part are easier to establish than those of the centroid for the resultant diagram.

**Fig. 38**

In a similar manner, we can also represent the resultant moment diagram for a *simply supported beam* by using a superposition of moment diagrams for each loading acting on a series of simply supported beams. For example, the beam loading shown at the top of Fig. 38a is equivalent to the sum of the beam loadings shown below it. Consequently, the sum of the moment diagrams for each of these three loadings can be used rather than the resultant moment diagram shown at the top of Fig. 38b.

The examples that follow should also clarify some of these points and illustrate how to use the moment-area theorems to obtain the redundant reactions on statically indeterminate beams and shafts. The solutions follow the procedure for analysis outlined in Sec. 4.

## EXAMPLE | 19

The beam is subjected to the concentrated force shown in Fig. 39a. Determine the reactions at the supports. $EI$ is constant.

Fig. 39

### SOLUTION

**M/EI Diagram.** The free-body diagram is shown in Fig. 39b. Using the method of superposition, the separate $M/EI$ diagrams for the redundant reaction $B_y$ and the load $P$ are shown in Fig. 39c.

**Elastic Curve.** The elastic curve for the beam is shown in Fig. 39d. The tangents at the supports $A$ and $B$ have been constructed. Since $\Delta_B = 0$, then

$$t_{B/A} = 0$$

**Moment-Area Theorem.** Applying Theorem 2, we have

$$t_{B/A} = \left(\frac{2}{3}L\right)\left[\frac{1}{2}\left(\frac{B_yL}{EI}\right)L\right] + \left(\frac{L}{2}\right)\left[\frac{-PL}{EI}(L)\right]$$

$$+ \left(\frac{2}{3}L\right)\left[\frac{1}{2}\left(\frac{-PL}{EI}\right)(L)\right] = 0$$

$$B_y = 2.5P \qquad\qquad\qquad Ans.$$

**Equations of Equilibrium.** Using this result, the reactions at $A$ on the free-body diagram, Fig. 39b, are

$$\stackrel{+}{\rightarrow} \Sigma F_x = 0; \qquad\qquad A_x = 0 \qquad\qquad Ans.$$

$$+\uparrow \Sigma F_y = 0; \qquad -A_y + 2.5P - P = 0$$

$$A_y = 1.5P \qquad\qquad Ans.$$

$$\zeta +\Sigma M_A = 0; \qquad -M_A + 2.5P(L) - P(2L) = 0$$

$$M_A = 0.5PL \qquad\qquad Ans.$$

## EXAMPLE 20

The beam is subjected to the couple moment at its end $C$ as shown in Fig. 40a. Determine the reaction at $B$. $EI$ is constant.

(a)

### SOLUTION

**M/EI Diagram.** The free-body diagram is shown in Fig. 40b. By inspection, the beam is indeterminate to the first degree. In order to obtain a direct solution, we will choose $B_y$ as the redundant. Using superposition, the $M/EI$ diagrams for $B_y$ and $M_0$, each applied to a simply supported beam, are shown in Fig. 40c. (Note that for such a beam $A_x$, $A_y$, and $C_y$ do not contribute to an $M/EI$ diagram.)

(b)

**Elastic Curve.** The elastic curve for the beam is shown in Fig. 40d. The tangents at $A$, $B$, and $C$ have been established. Since $\Delta_A = \Delta_B = \Delta_C = 0$, then the vertical distances shown must be proportional; i.e.,

$$t_{B/C} = \frac{1}{2} t_{A/C} \qquad (1)$$

(c)

From Fig. 40c, we have

$$t_{B/C} = \left(\frac{1}{3}L\right)\left[\frac{1}{2}\left(\frac{B_y L}{2EI}\right)(L)\right] + \left(\frac{2}{3}L\right)\left[\frac{1}{2}\left(\frac{-M_0}{2EI}\right)(L)\right]$$

$$+ \left(\frac{L}{2}\right)\left[\left(\frac{-M_0}{2EI}\right)(L)\right]$$

$$t_{A/C} = (L)\left[\frac{1}{2}\left(\frac{B_y L}{2EI}\right)(2L)\right] + \left(\frac{2}{3}(2L)\right)\left[\frac{1}{2}\left(\frac{-M_0}{EI}\right)(2L)\right]$$

(d)

Substituting into Eq. 1 and simplifying yields

$$B_y = \frac{3M_0}{2L} \qquad \qquad Ans.$$

(e)

**Fig. 40**

**Equations of Equilibrium.** The reactions at $A$ and $C$ can now be determined from the equations of equilibrium, Fig. 40b. Show that $A_x = 0$, $C_y = 5M_0/4L$, and $A_y = M_0/4L$.

Note from Fig. 40e that this problem can also be worked in terms of the vertical distances,

$$t_{B/A} = \frac{1}{2} t_{C/A}$$

# PROBLEMS

**111.** Determine the moment reactions at the supports $A$ and $B$. $EI$ is constant.

**Prob. 111**

**\*112.** Determine the moment reactions at the supports, and then draw the shear and moment diagrams. $EI$ is constant.

**Prob. 112**

**113.** Determine the reactions at the bearing support $A$ and fixed support $B$, then draw the shear and moment diagrams for the beam. $EI$ is constant.

**Prob. 113**

**114.** Determine the reactions at the supports $A$ and $B$, then draw the shear and moment diagrams. $EI$ is constant.

**Prob. 114**

**115.** Determine the vertical reactions at the bearing supports, then draw the shear and moment diagrams. $EI$ is constant.

**Prob. 115**

**\*116.** Determine the reactions at the journal bearing support $A$ and fixed support $B$, then draw the shear and moment diagrams for the shaft. $EI$ is constant.

**Prob. 116**

# 9 Statically Indeterminate Beams and Shafts—Method of Superposition

The method of superposition has been used previously to solve for the redundant loading on axially loaded bars and torsionally loaded shafts. In order to apply this method to the solution of statically indeterminate beams (or shafts), it is first necessary to identify the redundant support reactions as explained in Sec. 6. By *removing* them from the beam we obtain the so-called *primary beam*, which is statically determinate and stable, and is subjected *only* to the external load. If we add to this beam a succession of similarly supported beams, each loaded with a *separate* redundant, then by the principle of superposition, we obtain the actual loaded beam. Finally, in order to solve for the redundants, we must write the *conditions of compatibility* that exist at the supports where each of the redundants acts. Since the redundant forces are determined directly in this manner, this method of analysis is sometimes called the ***force method***. Once the redundants are obtained, the other reactions on the beam can then be determined from the three equations of equilibrium.

To clarify these concepts, consider the beam shown in Fig. 41a. If we choose the reaction $\mathbf{B}_y$ at the roller as the redundant, then the primary beam is shown in Fig. 41b, and the beam with the redundant $\mathbf{B}_y$ acting on it is shown in Fig. 41c. The displacement at the roller is to be zero, and since the displacement of point $B$ on the primary beam is $v_B$, and $\mathbf{B}_y$ causes point $B$ to be displaced upward $v_B'$, we can write the compatibility equation at $B$ as

$$(+\uparrow) \qquad 0 = -v_B + v_B'$$

The displacements $v_B$ and $v_B'$ can be related to the loads using any one of the methods discussed in Secs. 2 through 5. We have

$$v_B = \frac{5PL^3}{48EI} \quad \text{and} \quad v_B' = \frac{B_yL^3}{3EI}$$

Substituting into the compatibility equation, we get

$$0 = -\frac{5PL^3}{48EI} + \frac{B_y L^3}{3EI}$$

$$B_y = \frac{5}{16}P$$

Now that $\mathbf{B}_y$ is known, the reactions at the wall are determined from the three equations of equilibrium applied to the free-body diagram of the beam, Fig. 41d. The results are

$$A_x = 0 \qquad A_y = \frac{11}{16}P$$

$$M_A = \frac{3}{16}PL$$

Actual beam

(a)

=

Redundant $\mathbf{B}_y$ removed

(b)

+

Only redundant $\mathbf{B}_y$ applied

(c)

(d)

**Fig. 41**

(a) Actual beam

$\|$

(b) Redundant $\mathbf{M}_A$ removed

$+$

(c) Only redundant $\mathbf{M}_A$ applied

**Fig. 42**

As stated in Sec. 6, choice of the redundant is *arbitrary*, provided the primary beam remains stable. For example, the moment at $A$ for the beam in Fig. 42a can also be chosen as the redundant. In this case the capacity of the beam to resist $\mathbf{M}_A$ is removed, and so the primary beam is then pin supported at $A$, Fig. 42b. To it we add the beam with the redundant at $A$ acting on it, Fig. 42c. Referring to the slope at $A$ caused by the load $\mathbf{P}$ as $\theta_A$, and the slope at $A$ caused by the redundant $\mathbf{M}_A$ as $\theta_A'$, the compatibility equation for the slope at $A$ requires

$$(\zeta+) \qquad\qquad\qquad 0 = \theta_A + \theta_A'$$

We have

$$\theta_A = \frac{PL^2}{16EI} \quad \text{and} \quad \theta_A' = \frac{M_A L}{3EI}$$

Thus,

$$0 = \frac{PL^2}{16EI} + \frac{M_A L}{3EI}$$

$$M_A = -\frac{3}{16}PL$$

This is the same result determined previously. Here the negative sign for $M_A$ simply means that $\mathbf{M}_A$ acts in the opposite sense of direction of that shown in Fig. 42c.

(a) Actual beam

||

(b) Redundant $\mathbf{B}_y$ and $\mathbf{C}_y$ removed

+

(c) Only redundant $\mathbf{B}_y$ applied

+

(d) Only redundant $\mathbf{C}_y$ applied

**Fig. 43**

Another example that illustrates this method is given in Fig. 43a. In this case the beam is indeterminate to the second degree and therefore *two* compatibility equations will be necessary for the solution. We will choose the forces at the roller supports $B$ and $C$ as redundants. The primary (statically determinate) beam deforms as shown in Fig. 43b when the redundants are removed. Each redundant force deforms this beam as shown in Figs. 43c and 43d, respectively. By superposition, the compatibility equations for the displacements at $B$ and $C$ are

$$(+\downarrow) \qquad\qquad 0 = v_B + v_B' + v_B'' \qquad\qquad\qquad (20)$$

$$(+\downarrow) \qquad\qquad 0 = v_C + v_C' + v_C''$$

Here the displacement components $v_B'$ and $v_C'$ will be expressed in terms of the unknown $\mathbf{B}_y$, and the components $v_B''$ and $v_C''$ will be expressed in terms of the unknown $\mathbf{C}_y$. When these displacements have been determined and substituted into Eq. 20, these equations may then be solved simultaneously for the two unknowns $\mathbf{B}_y$ and $\mathbf{C}_y$.

## Procedure for Analysis

The following procedure provides a means for applying the method of superposition (or the force method) to determine the reactions on statically indeterminate beams or shafts.

Elastic Curve.

- Specify the unknown redundant forces or moments that must be removed from the beam in order to make it statically determinate and stable.

- Using the principle of superposition, draw the statically indeterminate beam and show it equal to a sequence of corresponding *statically determinate beams*.

- The first of these beams, the primary beam, supports the same external loads as the statically indeterminate beam, and each of the other beams "added" to the primary beam shows the beam loaded with a separate redundant force or moment.

- Sketch the deflection curve for each beam and indicate symbolically the displacement (slope) at the point of each redundant force (moment).

Compatibility Equations.

- Write a compatibility equation for the displacement (slope) at each point where there is a redundant force (moment).

Load-Displacement Equations.

- Relate all the displacements or slopes to the forces or moments using an appropriate method as explained in Secs. 2 through 5.

- Substitute the results into the compatibility equations and solve for the unknown redundants.

- If a numerical value for a redundant is *positive*, it has the *same sense of direction* as originally assumed. Similarly, a *negative* numerical value indicates the redundant acts *opposite* to its assumed *sense of direction*.

Equilibrium Equations.

- Once the redundant forces and/or moments have been determined, the remaining unknown reactions can be found from the equations of equilibrium applied to the loadings shown on the beam's free-body diagram.

The following examples illustrate application of this procedure. For brevity, all displacements and slopes have been found.

## EXAMPLE | 21

Determine the reactions at the roller support $B$ of the beam shown in Fig. 44$a$, then draw the shear and moment diagrams. $EI$ is constant.

(a)

Actual beam

||

### SOLUTION

**Principle of Superposition.** By inspection, the beam is statically indeterminate to the first degree. The roller support at $B$ will be chosen as the redundant so that $\mathbf{B}_y$ will be determined *directly*. Figures 44$b$ and 44$c$ show application of the principle of superposition. Here we have assumed that $\mathbf{B}_y$ acts upward on the beam.

(b)

Redundant $\mathbf{B}_y$ removed

+

(c)

Only redundant $\mathbf{B}_y$ applied

**Compatibility Equation.** Taking positive displacement as downward, the compatibility equation at $B$ is

$$(+\downarrow) \qquad\qquad 0 = v_B - v_B' \qquad\qquad (1)$$

**Load-Displacement Equations.** These displacements are as follows:

$$v_B = \frac{wL^4}{8EI} + \frac{5PL^3}{48EI}$$

$$= \frac{2 \text{ kip/ft}(10 \text{ ft})^4}{8EI} + \frac{5(8 \text{ kip})(10 \text{ ft})^3}{48EI} = \frac{3333 \text{ kip} \cdot \text{ft}^3}{EI} \downarrow$$

$$v_B' = \frac{PL^3}{3EI} = \frac{B_y (10 \text{ ft})^3}{3EI} = \frac{333.3 \text{ ft}^3 B_y}{EI} \uparrow$$

(d)

Substituting into Eq. 1 and solving yields

$$0 = \frac{3333}{EI} - \frac{333.3 B_y}{EI}$$

$$B_y = 10 \text{ kip} \qquad\qquad Ans.$$

(e)

Fig. 44

**Equilibrium Equations.** Using this result and applying the three equations of equilibrium, we obtain the results shown on the beam's free-body diagram in Fig. 44$d$. The shear and moment diagrams are shown in Fig. 44$e$.

EXAMPLE | 22

The beam in Fig. 45a is fixed supported to the wall at $A$ and pin connected to a $\frac{1}{2}$-in.-diameter rod $BC$. If $E = 29(10^3)$ ksi for both members, determine the force developed in the rod due to the loading. The moment of inertia of the beam about its neutral axis is $I = 475$ in$^4$.

**Fig. 45**

Actual beam and rod
(a)

Redundant $\mathbf{F}_{BC}$ removed
(b)

Only redundant $\mathbf{F}_{BC}$ applied
(c)

## SOLUTION I

**Principle of Superposition.** By inspection, this problem is indeterminate to the first degree. Here $B$ will undergo an unknown displacement $v_B''$, since the rod will stretch. The rod will be treated as the redundant and hence the force of the rod is removed from the beam at $B$, Fig. 45b, and then reapplied, Fig. 45c.

**Compatibility Equation.** At point $B$ we require

$$(+\downarrow) \qquad\qquad v_B'' = v_B - v_B' \qquad\qquad (1)$$

**Load-Displacement Equations.** $v_B''$ is calculated from is calculated from Eq. 2. Working in kilopounds and inches, we have

$$v_B'' = \frac{PL}{AE} = \frac{F_{BC}\,(8\text{ ft})(12\text{ in./ft})}{(\pi/4)\left(\frac{1}{2}\text{ in.}\right)^2[29(10^3)\text{ kip/in}^2]} = 0.01686 F_{BC} \downarrow$$

$$v_B = \frac{5PL^3}{48EI} = \frac{5(8\text{ kip})(10\text{ ft})^3\,(12\text{ in./ft})^3}{48[29(10^3)\text{ kip/in}^2](475\text{ in}^4)} = 0.1045\text{ in.} \downarrow$$

$$v_B' = \frac{PL^3}{3EI} = \frac{F_{BC}\,(10\text{ ft})^3\,(12\text{ in./ft})^3}{3[29(10)^3\text{ kip/in}^2](475\text{ in}^4)} = 0.04181 F_{BC} \uparrow$$

Thus, Eq. 1 becomes

$$(+\downarrow) \qquad\qquad 0.01686 F_{BC} = 0.1045 - 0.04181 F_{BC}$$
$$F_{BC} = 1.78\text{ kip} \qquad\qquad\qquad Ans.$$

**Fig. 45 (cont.)**

## SOLUTION II

**Principle of Superposition.** We can also solve this problem by removing the pin support at $C$ and keeping the rod attached to the beam. In this case the 8-kip load will cause points $B$ and $C$ to be displaced downward the *same amount* $v_C$, Fig. 45e, since no force exists in rod $BC$. When the redundant force $\mathbf{F}_{BC}$ is applied at point $C$, it causes the end $C$ of the rod to be displaced upward $v_C'$ and the end $B$ of the beam to be displaced upward $v_B'$, Fig. 45f. The difference in these two displacements, $v_{BC}$, represents the stretch of the rod due to $\mathbf{F}_{BC}$, so that $v_C' = v_{BC} + v_B'$. Hence, from Figs. 45d, 45e, and 45f, the compatibility of displacement at point $C$ is

$$(+\downarrow) \qquad\qquad 0 = v_C - (v_{BC} + v_B') \qquad\qquad (2)$$

From Solution I, we have

$$v_C = v_B = 0.1045 \text{ in.} \downarrow$$
$$v_{BC} = v_B'' = 0.01686 F_{BC} \uparrow$$
$$v_B' = 0.04181 F_{BC} \uparrow$$

Therefore, Eq. 2 becomes

$$(+\downarrow) \quad 0 = 0.1045 - (0.01686 F_{BC} + 0.04181 F_{BC})$$
$$F_{BC} = 1.78 \text{ kip} \qquad\qquad\qquad Ans.$$

EXAMPLE | 23

Determine the moment at $B$ for the beam shown in Fig. 46$a$. $EI$ is constant. Neglect the effects of axial load.

SOLUTION

**Principle of Superposition.** Since the axial load on the beam is neglected, there will be a vertical force and moment at $A$ and $B$. Here there are only two available equations of equilibrium ($\Sigma M = 0, \Sigma F_y = 0$) and so the problem is indeterminate to the second degree. We will assume that $B_y$ and $M_B$ are redundant, so that by the principle of superposition, the beam is represented as a cantilever, loaded *separately* by the distributed load and reactions $B_y$ and $M_B$, Figs. 46$b$, 46$c$, and 46$d$.

(a) $A$   3 kip/ft   $B$
    6 ft —+— 6 ft
    Actual beam

‖

(b) $A$   3 kip/ft
    6 ft —+— 6 ft   $v_B$
    $B$   $\theta_B$
    Redundants $M_B$ and $B_y$ removed

+

(c) $A$   $B_y$
    12 ft   $v_B'$
    $B$   $\theta_B'$
    Only redundant $B_y$ applied

+

(d) $A$   $M_B$
    12 ft   $v_B''$
    $B$   $\theta_B''$
    Only redundant $M_B$ applied

**Fig. 46**

**Compatibility Equations.**   Referring to the displacement and slope at $B$, we require

$$(\zeta+) \qquad\qquad 0 = \theta_B + \theta_B' + \theta_B'' \qquad\qquad (1)$$

$$(+\downarrow) \qquad\qquad 0 = v_B + v_B' + v_B'' \qquad\qquad (2)$$

**Load-Displacement Equations.** Calculating the slopes and displacements, we have

$$\theta_B = \frac{wL^3}{48EI} = \frac{3 \text{ kip/ft } (12 \text{ ft})^3}{48EI} = \frac{108 \text{ kip} \cdot \text{ft}^2}{EI} \; \zeta$$

$$v_B = \frac{7wL^4}{384EI} = \frac{7(3 \text{ kip/ft})(12 \text{ ft})^4}{384EI} = \frac{1134 \text{ kip} \cdot \text{ft}^3}{EI} \downarrow$$

$$\theta_B' = \frac{PL^2}{2EI} = \frac{B_y(12 \text{ ft})^2}{2EI} = \frac{72B_y}{EI} \; \zeta$$

$$v_B' = \frac{PL^3}{3EI} = \frac{B_y(12 \text{ ft})^3}{3EI} = \frac{576B_y}{EI} \downarrow$$

$$\theta_B'' = \frac{ML}{EI} = \frac{M_B(12 \text{ ft})}{EI} = \frac{12M_B}{EI} \; \zeta$$

$$v_B'' = \frac{ML^2}{2EI} = \frac{M_B(12 \text{ ft})^2}{2EI} = \frac{72M_B}{EI} \downarrow$$

Substituting these values into Eqs. 1 and 2 and canceling out the common factor $EI$, we get

$$(\zeta+) \qquad\qquad 0 = 108 + 72B_y + 12M_B$$

$$(+\downarrow) \qquad\qquad 0 = 1134 + 576B_y + 72M_B$$

Solving these equations simultaneously gives

$$B_y = -3.375 \text{ kip}$$

$$M_B = 11.25 \text{ kip} \cdot \text{ft} \qquad\qquad\qquad\qquad Ans.$$

**NOTE:** The reactions at $A$ can now be determined from the equilibrium equations.

# FUNDAMENTAL PROBLEMS

**F13.** Determine the reactions at the fixed support $A$ and the roller $B$. $EI$ is constant.

**F13**

**F14.** Determine the reactions at the fixed support $A$ and the roller $B$. $EI$ is constant.

**F14**

**F15.** Determine the reactions at the fixed support $A$ and the roller $B$. Support $B$ settles 2 mm. $E = 200$ GPa, $I = 65.0(10^{-6})$ m$^4$.

**F15**

**F16.** Determine the reaction at the roller $B$. $EI$ is constant.

**F16**

**F17.** Determine the reaction at the roller $B$. $EI$ is constant.

**F17**

**F18.** Determine the reaction at the roller support $B$ if it settles 5 mm. $E = 200$ GPa and $I = 65.0(10^{-6})$ m$^4$.

**F18**

# PROBLEMS

**117.** Determine the reactions at the bearing supports $A, B,$ and $C$ of the shaft, then draw the shear and moment diagrams. $EI$ is constant. Each bearing exerts only vertical reactions on the shaft.

**Prob. 117**

**118.** Determine the reactions at the supports $A$ and $B.$ $EI$ is constant.

**Prob. 118**

**119.** Determine the reactions at the supports $A$, $B$, and $C$, then draw the shear and moment diagrams. $EI$ is constant.

**Prob. 119**

**\*120.** Determine the moment reactions at the supports $A$ and $B.$ $EI$ is constant.

**Prob. 120**

**121.** Determine the deflection at the end $B$ of the clamped A-36 steel strip. The spring has a stiffness of $k = 2\,\text{N/mm}.$ The strip is 5 mm wide and 10 mm high. Also, draw the shear and moment diagrams for the strip.

**Prob. 121**

**122.** Determine the reactions at the supports $A$ and $B.$ $EI$ is constant.

**Prob. 122**

**123.** Determine the reactions at support *C*. *EI* is the same for both beams.

**Prob. 123**

**\*124.** Before the uniform distributed load is applied on the beam, there is a small gap of 0.2 mm between the beam and the post at *B*. Determine the support reactions at *A*, *B*, and *C*. The post at *B* has a diameter of 40 mm, and the moment of inertia of the beam is $I = 875(10^6)$ mm$^4$. The post and the beam are made of material having a modulus of elasticity of *E* = 200 GPa.

**Prob. 124**

**125.** The fixed supported beam *AB* is strengthened using the simply supported beam *CD* and the roller at *F* which is set in place just before application of the load **P**. Determine the reactions at the supports if *EI* is constant.

**Prob. 125**

**126.** Determine the force in the spring. *EI* is constant.

**Prob. 126**

**127.** The beam is supported by the bolted supports at its ends. When loaded these supports initially do not provide an actual fixed connection, but instead allow a slight rotation $\alpha$ before becoming fixed after the load is fully applied. Determine the moment at the connections and the maximum deflection of the beam.

**Prob. 127**

**\*128.** Each of the two members is made from 6061-T6 aluminum and has a square cross section 1 in. × 1 in. They are pin connected at their ends and a jack is placed between them and opened until the force it exerts on each member is 500 lb. Determine the greatest force *P* that can be applied to the center of the top member without causing either the two members to yield. For the analysis neglect the axial force in each member. Assume the jack is rigid.

**Prob. 128**

718

**129.** The beam is made from a soft linear elastic material having a constant $EI$. If it is originally a distance $\Delta$ from the surface of its end support, determine the length $a$ that rests on this support when it is subjected to the uniform load $w_0$, which is great enough to cause this to happen.

**131.** The 1-in.-diameter A-36 steel shaft is supported by bearings at $A$ and $C$. The bearing at $B$ rests on a simply supported A992 steel wide-flange beam having a moment of inertia of $I = 500$ in$^4$. If the belt loads on the pulley are 400 lb each, determine the vertical reactions at $A$, $B$, and $C$.

**Prob. 129**

**Prob. 131**

**130.** The A992 steel beam and rod are used to support the load of 8 kip. If it is required that the allowable normal stress for the steel is $\sigma_{\text{allow}} = 18$ ksi, and the maximum deflection not exceed 0.05 in., determine the smallest diameter rod that should be used. The beam is rectangular, having a height of 5 in. and a thickness of 3 in.

**\*132.** The assembly consists of three simply supported beams for which the bottom of the top beam rests on the top of the bottom two. if a uniform load of 3 kN/m is applied to the beam, determine the vertical reactions at each of the supports. $EI$ is constant.

**Prob. 130**

**Prob. 132**

# CHAPTER REVIEW

The elastic curve represents the centerline deflection of a beam or shaft. Its shape can be determined using the moment diagram. Positive moments cause the elastic curve to be concave upwards and negative moments cause it to be concave downwards. The radius of curvature at any point is determined from

$$\frac{1}{\rho} = \frac{M}{EI}$$

Moment diagram

Inflection point

Elastic curve

The equation of the elastic curve and its slope can be obtained by first finding the internal moment in the member as a function of $x$. If several loadings act on the member, then separate moment functions must be determined between each of the loadings. Integrating these functions once using $EI(d^2v/dx^2) = M(x)$ gives the equation for the slope of the elastic curve, and integrating again gives the equation for the deflection. The constants of integration are determined from the boundary conditions at the supports, or in cases where several moment functions are involved, continuity of slope and deflection at points where these functions join must be satisfied.

$\theta = 0$
$v = 0$

$v = 0$

Boundary conditions

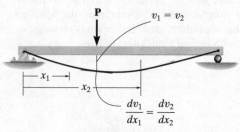

$v_1 = v_2$

$\dfrac{dv_1}{dx_1} = \dfrac{dv_2}{dx_2}$

Continuity conditions

Discontinuity functions allow one to express the equation of the elastic curve as a continuous function, regardless of the number of loadings on the member. This method eliminates the need to use continuity conditions, since the two constants of integration can be determined solely from the two boundary conditions.

The moment-area method is a semi-graphical technique for finding the slope of tangents or the vertical distance between tangents at specific points on the elastic curve. It requires finding area segments under the $M/EI$ diagram, or the moment of these segments about points on the elastic curve. The method works well for $M/EI$ diagrams composed of simple shapes, such as those produced by concentrated forces and couple moments.

The deflection or slope at a point on a member subjected to combinations of loadings can be determined using the method of superposition.

Statically indeterminate beams and shafts have more unknown support reactions than available equations of equilibrium. To solve, one first identifies the redundant reactions. The method of integration or the moment-area theorems can then be used to solve for the unknown redundants. It is also possible to determine the redundants by using the method of superposition, where one considers the conditions of continuity at the redundant. Here the displacement due to the external loading is determined with the redundant removed, and again with the redundant applied and the external loading removed.

# REVIEW PROBLEMS

**133.** The shaft supports the two pulley loads shown. Using discontinuity functions, determine the equation of the elastic curve. The bearings at $A$ and $B$ exert only vertical reactions on the shaft. $EI$ is constant.

**Prob. 133**

**134.** The shaft is supported by a journal bearing at $A$, which exerts only vertical reactions on the shaft, and by a thrust bearing at $B$, which exerts both horizontal and vertical reactions on the shaft. Draw the bending-moment diagram for the shaft and then, from this diagram, sketch the deflection or elastic curve for the shaft's centerline. Determine the equations of the elastic curve using the coordinates $x_1$ and $x_2$. $EI$ is constant. Use the method of integration.

**Prob. 134**

**135.** Determine the moment reactions at the supports $A$ and $B$. Use the method of integration. $EI$ is constant.

**Prob. 135**

**\*136.** Determine the equations of the elastic curve for the beam using the $x_1$ and $x_2$ coordinates. Specify the slope at $A$ and the maximum deflection. $EI$ is constant. Use the method of integration.

**Prob. 136**

**137.** Determine the maximum deflection between the supports $A$ and $B$. $EI$ is constant. Use the method of integration.

**Prob. 137**

**138.** If the bearings at $A$ and $B$ exert only vertical reactions on the shaft, determine the slope at $B$ and the deflection at $C$. Use the moment-area theorems.

**Prob. 138**

**139.** The bearing supports $A$, $B$, and $C$ exert only vertical reactions on the shaft. Determine these reactions, then draw the shear and moment diagrams. $EI$ is constant. Use the moment-area theorems.

**141.** Using the method of superposition, determine the deflection at $C$ of beam $AB$. The beams are made of wood having a modulus of elasticity of $E = 1.5(10^3)$ ksi.

Section $a$ – $a$

**Prob. 141**

**Prob. 139**

**142.** The rim on the flywheel has a thickness $t$, width $b$, and specific weight $\gamma$. If the flywheel is rotating at a constant rate of $\omega$, determine the maximum moment developed in the rim. Assume that the spokes do not deform. *Hint*: Due to symmetry of the loading, the slope of the rim at each spoke is zero. Consider the radius to be sufficiently large so that the segment $AB$ can be considered as a straight beam fixed at both ends and loaded with a uniform centrifugal force per unit length. Show that this force is $w = bt\gamma\omega^2 r/g$.

***140.** Using the method of superposition, determine the magnitude of $\mathbf{M}_0$ in terms of the distributed load $w$ and dimension $a$ so that the deflection at the center of the beam is zero. $EI$ is constant.

**Prob. 140**

**Prob. 142**

# Solutions and Answers for Preliminary Problems

**P1a.**

$$M = (8x - 32) \text{ kN} \cdot \text{m}$$
$$x = 0, \quad \frac{dy}{dx} = 0$$
$$x = 0, \quad y = 0$$

**P1b.**

$$M = (5x) \text{ kN} \cdot \text{m}$$
$$x = 0, \quad y = 0$$
$$x = 2 \text{ m}, \quad y = 0$$

**P1c.**

$$M = 4x - (2x)\left(\tfrac{1}{2}x\right)$$
$$M = (4x - x^2) \text{ kN} \cdot \text{m}$$
$$x = 0, \quad y = 0$$
$$x = 4 \text{ m}, \quad y = 0$$

**P1d.**

$$M_1 = (-2x_1) \text{ kN} \cdot \text{m}$$

$$M_2 = (-2x + 8) \text{ kN} \cdot \text{m}$$
$$x_1 = 0, \quad y_1 = 0$$
$$x_2 = 4 \text{ m}, \; y_2 = 0$$
$$x_1 = x_2 = 2 \text{ m}, \; \frac{dy_1}{dx_1} = \frac{dy_2}{dx_2}$$
$$x_1 = x_2 = 2 \text{ m}, \; y_1 = y_2$$

**P1e.**

$$M_1 = -2x_1 - (2x_1)\left(\tfrac{1}{2}x_1\right)$$
$$M_1 = (-2x_1 - x_1^2) \text{ kN} \cdot \text{m}$$

$$M_2 = 10(x_2 - 2) - 4(x_2 - 1) - 2x_2$$
$$M_2 = (4x_2 - 16) \text{ kN} \cdot \text{m}$$
$$x_1 = 0, \quad y_1 = 0$$
$$x_1 = 2 \text{ m}, \; y_1 = 0$$
$$x_2 = 2 \text{ m}, \; y_2 = 0$$
$$x_1 = x_2 = 2 \text{ m}, \; \frac{dy_1}{dx_1} = \frac{dy_2}{dx_2}$$

**P1f.**

$$M_1 = (1.5x_1)\,\text{kN}\cdot\text{m}$$

$$M_2 = 1.5x_2 - 3(x_2 - 2)\left(\frac{1}{2}\right)(x_2 - 2)$$

$$M_2 = -1.5x_2^2 + 7.5x_2 - 6$$

$$x_1 = 0,\ y_1 = 0$$

$$x_2 = 4\,\text{m},\ y_2 = 0$$

$$x_1 = x_2 = 2\,\text{m},\ \frac{dy_1}{dx_1} = \frac{dy_2}{dx_2}$$

$$x_1 = x_2 = 2\,\text{m},\ \ y_1 = y_2$$

---

## Selected Answers

1.    $\sigma = 3.02$ ksi
2.    $\sigma = 75.5$ ksi
3.    $\sigma = 582$ MPa
5.    $v_C = 6.11$ mm $\downarrow$
6.    $v_1 = \dfrac{Px_1}{12EI}(-x_1^2 + L^2)$,

     $v_3 = \dfrac{P}{12EI}(2x_3^3 - 9Lx_3^2 + 10L^2x_3 - 3L^3)$,

     $v_{\max} = \dfrac{PL^3}{8EI}\downarrow$

7.    $v_{\max} = \dfrac{P}{3EI_{AB}}\left\{\left(1 - \dfrac{I_{AB}}{I_{BC}}\right)l^3 - L^3\right\}$

9.    $v_1 = \dfrac{P}{12EI}(2x_1^3 - 3x_1^2)$, $v_2 = \dfrac{PL^2}{48EI}(-6x_2 + L)$

10.    $\theta_A = -\dfrac{M_0L}{3EI}$, $v = \dfrac{M_0}{6EIL}(3Lx^2 - x^3 - 2L^2x)$,

      $v_{\max} = \dfrac{-0.0642M_0L^2}{EI}$

11.    $\theta_B = \dfrac{M_0L}{6EI}$, $v|_{x=L/2} = \dfrac{-M_0L^2}{16EI}$

13.    $\theta_A = -\dfrac{M_0a}{2EI}$, $v_{\max} = -\dfrac{5M_0a^2}{8EI}$

14.    $v_{\max} = \dfrac{3PL^3}{256EI}\downarrow$

15.    $F = 1.375$ N

17.    $v_1 = \dfrac{M_0}{6EIL}(-x_1^3 + L^2x_1)$,

      $v_2 = \dfrac{M_0}{24EI}(-12x_2^2 + 20Lx_2 - 7L^2)$,

      $v_C = \dfrac{7M_0L^2}{24EI}\downarrow$

18.    $\theta_A = -\dfrac{3PL^2}{8EI}$, $v_C = \dfrac{-PL^3}{6EI}$

19.    $v_0 = -\dfrac{11PL^3}{48EI}$

21.    $v_{\max} = 11.5$ mm $\downarrow$

22.    $v = \dfrac{1}{EI}(2.25\,x^3 - 0.002778\,x^5 - 40.5\,x^2)$ kip·ft$^3$,

      $\theta = 0.00466$ rad (clockwise), $v_{\max} = 0.369$ in.

23.    $\theta_C = -\dfrac{4M_0L}{3EI}$, $v_1 = \dfrac{M_0}{6EIL}[-x_1^3 + L^2x_1]$,

      $v_2 = \dfrac{M_0}{6EIL}[-3Lx_2^2 + 8L^2x_2 - 5L^3]$,

$$v_C = -\frac{5M_0L^2}{6EI}$$

**25.** $v_{\max} = \dfrac{-18.8 \text{ kip} \cdot \text{ft}^3}{EI}$

**26.** $v_{\max} = 0.396 \text{ in.}\downarrow$

**27.** $v = \dfrac{w_0 x^2}{120EIL}(10L^2 x - x^3 - 20L^3),$

$v_{\max} = \dfrac{11w_0 L^4}{120EI}\downarrow$

**29.** $\theta_B = -\dfrac{wa^3}{6EI}, v_1 = \dfrac{w}{24EI}\left[-x_1^4 + 4ax_1^3 - 6a^2 x_1^2\right],$

$v_2 = \dfrac{wa^3}{24EI}\left[-4x_2 + a\right],$

$v_B = \dfrac{wa^3}{24EI}(-4L + a)$

**30.** $\theta_B = -\dfrac{wa^3}{6EI}, v_1 = \dfrac{wx_1^2}{24EI}\left[-x_1^2 + 4ax_1 - 6a^2\right].$

$v_2 = \dfrac{wa^3}{24EI}\left[4x_3 + a - 4L\right], v_B = \dfrac{wa^3}{24EI}(a - 4L)$

**31.** $v = \dfrac{1}{EI}\left[-\dfrac{Pb}{6a}x^3 + \dfrac{P(a+b)}{6a}<x-a>^3 + \dfrac{Pab}{6}x\right]$

**33.** $v = \dfrac{P}{6EI}\left[-x^3 + <x-a>^3 + <x-3a>^3 + 9a^2 x - 8a^3\right],$

$(v_{\max})_{BC} = \dfrac{Pa^3}{2EI}\uparrow, v_A = \dfrac{4Pa^3}{3EI}\downarrow$

**34.** $v = \dfrac{P}{12EI}\left[-2<x-a>^3 + 4<x-2a>^3 + a^2 x\right],$

$(v_{\max})_{AB} = \dfrac{0.106Pa^3}{EI}\uparrow, v_C = \dfrac{3Pa^3}{4EI}\downarrow$

**35.** $v = \dfrac{1}{EI}\left[-2.5x^2 + 2<x-4>^3 - \dfrac{1}{8}<x-4>^4\right.$

$+ 2<x-12>^3 + \dfrac{1}{8}<x-12>^4$

$\left. - 24x + 136\right] \text{kip} \cdot \text{ft}^3$

**37.** $v = \dfrac{M_0}{6EI}\left[3\left<x - \dfrac{L}{3}\right>^2 - 3\left<x - \dfrac{2}{3}L\right>^2 - Lx\right],$

$v_{\max} = \dfrac{5M_0 L^2}{72EI}\downarrow$

**38.** $v = \dfrac{1}{EI}\left[0.417x^3 - 0.333<x-8>^3\right.$

$\left. - 0.667<x-16>^3 - 169x\right] \text{kip} \cdot \text{ft}^3$

**39.** $v_{\max} = 12.9 \text{ mm}\downarrow$

**41.** $(v_{\max})_{AB} = 0.0867 \text{ in.}\uparrow$

**42.** $v = \dfrac{1}{EI}\left[-0.25x^4 + 0.208<x-1.5>^3\right.$

$+ 0.25<x-1.5>^4 + 4.625<x-4.5>^3$

$\left. + 25.1x - 36.4\right] \text{kN} \cdot \text{m}^3$

**43.** $v = \dfrac{1}{EI}\left[-0.0833x^3 + 3<x-8>^2\right.$

$\left. + 3<x-16>^2 + 8.00x\right]$

**45.** $v_C = -0.501 \text{ mm}, v_D = -0.698 \text{ mm},$
$v_E = -0.501 \text{ mm}$

**46.** $\theta_A = -0.128°, \theta_B = 0.128°$

**47.** $v_{\max} = -3.64 \text{ mm}$

**49.** $\theta_A = \dfrac{302}{EI} \text{ kip} \cdot \text{ft}^2, v_C = -\dfrac{3110}{EI} \text{ kip} \cdot \text{ft}^3$

**50.** $\dfrac{dv}{dx} = \dfrac{1}{EI}\left[2.25x^2 - 0.5x^3 + 5.25<x-5>^2\right.$

$\left. + 0.5<x-5>^3 - 3.125\right] \text{kN} \cdot \text{m}^2,$

$v = \dfrac{1}{EI}\left[0.75x^3 - 0.125x^4 + 1.75<x-5>^3\right.$

$\left. + 0.125<x-5>^4 - 3.125x\right] \text{kN} \cdot \text{m}^3$

**51.** $\theta_C = -\dfrac{3937.5}{EI}, \Delta_C = \dfrac{50\,625}{EI}\downarrow$

**53.** $\theta_B = -\dfrac{5PL^2}{8\,EI}, \Delta_B = \dfrac{7PL^3}{16EI}\downarrow$

**54.** $\theta_B = -\dfrac{Pa^2}{12EI}, \Delta_C = \dfrac{Pa^3}{12EI}$

**55.** $\Delta_{\max} = 12.2 \text{ mm}$

**57.** $\Delta_{\max} = \dfrac{11Pa^3}{48EI}$

**58.** $\Delta_C = -\dfrac{84}{EI}, \theta_A = \dfrac{8}{EI}, \theta_B = -\dfrac{16}{EI}, \theta_C = -\dfrac{40}{EI}$

**59.** $\theta_A = 0.00115 \text{ rad}$

**61.** $a = 0.858L$

**62.** $P = 6.43 \text{ lb}, \Delta_B = 2.14 \text{ in.}\downarrow$

**63.** $\theta_B = -\dfrac{3M_0 L}{2EI}, \Delta_B = \dfrac{7M_0 L^2}{8EI}\downarrow$

**65.** $\theta_A = -\dfrac{5Pa^2}{2EI}, \Delta_C = \dfrac{19Pa^3}{6EI}\downarrow$

**66.** $\Delta_C = -\dfrac{PL^3}{12EI}, \theta_A = \dfrac{PL^2}{24EI}, \theta_B = -\dfrac{PL^2}{12EI}$

**67.** $\Delta_{\max} = \dfrac{0.00802PL^3}{EI}$

**69.** $\theta_C = -\dfrac{5Pa^2}{2EI}, \Delta_B = \dfrac{25Pa^3}{6EI}\downarrow$

**70.** $\theta_A = -\dfrac{336 \text{ kip} \cdot \text{ft}^2}{EI}, v_{\max} = \dfrac{3048 \text{ kip} \cdot \text{ft}^3}{EI}\downarrow$

**71.** $E = \dfrac{Pa}{24I\Delta}(3L^2 - 4a^2)$

**73.** $\theta_A = -\dfrac{M_0 L}{6EI}, \Delta_{\max} = \dfrac{5M_0 L^2}{72EI}\downarrow$

**74.** $\theta_{\max} = \dfrac{5PL^2}{16EI}, \Delta_{\max} = \dfrac{3PL^3}{16EI}\downarrow$

**75.** $\theta_B = 0.00658$ rad, $\Delta_C = 13.8$ mm$\downarrow$

**77.** $a = 0.865\,L$

**78.** $\theta_B = \dfrac{7wa^3}{12EI}, \Delta_C = \dfrac{25wa^4}{48EI}\downarrow$

**79.** $\theta_C = -\dfrac{a^2}{6EI}(12P + wa),$

$\Delta_C = \dfrac{a^3}{24EI}(64P + 7wa)\downarrow$

**81.** $\theta_A = \dfrac{PL^2}{12EI}, \Delta_D = \dfrac{PL^3}{8EI}\downarrow$

**82.** $\Delta_{\max} = \dfrac{3wa^4}{8EI}$

**83.** $\theta_B = -0.00778$ rad, $v_B = 0.981$ in.$\downarrow$

**85.** $\theta_C = -\dfrac{wa^3}{6EI}, \Delta_C = \dfrac{wa^4}{8EI}\downarrow$

**86.** $\theta_A = \dfrac{wa^3}{6EI}, \Delta_D = \dfrac{wa^4}{12EI}\downarrow$

**87.** $\Delta_C = 0.895$ in.$\downarrow$

**89.** $\Delta_C = 1.90$ in.$\downarrow$

**90.** Use W14 $\times$ 34

**91.** $\Delta_C = 23.2$ mm$\downarrow$

**93.** $\Delta = PL^2\left(\dfrac{1}{k} + \dfrac{L}{3EI}\right)$

**94.** $\Delta_A = \dfrac{72}{EI}\downarrow, \theta_A = \dfrac{36}{EI}$↻

**95.** $\Delta_A = PL^3\left(\dfrac{1}{12EI} + \dfrac{1}{8GJ}\right)\downarrow$

**97.** $\dfrac{x_{\max}}{y_{\max}} = \dfrac{I_x}{I_y}\tan\theta,$

$y_{\max} = 0.736$ in., $x_{\max} = 3.09$ in.

**98.** $\Delta_A = \dfrac{Pa^2(3b + a)}{3EI}\downarrow$

**99.** $A_y = \dfrac{20}{27}P, M_A = \dfrac{4}{27}PL, B_y = \dfrac{7}{27}P, M_B = \dfrac{2}{27}PL$

**101.** $A_x = 0, C_y = \dfrac{5}{16}P, B_y = \dfrac{11}{8}P, A_y = \dfrac{5}{16}P$

**102.** $B_y = \dfrac{5}{16}P, A_y = \dfrac{11}{16}P, M_A = \dfrac{3PL}{16}$

**103.** $A_x = 0, B_y = \dfrac{3wL}{8}, A_y = \dfrac{5wL}{8}, M_A = \dfrac{wL^2}{8}$

**105.** $C_x = 0, A_y = 12.0$ kN, $B_y = 40.0$ kN, $C_y = 12.0$ kN

**106.** $A_x = 0, B_y = \dfrac{w_0L}{10}, A_y = \dfrac{2w_0L}{5}, M_A = \dfrac{w_0L^2}{15}$

**107.** $A_x = 0, A_y = \dfrac{7wL}{16}, C_y = -\dfrac{wL}{16}, B_y = \dfrac{5wL}{8}$

**109.** $T_{AC} = \dfrac{3A_2E_2wL_1^4}{8(A_2E_2L_1^3 + 3E_1I_1L_2)}$

**110.** $A_x = 0, F_C = 112$ kN, $A_y = 34.0$ kN, $B_y = 34.0$ kN

**111.** $M_A = \dfrac{5wL^2}{192}, M_B = \dfrac{11wL^2}{192}$

**113.** $A_y = 1.48$ kip, $B_x = 0, B_y = 3.52$ kip, $M_B = 7.67$ kip·ft

**114.** $B_y = \dfrac{2}{3}P, M_A = \dfrac{PL}{3}, A_y = \dfrac{4}{3}P, A_x = 0$

**115.** $B_y = \dfrac{11P}{16}, C_y = \dfrac{13P}{32}, A_y = \dfrac{3P}{32}$

**117.** $B_y = 550$ N, $A_y = 125$ N, $C_y = 125$ N

**118.** $A_x = 0, B_y = \dfrac{7P}{4}, A_y = \dfrac{3P}{4}, M_A = \dfrac{PL}{4}$

**119.** $C_x = 0, B_y = 30.75$ kip, $A_y = 2.625$ kip, $C_y = 14.6$ kip

**121.** $\Delta_B = 1.50$ mm$\downarrow$

**122.** $A_x = 0, B_y = \dfrac{3M_0}{2L}, A_y = \dfrac{3M_0}{2L}, M_A = \dfrac{M_0}{2}$

**123.** $C_x = 0, C_y = \dfrac{P}{3}$

**125.** $M_A = M_B = \dfrac{1}{24}PL, A_y = B_y = \dfrac{1}{6}P,$

$C_y = D_y = \dfrac{1}{3}P, D_x = 0$

**126.** $F_{sp} = \dfrac{3kwL^4}{24EI + 8kL^3}$

**127.** $M = \dfrac{PL}{8} - \dfrac{2EI}{L}\alpha, \Delta_{\max} = \dfrac{PL^3}{192EI} + \dfrac{\alpha L}{4}$

**129.** $a = L - \left(\dfrac{72\Delta EI}{w_o}\right)^{\frac{1}{4}}$

**130.** $d = 0.708$ in.

**131.** $B_y = 634$ lb , $A_y = 243$ lb , $C_y = 76.8$ lb

**133.** $v = \dfrac{1}{EI}(-30x^3 + 46.25 <x - 12>^3$
$- 11.7 <x - 24>^3 + 38{,}700x - 412{,}560)$ lb·in$^3$

**134.** $v_1 = \dfrac{1}{EI}(4.44x_1^3 - 640x_1)$ lb·in$^3$,
$v_2 = \dfrac{1}{EI}(-4.44x_2^3 + 640x_2)$ lb·in$^3$

**135.** $M_B = \dfrac{w_0L^2}{30}, M_A = \dfrac{w_0L^2}{20}$

**137.** $(v_2)_{\max} = \dfrac{wL^4}{18\sqrt{3}EI}$

**138.** $\theta_B = \dfrac{Pa^2}{4EI}, \Delta_C = \dfrac{Pa^3}{4EI}\uparrow$

**139.** $B_y = 138$ N, $A_y = 81.3$ N, $C_y = 18.8$ N

**141.** $\Delta_C = 0.644$ in$\downarrow$

**142.** $M_{\max} = \dfrac{\pi^2 br\gamma\omega^2 r^3}{108g}$

# Fundamental Problems Partial Solutions and Answers

## F1

$\zeta + \Sigma M_O = 0; \qquad M(x) = 30 \text{ kN} \cdot \text{m}$

$EI\dfrac{d^2v}{dx^2} = 30$

$EI\dfrac{dv}{dx} = 30x + C_1$

$EIv = 15x^2 + C_1 x + C_2$

At $x = 3$ m, $\dfrac{dv}{dx} = 0.$

$C_1 = -90 \text{ kN} \cdot \text{m}^2$

At $x = 3$ m, $v = 0.$

$C_2 = 135 \text{ kN} \cdot \text{m}^3$

$\dfrac{dv}{dx} = \dfrac{1}{EI}(30x - 90)$

$v = \dfrac{1}{EI}(15x^2 - 90x + 135)$

For end $A$, $x = 0$

$\theta_A = \dfrac{dv}{dx}\bigg|_{x=0} = -\dfrac{90(10^3)}{200(10^9)[65.0(10^{-6})]} = -0.00692 \text{ rad}$      *Ans.*

$v_A = v|_{x=0} = \dfrac{135(10^3)}{200(10^9)[65.0(10^{-6})]} = 0.01038 \text{ m} = 10.4 \text{ mm}$    *Ans.*

## F2

$\zeta + \Sigma M_O = 0; \qquad M(x) = (-10x - 10) \text{ kN} \cdot \text{m}$

$EI\dfrac{d^2v}{dx^2} = -10x - 10$

$EI\dfrac{dv}{dx} = -5x^2 - 10x + C_1$

$EIv = -\dfrac{5}{3}x^3 - 5x^2 + C_1 x + C_2$

At $x = 3$ m, $\dfrac{dv}{dx} = 0.$

$EI(0) = -5(3^2) - 10(3) + C_1 \qquad C_1 = 75 \text{ kN} \cdot \text{m}^2$

At $x = 3$ m, $v = 0.$

$EI(0) = -\dfrac{5}{3}(3^3) - 5(3^2) + 75(3) + C_2 \quad C_2 = -135 \text{ kN} \cdot \text{m}^3$

$\dfrac{dv}{dx} = \dfrac{1}{EI}(-5x^2 - 10x + 75)$

$v = \dfrac{1}{EI}\left(-\dfrac{5}{3}x^3 - 5x^2 + 75x - 135\right)$

For end $A$, $x = 0$

$\theta_A = \dfrac{dv}{dx}\bigg|_{x=0} = \dfrac{1}{EI}[-5(0) - 10(0) + 75]$

$\phantom{\theta_A} = \dfrac{75(10^3)}{200(10^9)[65.0(10^{-6})]} = 0.00577 \text{ rad}$      *Ans.*

$v_A = v|_{x=0} = \dfrac{1}{EI}\left[-\dfrac{5}{3}(0^3) - 5(0^2) + 75(0) - 135\right]$

$\phantom{v_A} = -\dfrac{135(10^3)}{200(10^9)[65.0(10^{-6})]} = -0.01038 \text{ m} = -10.4 \text{ mm}$

     *Ans.*

## F3

$\zeta + \Sigma M_O = 0; \qquad M(x) = \left(-\dfrac{3}{2}x^2 - 10x\right) \text{ kN} \cdot \text{m}$

$EI\dfrac{d^2v}{dx^2} = -\dfrac{3}{2}x^2 - 10x$

$EI\dfrac{dv}{dx} = -\dfrac{1}{2}x^3 - 5x^2 + C_1$

At $x = 3$ m, $\dfrac{dv}{dx} = 0.$

$EI(0) = -\dfrac{1}{2}(3^3) - 5(3^2) + C_1 \qquad C_1 = 58.5 \text{ kN} \cdot \text{m}^2$

$\dfrac{dv}{dx} = \dfrac{1}{EI}\left(-\dfrac{1}{2}x^3 - 5x^2 + 58.5\right)$

For end $A$, $x = 0$

$\theta_A = \dfrac{dv}{dx}\bigg|_{x=0} = \dfrac{58.5(10^3)}{200(10^9)[65.0(10^{-6})]} = 0.0045 \text{ rad}$      *Ans.*

## F4

$A_y = 600 \text{ lb}$

$\zeta + \Sigma M_O = 0; \qquad M(x) = (600x - 50x^2) \text{ lb} \cdot \text{ft}$

$EI\dfrac{d^2v}{dx^2} = 600x - 50x^2$

$EI\dfrac{dv}{dx} = 300x^2 - 16.667x^3 + C_1$

$EIv = 100x^3 - 4.1667x^4 + C_1 x + C_2$

At $x = 0$, $v = 0.$

$EI(0) = 100(0^3) - 4.1667(0^4) + C_1(0) + C_2 \qquad C_2 = 0$

At $x = 12$ ft, $v = 0.$

$EI(0) = 100(12^3) - 4.1667(12^4) + C_1(12)$

$\phantom{EI(0) = 100(12^3) - 4.1667(12^4) + C_1(12) xxxxxx} C_1 = -7200 \text{ lb} \cdot \text{ft}^2$

$\dfrac{dv}{dx} = \dfrac{1}{EI}(300x^2 - 16.667x^3 - 7200)$

$$v = \frac{1}{EI}(100x^3 - 4.1667x^4 - 7200x)$$

$v_{max}$ occurs where $\frac{dv}{dx} = 0$.

$$300x^2 - 16.667x^3 - 7200 = 0$$

$x = 6$ ft                                                    *Ans.*

$$v = \frac{1}{EI}[100(6^3) - 4.1667(6^4) - 7200(6)]$$

$$= \frac{-27\,000(12 \text{ in.}/\text{ft})^3}{1.5(10^6)\left[\frac{1}{12}(3)(6^3)\right]}$$

$$= -0.576 \text{ in.}$$                                       *Ans.*

## F5

$$\zeta + \Sigma M_O = 0; \qquad M(x) = (40 - 5x) \text{ kN} \cdot \text{m}$$

$$EI\frac{d^2v}{dx^2} = 40 - 5x$$

$$EI\frac{dv}{dx} = 40x - 2.5x^2 + C_1$$

$$EIv = 20x^2 - 0.8333x^3 + C_1x + C_2$$

At $x = 0$, $v = 0$.

$$EI(0) = 20(0^2) - 0.8333(0^3) + C_1(0) + C_2 \qquad C_2 = 0$$

At $x = 6$ m, $v = 0$.

$$EI(0) = 20(6^2) - 0.8333(6^3) + C_1(6) + 0$$

$$C_1 = -90 \text{ kN} \cdot \text{m}^2$$

$$\frac{dv}{dx} = \frac{1}{EI}(40x - 2.5x^2 - 90)$$

$$v = \frac{1}{EI}(20x^2 - 0.8333x^3 - 90x)$$

$v_{max}$ occurs where $\frac{dv}{dx} = 0$.

$$40x - 2.5x^2 - 90 = 0$$

$$x = 2.7085 \text{ m}$$

$$v = \frac{1}{EI}[20(2.7085^2) - 0.83333(2.7085^3) - 90(2.7085)]$$

$$= -\frac{113.60(10^3)}{200(10^9)[39.9(10^{-6})]} = -0.01424 \text{ m} = -14.2 \text{ mm}$$

*Ans.*

## F6

$$\zeta + \Sigma M_O = 0; \qquad M(x) = (10x + 10) \text{ kN} \cdot \text{m}$$

$$EI\frac{d^2v}{dx^2} = 10x + 10$$

$$EI\frac{dv}{dx} = 5x^2 + 10x + C_1$$

Due to symmetry, $\frac{dv}{dx} = 0$ at $x = 3$ m.

$$EI(0) = 5(3^2) + 10(3) + C_1 \quad C_1 = -75 \text{ kN} \cdot \text{m}^2$$

$$\frac{dv}{dx} = \frac{1}{EI}[5x^2 + 10x - 75]$$

At $x = 0$,

$$\frac{dv}{dx} = \frac{-75(10^3)}{200(10^9)(39.9(10^{-6}))} = -9.40(10^{-3}) \text{ rad} \qquad \textit{Ans.}$$

## F7

Since $B$ is a fixed support, $\theta_B = 0$.

$$\theta_A = |\theta_{A/B}| = \frac{1}{2}\left(\frac{38}{EI} + \frac{20}{EI}\right)(3) = \frac{87 \text{ kN} \cdot \text{m}^2}{EI}$$

$$= \frac{87(10^3)}{200(10^9)[65(10^{-6})]} = 0.00669 \text{ rad} \,\rotatebox{0}{$\circlearrowright$} \qquad \textit{Ans.}$$

$$\Delta_A = |t_{A/B}| = (1.5)\left[\frac{20}{EI}(3)\right] + 2\left[\frac{1}{2}\left(\frac{18}{EI}\right)(3)\right]$$

$$= \frac{144(10^3)}{200(10^9)[65(10^{-6})]} = 0.01108 \text{ m} = 11.1 \text{ mm} \downarrow$$

*Ans.*

## F8

Since $B$ is a fixed support, $\theta_B = 0$.

$$\theta_A = |\theta_{A/B}| = \frac{1}{2}\left(\frac{50}{EI} + \frac{20}{EI}\right)(1) + \frac{1}{2}\left(\frac{20}{EI}\right)(1) = \frac{45 \text{ kN} \cdot \text{m}^2}{EI}$$

$$= \frac{45(10^3)}{200(10^9)[126(10^{-6})]} = 0.00179 \text{ rad} \,\rotatebox{0}{$\circlearrowright$} \qquad \textit{Ans.}$$

$$\Delta_A = |t_{A/B}| =$$

$$(1.6667)\left[\frac{1}{2}\left(\frac{30}{EI}\right)(1)\right] + 1.5\left[\frac{20}{EI}(1)\right] + 0.6667\left[\frac{1}{2}\left(\frac{20}{EI}\right)(1)\right]$$

$$= \frac{61.667 \text{ kN} \cdot \text{m}^3}{EI} = \frac{61.667(10^3)}{200(10^9)[126(10^{-6})]}$$

$$= 0.002447 \text{ m} = 2.48 \text{ mm} \downarrow \qquad \textit{Ans.}$$

## F9

Since $B$ is a fixed support, $\theta_B = 0$.

$$\theta_A = |\theta_{A/B}| = \frac{1}{2}\left[\frac{60}{EI}(1)\right] + \frac{30}{EI}(2) = \frac{90 \text{ kN} \cdot \text{m}^2}{EI}$$

$$= \frac{90(10^3)}{200(10^9)[121(10^{-6})]} = 0.00372 \text{ rad} \,\rotatebox{0}{$\circlearrowright$} \qquad \textit{Ans.}$$

$$\Delta_A = |t_{A/B}| = 1.6667\left[\frac{1}{2}\left(\frac{60}{EI}\right)(1)\right] + (1)\left[\frac{30}{EI}(2)\right]$$

$$= \frac{110 \text{ kN} \cdot \text{m}^3}{EI}$$

$$= \frac{110(10^3)}{200(10^9)[121(10^{-6})]} = 0.004545 \text{ m} = 4.55 \text{ mm} \downarrow \quad Ans.$$

$$= \frac{113.60(10^3)}{200(10^9)[39.9(10^{-6})]} = 0.01424 \text{ m} = 14.2 \text{ mm} \downarrow \quad Ans.$$

**F10**

Since $B$ is a fixed support, $\theta_B = 0$.

$$\theta_A = |\theta_{A/B}| = \frac{1}{2}\left(\frac{18}{EI}\right)(6) + \frac{1}{3}\left(\frac{9}{EI}\right)(3) = \frac{63 \text{ kip} \cdot \text{ft}^2}{EI}$$

$$= \frac{63(12^2)}{29(10^3)(245)} = 0.00128 \text{ rad} \curvearrowright \quad Ans.$$

$$\Delta_A = |t_{A/B}| = 4\left[\frac{1}{2}\left(\frac{18}{EI}\right)(6)\right] + (3 + 2.25)\left[\frac{1}{3}\left(\frac{9}{EI}\right)(3)\right]$$

$$= \frac{263.25 \text{ kip} \cdot \text{ft}^3}{EI} = \frac{263.25(12^3)}{29(10^3)(245)} = 0.0640 \text{ in.} \downarrow \quad Ans.$$

**F11**

Due to symmetry, the slope at the midspan of the beam (point $C$) is zero, i.e., $\theta_C = 0$.

$$\Delta_{\max} = \Delta C = |t_{A/C}| = (2)\left[\frac{1}{2}\left(\frac{30}{EI}\right)(3)\right] + 1.5\left[\frac{10}{EI}(3)\right]$$

$$= \frac{135 \text{ kN} \cdot \text{m}^3}{EI}$$

$$= \frac{135(10^3)}{200(10^9)[42.8(10^{-6})]} = 0.0158 \text{ m} = 15.8 \text{ mm} \downarrow \quad Ans.$$

**F12**

$$t_{A/B} = 2\left[\frac{1}{2}\left(\frac{30}{EI}\right)(6)\right] + 3\left[\frac{10}{EI}(6)\right] = \frac{360}{EI}$$

$$\theta_B = \frac{|t_{A/B}|}{L} = \frac{\dfrac{360}{EI}}{6} = \frac{60}{EI}$$

The maximum deflection occurs at point $C$ where the slope of the elastic curve is zero.

$$\theta_B = \theta_{B/C}$$

$$\frac{60}{EI} = \left(\frac{10}{EI}\right)x + \frac{1}{2}\left(\frac{5x}{EI}\right)x$$

$$2.5x^2 + 10x - 60 = 0$$

$$x = 3.2915 \text{ m}$$

$$\Delta_{\max} = |t_{B/C}| =$$

$$\frac{2}{3}(3.2915)\left\{\frac{1}{2}\left[\frac{5(3.2915)}{EI}\right](3.2915)\right\} + \frac{1}{2}(3.2915)\left[\frac{10}{EI}(3.2915)\right]$$

$$= \frac{113.60 \text{ kN} \cdot \text{m}^3}{EI}$$

**F13**

$$(v_B)_1 = \frac{Px^2}{6EI}(3L - x) = \frac{40(4^2)}{6EI}[3(6) - 4] = \frac{1493.33}{EI} \downarrow$$

$$(v_B)_2 = \frac{PL^3}{3EI} = \frac{B_y(4^3)}{3EI} = \frac{21.33B_y}{EI} \uparrow$$

$$(+\uparrow) \quad v_B = 0 = (v_B)_1 + (v_B)_2$$

$$0 = -\frac{1493.33}{EI} + \frac{21.33B_y}{EI}$$

$$B_y = 70 \text{ kN} \quad\quad Ans.$$

$$\xrightarrow{+} \Sigma F_x = 0; \quad\quad A_x = 0 \quad\quad Ans.$$

$$+\uparrow \Sigma F_y = 0; \quad 70 - 40 - A_y = 0 \quad A_y = 30 \text{ kN} \quad Ans.$$

$$\zeta + \Sigma M_A = 0; \quad 70(4) - 40(6) - M_A = 0$$

$$M_A = 40 \text{ kN} \cdot \text{m} \quad\quad Ans.$$

**F14**

To use the deflection tables, consider loading as a superposition of uniform distributed load minus a triangular load.

$$(v_B)_1 = \frac{w_0 L^4}{8EI}\downarrow \quad (v_B)_2 = \frac{w_0 L^4}{30EI}\uparrow \quad (v_B)_3 = \frac{B_y L^3}{3EI}\uparrow$$

$$(+\uparrow) \quad v_B = 0 = (v_B)_1 + (v_B)_2 + (v_B)_3$$

$$0 = -\frac{w_0 L^4}{8EI} + \frac{w_0 L^4}{30EI} + \frac{B_y L^3}{3EI}$$

$$B_y = \frac{11w_0 L}{40} \quad\quad Ans.$$

$$\xrightarrow{+} \Sigma F_x = 0; \quad\quad A_x = 0 \quad\quad Ans.$$

$$+\uparrow \Sigma F_y = 0; \quad A_y + \frac{11w_0 L}{40} - \frac{1}{2}w_0 L = 0$$

$$A_y = \frac{9w_0 L}{40} \quad\quad Ans.$$

$$\zeta + \Sigma M_A = 0; \quad M_A + \frac{11w_0 L}{40}(L) - \frac{1}{2}w_0 L\left(\frac{2}{3}L\right) = 0$$

$$M_A = \frac{7w_0 L^2}{120} \quad\quad Ans.$$

**F15**

$$(v_B)_1 = \frac{wL^4}{8EI} = \frac{[10(10^3)](6^4)}{8[200(10^9)][65.0(10^{-6})]} = 0.12461 \text{ m} \downarrow$$

$$(v_B)_2 = \frac{B_y L^3}{3EI} = \frac{B_y(6^3)}{3[200(10^9)][65.0(10^{-6})]} = 5.5385(10^{-6})B_y \uparrow$$

$$(+\downarrow) \quad v_B = (v_B)_1 + (v_B)_2$$

$$0.002 = 0.12461 - 5.5385(10^{-6})B_y$$

$$B_y = 22.14(10^3) \text{ N} = 22.1 \text{ kN} \qquad \qquad Ans.$$

$$\xrightarrow{+} \Sigma F_x = 0; \qquad A_x = 0 \qquad \qquad Ans.$$

$$+\uparrow \Sigma F_y = 0; \qquad A_y + 22.14 - 10(6) = 0 \qquad A_y = 37.9 \text{ kN}$$
$$Ans.$$

$$\zeta + \Sigma M_A = 0; \qquad M_A + 22.14(6) - 10(6)(3) = 0$$
$$M_A = 47.2 \text{ kN} \cdot \text{m} \qquad \qquad Ans.$$

**F16**

$$(v_B)_1 = \frac{M_O L}{6EI(2L)} [(2L)^2 - L^2] = \frac{M_O L^2}{4EI} \downarrow$$

$$(v_B)_2 = \frac{B_y (2L)^3}{48EI} = \frac{B_y L^3}{6EI} \uparrow$$

$$(+\uparrow) \qquad v_B = 0 = (v_B)_1 + (v_B)_2$$

$$0 = -\frac{M_O L^2}{4EI} + \frac{B_y L^3}{6EI}$$

$$B_y = \frac{3M_O}{2L} \qquad \qquad Ans.$$

**F17**

$$(v_B)_1 = \frac{Pbx}{6EIL} (L^2 - b^2 - x^2) = \frac{50(4)(6)}{6EI(12)} (12^2 - 4^2 - 6^2)$$

$$= \frac{1533.3 \text{ kN} \cdot \text{m}^3}{EI} \downarrow$$

$$(v_B)_2 = \frac{B_y L^3}{48EI} = \frac{B_y (12^3)}{48EI} = \frac{36B_y}{EI} \uparrow$$

$$(+\uparrow) \qquad v_B = 0 = (v_B)_1 + (v_B)_2$$

$$0 = -\frac{1533.3 \text{ kN} \cdot \text{m}^3}{EI} + \frac{36B_y}{EI}$$

$$B_y = 42.6 \text{ kN} \qquad \qquad Ans.$$

**F18**

$$(v_B)_1 = \frac{5wL^4}{384EI} = \frac{5[10(10^3)](12^4)}{384[200(10^9)][65.0(10^{-6})]} = 0.20769 \downarrow$$

$$(v_B)_2 = \frac{B_y L^3}{48EI} = \frac{B_y (12^3)}{48[200(10^9)][65.0(10^{-6})]} = 2.7692(10^{-6})B_y \uparrow$$

$$(+\uparrow) \qquad v_B = (v_B)_1 + (v_B)_2$$

$$-0.005 = -0.20769 + 2.7692(10^{-6})B_y$$

$$B_y = 73.19(10^3) \text{ N} = 73.2 \text{ kN} \qquad \qquad Ans.$$

# Buckling of Columns

From Chapter 13 of *Mechanics of Materials*, Ninth Edition. R. C. Hibbeler. Copyright © 2014 by Pearson Education, Inc. Published by Pearson Prentice Hall. All rights reserved.

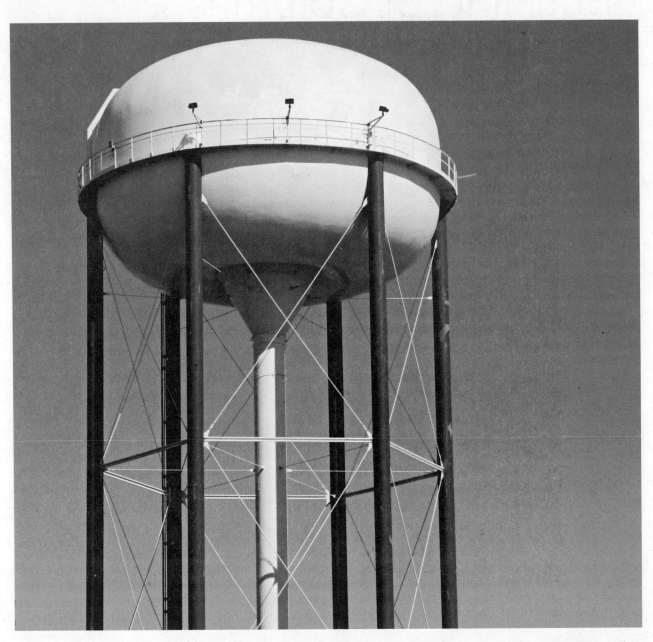

The columns of this water tank are braced at their length in order to reduce their chance of buckling.

# Buckling of Columns

## CHAPTER OBJECTIVES

■ In this chapter, we will discuss the behavior of columns and indicate some of the methods used for their design. The chapter begins with a general discussion of buckling, followed by a determination of the axial load needed to buckle a so-called ideal column. Afterwards, a more realistic analysis is considered, which accounts for any bending of the column. Also, inelastic buckling of a column is presented as a special topic. At the end of the chapter we will discuss some of the methods used to design both concentrically and eccentrically loaded columns made of common engineering materials.

## 1 Critical Load

Whenever a member is designed, it is necessary that it satisfy specific strength, deflection, and stability requirements. There are various methods used to determine a member's strength and deflection; these methods assume that the member is always in stable equilibrium. Some members, however, may be subjected to compressive loadings, and if these members are long and slender the loading may be large enough to cause the member to deflect laterally or sidesway. To be specific, long slender members subjected to an axial compressive force are called *columns*, and the lateral deflection that occurs is called *buckling*. Quite often the buckling of a column can lead to a sudden and dramatic failure of a structure or mechanism, and as a result, special attention must be given to the design of columns so that they can safely support their intended loadings without buckling.

$P_{cr}$

$P > P_{cr}$

$P_{cr}$

$P > P_{cr}$

(a)

(b)

**Fig. 1**

The maximum axial load that a column can support when it is on the *verge* of buckling is called the **critical load**, $P_{cr}$, Fig. 1*a*. Any additional loading will cause the column to buckle and therefore deflect laterally as shown in Fig. 1*b*. In order to better understand the nature of this instability, consider a two-bar mechanism consisting of weightless bars that are rigid and pin connected as shown in Fig. 2*a*. When the bars are in the vertical position, the spring, having a stiffness $k$, is unstretched, and a *small* vertical force **P** is applied at the top of one of the bars. We can upset this equilibrium position by displacing the pin at $A$ by a small amount $\Delta$, Fig. 2*b*. As shown on the free-body diagram of the pin when the bars are displaced, Fig. 2*c*, the spring will produce a restoring force $F = k\Delta$, while the applied load **P** develops two horizontal components, $P_x = P \tan \theta$, which tend to push the pin (and the bars) further out of equilibrium. Since $\theta$ is small, $\Delta \approx \theta(L/2)$ and $\tan \theta \approx \theta$. Thus the *restoring* spring force becomes $F = k\theta L/2$, and the *disturbing* force is $2P_x = 2P\theta$.

If the restoring force is greater than the disturbing force, that is, $k\theta L/2 > 2P\theta$, then, noticing that $\theta$ cancels out, we can solve for $P$, which gives

$$P < \frac{kL}{4} \qquad \text{stable equilibrium}$$

This is a condition for *stable equilibrium* since the force developed by the spring would be adequate to restore the bars back to their vertical position. However, if $kL\theta/2 < 2P\theta$, or

$$P > \frac{kL}{4} \qquad \text{unstable equilibrium}$$

then the mechanism would be in *unstable equilibrium*. In other words, if this load **P** is applied, and a slight displacement occurs at $A$, the mechanism will tend to move out of equilibrium and not be restored to its original position.

**Fig. 2**

The intermediate value of $P$, which requires $kL\theta/2 = 2P\theta$, is the *critical load*. Here

$$P_{cr} = \frac{kL}{4} \qquad \text{neutral equilibrium}$$

This loading represents a case of the mechanism being in *neutral equilibrium*. Since $P_{cr}$ is *independent* of the (small) displacement $\theta$ of the bars, any slight disturbance given to the mechanism will not cause it to move further out of equilibrium, nor will it be restored to its original position. Instead, the bars will *remain* in the deflected position.

These three different states of equilibrium are represented graphically in Fig. 3. The transition point where the load is equal to the critical value $P = P_{cr}$ is called the *bifurcation point*. At this point the mechanism will be in equilibrium for any *small value* of $\theta$, measured either to the right or to the left of the vertical. Physically, $P_{cr}$ represents the load for which the mechanism is on the verge of buckling. It is quite reasonable to determine this value by assuming *small displacements* as done here; however, it should be understood that $P_{cr}$ may *not* be the largest value of $P$ that the mechanism can support. Indeed, if a larger load is placed on the bars, then the mechanism may have to undergo a further deflection before the spring is compressed or elongated enough to hold the mechanism in equilibrium.

Like the two-bar mechanism just discussed, the critical buckling loads on columns supported in various ways can be obtained, and the method used to do this will be explained in the next section. Although in engineering design the critical load may be considered to be the largest load the column can support, realize that, like the two-bar mechanism in the deflected or buckled position, a column may actually support an

**Fig. 3**

even greater load than $P_{cr}$. Unfortunately, however, this loading may require the column to undergo a *large* deflection, which is generally not tolerated in engineering structures or machines. For example, it may take only a few newtons of force to buckle a meterstick, but the additional load it may support can be applied only after the stick undergoes a relatively large lateral deflection.

## 2 Ideal Column with Pin Supports

In this section we will determine the critical buckling load for a column that is pin supported as shown in Fig. 4*a*. The column to be considered is an *ideal column*, meaning one that is perfectly straight before loading, is made of homogeneous material, and upon which the load is applied through the centroid of the cross section. It is further assumed that the material behaves in a linear-elastic manner and that the column buckles or bends in a single plane. In reality, the conditions of column straightness and load application are never accomplished; however, the analysis to be performed on an "ideal column" is similar to that used to analyze initially crooked columns or those having an eccentric load application. These more realistic cases will be discussed later in this chapter.

Since an ideal column is straight, theoretically the axial load $P$ could be increased until failure occurs by either fracture or yielding of the material. However, when the critical load $P_{cr}$ is reached, the column will be on the verge of becoming unstable, so that a small lateral force $F$, Fig. 4*b*, will cause the column to remain in the deflected position when $F$ is removed, Fig. 4*c*. Any slight reduction in the axial load $P$ from $P_{cr}$ will allow the column to straighten out, and any slight increase in $P$, beyond $P_{cr}$, will cause further increases in lateral deflection.

The dramatic failure of this off-shore oil platform was caused by the horizontal forces of hurricane winds, which led to buckling of its supporting columns.

(a)                    (b)                    (c)

**Fig. 4**

Whether or not a column will remain stable or become unstable when subjected to an axial load will depend on its ability to restore itself, which is based on its resistance to bending. Hence, in order to determine the critical load and the buckled shape of the column, we will apply the Equation 10, which relates the internal moment in the column to its deflected shape, i.e.,

$$EI\frac{d^2v}{dx^2} = M \tag{1}$$

This equation assumes that the slope of the elastic curve is small and that deflections occur only by bending. When the column is in its deflected position, Fig. 5a, the internal bending moment can be determined by using the method of sections. The free-body diagram of a segment in the deflected position is shown in Fig. 5b. Here both the deflection $v$ and the internal moment $M$ are shown in the *positive direction* according to the sign convention used to establish Eq. 1. Moment equilibrium requires $M = -Pv$. Thus Eq. 1 becomes

$$EI\frac{d^2v}{dx^2} = -Pv$$

$$\frac{d^2v}{dx^2} + \left(\frac{P}{EI}\right)v = 0 \tag{2}$$

**Fig. 5**

This is a homogeneous, second-order, linear differential equation with constant coefficients. It can be shown by using the methods of differential equations, or by direct substitution into Eq. 2, that the general solution is

$$v = C_1 \sin\left(\sqrt{\frac{P}{EI}}x\right) + C_2 \cos\left(\sqrt{\frac{P}{EI}}x\right) \tag{3}$$

The two constants of integration are determined from the boundary conditions at the ends of the column. Since $v = 0$ at $x = 0$, then $C_2 = 0$. And since $v = 0$ at $x = L$, then

$$C_1 \sin\left(\sqrt{\frac{P}{EI}}L\right) = 0$$

This equation is satisfied if $C_1 = 0$; however, then $v = 0$, which is a *trivial solution* that requires the column to always remain straight, even though the load may cause the column to become unstable. The other possibility is for

$$\sin\left(\sqrt{\frac{P}{EI}}L\right) = 0$$

which is satisfied if

$$\sqrt{\frac{P}{EI}}L = n\pi$$

or

$$P = \frac{n^2\pi^2 EI}{L^2} \quad n = 1, 2, 3, \ldots \quad (4)$$

The *smallest value* of $P$ is obtained when $n = 1$, so the *critical load* for the column is therefore*

$$P_{cr} = \frac{\pi^2 EI}{L^2}$$

This load is sometimes referred to as the *Euler load*, named after the Swiss mathematician Leonhard Euler, who originally solved this problem in 1757. The corresponding buckled shape is defined by the equation

$$v = C_1 \sin \frac{\pi x}{L}$$

Here the constant $C_1$ represents the maximum deflection, $v_{max}$, which occurs at the midpoint of the column, Fig. 5c. Specific values for $C_1$ cannot be obtained, since the exact deflected form for the column is unknown once it has buckled. It has been assumed, however, that this deflection is small.

Note that the critical load is independent of the strength of the material; rather it only depends on the column's dimensions ($I$ and $L$) and the material's stiffness or modulus of elasticity $E$. For this reason, as far as elastic buckling is concerned, columns made, for example, of high-strength steel offer no advantage over those made of lower-strength steel, since the modulus of elasticity for both is approximately the same. Also note that the load-carrying capacity of a column will increase as the moment of inertia of the cross section increases. Thus, efficient columns are designed so that most of the column's cross-sectional area is located as far away as possible from the principal centroidal axes for the section. This is why hollow sections such as tubes are more economical than solid sections. Furthermore, wide-flange sections, and columns that are "built up" from channels, angles, plates, etc., are better than sections that are solid and rectangular.

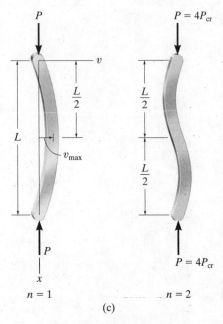

**Fig. 5 (cont.)**

*$n$ represents the number of curves in the deflected shape of the column. For example, if $n = 2$, then *two* curves will appear, Fig. 5c. Here the critical load is 4 $P_{cr}$ just prior to buckling, which practically speaking will not exist.

It is also important to realize that a column will buckle about the principal axis of the cross section having the *least moment of inertia* (the weakest axis) provided it is supported the same way about each axis. For example, a column having a rectangular cross section, like a meter stick, as shown in Fig. 6, will buckle about the *a–a* axis, not the *b–b* axis. As a result, engineers usually try to achieve a balance, keeping the moments of inertia the same in all directions. Geometrically, then, circular tubes would make excellent columns. Also, square tubes or those shapes having $I_x \approx I_y$ are often selected for columns.

Summarizing the above discussion, the buckling equation for a pin-supported long slender column can be rewritten, and the terms defined as follows:

$$P_{cr} = \frac{\pi^2 EI}{L^2} \qquad (5)$$

where

$P_{cr}$ = critical or maximum axial load on the column just before it begins to buckle. This load must *not* cause the stress in the column to exceed the proportional limit

$E$ = modulus of elasticity for the material

$I$ = *least* moment of inertia for the column's cross-sectional area

$L$ = unsupported length of the column, whose ends are pinned

For purposes of design, the above equation can also be written in a more useful form by expressing $I = A r^2$, where $A$ is the cross-sectional area and $r$ is the *radius of gyration* of the cross-sectional area. Thus,

$$P_{cr} = \frac{\pi^2 E (A r^2)}{L^2}$$

$$\left(\frac{P}{A}\right)_{cr} = \frac{\pi^2 E}{(L/r)^2}$$

or

$$\sigma_{cr} = \frac{\pi^2 E}{(L/r)^2} \qquad (6)$$

Here

$\sigma_{cr}$ = critical stress, which is an average normal stress in the column just before the column buckles. This stress is an *elastic stress* and therefore $\sigma_{cr} \leq \sigma_Y$

$E$ = modulus of elasticity for the material

$L$ = unsupported length of the column, whose ends are pinned

$r$ = *smallest* radius of gyration of the column, determined from $r = \sqrt{I/A}$, where $I$ is the *least* moment of inertia of the column's cross-sectional area $A$

The geometric ratio $L/r$ in Eq. 6 is known as the *slenderness ratio*. It is a measure of the column's flexibility, and as will be discussed later, it serves to classify columns as long, intermediate, or short.

**Fig. 6**

Failure of this crane boom was caused by the localized buckling of one of its tubular struts.

It is possible to graph Eq. 6 using axes that represent the critical stress versus the slenderness ratio. Examples of this graph for columns made of a typical structural steel and aluminum alloy are shown in Fig. 7. Note that the curves are hyperbolic and are valid only for critical stresses below the material's yield point (proportional limit), since the material must behave elastically. For the steel the yield stress is $(\sigma_Y)_{st} = 36$ ksi $[E_{st} = 29(10^3)$ ksi$]$, and for the aluminum it is $(\sigma_Y)_{al} = 27$ ksi $[E_{al} = 10(10^3)$ ksi$]$. Substituting $\sigma_{cr} = \sigma_Y$ into Eq. 6, the *smallest* allowable slenderness ratios for the steel and aluminum columns are therefore $(L/r)_{st} = 89$ and $(L/r)_{al} = 60.5$, respectively. Thus, for a steel column, if $(L/r)_{st} \geq 89$, Euler's formula can be used to determine the critical load since the stress in the column remains elastic. On the other hand, if $(L/r)_{st} < 89$, the column's stress will exceed the yield point before buckling can occur, and therefore the Euler formula is not valid in this case.

Fig. 7

## Important Points

- *Columns* are long slender members that are subjected to axial compressive loads.

- The *critical load* is the maximum axial load that a column can support when it is on the verge of buckling. This loading represents a case of *neutral equilibrium*.

- An *ideal column* is initially perfectly straight, made of homogeneous material, and the load is applied through the centroid of the cross section.

- A pin-connected column will buckle about the principal axis of the cross section having the *least* moment of inertia.

- The *slenderness ratio* is $L/r$, where $r$ is the smallest radius of gyration of the cross section. Buckling will occur about the axis where this ratio gives the greatest value.

## EXAMPLE 1

The A992 steel W8 × 31 member shown in Fig. 8 is to be used as a pin-connected column. Determine the largest axial load it can support before it either begins to buckle or the steel yields.

12 ft

**Fig. 8**

### SOLUTION

The column's cross-sectional area and moments of inertia are $A = 9.13 \text{ in}^2$, $I_x = 110 \text{ in}^4$, and $I_y = 37.1 \text{ in}^4$. By inspection, buckling will occur about the $y$–$y$ axis. Why? Applying Eq. 5, we have

$$P_{cr} = \frac{\pi^2 EI}{L^2} = \frac{\pi^2[29(10^3) \text{ kip/in}^2](37.1 \text{ in}^4)}{[12 \text{ ft}(12 \text{ in./ft})]^2} = 512 \text{ kip}$$

When fully loaded, the average compressive stress in the column is

$$\sigma_{cr} = \frac{P_{cr}}{A} = \frac{512 \text{ kip}}{9.13 \text{ in}^2} = 56.1 \text{ ksi}$$

Since this stress exceeds the yield stress (50 ksi), the load $P$ is determined from simple compression:

$$50 \text{ ksi} = \frac{P}{9.13 \text{ in}^2}; \qquad P = 456 \text{ kip} \qquad\qquad Ans.$$

In actual practice, a factor of safety would be placed on this loading.

743

# 3 Columns Having Various Types of Supports

The Euler load was derived for a column that is pin connected or free to rotate at its ends. Oftentimes, however, columns may be supported in some other way. For example, consider the case of a column fixed at its base and free at the top, Fig. 9a. As the column buckles the load displaces $\delta$ and at $x$ the displacement is $v$. From the free-body diagram in Fig. 9b, the internal moment at the arbitrary section is $M = P(\delta - v)$. Consequently, the differential equation for the deflection curve is

$$EI\frac{d^2v}{dx^2} = P(\delta - v)$$

$$\frac{d^2v}{dx^2} + \frac{P}{EI}v = \frac{P}{EI}\delta \tag{7}$$

Unlike Eq. 2, this equation is nonhomogeneous because of the nonzero term on the right side. The solution consists of both a complementary and a particular solution, namely,

$$v = C_1\sin\left(\sqrt{\frac{P}{EI}}x\right) + C_2\cos\left(\sqrt{\frac{P}{EI}}x\right) + \delta$$

The constants are determined from the boundary conditions. At $x = 0$, $v = 0$, so that $C_2 = -\delta$. Also,

$$\frac{dv}{dx} = C_1\sqrt{\frac{P}{EI}}\cos\left(\sqrt{\frac{P}{EI}}x\right) - C_2\sqrt{\frac{P}{EI}}\sin\left(\sqrt{\frac{P}{EI}}x\right)$$

At $x = 0$, $dv/dx = 0$, so that $C_1 = 0$. The deflection curve is therefore

$$v = \delta\left[1 - \cos\left(\sqrt{\frac{P}{EI}}x\right)\right] \tag{8}$$

Since the deflection at the top of the column is $\delta$, that is, at $x = L$, $v = \delta$, we require

$$\delta\cos\left(\sqrt{\frac{P}{EI}}L\right) = 0$$

The trivial solution $\delta = 0$ indicates that no buckling occurs, regardless of the load $P$. Instead,

$$\cos\left(\sqrt{\frac{P}{EI}}L\right) = 0 \quad \text{or} \quad \sqrt{\frac{P}{EI}}L = \frac{n\pi}{2}, \quad n = 1, 3, 5\ldots$$

The smallest critical load occurs when $n = 1$, so that

$$P_{cr} = \frac{\pi^2EI}{4L^2} \tag{9}$$

By comparison with Eq. 5, it is seen that a column fixed supported at its base and free at its top will support only one-fourth the critical load that can be applied to a column pin supported at both ends.

(a)

(b)

**Fig. 9**

The tubular columns used to support this water tank have been braced at three locations along their length to prevent them from buckling.

Other types of supported columns are analyzed in much the same way and will not be covered in detail here.* Instead, we will tabulate the results for the most common types of column support and show how to apply these results by writing Euler's formula in a general form.

**Effective Length.** As stated previously, the Euler formula, Eq. 5, was developed for the case of a column having ends that are pinned or free to rotate. In other words, $L$ in the equation represents the unsupported distance between the points of zero moment. This formula can be used to determine the critical load on columns having other types of support provided "$L$" represents the distance between the zero-moment points. This distance is called the column's *effective length*, $L_e$. Obviously, for a pin-ended column $L_e = L$, Fig. 10a. For the fixed- and free-ended column, the deflection curve, Eq. 8, was found to be one-half that of a column that is pin connected and has a length of $2L$, Fig. 10b. Thus the effective length between the points of zero moment is $L_e = 2L$. Examples for two other columns with different end supports are also shown in Fig. 10. The column fixed at its ends, Fig. 10c, has inflection points or points of zero moment $L/4$ from each support. The effective length is therefore represented by the middle half of its length, that is, $L_e = 0.5L$. Lastly, the pin- and fixed-ended column, Fig. 10d, has an inflection point at approximately $0.7L$ from its pinned end, so that $L_e = 0.7L$.

Rather than specifying the column's effective length, many design codes provide column formulas that employ a dimensionless coefficient $K$ called the *effective-length factor*. This factor is defined from

$$L_e = KL \qquad (10)$$

Specific values of $K$ are also given in Fig. 10. Based on this generality, we can therefore write Euler's formula as

$$P_{cr} = \frac{\pi^2 EI}{(KL)^2} \qquad (11)$$

or

$$\sigma_{cr} = \frac{\pi^2 E}{(KL/r)^2} \qquad (12)$$

Here $(KL/r)$ is the column's *effective-slenderness ratio*. For example, if the column is fixed at its base and free at its end, we have $K = 2$, and therefore Eq. 11 gives the same result as Eq. 9.

Pinned ends
$K = 1$
(a)

Fixed and free ends
$K = 2$
(b)

$L = L_e$

$L_e = 2L$

Fixed ends
$K = 0.5$
(c)

Pinned and fixed ends
$K = 0.7$
(d)

$L_e = 0.5L$

$L_e = 0.7L$

**Fig. 10**

## EXAMPLE | 2

12 ft

12 ft

(a)

12 ft

x–x axis buckling

(b)

8.40 ft

y–y axis buckling

(c)

**Fig. 11**

A W6 × 15 steel column is 24 ft long and is fixed at its ends as shown in Fig. 11a. Its load-carrying capacity is increased by bracing it about the y–y (weak) axis using struts that are assumed to be pin connected to its midheight. Determine the load it can support so that the column does not buckle nor the material exceed the yield stress. Take $E_{st} = 29(10^3)$ ksi and $\sigma_Y = 60$ ksi.

### SOLUTION

The buckling behavior of the column will be *different* about the x–x and y–y axes due to the bracing. The buckled shape for each of these cases is shown in Figs. 11b and 11c. From Fig. 11b, the effective length for buckling about the x–x axis is $(KL)_x = 0.5(24 \text{ ft}) = 12 \text{ ft} = 144$ in., and from Fig. 11c, for buckling about the y–y axis, $(KL)_y = 0.7(24 \text{ ft}/2) = 8.40 \text{ ft} = 100.8$ in. We have $I_x = 29.1 \text{ in}^4$, $I_y = 9.32 \text{ in}^4$.

Applying Eq. 11,

$$(P_{cr})_x = \frac{\pi^2 E I_x}{(KL)_x^2} = \frac{\pi^2[29(10^3) \text{ ksi}]29.1 \text{ in}^4}{(144 \text{ in.})^2} = 401.7 \text{ kip} \qquad (1)$$

$$(P_{cr})_y = \frac{\pi^2 E I_y}{(KL)_y^2} = \frac{\pi^2[29(10^3) \text{ ksi}]9.32 \text{ in}^4}{(100.8 \text{ in.})^2} = 262.5 \text{ kip} \qquad (2)$$

By comparison, buckling will occur about the y–y axis.

The area of the cross section is 4.43 in², so the average compressive stress in the column is

$$\sigma_{cr} = \frac{P_{cr}}{A} = \frac{262.5 \text{ kip}}{4.43 \text{ in}^2} = 59.3 \text{ ksi}$$

Since this stress is less than the yield stress, buckling will occur before the material yields. Thus,

$$P_{cr} = 263 \text{ kip} \qquad\qquad\qquad Ans.$$

**NOTE:** From Eq. 12 it can be seen that buckling will always occur about the column axis having the *largest* slenderness ratio, since a large slenderness ratio will give a small critical stress. We have

$$\left(\frac{KL}{r}\right)_x = \frac{144 \text{ in.}}{2.56 \text{ in.}} = 56.2$$

$$\left(\frac{KL}{r}\right)_y = \frac{100.8 \text{ in.}}{1.46 \text{ in.}} = 69.0$$

Hence, y–y axis buckling will occur, which is the same conclusion reached by comparing Eqs. 1 and 2.

## EXAMPLE | 3

The aluminum column is braced at its top by cables so as to prevent movement at the top along the $x$ axis, Fig. 12a. If it is assumed to be fixed at its base, determine the largest allowable load $P$ that can be applied. Use a factor of safety for buckling of F.S. = 3.0. Take $E_{al} = 70$ GPa, $\sigma_Y = 215$ MPa, $A = 7.5(10^{-3})$ m$^2$, $I_x = 61.3(10^{-6})$ m$^4$, $I_y = 23.2(10^{-6})$ m$^4$.

### SOLUTION

Buckling about the $x$ and $y$ axes is shown in Figs. 12b and 12c, respectively. Using Fig. 10a, for $x$–$x$ axis buckling, $K = 2$, so $(KL)_x = 2(5\text{ m}) = 10$ m. Also, for $y$–$y$ axis buckling, $K = 0.7$, so $(KL)_y = 0.7(5\text{ m}) = 3.5$ m.

Applying Eq. 11, the critical loads for each case are

$$(P_{cr})_x = \frac{\pi^2 E I_x}{(KL)_x^2} = \frac{\pi^2 [70(10^9)\text{ N/m}^2](61.3(10^{-6})\text{ m}^4)}{(10\text{ m})^2}$$

$$= 424\text{ kN}$$

$$(P_{cr})_y = \frac{\pi^2 E I_y}{(KL)_y^2} = \frac{\pi^2 [70(10^9)\text{ N/m}^2](23.2(10^{-6})\text{ m}^4)}{(3.5\text{ m})^2}$$

$$= 1.31\text{ MN}$$

**Fig. 12**

By comparison, as $P$ is increased the column will buckle about the $x$–$x$ axis. The allowable load is therefore

$$P_{allow} = \frac{P_{cr}}{\text{F.S.}} = \frac{424\text{ kN}}{3.0} = 141\text{ kN} \qquad \textit{Ans.}$$

Since

$$\sigma_{cr} = \frac{P_{cr}}{A} = \frac{424\text{ kN}}{7.5(10^{-3})\text{ m}^2} = 56.5\text{ MPa} < 215\text{ MPa}$$

Euler's equation can be applied.

$L_e = 3.5$ m

$y$–$y$ axis buckling

(c)

$L_e = 10$ m

$x$–$x$ axis buckling

(b)

# FUNDAMENTAL PROBLEMS

**F1.** A 50-in.-long rod is made from a 1-in.-diameter steel rod. Determine the critical buckling load if the ends are fixed supported. $E = 29(10^3)$ ksi, $\sigma_Y = 36$ ksi.

**F2.** A 12-ft wooden rectangular column has the dimensions shown. Determine the critical load if the ends are assumed to be pin connected. $E = 1.6(10^3)$ ksi. Yielding does not occur.

**F2**

**F3.** The A992 steel column can be considered pinned at its top and bottom and braced against its weak axis at the mid-height. Determine the maximum allowable force **P** that the column can support without buckling. Apply a F.S. = 2 against buckling. Take $A = 7.4(10^{-3})$ m$^2$, $I_x = 87.3(10^{-6})$ m$^4$, and $I_y = 18.8(10^{-6})$ m$^4$.

**F3**

**F4.** A steel pipe is fixed supported at its ends. If it is 5 m long and has an outer diameter of 50 mm and a thickness of 10 mm, determine the maximum axial load $P$ that it can carry without buckling. $E_{st} = 200$ GPa, $\sigma_Y = 250$ MPa.

**F5.** Determine the maximum force **P** that can be supported by the assembly without risk of causing member $AC$ to buckle. The member is made of A992 steel and has a diameter of 2 in. Take F.S. = 2 against buckling.

**F5**

**F6.** The A992 steel rod $BC$ has a diameter of 50 mm and is used as a strut to support the beam. Determine the maximum intensity $w$ of the uniform distributed load that can be applied to the beam without risk of causing the strut to buckle. Take F.S. = 2 against buckling.

**F6**

# PROBLEMS

**1.** Determine the critical buckling load for the column. The material can be assumed rigid.

**3.** The aircraft link is made from an A992 steel rod. Determine the smallest diameter of the rod, to the nearest $\frac{1}{16}$ in., that will support the load of 4 kip without buckling. The ends are pin connected.

**Prob. 3**

**Prob. 1**

*4.** Rigid bars $AB$ and $BC$ are pin connected at $B$. If the spring at $D$ has a stiffness $k$, determine the critical load $P_{cr}$ for the system.

**2.** The column consists of a rigid membr that is pinned at its bottom and attached to a spring at its top. If the spring is unstretched when the column is in the vertical position, determine the critical load that can be placed on the column.

**Prob. 2**

**Prob. 4**

**5.** A rod made from polyurethane has a stress-strain diagram in compression as shown. If the rod is pinned at its ends and is 37 in. long, determine its smallest diameter so it does not fail from elastic buckling.

**6.** A rod made from polyurethane has a stress-strain diagram in compression as shown. If the rod is pinned at its top and fixed at its base, and is 37 in. long, determine its smallest diameter so it does not fail from elastic buckling.

**9.** A column is constructed using four A992 steel angles that are laced together as shown. The length of the column is to be 25 ft and the ends are assumed to be pin connected. Each angle shown below has an area of $A = 2.75$ in$^2$ and moments of inertia of $I_x = I_y = 2.22$ in$^4$. Determine the distance $d$ between the centroids $C$ of the angles so that the column can support an axial load of $P = 350$ kip without buckling. Neglect the effect of the lacing.

**10.** A column is constructed using four A992 steel angles that are laced together as shown. The length of the column is to be 40 ft and the ends are assumed to be fixed connected. Each angle shown below has an area of $A = 2.75$ in$^2$ and moments of inertia of $I_x = I_y = 2.22$ in$^4$. Determine the distance $d$ between the centroids $C$ of the angles so that the column can support an axial load of $P = 350$ kip without buckling. Neglect the effect of the lacing.

**Probs. 5/6**

**Probs. 9/10**

**11.** The A992 steel angle has a cross-sectional area of $A = 2.48$ in$^2$ and a radius of gyration about the $x$ axis of $r_x = 1.26$ in. and about the $y$ axis of $r_y = 0.879$ in. The smallest radius of gyration occurs about the $a$–$a$ axis and is $r_a = 0.644$ in. If the angle is to be used as a pin-connected 10-ft-long column, determine the largest axial load that can be applied through its centroid $C$ without causing it to buckle.

**7.** A 2014-T6 aluminum alloy hollow circular tube has an outer diameter of 150 mm and inner diameter of 100 mm. If it is pinned at both ends, determine the largest axial load that can be applied to the tube without causing it to buckle. The tube is 6 m long.

**\*8.** A 2014-T6 aluminum alloy hollow circular tube has an outer diameter of 150 mm and inner diameter of 100 mm. If it is pinned at one end and fixed at the other end, determine the largest axial load that can be applied to the tube without causing it to buckle. The tube is 6 m long.

**Prob. 11**

**\*12.** The control linkage for a machine consists of two L2 steel rods $BE$ and $FG$, each with a diameter of 1 in. If a device at $G$ causes the end $G$ to freeze up and become pin connected, determine the maximum horizontal force $P$ that could be applied to the handle without causing either of the two rods to buckle. The members are pin connected at $A, B, D, E,$ and $F$.

**14.** The two steel channels are to be laced together to form a 30-ft-long bridge column assumed to be pin connected at its ends. Each channel has a cross-sectional area of $A = 3.10$ in$^2$ and moments of inertia $I_x = 55.4$ in$^4$, $I_y = 0.382$ in$^4$. The centroid $C$ of its area is located in the figure. Determine the proper distance $d$ between the centroids of the channels so that buckling occurs about the $x$–$x$ and $y'$–$y'$ axes due to the same load. What is the value of this critical load? Neglect the effect of the lacing. $E_{st} = 29(10^3)$ ksi, $\sigma_y = 50$ ksi.

**Prob. 14**

**Prob. 12**

**15.** An A992 steel W200 $\times$ 46 column of length 9 m is pinned at both of its ends. Determine the allowable axial load the column can support if F.S. $= 2$ is to be used against buckling.

**\*16.** An A992 steel W200 $\times$ 46 column of length 9 m is fixed at one end and free at its other end. Determine the allowable axial load the column can support if F.S. $= 2$ is to be used against buckling.

**17.** The 10-ft wooden rectangular column has the dimensions shown. Determine the critical load if the ends are assumed to be pin connected. $E_w = 1.6(10^3)$ ksi, $\sigma_y = 5$ ksi.

**13.** An A992 steel column has a length of 5 m and is fixed at both ends. If the cross-sectional area has the dimensions shown, determine the critical load.

**18.** The 10-ft wooden column has the dimensions shown. Determine the critical load if the bottom is fixed and the top is pinned. $E_w = 1.6(10^3)$ ksi, $\sigma_Y = 5$ ksi.

**Prob. 13**

**Probs. 17/18**

**19.** Determine the maximum force $P$ that can be applied to the handle so that the A992 steel control rod $AB$ does not buckle. The rod has a diameter of 1.25 in. It is pin connected at its ends.

**Prob. 19**

**22.** The linkage is made using two A992 steel rods, each having a circular cross section. Determine the diameter of each rod to the nearest $\frac{1}{8}$ in. that will support a load of $P = 6$ kip. Assume that the rods are pin connected at their ends. Use a factor of safety with respect to buckling of 1.8.

**23.** The linkage is made using two A992 steel rods, each having a circular cross section. If each rod has a diameter of $\frac{3}{4}$ in., determine the largest load it can support without causing any rod to buckle. Assume that the rods are pin connected at their ends.

**Probs. 22/23**

**\*20.** The A992 steel tube has the cross-sectional area shown. If it has a length of 15 ft and is pinned at both ends, determine the maximum axial load that the tube can support without causing it to buckle.

**21.** The A992 steel tube has the cross-sectional area shown. If it has a length of 15 ft and is fixed at one end and free at the other end, determine the maximum axial load that the tube can support without causing it to buckle.

**\*24.** An L-2 tool steel link in a forging machine is pin connected to the forks at its ends as shown. Determine the maximum load $P$ it can carry without buckling. Use a factor of safety with respect to buckling of F.S. $= 1.75$. Note from the figure on the left that the ends are pinned for buckling, whereas from the figure on the right the ends are fixed.

**Probs. 20/21**

**Prob. 24**

**25.** The W14 × 30 is used as a structural A992 steel column that can be assumed pinned at both of its ends. Determine the largest axial force $P$ that can be applied without causing it to buckle.

**P**

25 ft

**Prob. 25**

**26.** The A992 steel bar $AB$ has a square cross section. If it is pin connected at its ends, determine the maximum allowable load $P$ that can be applied to the frame. Use a factor of safety with respect to buckling of 2.

C

1.5 in.   30°

A

B   1.5 in.

10 ft   1.5 in.

P

**Prob. 26**

**27.** The strongback $BC$ is made of an A992 steel hollow circular section with $d_o = 60$ mm and $d_i = 40$ mm. Determine the allowable maximum lifting force **P** without causing the strong back to buckle. F.S. $= 2$ against buckling is desired.

**\*28.** The strongback is made of an A992 steel hollow circular section with the outer diameter of $d_o = 60$ mm. If it is designed to withstand the lifting force of $P = 60$ kN, determine the minimum required wall thickness of the strong back so that it will not buckle. Use F.S. $= 2$ against buckling.

**P**

A

45°   $\lceil a$   45°

B   C

$\lfloor a$

4 m

D   E

$d_o$

$d_i$

Section $a$ – $a$

**Probs. 27/28**

**29.** The beam supports the load of $P = 6$ kip. As a result, the A992 steel member $BC$ is subjected to a compressive load. Due to the forked ends on the member, consider the supports at $B$ and $C$ to act as pins for $x$–$x$ axis buckling and as fixed supports for $y$–$y$ axis buckling. Determine the factor of safety with respect to buckling about each of these axes.

**30.** Determine the greatest load $P$ the beam will support without causing the A992 steel member $BC$ to buckle. Due to the forked ends on the member, consider the supports at $B$ and $C$ to act as pins for $x$–$x$ axis buckling and as fixed supports for $y$–$y$ axis buckling.

4 ft   4 ft   **P**

A   B

3 ft   y   3 in.

C   y

x   1 in.

x

**Probs. 29/30**

**31.** The steel bar $AB$ has a rectangular cross section. If it is pin connected at its ends, determine the maximum allowable intensity $w$ of the distributed load that can be applied to $BC$ without causing bar $AB$ to buckle. Use a factor of safety with respect to buckling of 1.5. $E_{st} = 200$ GPa, $\sigma_Y = 360$ MPa.

**Prob. 31**

**\*32.** The frame supports the load of $P = 4$ kN. As a result, the A992 steel member $BC$ is subjected to a compressive load. Due to the forked ends on this member, consider the supports at $B$ and $C$ to act as pins for $x$–$x$ axis buckling and as fixed supports for $y$–$y$ axis buckling. Determine the factor of safety with respect to buckling about each of these axes.

**33.** Determine the greatest load $P$ the frame will support without causing the A992 steel member $BC$ to buckle. Due to the forked ends on the member, consider the supports at $B$ and $C$ to act as pins for $x$–$x$ axis buckling and as fixed supports for $y$–$y$ axis buckling.

**Probs. 32/33**

**34.** A 6061-T6 aluminum alloy solid circular rod of length

4 m is pinned at both of its ends. If it is subjected to an axial load of 15 kN and F.S. = 2 is required against buckling, determine the minimum required diameter of the rod to the nearest mm.

**35.** A 6061-T6 aluminum alloy solid circular rod of length 4 m is pinned at one end while fixed at the other end. If it is subjected to an axial load of 15 kN and F.S. = 2 is required against buckling, determine the minimum required diameter of the rod to the nearest mm.

**\*36.** The members of the truss are assumed to be pin connected. If member $BD$ is an A992 steel rod of radius 2 in., determine the maximum load $P$ that can be supported by the truss without causing the member to buckle.

**37.** Solve Prob. 36 in the case of member $AB$, which has a radius of 2 in.

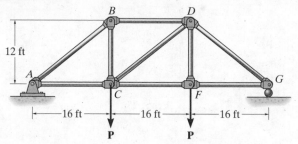

**Probs. 36/37**

**38.** The truss is made from A992 steel bars, each of which has a circular cross section with a diameter of 1.5 in. Determine the maximum force $P$ that can be applied without causing any of the members to buckle. The members are pin connected at their ends.

**39.** The truss is made from A992 steel bars, each of which has a circular cross section. If the applied load $P = 10$ kip, determine the diameter of member $AB$ to the nearest $\frac{1}{8}$ in. that will prevent this member from buckling. The members are pin connected at their ends.

**Probs. 38/39**

**\*40.** The steel bar $AB$ of the frame is assumed to be pin connected at its ends for $y$–$y$ axis buckling. If $P = 18$ kN, determine the factor of safety with respect to buckling about the $y$–$y$ axis due to the applied loading. $E_{st} = 200$ GPa, $\sigma_Y = 360$ MPa.

**Prob. 40**

**41.** The ideal column has a weight $w$ (force/length) and rests in the horizontal position when it is subjected to the axial load **P**. Determine the maximum moment in the column at midspan. $EI$ is constant. *Hint:* Establish the differential equation for deflection, Eq. 1, with the origin at the mid span. The general solution is $v = C_1 \sin kx + C_2 \cos kx + (w/(2P))x^2 - (wL/(2P))x - (wEI/P^2)$ where $k^2 = P/EI$.

**Prob. 41**

**42.** The ideal column is subjected to the force **F** at its midpoint and the axial load **P**. Determine the maximum moment in the column at midspan. $EI$ is constant. *Hint:* Establish the differential equation for deflection, Eq. 1. The general solution is $v = C_1 \sin kx + C_2 \cos kx - c^2x/k^2$, where $c^2 = F/2EI, k^2 = P/EI$.

**Prob. 42**

**43.** The column with constant $EI$ has the end constraints shown. Determine the critical load for the column.

**Prob. 43**

**\*44.** Consider an ideal column as in Fig. 10$c$, having both ends fixed. Show that the critical load on the column is given by $P_{cr} = 4\pi^2EI/L^2$. *Hint:* Due to the vertical deflection of the top of the column, a constant moment **M′** will be developed at the supports. Show that $d^2v/dx^2 + (P/EI)v = M'/EI$. The solution is of the form $v = C_1 \sin(\sqrt{P/EI}x) + C_2 \cos(\sqrt{P/EI}x) + M'/P$.

**45.** Consider an ideal column as in Fig. 10$d$, having one end fixed and the other pinned. Show that the critical load on the column is given by $P_{cr} = 20.19EI/L^2$. *Hint:* Due to the vertical deflection at the top of the column, a constant moment **M′** will be developed at the fixed support and horizontal reactive forces **R′** will be developed at both supports. Show that $d^2v/dx^2 + (P/EI)v = (R'/EI)(L - x)$. The solution is of the form $v = C_1\sin(\sqrt{P/EI}x) + C_2 \cos(\sqrt{P/EI}x) + (R'/P)(L - x)$. After application of the boundary conditions show that $\tan(\sqrt{P/EI}L) = \sqrt{P/EI}L$. Solve by trial and error for the smallest nonzero root.

# *4 The Secant Formula

The Euler formula was derived assuming the load $P$ is always applied through the centroid of the column's cross-sectional area and that the column is perfectly straight. This is actually quite unrealistic, since manufactured columns are never perfectly straight, nor is the application of the load known with great accuracy. In reality, then, columns never suddenly buckle; instead they begin to bend, although ever so slightly, immediately upon application of the load. As a result, the actual criterion for load application should be limited either to a specified deflection of the column or by not allowing the maximum stress in the column to exceed an allowable stress.

To study this effect, we will apply the load $P$ to the column at a short *eccentric distance e* from its centroid, Fig. 13a. This loading on the column is statically equivalent to the axial load $P$ and bending moment $M' = Pe$ shown in Fig. 13b. As shown, in both cases, the ends $A$ and $B$ are supported so that they are free to rotate (pin supported). As before, we will only consider small slopes and deflections and linear-elastic material behavior. Furthermore, the $x$–$v$ plane is a plane of symmetry for the cross-sectional area.

From the free-body diagram of the arbitrary section, Fig. 13c, the internal moment in the column is

$$M = -P(e + v) \tag{13}$$

The differential equation for the deflection curve is therefore

$$EI\frac{d^2v}{dx^2} = -P(e + v)$$

The column supporting this crane is unusually long. It will be subjected not only to uniaxial load, but also a bending moment. To ensure it will not buckle, it should be braced at the roof as a pin connection.

(a)

(b)

(c)

**Fig. 13**

or

$$\frac{d^2v}{dx^2} + \frac{P}{EI}v = -\frac{P}{EI}e$$

This equation is similar to Eq. 7 and has a general solution consisting of the complementary and particular solutions, namely,

$$v = C_1 \sin\sqrt{\frac{P}{EI}}x + C_2 \cos\sqrt{\frac{P}{EI}}x - e \tag{14}$$

To evaluate the constants we must apply the boundary conditions. At $x = 0, v = 0$, so $C_2 = e$. And at $x = L, v = 0$, which gives

$$C_1 = \frac{e[1 - \cos(\sqrt{P/EI}L)]}{\sin(\sqrt{P/EI}L)}$$

Since $1 - \cos(\sqrt{P/EI}L) = 2\sin^2(\sqrt{P/EI}\,L/2)$ and $\sin(\sqrt{P/EI}L) = 2\sin(\sqrt{P/EI}L/2)\cos(\sqrt{P/EI}L/2)$, we have

$$C_1 = e\tan\left(\sqrt{\frac{P}{EI}}\frac{L}{2}\right)$$

Hence, the deflection curve, Eq. 14, can be written as

$$v = e\left[\tan\left(\sqrt{\frac{P}{EI}}\frac{L}{2}\right)\sin\left(\sqrt{\frac{P}{EI}}x\right) + \cos\left(\sqrt{\frac{P}{EI}}x\right) - 1\right] \tag{15}$$

**Maximum Deflection.** Due to symmetry of loading, both the maximum deflection and maximum stress occur at the column's midpoint. Therefore, when $x = L/2, v = v_{max}$, so

$$\boxed{v_{max} = e\left[\sec\left(\sqrt{\frac{P}{EI}}\frac{L}{2}\right) - 1\right]} \tag{16}$$

Notice that if $e$ approaches zero, then $v_{max}$ approaches zero. However, if the terms in the brackets approach infinity as $e$ approaches zero, then $v_{max}$ will have a nonzero value. Mathematically, this would represent the behavior of an axially loaded column at failure when subjected to the critical load $P_{cr}$. Therefore, to find $P_{cr}$ we require

$$\sec\left(\sqrt{\frac{P_{cr}}{EI}}\frac{L}{2}\right) = \infty$$

$$\sqrt{\frac{P_{cr}}{EI}}\frac{L}{2} = \frac{\pi}{2}$$

$$P_{cr} = \frac{\pi^2 EI}{L^2} \tag{17}$$

which is the same result found from the Euler formula, Eq. 5.

If Eq. 16 is plotted as load $P$ versus deflection $v_{max}$ for various values of eccentricity $e$, the family of colored curves shown in Fig. 14 results. Here the critical load becomes an asymptote to the curves, and of

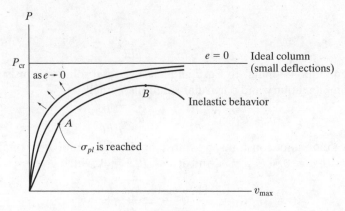

**Fig. 14**

course represents the unrealistic case of an ideal column ($e = 0$). As stated earlier, $e$ is *never zero* due to imperfections in initial column straightness and load application; however, as $e \rightarrow 0$, the curves tend to approach the ideal case. Furthermore, these curves are appropriate only for *small deflections*, since the curvature was approximated by $d^2v/dx^2$ when Eq. 16 was developed. Had a more exact analysis been performed, all these curves would tend to turn upward, intersecting and then rising above the line $P = P_{cr}$. This, of course, indicates that a larger load $P$ is needed to create larger column deflections. We have not considered this analysis here, however, since most often engineering design restricts the deflection of columns to small values.

It should also be noted that the colored curves in Fig. 14 apply only for linear-elastic material behavior. Such is the case if the column is long and slender. However, if a short or intermediate-length stocky column is considered, then the applied load, as it is increased, may eventually cause the material to yield, and the column will begin to behave in an *inelastic manner*. This occurs at point $A$ for the black curve in Fig. 14. As the load is further increased, the curve never reaches the critical load, and instead the load reaches a maximum value at $B$. Afterwards, a sudden decrease in load-carrying capacity occurs as the column continues to yield and deflect by larger amounts.

Lastly, the colored curves in Fig. 14 also illustrate that a *nonlinear* relationship occurs between the load $P$ and the deflection $v$. As a result, the principle of superposition *cannot be used* to determine the total deflection of a column caused by applying *successive loads* to the column. Instead, the loads must first be added, and then the corresponding deflection due to their resultant can be determined. Physically, the reason that successive loads and deflections cannot be superimposed is that the column's internal moment *depends* on *both* the *load P* and the *deflection v*, that is, $M = -P(e + v)$, Eq. 13.

## The Secant Formula.

The maximum stress in the column can be determined by realizing that it is caused by both the axial load and the moment, Fig. 15a. Maximum moment occurs at the column's midpoint, and using Eqs. 13 and 16, it has a magnitude of

$$M = |P(e + v_{max})| \qquad M = Pe \sec\left(\sqrt{\frac{P}{EI}}\frac{L}{2}\right) \qquad (18)$$

As shown in Fig. 15b, the maximum stress in the column is compressive, and it has a value of

$$\sigma_{max} = \frac{P}{A} + \frac{Mc}{I}; \qquad \sigma_{max} = \frac{P}{A} + \frac{Pec}{I}\sec\left(\sqrt{\frac{P}{EI}}\frac{L}{2}\right)$$

Since the radius of gyration is defined as $r^2 = I/A$, the above equation can be written in a form called the *secant formula*:

$$\sigma_{max} = \frac{P}{A}\left[1 + \frac{ec}{r^2}\sec\left(\frac{L}{2r}\sqrt{\frac{P}{EA}}\right)\right] \qquad (19)$$

Here

$\sigma_{max}$ = maximum *elastic stress* in the column, which occurs at the inner concave side at the column's midpoint. This stress is compressive.

$P$ = vertical load applied to the column. $P < P_{cr}$ unless $e = 0$; then $P = P_{cr}$ (Eq. 5).

$e$ = eccentricity of the load $P$, measured from the centroidal axis of the column's cross-sectional area to the line of action of $P$

$c$ = distance from the centroidal axis to the outer fiber of the column where the maximum compressive stress $\sigma_{max}$ occurs

$A$ = cross-sectional area of the column

$L$ = unsupported length of the column *in the plane of bending*. Application is restricted to members that are pin connected, $L_e = L$ or have one end free and the other end fixed, $L_e = 2L$.

$E$ = modulus of elasticity for the material

$r$ = radius of gyration, $r = \sqrt{I/A}$, where $I$ is calculated about the centroidal or bending axis

Like Eq. 16, Eq. 19 indicates that there is a nonlinear relationship between the load and the stress. Hence, the principle of superposition does not apply, and therefore the loads have to be added *before* the stress is determined. Furthermore, due to this nonlinear relationship, any factor of safety used for design purposes applies to the load and not to the stress.

For a given value of $\sigma_{max}$, graphs of Eq. 19 can be plotted as the slenderness ratio $KL/r$ versus the average stress $P/A$ for various values of the *eccentricity ratio* $ec/r^2$. A specific set of graphs for a structural-grade A-36 steel having a yield point of $\sigma_{max} = \sigma_Y = 36$ ksi

(a)

Axial
stress

+

Bending
stress

=

$\sigma_{max}$

Resultant
stress

(b)

**Fig. 15**

$\frac{P}{A}$(ksi)

$\dfrac{ec}{r^2} = 0.1$

Euler's formula
Eq. 13–6

$\dfrac{ec}{r^2} = 0$

0.5

1.0

1.5

$\dfrac{KL}{r}$

A-36 structural steel
$E_{st} = 29\,(10^3)$ ksi, $\sigma_Y = 36$ ksi

**Fig. 16**

and a modulus of elasticity of $E_{st} = 29(10^3)$ ksi is shown in Fig. 16. Note that when $e \to 0$, or when $ec/r^2 \to 0$, Eq. 19 gives $\sigma_{max} = P/A$, where $P$ is the critical load on the column, defined by Euler's formula. This results in Eq. 6, which has been plotted in Fig. 7 and repeated in Fig. 16. Since both Eqs. 6 and 19 are valid only for elastic loadings, the stresses shown in Fig. 16 cannot exceed $\sigma_Y = 36$ ksi, represented here by the horizontal line.

The curves in Fig. 16 indicate that differences in the eccentricity ratio have a marked effect on the load-carrying capacity of columns that have small slenderness ratios. However, columns that have large slenderness ratios tend to fail at or near the Euler critical load regardless of the eccentricity ratio. When using Eq. 19 for design purposes, it is therefore important to have a somewhat accurate value for the eccentricity ratio for shorter-length columns.

**Design.**  Once the eccentricity ratio has been determined, the column data can be substituted into Eq. 9. If a value of $\sigma_{max} = \sigma_Y$ is chosen, then the corresponding load $P_Y$ can be determined from a trial-and-error procedure, since the equation is transcendental and cannot be solved explicitly for $P_Y$. As a design aid, computer software, or graphs such as those in Fig. 16, can also be used to determine $P_Y$ directly.

Realize that $P_Y$ is the load that will cause the column to develop a maximum compressive stress of $\sigma_Y$ at its inner concave fibers. Due to the eccentric application of $P_Y$, this load will always be smaller than the critical load $P_{cr}$, which is determined from the Euler formula that assumes (unrealistically) that the column is axially loaded.

## Important Points

- Due to imperfections in manufacturing or specific application of the load, a column will never suddenly buckle; instead, it begins to bend.

- The load applied to a column is related to its deflection in a nonlinear manner, and so the principle of superposition does not apply.

- As the slenderness ratio increases, eccentrically loaded columns tend to fail at or near the Euler buckling load.

# EXAMPLE | 4

The W8 × 40 A992 steel column shown in Fig. 17a is fixed at its base and braced at the top so that it is fixed from displacement, yet free to rotate about the y–y axis. Also, it can sway to the side in the y–z plane. Determine the maximum eccentric load the column can support before it either begins to buckle or the steel yields.

(a)

## SOLUTION

From the support conditions it is seen that about the y–y axis the column behaves as if it were pinned at its top and fixed at the bottom and subjected to an axial load $P$, Fig. 17b. About the x–x axis the column is free at the top and fixed at the bottom, and it is subjected to both an axial load $P$ and moment $M = P(9 \text{ in.})$, Fig. 17c.

**y–y Axis Buckling.** From Fig. 10d the effective length factor is $K_y = 0.7$, so $(KL)_y = 0.7(12) \text{ ft} = 8.40 \text{ ft} = 100.8 \text{ in.}$ Determining $I_y$ for the W8 × 40 section and applying Eq. 11, we have

$$(P_{cr})_y = \frac{\pi^2 E I_y}{(KL)_y^2} = \frac{\pi^2 [29(10^3) \text{ ksi}](49.1 \text{ in}^4)}{(100.8 \text{ in.})^2} = 1383 \text{ kip}$$

(b)   y–y axis buckling

**x–x Axis Yielding.** From Fig. 10b, $K_x = 2$, so $(KL)_x = 2(12) \text{ ft} = 24 \text{ ft} = 288 \text{ in.}$ Determining $A = 11.7 \text{ in}^2$, $c = 8.25 \text{ in.}/2 = 4.125 \text{ in.}$, and $r_x = 3.53 \text{ in.}$, and applying the secant formula, we have

$$\sigma_Y = \frac{P_x}{A}\left[1 + \frac{ec}{r_x^2} \sec\left(\frac{(KL)_x}{2r_x}\sqrt{\frac{P_x}{EA}}\right)\right]$$

Substituting the data and simplifying yields

$$585 = P_x[1 + 2.979 \sec(0.0700\sqrt{P_x})]$$

Solving for $P_x$ by trial and error, noting that the argument for the secant is in radians, we get

$$P_x = 115 \text{ kip} \qquad\qquad Ans.$$

Since this value is less than $(P_{cr})_y = 1383 \text{ kip}$, failure will occur about the x–x axis.

(c)   x–x axis yielding

**Fig. 17**

## *5    Inelastic Buckling

In engineering practice, columns are generally classified according to the type of stresses developed within the column at the time of failure. *Long slender columns* will become unstable when the compressive stress remains elastic. The failure that occurs is referred to as *elastic instability*. *Intermediate columns* fail due to *inelastic instability*, meaning that the compressive stress at failure is greater than the material's proportional limit. And *short columns*, sometimes called *posts*, do not become unstable; rather the material simply yields or fractures.

Application of the Euler equation requires that the stress in the column remain *below* the material's yield point (actually the proportional limit) when the column buckles, and so this equation applies only to long columns. In practice, however, most columns are selected to have intermediate lengths. The behavior of these columns can be studied by modifying the Euler equation so that it applies for inelastic buckling. To show how this can be done, consider the material to have a stress–strain diagram as shown in Fig. 18a. Here the proportional limit is $\sigma_{pl}$, and the modulus of elasticity, or slope of the line $AB$, is $E$.

If the column has a slenderness ratio that is *less* than $(KL/r)_{pl}$, then the critical stress in the column must be greater than $\sigma_{pl}$. For example, suppose a column has a slenderness ratio of $(KL/r)_1 < (KL/r)_{pl}$, with corresponding critical stress $\sigma_D > \sigma_{pl}$ needed to cause instability. When the column is *about to buckle*, the change in stress and strain that occurs in the column is within a *small range* $\Delta\sigma$ and $\Delta\epsilon$, so that the modulus of elasticity or stiffness for the material can be taken as the **tangent modulus** $E_t = \Delta\sigma/\Delta\epsilon$ defined as the slope of the $\sigma-\epsilon$ diagram at point $D$, Fig. 18a. In other words, at the time of failure, the column behaves as if it were made from a material that has a *lower stiffness* than when it behaves elastically, $E_t < E$.

This crane boom failed by buckling caused by an overload. Note the region of localized collapse.

(a)

**Fig. 18**

In general, therefore, as the slenderness ratio $(KL/r)$ decreases, the *critical stress* for a column continues to rise; and from the $\sigma-\epsilon$ diagram, the *tangent modulus* for the material *decreases*. Using this idea, we can modify Euler's equation to include these cases of inelastic buckling by substituting the material's tangent modulus $E_t$ for $E$, so that

$$\sigma_{cr} = \frac{\pi^2 E_t}{(KL/r)^2} \tag{20}$$

This is the so-called *tangent modulus* or *Engesser equation*, proposed by F. Engesser in 1889. A plot of this equation for intermediate and short-length columns of a material defined by the $\sigma-\epsilon$ diagram in Fig. 18a is shown in Fig. 18b.

No *actual column* can be considered to be either perfectly straight or loaded along its centroidal axis, as assumed here, and therefore it is indeed very difficult to develop an expression that will provide a complete analysis of this phenomenon. As a result, other methods of describing the inelastic buckling of columns have been considered. One of these methods was developed by the aeronautical engineer F. R. Shanley and is called the *Shanley theory* of inelastic buckling. Although it provides a better description of the phenomenon than the tangent modulus theory, as explained here, experimental testing of a large number of columns, each of which approximates the ideal column, has shown that Eq. 20 is *reasonably accurate* in predicting the column's critical stress. Furthermore, the tangent modulus approach to modeling inelastic column behavior is relatively easy to apply.

(b)

**Fig. 18 (cont.)**

## EXAMPLE 5

**Fig. 19**

A solid rod has a diameter of 30 mm and is 600 mm long. It is made of a material that can be modeled by the stress–strain diagram shown in Fig. 19. If it is used as a pin-supported column, determine the critical load.

SOLUTION

The radius of gyration is

$$r = \sqrt{\frac{I}{A}} = \sqrt{\frac{(\pi/4)(15 \text{ mm})^4}{\pi(15 \text{ mm})^2}} = 7.5 \text{ mm}$$

and therefore the slenderness ratio is

$$\frac{KL}{r} = \frac{1(600 \text{ mm})}{7.5 \text{ mm}} = 80$$

Applying Eq. 20 we have,

$$\sigma_{cr} = \frac{\pi^2 E_t}{(KL/r)^2} = \frac{\pi^2 E_t}{(80)^2} = 1.542(10^{-3})E_t \qquad (1)$$

First we will assume that the critical stress is elastic. From Fig. 19,

$$E = \frac{150 \text{ MPa}}{0.001} = 150 \text{ GPa}$$

Thus, Eq. 1 becomes

$$\sigma_{cr} = 1.542(10^{-3})[150(10^3)] \text{ MPa} = 231.3 \text{ MPa}$$

Since $\sigma_{cr} > \sigma_{pl} = 150$ MPa, inelastic buckling occurs.
From the second line segment of the $\sigma-\epsilon$ diagram, Fig. 19, we have

$$E_t = \frac{\Delta\sigma}{\Delta\epsilon} = \frac{270 \text{ MPa} - 150 \text{ MPa}}{0.002 - 0.001} = 120 \text{ GPa}$$

Applying Eq. 1 yields

$$\sigma_{cr} = 1.542(10^{-3})[120(10^3)] \text{ MPa} = 185.1 \text{ MPa}$$

Since this value falls within the limits of 150 MPa and 270 MPa, it is indeed the critical stress.
The critical load on the rod is therefore

$$P_{cr} = \sigma_{cr}A = 185.1(10^6) \text{ Pa}[\pi(0.015 \text{ m})^2] = 131 \text{ kN} \qquad Ans.$$

## PROBLEMS

**46.** The wood column has a square cross section with dimensions 100 mm by 100 mm. It is fixed at its base and free at its top. Determine the load $P$ that can be applied to the edge of the column without causing the column to fail either by buckling or by yielding. $E_w = 12$ GPa, $\sigma_Y = 55$ MPa.

**Prob. 46**

**47.** The hollow red brass C83400 copper alloy shaft is fixed at one end but free at the other end. Determine the maximum eccentric force $P$ the shaft can support without causing it to buckle or yield. Also, find the corresponding maximum deflection of the shaft.

**\*48.** The hollow red brass C83400 copper alloy shaft is fixed at one end but free at the other end. If the eccentric force $P = 5$ kN is applied to the shaft as shown, determine the maximum normal stress and the maximum deflection.

**Probs. 47/48**

**49.** The tube is made of copper and has an outer diameter of 35 mm and a wall thickness of 7 mm. Determine the eccentric load $P$ that it can support without failure. The tube is pin supported at its ends. $E_{cu} = 120$ GPa, $\sigma_Y = 750$ MPa.

**50.** Solve Prob. 49 if instead the left end is free and the right end is fixed-supported.

**Probs. 49/50**

**51.** Assume that the wood column is pin connected at its base and top. Determine the maximum eccentric load $P$ that can be applied without causing the column to buckle or yield. $E_w = 1.8(10^3)$ ksi, $\sigma_Y = 8$ ksi.

**\*52.** Assume that the wood column is pinned top and bottom for movement about the $x$–$x$ axis, and fixed at the bottom and free at the top for movement about the $y$–$y$ axis. Determine the maximum eccentric load $P$ that can be applied without causing the column to buckle or yield. $E_w = 1.8(10^3)$ ksi, $\sigma_Y = 8$ ksi.

**Probs. 51/52**

BUCKLING OF COLUMNS

**53.** A W12 × 26 structural A992 steel column is pin connected at its ends and has a length $L = 11.5$ ft. Determine the maximum eccentric load $P$ that can be applied so the column does not buckle or yield. Compare this value with an axial critical load $P'$ applied through the centroid of the column.

**Prob. 53**

**54.** A W14 × 30 structural A-36 steel column is pin connected at its ends and has a length $L = 10$ ft. Determine the maximum eccentric load $P$ that can be applied so the column does not buckle or yield. Compare this value with an axial critical load $P'$ applied through the centroid of the column.

**Prob. 54**

**55.** The wood column is pinned at its base and top. If the eccentric force $P = 10$ kN is applied to the column, investigate whether the column is adequate to support this loading without buckling or yielding. Take $E = 10$ GPa and $\sigma_Y = 15$ MPa.

**\*56.** The wood column is pinned at its base and top. Determine the maximum eccentric force $P$ the column can support without causing it to either buckle or yield. Take $E = 10$ GPa and $\sigma_Y = 15$ MPa.

**Probs. 55/56**

**57.** The 6061-T6 aluminum alloy solid shaft is fixed at one end but free at the other end. If the shaft has a diameter of 100 mm, determine its maximum allowable length $L$ if it is subjected to the eccentric force $P = 80$ kN.

**58.** The 6061-T6 aluminum alloy solid shaft is fixed at one end but free at the other end. If the length is $L = 3$ m, determine its minimum required diameter if it is subjected to the eccentric force $P = 60$ kN.

**Probs. 57/58**

766

**59.** The wood column is pinned at its base and top. If $L = 7$ ft, determine the maximum eccentric load $P$ that can be applied without causing the column to buckle or yield. $E_w = 1.8(10^3)$ ksi, $\sigma_Y = 8$ ksi.

**Prob. 59**

**\*60.** The wood column is pinned at its base and top. If $L = 5$ ft, determine the maximum eccentric load $P$ that can be applied without causing the column to buckle or yield. $E_w = 1.8(10^3)$ ksi, $\sigma_Y = 8$ ksi.

**Prob. 60**

**61.** The A992 steel rectangular hollow section column is pinned at both ends. If it has a length of $L = 14$ ft, determine the maximum allowable eccentric force **P** it can support without causing it to either buckle or yield.

**62.** The A992 steel rectangular hollow section column is pinned at both ends. If it is subjected to the eccentric force $P = 45$ kip, determine its maximum allowable length $L$ without causing it to either buckle or yield.

**Probs. 61/62**

**63.** The W10 × 30 structural A992 steel column is pinned at its top and bottom. Determine the maximum load $P$ it can support.

**\*64.** The W10 × 30 structural A992 steel column is fixed at its bottom and free at its top. If it is subjected to the eccentric load of $P = 85$ kip, determine if the column fails by yielding. The column is braced so that it does not buckle about the $y$–$y$ axis.

**Probs. 63/64**

**65.** Determine the maximum eccentric load $P$ the 2014-T6-aluminum-alloy strut can support without causing it either to buckle or yield. The ends of the strut are pin connected.

Section $a$ – $a$

**Prob. 65**

**66.** The W10 × 45 structural A992 steel column is assumed to be pinned at its top and bottom. If the 12-kip load is applied at an eccentric distance of 8 in., determine the maximum stress in the column. Take $L = 12.6$ ft.

**67.** The W10 × 45 structural A992 steel column is assumed to be pinned at its top and bottom. If the 12-kip load is applied at an eccentric distance of 8 in., determine the maximum stress in the column. Take $L = 9$ ft.

**Probs. 66/67**

**\*68.** The W14 × 53 structural A992 steel column is fixed at its base and free at its top. If $P = 75$ kip, determine the sidesway deflection at its top and the maximum stress in the column.

**69.** The W14 × 53 column is fixed at its base and free at its top. Determine the maximum eccentric load $P$ that it can support without causing it to buckle or yield. $E_{st} = 29(10^3)$ ksi, $\sigma_Y = 50$ ksi.

**Probs. 68/69**

**70.** A column of intermediate length buckles when the compressive stress is 40 ksi. If the slenderness ratio is 60, determine the tangent modulus.

**71.** The aluminum rod is fixed at its base free at its top. If the eccentric load $P = 200$ kN is applied, determine the greatest allowable length $L$ of the rod so that it does not buckle or yield. $E_{al} = 72$ GPa, $\sigma_Y = 410$ MPa.

**\*72.** The aluminum rod is fixed at its base free at its top. If the length of the rod is $L = 2$ m, Determine the greatest allowable load $P$ that can be applied so that the rod does not buckle or yield. Also, determine the largest sidesway deflection of the rod due to the loading. $E_{al} = 72$ GPa, $\sigma_Y = 410$ MPa.

**Probs. 71/72**

**73.** The stress-strain diagram of the material of a column can be approximated as shown. Plot $P/A$ vs. $KL/r$ for the column.

**Prob. 73**

**74.** Construct the buckling curve, $P/A$ versus $L/r$, for a column that has a bilinear stress–strain curve in compression as shown.

**Prob. 74**

**75.** The stress–strain diagram of the material can be approximated by the two line segments shown. If a bar having a diameter of 80 mm and a length of 1.5 m is made from this material, determine the critical load provided the ends are pinned. Assume that the load acts through the axis of the bar. Use Engesser's equation.

**Prob. 75**

**\*76.** The stress–strain diagram of the material can be approximated by the two line segments shown. If a bar having a diameter of 80 mm and a length of 1.5 m is made from this material, determine the critical load provided the ends are fixed. Assume that the load acts through the axis of the bar. Use Engesser's equation.

**Prob. 76**

**77.** The stress–strain diagram of the material can be approximated by the two line segments shown. If a bar having a diameter of 80 mm and a length of 1.5 m is made from this material, determine the critical load provided one end is pinned and the other is fixed. Assume that the load acts through the axis of the bar. Use Engesser's equation.

**Prob. 77**

## *6 Design of Columns for Concentric Loading

These long unbraced timber columns are used to support the roof of this building.

The theory presented thus far applies to columns that are perfectly straight, made of homogeneous material, and originally stress free. Practically speaking, though, as stated previously, columns are not perfectly straight, and most have residual stresses in them, primarily due to nonuniform cooling during manufacture. Also, the supports for columns are less than exact, and the points of application and directions of loads are not known with absolute certainty. In order to compensate for these effects, which actually vary from one column to the next, many design codes specify the use of column formulas that are empirical. By performing experimental tests on a large number of axially loaded columns, the results may be plotted and a design formula developed by curve-fitting the mean of the data.

An example of such tests for wide-flange steel columns is shown in Fig. 20. Notice the similarity between these results and those of the family of curves determined from the secant formula, Fig. 16. The reason for this similarity has to do with the influence of an "accidental" eccentricity ratio on the column's strength. As stated in Sec. 4, this ratio has more of an effect on the strength of short and intermediate-length columns than on those that are long. Tests have indicated that $ec/r^2$ can range from 0.1 to 0.6 for most axially loaded columns.

In order to account for the behavior of different-length columns, design codes usually specify several formulas that will best fit the data within the short, intermediate, and long column range. Hence, each formula will apply only for a specific *range* of slenderness ratios, and so it is important that the engineer carefully observe the $KL/r$ limits for which a particular formula is valid. Examples of design formulas for steel, aluminum, and wood columns that are currently in use will now be discussed. The purpose is to give some idea as to how columns are designed in practice. These formulas should not, however, be used for the design of actual columns, unless the code from which they are referenced is consulted.

**Fig. 20**

**Steel Columns.** Columns made of structural steel can be designed on the basis of formulas proposed by the Structural Stability Research Council (SSRC). Factors of safety have been applied to these formulas and adopted as specifications for building construction by the American Institute of Steel Construction (AISC). Basically these specifications provide two formulas for column design, each of which gives the maximum allowable stress in the column for a specific range of slenderness ratios.*

For long columns the Euler formula is proposed, i.e., $\sigma_{\max} = \pi^2 E/(KL/r)^2$.

Application of this formula requires that a factor of safety F.S. $= \frac{23}{12} \approx 1.92$ be applied. Thus, for design,

$$\sigma_{\text{allow}} = \frac{12\pi^2 E}{23(KL/r)^2} \qquad \left(\frac{KL}{r}\right)_c \leq \frac{KL}{r} \leq 200 \qquad (21)$$

As stated, this equation is applicable for a slenderness ratio bounded by 200 and $(KL/r)_c$. A specific value of $(KL/r)_c$ is obtained by requiring the Euler formula to be used only for elastic material behavior. Through experiments it has been determined that compressive residual stresses can exist in rolled-formed steel sections that may be as much as one-half the yield stress. Consequently, if the stress in the Euler formula is greater than $\frac{1}{2}\sigma_Y$, the equation will not apply. Therefore the value of $(KL/r)_c$ is determined as follows:

$$\frac{1}{2}\sigma_Y = \frac{\pi^2 E}{(KL/r)_c^2} \qquad \text{or} \qquad \left(\frac{KL}{r}\right)_c = \sqrt{\frac{2\pi^2 E}{\sigma_Y}} \qquad (22)$$

Columns having slenderness ratios less than $(KL/r)_c$ are designed on the basis of an empirical formula that is parabolic and has the form

$$\sigma_{\max} = \left[1 - \frac{(KL/r)^2}{2(KL/r)_c^2}\right]\sigma_Y$$

Since there is more uncertainty in the use of this formula for longer columns, it is divided by a factor of safety defined as follows:

$$\text{F.S.} = \frac{5}{3} + \frac{3}{8}\frac{(KL/r)}{(KL/r)_c} - \frac{(KL/r)^3}{8(KL/r)_c^3}$$

Here it is seen that F.S. $= \frac{5}{3} \approx 1.67$ at $KL/r = 0$ and increases to F.S. $= \frac{23}{12} \approx 1.92$ at $(KL/r)_c$. Hence, for design purposes,

$$\sigma_{\text{allow}} = \frac{\left[1 - \dfrac{(KL/r)^2}{2(KL/r)_c^2}\right]\sigma_Y}{(5/3) + [(3/8)(KL/r)/(KL/r)_c] - \left[(KL/r)^3/8(KL/r)_c^3\right]} \qquad (23)$$

Equations 21 and 23 are plotted in Fig. 21. When applying any of these equations, either FPS or SI units can be used for the calculations.

**Fig. 21**

*The current AISC code enables engineers to use one of two methods for design, namely, Load and Resistance Factor Design, and Allowable Stress Design. The latter is explained here.

## Aluminum Columns.

Column design for structural aluminum is specified by the Aluminum Association using three equations, each applicable for a specific range of slenderness ratios. Since several types of aluminum alloy exist, there is a unique set of formulas for each type. For a common alloy (2014-T6) used in building construction, the formulas are

$\sigma_{allow}(\text{ksi})$

Eq. 24

Eq. 25

Eq. 26

**Fig. 22**

$$\sigma_{allow} = 28 \text{ ksi} \qquad 0 \le \frac{KL}{r} \le 12 \tag{24}$$

$$\sigma_{allow} = \left[ 30.7 - 0.23\left(\frac{KL}{r}\right) \right] \text{ksi} \qquad 12 < \frac{KL}{r} < 55 \tag{25}$$

$$\sigma_{allow} = \frac{54\,000 \text{ ksi}}{(KL/r)^2} \qquad 55 \le \frac{KL}{r} \tag{26}$$

These equations are plotted in Fig. 22. As shown, the first two represent straight lines and are used to model the effects of columns in the short and intermediate range. The third formula has the same form as the Euler formula and is used for long columns.

## Timber Columns.

Columns used in timber construction are designed on the basis of formulas published by the National Forest Products Association (NFPA) or the American Institute of Timber Construction (AITC). For example, the NFPA formulas for the allowable stress in short, intermediate, and long columns having a rectangular cross section of dimensions $b$ and $d$, where $d$ is the *smallest* dimension of the cross section, are

$\sigma_{allow}(\text{ksi})$

Eq. 27

Eq. 28

Eq. 29

**Fig. 23**

$$\sigma_{allow} = 1.20 \text{ ksi} \qquad 0 \le \frac{KL}{d} \le 11 \tag{27}$$

$$\sigma_{allow} = 1.20\left[ 1 - \frac{1}{3}\left(\frac{KL/d}{26.0}\right)^2 \right] \text{ksi} \qquad 11 < \frac{KL}{d} \le 26 \tag{28}$$

$$\sigma_{allow} = \frac{540 \text{ ksi}}{(KL/d)^2} \qquad 26 < \frac{KL}{d} \le 50 \tag{29}$$

Here wood has a modulus of elasticity of $E_w = 1.8(10^3)$ ksi and an allowable compressive stress of 1.2 ksi parallel to the grain. In particular, Eq. 29 is simply Euler's equation having a factor of safety of 3. These three equations are plotted in Fig. 23.

## Procedure for Analysis

### Column Analysis.

- When using any formula to *analyze* a column, that is, to find its allowable load, it is first necessary to calculate the slenderness ratio in order to determine which column formula applies.

- Once the average allowable stress has been calculated, the allowable load on the column is determined from $P = \sigma_{\text{allow}} A$.

### Column Design.

- If a formula is used to *design* a column, that is, to determine the column's cross-sectional area for a given loading and effective length, then a trial-and-check procedure generally must be followed when the column has a composite shape, such as a wide-flange section.

- One possible way to apply a trial-and-check procedure would be to *assume* the column's cross-sectional area, $A'$, and calculate the corresponding stress $\sigma' = P/A'$. Also, use an appropriate design formula to determine the allowable stress $\sigma_{\text{allow}}$. From this, calculate the *required* column area $A_{\text{req'd}} = P/\sigma_{\text{allow}}$.

- If $A' > A_{\text{req'd}}$, the design is safe. When making the comparison, it is practical to require $A'$ to be close to but greater than $A_{\text{req'd}}$, usually within 2–3%. A redesign is necessary if $A' < A_{\text{req'd}}$.

- Whenever a trial-and-check procedure is repeated, the choice of an area is determined by the previously calculated required area. In engineering practice this method for design is usually shortened through the use of computer software or published tables and graphs.

These timber columns can be considered pinned at their bottom and fixed connected to the beams at their tops.

## EXAMPLE | 6

$P$

$x$    $y$

$y$    $x$

16 ft

$P$

**Fig. 24**

An A992 steel W10 × 100 member is used as a pin-supported column, Fig. 24. Using the AISC column design formulas, determine the largest load that it can safely support.

### SOLUTION

The following data for a W10 × 100 is taken from the table in Appendix: Geometric Properties of Structural Shapes.

$$A = 29.4 \text{ in}^2 \quad r_x = 4.60 \text{ in.} \quad r_y = 2.65 \text{ in.}$$

Since $K = 1$ for both $x$ and $y$ axis buckling, the slenderness ratio is largest if $r_y$ is used. Thus,

$$\frac{KL}{r} = \frac{1(16 \text{ ft})(12 \text{ in.}/\text{ft})}{2.65 \text{ in.}} = 72.45$$

From Eq. 22, we have

$$\left(\frac{KL}{r}\right)_c = \sqrt{\frac{2\pi^2 E}{\sigma_Y}}$$

$$= \sqrt{\frac{2\pi^2[29(10^3) \text{ ksi}]}{50 \text{ ksi}}}$$

$$= 107$$

Here $0 < KL/r < (KL/r)_c$, so Eq. 23 applies.

$$\sigma_{\text{allow}} = \frac{\left[1 - \dfrac{(KL/r)^2}{2(KL/r)_c^2}\right]\sigma_Y}{(5/3) + [(3/8)(KL/r)/(KL/r)_c] - \left[(KL/r)^3/8(KL/r_c)^3\right]}$$

$$= \frac{[1 - (72.45)^2/2(107)^2] \, 50 \text{ ksi}}{(5/3) + [(3/8)(72.45/107)] - [(72.45)^3/8(107)^3]}$$

$$= 23.93 \text{ ksi}$$

The allowable load $P$ on the column is therefore

$$\sigma_{\text{allow}} = \frac{P}{A}; \qquad 23.93 \text{ kip/in}^2 = \frac{P}{29.4 \text{ in}^2}$$

$$P = 704 \text{ kip} \qquad\qquad\qquad Ans.$$

## EXAMPLE | 7

The steel rod in Fig. 25 is to be used to support an axial load of 18 kip. If $E_{st} = 29(10^3)$ ksi and $\sigma_Y = 50$ ksi, determine the smallest diameter of the rod as allowed by the AISC specification. The rod is fixed at both ends.

**Fig. 25**

### SOLUTION

For a circular cross section the radius of gyration becomes

$$r = \sqrt{\frac{I}{A}} = \sqrt{\frac{(1/4)\pi(d/2)^4}{(1/4)\pi d^2}} = \frac{d}{4}$$

Applying Eq. 22, we have

$$\left(\frac{KL}{r}\right)_c = \sqrt{\frac{2\pi^2 E}{\sigma_Y}} = \sqrt{\frac{2\pi^2[29(10^3)\text{ ksi}]}{50\text{ ksi}}} = 107.0$$

Since the rod's radius of gyration is unknown, $KL/r$ is unknown, and therefore a choice must be made as to whether Eq. 21 or Eq. 23 applies. We will consider Eq. 21. For a fixed-end column $K = 0.5$, so

$$\sigma_{allow} = \frac{12\pi^2 E}{23(KL/r)^2}$$

$$\frac{18\text{ kip}}{(1/4)\pi d^2} = \frac{12\pi^2[29(10^3)\text{ kip/in}^2]}{23[0.5(15\text{ ft})(12\text{ in./ft})/(d/4)]^2}$$

$$\frac{22.92}{d^2} = 1.152d^2$$

$$d = 2.11\text{ in.}$$

Use

$$d = 2.25\text{ in.} = 2\tfrac{1}{4}\text{ in.} \qquad \qquad Ans.$$

For this design, we must check the slenderness-ratio limits; i.e.,

$$\frac{KL}{r} = \frac{0.5(15\text{ ft})(12\text{ in./ft})}{(2.25\text{ in.}/4)} = 160$$

Since $107.0 < 160 < 200$, use of Eq. 21 is appropriate.

# EXAMPLE | 8

12 kip

$b$ · $2b$

$x$ · $y$

30 in.

12 kip

**Fig. 26**

A bar having a length of 30 in. is used to support an axial compressive load of 12 kip, Fig. 26. It is pin supported at its ends and made of a 2014-T6 aluminum alloy. Determine the dimensions of its cross-sectional area if its width is to be twice its thickness.

## SOLUTION

Since $KL = 30$ in. is the same for both $x$ and $y$ axis buckling, the larger slenderness ratio is determined using the smaller radius of gyration, i.e., using $I_{min} = I_y$:

$$\frac{KL}{r_y} = \frac{KL}{\sqrt{I_y/A}} = \frac{1(30)}{\sqrt{(1/12)2b(b^3)/[2b(b)]}} = \frac{103.9}{b} \qquad (1)$$

Here we must apply Eq. 24, 25, or 26. Since we do not as yet know the slenderness ratio, we will begin by using Eq. 24.

$$\frac{P}{A} = 28 \text{ ksi}$$

$$\frac{12 \text{ kip}}{2b(b)} = 28 \text{ kip/in}^2$$

$$b = 0.463 \text{ in.}$$

Checking the slenderness ratio, we have

$$\frac{KL}{r} = \frac{103.9}{0.463} = 224.5 > 12$$

Try Eq. 26, which is valid for $KL/r \geq 55$,

$$\frac{P}{A} = \frac{54\,000 \text{ ksi}}{(KL/r)^2}$$

$$\frac{12}{2b(b)} = \frac{54\,000}{(103.9/b)^2}$$

$$b = 1.05 \text{ in.} \qquad \qquad Ans.$$

From Eq. 1,

$$\frac{KL}{r} = \frac{103.9}{1.05} = 99.3 > 55 \quad \text{OK}$$

**NOTE:** It would be satisfactory to choose the cross section with dimensions 1 in. by 2 in.

## EXAMPLE | 9

A board having cross-sectional dimensions of 5.5 in. by 1.5 in. is used to support an axial load of 5 kip, Fig. 27. If the board is assumed to be pin supported at its top and bottom, determine its *greatest* allowable length $L$ as specified by the NFPA.

**Fig. 27**

### SOLUTION

By inspection, the board will buckle about the $y$ axis. In the NFPA equations, $d = 1.5$ in. Assuming that Eq. 29 applies, we have

$$\frac{P}{A} = \frac{540 \text{ ksi}}{(KL/d)^2}$$

$$\frac{5 \text{ kip}}{(5.5 \text{ in.})(1.5 \text{ in.})} = \frac{540 \text{ ksi}}{(1 \, L/1.5 \text{ in.})^2}$$

$$L = 44.8 \text{ in.} \qquad\qquad\qquad Ans.$$

Here

$$\frac{KL}{d} = \frac{1(44.8 \text{ in.})}{1.5 \text{ in.}} = 29.8$$

Since $26 < KL/d \le 50$, the solution is valid.

## PROBLEMS

**78.** Determine the largest length of a W10 × 12 structural A992 steel section if it is pin supported and is subjected to an axial load of 28 kip. Use the AISC equations.

**79.** Using the AISC equations, select from Appendix: Geometric Properties of Structural Shapes the lightest-weight structural A992 steel column that is 14 ft long and supports an axial load of 40 kip. The ends are fixed.

**\*80.** Using the AISC equations, select from Appendix: Geometric Properties of Structural Shapes the lightest-weight structural A992 steel column that is 14 ft long and supports an axial load of 40 kip. The ends are pinned. Take $\sigma_Y = 50$ ksi.

**81.** Determine the largest length of a W8 × 31 structural A992 steel section if it is pin supported and is subjected to an axial load of 130 kip. Use the AISC equations.

**82.** Using the AISC equations, select from Appendix: Geometric Properties of Structural Shapes the lightest-weight structural A992 steel column that is 12 ft long and supports an axial load of 20 kip. The ends are pinned.

**83.** Determine the largest length of a W10 × 12 structural A992 steel section if it is fixed supported and is subjected to an axial load of 28 kip. Use the AISC equations.

**\*84.** Using the AISC equations, select the lightest-weight structural A992 steel column that is 30 ft long and supports an axial load of 200 kip. The ends are fixed.

**85.** Determine the largest length of a W8 × 31 structural A992 steel section if it is pin supported and is subjected to an axial load of 18 kip. Use the AISC equations.

**86.** Using the AISC equations, select the lightest-weight structural A992 steel column that is 12 ft long and supports an axial load of 40 kip. The ends are fixed.

**87.** A 5-ft-long rod is used in a machine to transmit an axial compressive load of 3 kip. Determine its smallest diameter if it is pin connected at its ends and is made of a 2014-T6 aluminum alloy.

**\*88.** Determine the largest length of a W8 × 31 structural A992 steel column if it is to support an axial load of 10 kip. The ends are pinned.

**89.** Using the AISC equations, check if a column having the cross section shown can support an axial force of 1500 kN. The column has a length of 4 m, is made from A992 steel, and its ends are pinned.

**Prob. 89**

**90.** The A992-steel tube is pinned at both ends. If it is subjected to an axial force of 150 kN, determine the maximum length of the tube using the AISC column design formulas.

**Prob. 90**

**91.** The bar is made of a 2014-T6 aluminum alloy. Determine its smallest thickness *b* if its width is 5*b*. Assume that it is pin connected at its ends.

**\*92.** The bar is made of a 2014-T6 aluminum alloy. Determine its smallest thickness *b* if its width is 5*b*. Assume that it is fixed connected at its ends.

**Probs. 91/92**

**93.** The 2014-T6 aluminum column of 3-m length has the cross section shown. If the column is pinned at both ends and braced against the weak axis at its mid-height, determine the allowable axial force *P* that can be safely supported by the column.

**94.** The 2014-T6 aluminum column has the cross section shown. If the column is pinned at both ends and subjected to an axial force *P* = 100 kN, determine the maximum length the column can have to safely support the loading.

**Probs. 93/94**

**95.** The tube is 0.5 in. thick, is made of aluminum alloy 2014-T6, and is fixed connected at its ends. Determine the largest axial load that it can support.

**\*96.** The tube is 0.5 in. thick, is made from aluminum alloy 2014-T6, and is fixed at its bottom and pinned at its top. Determine the largest axial load that it can support.

**Probs. 95/96**

**97.** The tube is 0.25 in. thick, is made of a 2014-T6 aluminum alloy, and is fixed at its bottom and pinned at its top. Determine the largest axial load that it can support.

**98.** The tube is 0.25 in. thick, is made of a 2014-T6 aluminum alloy, and is fixed connected at its ends. Determine the largest axial load that it can support.

**99.** The tube is 0.25 in. thick, is made of 2014-T6 aluminum alloy and is pin connected at its ends. Determine the largest axial load it can support.

**Probs. 97/98/99**

**\*100.** A rectangular wooden column has the cross section shown. If the column is 6 ft long and subjected to an axial force of $P = 15$ kip, determine the required minimum dimension $a$ of its cross-sectional area to the nearest $\frac{1}{16}$ in. so that the column can safely support the loading. The column is pinned at both ends.

**101.** A rectangular wooden column has the cross section shown. If $a = 3$ in. and the column is 12 ft long, determine the allowable axial force $P$ that can be safely supported by the column if it is pinned at its top and fixed at its base.

**102.** A rectangular wooden column has the cross section shown. If $a = 3$ in. and the column is subjected to an axial force of $P = 15$ kip, determine the maximum length the column can have to safely support the load. The column is pinned at its top and fixed at its base.

**Probs. 100/101/102**

**103.** The timber column has a square cross section and is assumed to be pin connected at its top and bottom. If it supports an axial load of 50 kip, determine its smallest side dimension $a$ to the nearest $\frac{1}{2}$ in. Use the NFPA formulas.

**Prob. 103**

**\*104.** The bar is made of aluminum alloy 2014-T6.

Determine its thickness $b$ if its width is $1.5b$. Assume that it is fixed connected at its ends.

**Prob. 104**

**105.** The column is made of wood. It is fixed at its bottom and free at its top. Use the NFPA formulas to determine its greatest allowable length if it supports an axial load of $P = 6$ kip.

**106.** The column is made of wood. It is fixed at its bottom and free at its top. Use the NFPA formulas to determine the largest allowable axial load $P$ that it can support if it has a length $L = 6$ ft.

**Probs. 105/106**

# *7 Design of Columns for Eccentric Loading

Occasionally a column may be required to support a load acting either at its edge or on an angle bracket attached to its side, such as shown in Fig. 28*a*. The bending moment $M = Pe$, which is caused by the eccentric loading, must be accounted for when the column is designed. There are several acceptable ways in which this is done in engineering practice. We will discuss two of the most common methods.

## Use of Available Column Formulas.

The stress distribution acting over the cross-sectional area of the column shown in Fig. 28*a* is determined from a superposition of both the axial force $P$ and the bending moment $M = Pe$. In particular, the maximum compressive stress is

$$\sigma_{max} = \frac{P}{A} + \frac{Mc}{I} \qquad (30)$$

A typical stress profile is shown in Fig. 28*b*. If we conservatively *assume* that the entire cross section is subjected to the uniform stress $\sigma_{max}$ as determined from Eq. 30, then we can compare $\sigma_{max}$ with $\sigma_{allow}$, which is determined using the formulas given in Sec. 6. Calculation of $\sigma_{allow}$ is usually done using the *largest* slenderness ratio for the column, regardless of the axis about which the column experiences bending. This requirement is normally specified in design codes and will in most cases lead to a conservative design. If

$$\sigma_{max} \leq \sigma_{allow}$$

then the column can carry the specified loading. If this inequality does not hold, then the column's area $A$ must be increased, and a new $\sigma_{max}$ and $\sigma_{allow}$ must be calculated. This method of design is rather simple to apply and works well for columns that are short or of intermediate length.

## Interaction Formula.

When *designing* an eccentrically loaded column it is desirable to see how the bending and axial loads *interact*, so that a balance between these two effects can be achieved. To do this, we will consider the separate contributions made to the total column area by the axial force and moment. If the allowable stress for the axial load is $(\sigma_a)_{allow}$, then the required area for the column needed to support the load $P$ is

$$A_a = \frac{P}{(\sigma_a)_{allow}}$$

Similarly, if the allowable bending stress is $(\sigma_b)_{allow}$, then since $I = A r^2$, the required area of the column needed to support the eccentric moment is determined from the flexure formula, that is,

(a)

(b)

**Fig. 28**

$$A_b = \frac{Mc}{(\sigma_b)_{\text{allow}} \, r^2}$$

The total area $A$ for the column needed to resist *both* the axial load and moment requires that

$$A_a + A_b = \frac{P}{(\sigma_a)_{\text{allow}}} + \frac{Mc}{(\sigma_b)_{\text{allow}} \, r^2} \leq A$$

or

$$\frac{P/A}{(\sigma_a)_{\text{allow}}} + \frac{Mc/A r^2}{(\sigma_b)_{\text{allow}}} \leq 1$$

$$\frac{\sigma_a}{(\sigma_a)_{\text{allow}}} + \frac{\sigma_b}{(\sigma_b)_{\text{allow}}} \leq 1 \tag{31}$$

Here

$\sigma_a$ = axial stress caused by the force $P$ and determined from $\sigma_a = P/A$, where $A$ is the cross-sectional area of the column

$\sigma_b$ = bending stress caused by an eccentric load or applied moment $M$; $\sigma_b$ is found from $\sigma_b = Mc/I$, where $I$ is the moment of inertia of the cross-sectional area calculated about the bending or centroidal axis

$(\sigma_a)_{\text{allow}}$ = allowable axial stress as defined by formulas given in Sec. 6 or by other design code specifications. For this purpose, always use the *largest* slenderness ratio for the column, regardless of the axis about which the column experiences bending

$(\sigma_b)_{\text{allow}}$ = allowable bending stress as defined by code specifications

Notice that, if the column is subjected only to an axial load, then the bending-stress ratio in Eq. 31 would be equal to zero and the design will be based only on the allowable axial stress. Likewise, when no axial load is present, the axial-stress ratio is zero and the stress requirement will be based on the allowable bending stress. Hence, each stress ratio indicates the contribution of axial load or bending moment. Since Eq. 31 shows how these loadings interact, this equation is sometimes referred to as the **interaction formula**. This design approach requires a trial-and-check procedure, where it is required that the designer *pick* an available column and then check to see if the inequality is satisfied. If it is not, a larger section is then picked and the process repeated. An economical choice is made when the left side is close to but less than 1.

The interaction method is often specified in codes for the design of columns made of steel, aluminum, or timber. In particular, for allowable stress design, the American Institute of Steel Construction specifies the use of this equation only when the axial-stress ratio $\sigma_a / (\sigma_a)_{\text{allow}} \leq 0.15$. For other values of this ratio, a modified form of Eq. 31 is used.

Typical example of a column used to support an eccentric roof loading.

## EXAMPLE | 10

The column in Fig. 29 is made of aluminum alloy 2014-T6 and is used to support an eccentric load **P**. Determine the maximum magnitude of **P** that can be supported if the column is fixed at its base and free at its top. Use Eq. 30.

**Fig. 29**

### SOLUTION

From Fig. 10b, $K = 2$. The largest slenderness ratio for the column is therefore

$$\frac{KL}{r} = \frac{2(80 \text{ in.})}{\sqrt{[(1/12)(4 \text{ in.})(2 \text{ in.})^3][(2 \text{ in.})\, 4 \text{ in.}]}} = 277.1$$

By inspection, Eq. 26 must be used ($277.1 > 55$). Thus,

$$\sigma_{allow} = \frac{54\,000 \text{ ksi}}{(KL/r)^2} = \frac{54\,000 \text{ ksi}}{(277.1)^2} = 0.7031 \text{ ksi}$$

The maximum compressive stress in the column is determined from the combination of axial load and bending. We have

$$\sigma_{max} = \frac{P}{A} + \frac{(Pe)c}{I}$$

$$= \frac{P}{2 \text{ in.}(4 \text{ in.})} + \frac{P(1 \text{ in.})(2 \text{ in.})}{(1/12)(2 \text{ in.})(4 \text{ in.})^3}$$

$$= 0.3125P$$

*Assuming* that this stress is *uniform* over the cross section, we require

$$\sigma_{allow} = \sigma_{max}; \qquad 0.7031 = 0.3125P$$
$$P = 2.25 \text{ kip} \qquad\qquad Ans.$$

# EXAMPLE | 11

$P$

30 in.

$y$

$x$

15 ft

$M = P(30\text{ in.})$

$P$

**Fig. 30**

The A-36 steel W6 × 20 column in Fig. 30 is pin connected at its ends and is subjected to the eccentric load $P$. Determine the maximum allowable value of $P$ using the interaction method if the allowable bending stress is $(\sigma_b)_{\text{allow}} = 22$ ksi.

## SOLUTION

Here $K = 1$. The necessary geometric properties for the W6 × 20 are as follows:

$$A = 5.87\text{ in}^2 \qquad I_x = 41.4\text{ in}^4 \qquad r_y = 1.50\text{ in.} \qquad d = 6.20\text{ in.}$$

We will consider $r_y$ because this will lead to the *largest* value of the slenderness ratio. Also, $I_x$ is needed since bending occurs about the $x$ axis ($c = 6.20\text{ in.}/2 = 3.10\text{ in.}$). To determine the allowable compressive stress, we have

$$\frac{KL}{r} = \frac{1[15\text{ ft}(12\text{ in.}/\text{ft})]}{1.50\text{ in.}} = 120$$

Since

$$\left(\frac{KL}{r}\right)_c = \sqrt{\frac{2\pi^2 E}{\sigma_Y}} = \sqrt{\frac{2\pi^2\,[29(10^3)\text{ ksi}]}{36\text{ ksi}}} = 126.1$$

then $KL/r < (KL/r)_c$ and so Eq. 23 must be used.

$$\sigma_{\text{allow}} = \frac{[1 - (KL/r)^2/2(KL/r)_c]^2\sigma_Y}{(5/3) + [(3/8)(KL/r)/(KL/r)_c] - \left[(KL/r)^3/8(KL/r)_c^3\right]}$$

$$= \frac{[1 - (120)^2/2(126.1)^2]\,36\text{ ksi}}{(5/3) + [(3/8)(120)/(126.1)] - [(120)^3/8(126.1)^3]}$$

$$= 10.28\text{ ksi}$$

Applying the interaction Eq. 31 yields

$$\frac{\sigma_a}{(\sigma_a)_{\text{allow}}} + \frac{\sigma_b}{(\sigma_b)_{\text{allow}}} \leq 1$$

$$\frac{P/5.87\text{ in}^2}{10.28\text{ ksi}} + \frac{P(30\text{ in.})(3.10\text{ in.})/(41.4\text{ in}^4)}{22\text{ ksi}} = 1$$

$$P = 8.43\text{ kip} \qquad\qquad\qquad \textit{Ans.}$$

Checking the application of the interaction method for the steel section, we require

$$\frac{\sigma_a}{(\sigma_a)_{\text{allow}}} = \frac{8.43\text{ kip}/(5.87\text{ in.})}{10.28\text{ kip/in}^2} = 0.140 < 0.15 \qquad \text{OK}$$

## EXAMPLE | 12

The timber column in Fig. 31 is made from two boards nailed together so that the cross section has the dimensions shown. If the column is fixed at its base and free at its top, use Eq. 30 to determine the eccentric load **P** that can be supported.

**Fig. 31**

### SOLUTION

From Fig. 10b, $K = 2$. Here we must calculate $KL/d$ to determine which equation from Eqs. 27 through 29 should be used. Since $\sigma_{allow}$ is determined using the largest slenderness ratio, we choose $d = 3$ in. This is done to make this ratio as large as possible, and thereby yields the lowest possible allowable axial stress. We have

$$\frac{KL}{d} = \frac{2(60 \text{ in.})}{3 \text{ in.}} = 40$$

Since $26 < KL/d < 50$ the allowable axial stress is determined using Eq. 29. Thus,

$$\sigma_{allow} = \frac{540 \text{ ksi}}{(KL/d)^2} = \frac{540 \text{ ksi}}{(40)^2} = 0.3375 \text{ ksi}$$

Applying Eq. 30 with $\sigma_{allow} = \sigma_{max}$, we have

$$\sigma_{allow} = \frac{P}{A} + \frac{Mc}{I}$$

$$0.3375 \text{ ksi} = \frac{P}{(3 \text{ in.})(6 \text{ in.})} + \frac{P(4 \text{ in.})(3 \text{ in.})}{(1/12)(3 \text{ in.})(6 \text{ in.})^3}$$

$$P = 1.22 \text{ kip} \qquad\qquad Ans.$$

# PROBLEMS

**107.** The W8×15 structural A992 steel column is assumed to be pinned at its top and bottom. Determine the largest eccentric load $P$ that can be applied using Eq. 30 and the AISC equations of Sec. 6. The load at the top consists of a force $P$ and a moment $M = P(8 \text{ in.})$.

***108.** Solve Prob. 107 if the column is fixed at its top and bottom.

**109.** Solve Prob. 107 if the column is fixed at its bottom and pinned at its top.

**Probs. 107/108/109**

**110.** The W10 × 19 structural A992 steel column is assumed to be pinned at its top and bottom. Determine the largest eccentric load $P$ that can be applied using Eq. 30 and the AISC equations of Sec. 6.

**Prob. 110**

**111.** The W8×15 structural A992 steel column is fixed at its top and bottom. If it supports end moments of $M = 5$ kip·ft, determine the axial force $P$ that can be applied. Bending is about the $x$–$x$ axis. Use the AISC equations of Sec. 6 and Eq. 30.

**Prob. 111**

***112.** The W8 × 15 structural A992 steel column is fixed at its top and bottom. If it supports end moments of $M = 23$ kip·ft, determine the axial force $P$ that can be applied. Bending is about the $x$–$x$ axis. Use the interaction formula with $(\sigma_b) = 24$ ksi.

**Prob. 112**

**113.** The A992-steel W10 × 45 column is fixed at its base. Its top is constrained so that it cannot move along the *x–x* axis but it is free to rotate about and move along the *y–y* axis. Determine the maximum eccentric force *P* that can be safely supported by the column using the allowable stress method.

**114.** The A992-steel W10 × 45 column is fixed at its base. Its top is constrained so that it cannot move along the *x–x* axis but it is free to rotate about and move along the *y–y* axis. Determine the maximum eccentric force *P* that can be safely supported by the column using an interaction formula. The allowable bending stress is $(\sigma_b)_{allow} = 15$ ksi.

**115.** The A-36-steel W12 × 50 column is fixed at its base. Its top is constrained so that it cannot move along the *x–x* axis but it is free to rotate about and move along the *y–y* axis. If the eccentric force *P* = 15 kip is applied to the column, investigate if the column is adequate to support the loading. Use the allowable stress method.

***116.** The A-36-steel W12 × 50 column is fixed at its base. Its top is constrained so that it cannot move along the *x–x* axis but it is free to rotate about and move along the *y–y* axis. If the eccentric force *P* = 15 kip is applied to the column, investigate if the column is adequate to support the loading. Use the interaction formula. The allowable bending stress is $(\sigma_b)_{allow} = 15$ ksi.

**117.** A 16-ft-long column is made of aluminum alloy 2014-T6. If it is fixed at its top and bottom, and a concentric load **P** and a moment *M* = *P*(4.5 in.) are applied at point *A*, determine the maximum allowable magnitude of **P** using the equations of Sec. 6 and Eq. 30.

**118.** A 16-ft-long column is made of aluminum alloy 2014-T6. If it is fixed at its top and bottom, and a concentric load **P** and a moment *M* = *P*(4.5 in.) are applied at point *A*, determine the maximum allowable magnitude of **P** using the equations of Sec. 6 and the interaction formula with $(\sigma_b)_{allow} = 20$ ksi.

**Probs. 117/118**

**119.** The 2014-T6 aluminum hollow column is fixed at its base and free at its top. Determine the maximum eccentric force *P* that can be safely supported by the column. Use the allowable stress method. The thickness of the wall for the section is *t* = 0.5 in.

***120.** The 2014-T6 aluminum hollow column is fixed at its base and free at its top. Determine the maximum eccentric force *P* that can be safely supported by the column. Use the interaction formula. The allowable bending stress is $(\sigma_b)_{allow} = 30$ ksi. The thickness of the wall for the section is *t* = 0.5 in.

**Probs. 113/114/115/116**

**Probs. 119/120**

**121.** The 10-ft-long bar is made of aluminum alloy 2014-T6. If it is fixed at its bottom and pinned at the top, determine the maximum allowable eccentric load **P** that can be applied using the formulas in Sec. 6 and Eq. 30.

**122.** The 10-ft-long bar is made of aluminum alloy 2014-T6. If it is fixed at its bottom and pinned at the top, determine the maximum allowable eccentric load **P** that can be applied using the equations of Sec. 6 and the interaction formula with $(\sigma_b)_{\text{allow}} = 18$ ksi.

Probs. 121/122

**123.** Determine if the column can support the eccentric compressive load of 1.5 kip. Assume that the ends are pin connected. Use the NFPA equations in Sec. 6 and Eq. 30.

**\*124.** Determine if the column can support the eccentric compressive load of 1.5 kip. Assume that the bottom is fixed and the top is pinned. Use the NFPA equations in Sec. 6 and Eq. 30.

Probs. 123/124

**125.** The 10-in.-diameter utility pole supports the transformer that has a weight of 600 lb and center of gravity at $G$. If the pole is fixed to the ground and free at its top, determine if it is adequate according to the NFPA equations of Sec. 6 and Eq. 30.

Prob. 125

**126.** Using the NFPA equations of Sec. 6 and Eq. 30, determine the maximum allowable eccentric load $P$ that can be applied to the wood column. Assume that the column is pinned at both its top and bottom.

**127.** Using the NFPA equations of Sec. 6 and Eq. 30, determine the maximum allowable eccentric load $P$ that can be applied to the wood column. Assume that the column is pinned at the top and fixed at the bottom.

Probs. 126/127

## CHAPTER REVIEW

| | | |
|---|---|---|
| Buckling is the sudden instability that occurs in columns or members that support an axial compressive load. The maximum axial load that a member can support just before buckling is called the critical load $P_{cr}$. | | |
| The critical load for an ideal column is determined from Euler's formula, where $K = 1$ for pin supports, $K = 0.5$ for fixed supports, $K = 0.7$ for a pin and a fixed support, and $K = 2$ for a fixed support and a free end. | $P_{cr} = \dfrac{\pi^2 EI}{(KL)^2}$ | |
| If the axial loading is applied eccentrically to the column, then the secant formula can be used to determine the maximum stress in the column. | $\sigma_{max} = \dfrac{P}{A}\left[1 + \dfrac{ec}{r^2}\sec\left(\dfrac{L}{2r}\sqrt{\dfrac{P}{EA}}\right)\right]$ | |
| When the axial load causes yielding of the material, then the tangent modulus should be used with Euler's formula to determine the critical load for the column. This is referred to as Engesser's equation. | $\sigma_{cr} = \dfrac{\pi^2 E_t}{(KL/r)^2}$ | |
| Empirical formulas based on experimental data have been developed for use in the design of steel, aluminum, and timber columns. | | |

## REVIEW PROBLEMS

**\*128.** The wood column has a thickness of 4 in. and a width of 6 in. Using the NFPA equations of Sec. 6 and Eq. 30, determine the maximum allowable eccentric load $P$ that can be applied. Assume that the column is pinned at both its top and bottom.

**Prob. 128**

**129.** The wood column has a thickness of 4 in. and a width of 6 in. Using the NFPA equations of Sec. 6 and Eq. 30, determine the maximum allowable eccentric load $P$ that can be applied. Assume that the column is pinned at the top and fixed at the bottom.

**Prob. 129**

**130.** A steel column has a length of 5 m and is free at one end and fixed at the other end. If the cross-sectional area has the dimensions shown, determine the critical load. $E_{st} = 200$ GPa, $\sigma_Y = 360$ MPa.

**Prob. 130**

**131.** The square structural A992 steel tubing has outer dimensions of 8 in. by 8 in. Its cross-sectional area is 14.40 in$^2$ and its moments of inertia are $I_x = I_y = 131$ in$^4$. Determine the maximum load $P$ it can support. The column can be assumed fixed at its base and free at its top.

**Prob. 131**

**\*132.** If the A-36 steel solid circular rod *BD* has a diameter of 2 in., determine the allowable maximum force **P** that can be supported by the frame without causing the rod to buckle. Use F.S. = 2 against buckling.

**133.** If *P* = 15 kip, determine the required minimum diameter of the A992 steel solid circular rod *BD* to the nearest $\frac{1}{16}$ in. Use F.S. = 2 against buckling.

4.5 in.

4 ft

3 ft     3 ft

**P**

**Probs. 132/133**

**135.** The W200 × 46 A992-steel column can be considered pinned at its top and fixed at its base. Also, the column is braced at its mid-height against the weak axis. Determine the maximum axial load the column can support without causing it to buckle.

6 m

6 m

**Prob. 135**

**134.** The steel pipe is fixed supported at its ends. If it is 4 m long and has an outer diameter of 50 mm, determine its required thickness so that it can support an axial load of $P = 100$ kN without buckling. $E_{st} = 200$ GPa, $\sigma_Y = 250$ MPa.

*P*

4 m

*P*

**Prob. 134**

**\*136.** The structural A992 steel column has the cross section shown. If it is fixed at the bottom and free at the top, determine the maximum force *P* that can be applied at *A* without causing it to buckle or yield. Use a factor of safety of 3 with respect to buckling and yielding.

**137.** The structural A992 steel column has the cross section shown. If it is fixed at the bottom and free at the top, determine if the column will buckle or yield when the load $P = 10$ kN is applied. Use a factor of safety of 3 with respect to buckling and yielding.

**P**

20 mm

*A*

4 m

10 mm     150 mm     10 mm

100 mm

*A*

100 mm

100 mm

10 mm

**Probs. 136/137**

# Selected Answers

**1.** $P_{cr} = \dfrac{kL}{4}$

**2.** $P_{cr} = kL$

**3.** Use $d = \dfrac{9}{16}$ in.

**5.** $d = 2.58$ in.

**6.** $d = 1.81$ in.

**7.** $P_{cr} = 400$ kN

**9.** $d = 6.07$ in.

**10.** $d = 4.73$ in.

**11.** $P_{cr} = 20.4$ kip

**13.** $P_{cr} = 272$ kN

**14.** $d = 8.43$ in., $P_{cr} = 245$ kip

**15.** $P_{allow} = 186$ kN

**17.** $P_{cr} = 2.92$ kip

**18.** $P_{cr} = 5.97$ kip

**19.** $P = 17.6$ kip

**21.** $P_{cr} = 32.2$ kip

**22.** Use $d_{AB} = 2\dfrac{1}{8}$ in., $d_{BC} = 2$ in.

**23.** $P = 207$ lb

**25.** $P = 62.3$ kip

**26.** $P = 2.42$ kip

**27.** $P = 63.0$ kN

**29.** $x-x$ axis buckling: F.S. = 8.94
$y-y$ axis buckling: F.S. = 3.98

**30.** $P = 23.9$ kip

**31.** $w = 1.17$ kN/m

**33.** $P = 8.46$ kN

**34.** Use $d = 62$ mm

**35.** Use $d = 52$ mm

**37.** $P = 37.5$ kip

**38.** $P = 5.79$ kip

**39.** Use $d = 1\dfrac{3}{4}$ in.

**41.** $M_{max} = -\dfrac{wEI}{P}\left[ \sec\left( \dfrac{L}{2}\sqrt{\dfrac{P}{EI}} \right) - 1 \right]$

**42.** $M_{max} = -\dfrac{F}{2}\sqrt{\dfrac{EI}{P}}\tan\left( \dfrac{L}{2}\sqrt{\dfrac{P}{EI}} \right)$

**43.** $P_{cr} = \dfrac{\pi^2 EI}{4L^2}$

**46.** $P = 31.4$ kN

**47.** $P = 5.87$ kN, $v_{max} = 42.1$ mm

**49.** $P_{max} = 16.9$ kN

**50.** $P_{max} = 4.60$ kN

**51.** $\sigma_{max} = 65.8$ kip

**53.** $P = 156$ kip

**54.** $P' = 390$ kip, $P = 139$ kip

**55.** Yes.

**57.** $L = 2.53$ m

**58.** $d = 98.3$ mm

**59.** $P = 73.5$ kip

**61.** $P_{max} = 61.2$ kip

**62.** $L = 21.2$ ft

**63.** $P = 129$ kip

**65.** $P_{cr} = 83.5$ kN

**66.** $\sigma_{max} = 2.86$ ksi

**67.** $\sigma_{max} = 2.86$ ksi

**69.** $P = 88.5$ kip

**70.** $E_t = 14.6(10^3)$ ksi

**71.** $L = 8.34$ m

**75.** $P_{cr} = 661$ kN

**77.** $P_{cr} = 1350$ kN

**78.** $L = 8.99$ ft

**79.** Use W6 × 9

**81.** $L = 15.1$ ft

**82.** Use W6 × 12

**83.** $L = 18.0$ ft

**85.** $L = 33.7$ ft

**86.** Use W6 × 9

**87.** $d = 1.42$ in.

**89.** Yes.

**90.** $L = 4.46$ m

**91.** $b = 0.704$ in.

**93.** $P_{allow} = 422$ kN

**94.** $L = 3.08$ m

**95.** $P_{allow} = 380$ kip

**97.** $P_{allow} = 129$ kip

**98.** $P_{allow} = 143$ kip

**99.** $P_{allow} = 109$ kip

**101.** $P_{allow} = 8.61$ kip

**102.** $L = 8.89$ ft

**103.** Use $a = 7\dfrac{1}{2}$ in.

**105.** $L = 5.03$ ft

**106.** $P_{allow} = 4.22$ kip

**107.** $P = 8.83$ kip

**109.** $P = 17.4$ kip

**110.** $P = 3.91$ kip

**111.** $P = 29.6$ kip

**113.** $P = 8.60$ kip

**114.** $P = 14.6$ kip

**115.** No.

**117.** $P = 95.7$ kip

**118.** $P = 98.6$ kip

| | | | | |
|---|---|---|---|---|
| 119. | $P = 2.79$ kip | | 130. | $P_{cr} = 12.1$ kN |
| 121. | $P = 98.0$ kip | | 131. | $P = 161$ kip |
| 122. | $P = 132$ kip | | 133. | Use $d = 2\frac{1}{8}$ in. |
| 123. | Yes. | | | |
| 125. | Yes. | | 134. | $t = 5.92$ mm |
| 126. | $P = 1.69$ kip | | 135. | $P_{cr} = 839$ kN |
| 127. | $P = 3.44$ kip | | 137. | No, it does not buckle or yield. |
| 129. | $P = 9.01$ kip | | | |

# Fundamental Problems Partial Solutions and Answers

## F1

$$P = \frac{\pi^2 EI}{(KL)^2} = \frac{\pi^2 \left[29(10^3)\right]\left[\frac{\pi}{4}(0.5)^4\right]}{[0.5(50)]^2} = 22.5 \text{ kip} \qquad Ans.$$

$$\sigma = \frac{P}{A} = \frac{22.5}{\pi(0.5)^2} = 28.6 \text{ ksi} < \sigma_Y \quad \text{OK}$$

## F2

$$P = \frac{\pi^2 EI}{(KL)^2} = \frac{\pi^2 \left[1.6(10^3)\right]\left[\frac{1}{12}(4)(2)^3\right]}{[1(12)(12)]^2}$$

$$= 2.03 \text{ kip} \qquad Ans.$$

## F3

For buckling about the $x$ axis, $K_x = 1$ and $L_x = 12$ m.

$$P_{cr} = \frac{\pi^2 EI_x}{(K_x L_x)^2} = \frac{\pi^2 [200(10^9)][87.3(10^{-6})]}{[1(12)]^2} = 1.197(10^6) \text{ N}$$

For buckling about the $y$ axis, $L = 6$ m and $K_y = 1$.

$$P_{cr} = \frac{\pi^2 EI_y}{(K_y L_y)^2} = \frac{\pi^2 [200(10^9)][18.8(10^{-6})]}{[1(6)]^2}$$

$$= 1.031(10^6) \text{ N (controls)}$$

$$P_{allow} = \frac{P_{cr}}{\text{F.S.}} = \frac{1.031(10^6)}{2} = 515 \text{ kN} \qquad Ans.$$

$$\sigma_{cr} = \frac{P_{cr}}{A} = \frac{1.031(10^6)}{7.4(10^{-3})} = 139.30 \text{ MPa} < \sigma_Y = 345 \text{ MPa}$$

$$\text{(OK)}$$

## F4

$$A = \pi[(0.025)^2 - (0.015)^2] = 1.257(10^{-3}) \text{ m}^2$$

$$I = \frac{1}{4}\pi\left[(0.025)^4 - (0.015)^4\right] = 267.04(10^{-9}) \text{ m}^4$$

$$P = \frac{\pi^2 EI}{(KL)^2} = \frac{\pi^2 \left[200(10^9)\right]\left[267.04(10^{-9})\right]}{[0.5(5)]^2} = 84.3 \text{ kN} \quad Ans.$$

$$\sigma = \frac{P}{A} = \frac{84.3(10^3)}{1.257(10^{-3})} = 67.1 \text{ MPa} < 250 \text{ MPa} \quad \text{(OK)}$$

## F5

$$+\uparrow \Sigma F_y = 0; \qquad F_{AB}\left(\frac{3}{5}\right) - P = 0 \quad F_{AB} = 1.6667P \text{ (T)}$$

$$\xrightarrow{+} \Sigma F_x = 0; \qquad 1.6667P\left(\frac{4}{5}\right) - F_{AC} = 0$$

$$F_{AC} = 1.3333P \text{ (C)}$$

$$A = \frac{\pi}{4}(2^2) = \pi \text{ in}^2 \qquad I = \frac{\pi}{4}(1^4) = \frac{\pi}{4} \text{ in}^4$$

$$P_{cr} = F(\text{F.S.}) = 1.3333P(2) = 2.6667P$$

$$P_{cr} = \frac{\pi^2 EI}{(KL)^2}$$

$$2.6667P = \frac{\pi^2 [29(10^3)]\left(\frac{\pi}{4}\right)}{[1(4)(12)]^2}$$

$$P = 36.59 \text{ kip} = 36.6 \text{ kip} \qquad Ans.$$

$$\sigma_{cr} = \frac{P_{cr}}{A} = \frac{2.6667(36.59)}{\pi} = 31.06 \text{ ksi} < \sigma_Y = 50 \text{ ksi}$$

$$\text{(OK)}$$

**F6**

$\zeta + \Sigma M_A = 0;$ $\quad w(6)(3) - F_{BC}(6) = 0$ $\quad F_{BC} = 3w$

$A = \dfrac{\pi}{4}(0.05^2) = 0.625(10^{-3})\pi \text{ m}^2$ $\quad I = \dfrac{\pi}{4}(0.025^4)$

$\qquad\qquad\qquad\qquad\qquad\qquad\qquad = 97.65625(10^{-9})\pi \text{ m}^4$

$P_{cr} = F_{BC}(\text{F.S.}) = 3w(2) = 6w$

$P_{cr} = \dfrac{\pi^2 EI}{(KL)^2}$

$6w = \dfrac{\pi^2[200(10^9)][97.65625(10^{-9})\pi]}{[1(3)]^2}$

$w = 11.215(10^3) \text{ N/m} = 11.2 \text{ kN/m}$ *Ans.*

$\sigma_{cr} = \dfrac{P_{cr}}{A} = \dfrac{6[11.215(10^3)]}{0.625(10^{-3})\pi} = 34.27 \text{ MPa} < \sigma_Y = 345 \text{ MPa}$

(OK)

# Energy Methods

From Chapter 14 of *Mechanics of Materials*, Ninth Edition. R. C. Hibbeler. Copyright © 2014 by Pearson Education, Inc. Published by Pearson Prentice Hall. All rights reserved.

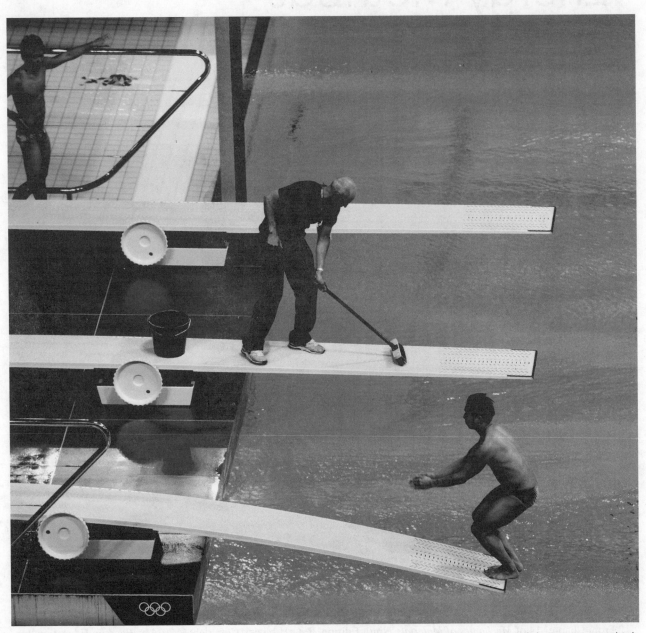

These diving boards must be made from a material that can store a high value of elastic strain energy due to bending. This allows it to have a large flexure, and thereby transfer this energy to the diver, as the board begins to straighten out.

# Energy Methods

## CHAPTER OBJECTIVES

■ In this chapter, we will show how to apply energy methods to solve problems involving deflection. The chapter begins with a discussion of work and strain energy, followed by a development of the principle of conservation of energy. Using this principle, the stress and deflection of a member are determined when the member is subjected to impact. The method of virtual work and Castigliano's theorem are then developed, and these methods are used to determine the displacement and slope at points on structural members and mechanical elements.

## 1 External Work and Strain Energy

The deflection of joints on a truss or points on a beam or shaft can be determined using energy methods. Before developing any of these methods, however, we will first define the work caused by an external force and couple moment and show how to express this work in terms of a body's strain energy. The formulations to be presented here and in the next section will provide the basis for applying the work and energy methods that follow throughout the chapter.

(a)        (b)

(c)

**Fig. 1**

**Work of a Force.** In mechanics, a force does *work* when it undergoes a displacement $dx$ that is in the *same direction* as the force. The work done is a scalar, defined as $dU_e = F\,dx$. If the total displacement is $\Delta$, the work becomes

$$U_e = \int_0^{\Delta} F\,dx \tag{1}$$

To show how to apply this equation, we will calculate the work done by an axial force applied to the end of the bar shown in Fig. 1a. As the magnitude of the force is *gradually* increased from zero to some limiting value $F = P$, the final displacement of the end of the bar becomes $\Delta$. If the material behaves in a linear-elastic manner, then the force will be directly proportional to the displacement; that is, $F = (P/\Delta)x$. Substituting into Eq. 1 and integrating from 0 to $\Delta$, we get

$$U_e = \frac{1}{2}P\Delta \tag{2}$$

Therefore, as the force is gradually applied to the bar, its magnitude builds from zero to some value $P$, and consequently, the work done is equal to the *average force magnitude*, $P/2$, times the total displacement $\Delta$. We can represent this graphically as the light-blue shaded area of the triangle in Fig. 1c.

Suppose, however, that **P** is already applied to the bar and that *another force* **P′** is now applied, so that the end of the bar is displaced *further* by an amount $\Delta'$, Fig. 1b. The work done by **P′** is equal to the gray shaded triangular area, but now the work done by **P** when the bar undergoes this further displacement is

$$U_e' = P\Delta' \tag{3}$$

Here the work represents the dark-blue shaded *rectangular area* in Fig. 1c. In this case **P** does not change its magnitude, since the bar's displacement $\Delta'$ is caused only by **P′**. Therefore, work here is simply the force magnitude $P$ times the displacement $\Delta'$.

## Work of a Couple Moment.

A couple moment **M** does work when it undergoes an angular displacement $d\theta$ along its line of action. The work is defined as $dU_e = M\,d\theta$, Fig. 2. If the total angular displacement is $\theta$ rad, the work becomes

$$U_e = \int_0^\theta M\,d\theta \qquad (4)$$

**Fig. 2**

As in the case of force, if the couple moment is applied to a *body* having linear elastic material behavior, such that its magnitude is increased gradually from zero at $\theta = 0$ to $M$ at $\theta$, then the work is

$$U_e = \frac{1}{2}M\theta \qquad (5)$$

However, if the couple moment is already applied to the body and other loadings further rotate the body by an amount $\theta'$, then the work is

$$U_e' = M\theta'$$

## Strain Energy.

When loads are applied to a body, they will deform the material. Provided no energy is lost in the form of heat, the external work done by the loads will be converted into internal work called **strain energy**. This energy, which is *always positive*, is stored in the body and is caused by the action of either normal or shear stress.

**Fig. 3**

## Normal Stress.

If the volume element shown in Fig. 3 is subjected to the normal stress $\sigma_z$, then the force created on the element's top and bottom faces is $dF_z = \sigma_z\,dA = \sigma_z\,dx\,dy$. If this force is applied gradually to the element, like the force **P** discussed previously, its magnitude is increased from zero to $dF_z$, while the element undergoes an elongation $d\Delta_z = \epsilon_z\,dz$. The work done by $dF_z$ is therefore $dU_i = \frac{1}{2}dF_z\,d\Delta_z = \frac{1}{2}[\sigma_z\,dx\,dy]\epsilon_z\,dz$. Since the volume of the element is $dV = dx\,dy\,dz$, we have

$$dU_i = \frac{1}{2}\sigma_z\epsilon_z\,dV \qquad (6)$$

Notice that $dU_i$ is *always positive*, even if $\sigma_z$ is compressive, since $\sigma_z$ and $\epsilon_z$ will always be in the same direction.

In general then, if the body is subjected only to a uniaxial *normal stress* $\sigma$, the strain energy in the body is then

$$U_i = \int_V \frac{\sigma\epsilon}{2}\,dV \qquad (7)$$

Also, if the material behaves in a linear-elastic manner, then Hooke's law applies, and we can express the strain energy in terms of the normal stress as

$$U_i = \int_V \frac{\sigma^2}{2E} dV \qquad (8)$$

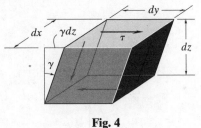

**Fig. 4**

**Shear Stress.** A strain-energy expression similar to that for normal stress can also be established for the material when it is subjected to shear stress. Consider the volume element shown in Fig. 4. Here the shear stress causes the element to deform such that only the shear force $dF = \tau(dx\,dy)$, acting on the top face of the element, is displaced $\gamma\,dz$ relative to the bottom face. The *vertical faces* only rotate, and therefore the shear forces on these faces do no work. Hence, the strain energy stored in the element is

$$dU_i = \frac{1}{2}[\tau(dx\,dy)]\gamma\,dz$$

or since $dV = dx\,dy\,dz$

$$dU_i = \frac{1}{2}\tau\gamma\,dV \qquad (9)$$

The strain energy stored in the body is therefore

$$U_i = \int_V \frac{\tau\gamma}{2} dV \qquad (10)$$

Like the case for normal strain energy, shear strain energy is always positive since $\tau$ and $\gamma$ are always in the same direction. If the material is linear elastic, then, applying Hooke's law, $\gamma = \tau/G$, we can express the strain energy in terms of the shear stress as

$$U_i = \int_V \frac{\tau^2}{2G} dV \qquad (11)$$

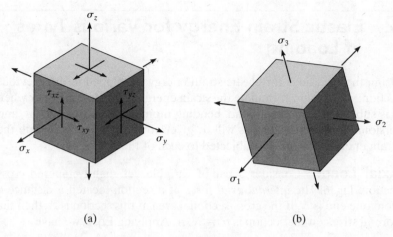

(a)                                        (b)

**Fig. 5**

In the next section, we will use Eqs. 8 and 11 to obtain formal expressions for the strain energy stored in members subjected to several types of loads. Once this is done we will then be able to develop the energy methods necessary to determine the displacement and slope at points on a body.

## Multiaxial Stress.

The previous development may be expanded to determine the strain energy in a body when it is subjected to a general state of stress, Fig. 5a. The strain energies associated with each of the normal and shear stress components can be obtained from Eqs. 6 and 9. Since energy is a scalar, the total strain energy in the body is therefore

$$U_i = \int_V \left[ \frac{1}{2}\sigma_x\epsilon_x + \frac{1}{2}\sigma_y\epsilon_y + \frac{1}{2}\sigma_z\epsilon_z \right.$$
$$\left. + \frac{1}{2}\tau_{xy}\gamma_{xy} + \frac{1}{2}\tau_{yz}\gamma_{yz} + \frac{1}{2}\tau_{xz}\gamma_{xz} \right] dV \qquad (12)$$

The strains can be eliminated by using the generalized form of Hooke's law. After substituting and combining terms, we have

$$U_i = \int_V \left[ \frac{1}{2E}\left(\sigma_x^2 + \sigma_y^2 + \sigma_z^2\right) - \frac{\nu}{E}(\sigma_x\sigma_y + \sigma_y\sigma_z + \sigma_x\sigma_z) \right.$$
$$\left. + \frac{1}{2G}\left(\tau_{xy}^2 + \tau_{yz}^2 + \tau_{xz}^2\right) \right] dV \qquad (13)$$

If only the principal stresses $\sigma_1, \sigma_2, \sigma_3$ act on the element, Fig. 5b, this equation reduces to a simpler form, namely,

$$U_i = \int_V \left[ \frac{1}{2E}\left(\sigma_1^2 + \sigma_2^2 + \sigma_3^2\right) - \frac{\nu}{E}(\sigma_1\sigma_2 + \sigma_2\sigma_3 + \sigma_1\sigma_3) \right] dV \qquad (14)$$

This equation can be used as a basis for developing the maximum-distortion-energy theory.

## 2 Elastic Strain Energy for Various Types of Loading

Using the equations for elastic strain energy developed in the previous section, we will now formulate the strain energy stored in a member when it is subjected to an axial load, bending moment, transverse shear, and torsional moment. Examples will be given to show how to calculate the strain energy in members subjected to each of these loadings.

**Axial Load.** Consider a bar of variable yet slightly tapered cross section, Fig. 6. The *internal axial force* at a section located a distance $x$ from one end is $N$. If the cross-sectional area at this section is $A$, then the normal stress on the section is $\sigma = N/A$. Applying Eq. 8, we have

**Fig. 6**

$$U_i = \int_V \frac{\sigma_x^2}{2E} dV = \int_V \frac{N^2}{2EA^2} dV$$

If we choose an element or differential slice having a volume $dV = A\,dx$, the general formula for the strain energy in the bar is therefore

$$U_i = \int_0^L \frac{N^2}{2A E} dx \qquad (15)$$

For the more common case of a prismatic bar of constant cross-sectional area $A$, length $L$, and constant axial load $N$, Fig. 7, Eq. 15, when integrated, gives

**Fig. 7**

$$U_i = \frac{N^2 L}{2A E} \qquad (16)$$

Notice that the bar's elastic strain energy will *increase* if the length of the bar is increased, or if the modulus of elasticity or cross-sectional area is decreased. For example, an aluminum rod [$E_{al} = 10(10^3)$ ksi] will store approximately three times as much energy as a steel rod [$E_{st} = 29(10^3)$ ksi] having the same size and subjected to the same load. However, doubling the cross-sectional area of a rod will decrease its ability to store energy by one-half. The following example illustrates this point numerically.

## EXAMPLE | 1

One of the two high-strength steel bolts $A$ and $B$ shown in Fig. 8 is to be chosen to support a sudden tensile loading. For the choice it is necessary to determine the greatest amount of elastic strain energy that each bolt can absorb. Bolt $A$ has a diameter of 0.875 in. for 2 in. of its length and a root (or smallest) diameter of 0.731 in. within the 0.25-in. threaded region. Bolt $B$ has "upset" threads, such that the diameter throughout its 2.25-in. length can be taken as 0.731 in. In both cases, neglect the extra material that makes up the threads. Take $E_{st} = 29(10^3)$ ksi, $\sigma_Y = 44$ ksi.

**Fig. 8**

## SOLUTION

**Bolt A.** If the bolt is subjected to its maximum tension, the maximum stress of $\sigma_Y = 44$ ksi will occur within the 0.25-in. region. This tension force is

$$P_{max} = \sigma_Y A = 44 \text{ ksi} \left[ \pi \left( \frac{0.731 \text{ in.}}{2} \right)^2 \right] = 18.47 \text{ kip}$$

Applying Eq. 16 to each region of the bolt, we have

$$U_i = \sum \frac{N^2 L}{2AE}$$

$$= \frac{(18.47 \text{ kip})^2 (2 \text{ in.})}{2[\pi(0.875 \text{ in.}/2)^2][29(10^3) \text{ ksi}]} + \frac{(18.47 \text{ kip})^2 (0.25 \text{ in.})}{2[\pi(0.731 \text{ in.}/2)^2][29(10^3) \text{ ksi}]}$$

$$= 0.0231 \text{ in.} \cdot \text{kip} \hspace{4cm} Ans.$$

**Bolt B.** Here the bolt is assumed to have a uniform diameter of 0.731 in. throughout its 2.25-in. length. Also, from the calculation above, it can support a maximum tension force of $P_{max} = 18.47$ kip. Thus,

$$U_i = \frac{N^2 L}{2AE} = \frac{(18.47 \text{ kip})^2 (2.25 \text{ in.})}{2[\pi(0.731 \text{ in.}/2)^2][29(10^3) \text{ ksi}]} = 0.0315 \text{ in.} \cdot \text{kip} \quad Ans.$$

**NOTE:** By comparison, bolt $B$ can absorb 36% more elastic energy than bolt $A$, because it has a smaller cross section along its shank.

**Bending Moment.**  Since a bending moment applied to a straight prismatic member develops *normal stress* in the member, we can use Eq. 8 to determine the strain energy stored in the member due to bending. For example, consider the axisymmetric beam shown in Fig. 9. Here the internal moment is $M$, and the normal stress acting on the arbitrary element a distance $y$ from the neutral axis is $\sigma = My/I$. If the volume of the element is $dV = dA\ dx$, where $dA$ is the area of its exposed face and $dx$ is its length, the elastic strain energy in the beam is

$$U_i = \int_V \frac{\sigma^2}{2E} dV = \int_V \frac{1}{2E}\left(\frac{My}{I}\right)^2 dA\ dx$$

or

$$U_i = \int_0^L \frac{M^2}{2EI^2}\left(\int_A y^2\ dA\right) dx$$

Realizing that the area integral represents the moment of inertia of the area about the neutral axis, the final result can be written as

$$U_i = \int_0^L \frac{M^2\ dx}{2EI} \tag{17}$$

To evaluate the strain energy, therefore, we must first express the internal moment as a function of its position $x$ along the beam, and then perform the integration over the beam's entire length.* The following examples illustrate this procedure.

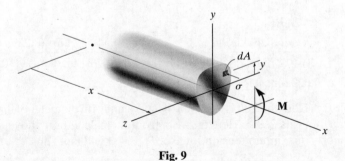

**Fig. 9**

*Recall that the flexure formula, as used here, can also be used with justifiable accuracy to determine the stress in slightly tapered beams. So in the general sense, $I$ in Eq. 17 may also have to be expressed as a function of $x$.

## EXAMPLE | 2

Determine the elastic strain energy due to bending of the cantilevered beam in Fig. 10*a*. *EI* is constant.

(a)

**Fig. 10**

### SOLUTION

The internal moment in the beam is determined by establishing the $x$ coordinate with origin at the left side. The left segment of the beam is shown in Fig. 10*b*. We have

(b)

$$\zeta + \Sigma M_{NA} = 0; \qquad M + wx\left(\frac{x}{2}\right) = 0$$

$$M = -w\left(\frac{x^2}{2}\right)$$

Applying Eq. 17 yields

$$U_i = \int_0^L \frac{M^2\,dx}{2EI} = \int_0^L \frac{[-w(x^2/2)]^2\,dx}{2EI} = \frac{w^2}{8EI}\int_0^L x^4\,dx$$

or

$$U_i = \frac{w^2 L^5}{40EI} \qquad\qquad Ans.$$

We can also obtain the strain energy using an $x$ coordinate having its origin at the right side of the beam and extending positive to the left, Fig. 10*c*. In this case,

$$\zeta + \Sigma M_{NA} = 0; \qquad -M - wx\left(\frac{x}{2}\right) + wL(x) - \frac{wL^2}{2} = 0$$

$$M = -\frac{wL^2}{2} + wLx - w\left(\frac{x^2}{2}\right)$$

(c)

Applying Eq. 17, we obtain the same result as before; however, more calculations are involved in this case.

# EXAMPLE | 3

(a)

(b)

(c)

(d)

(e)

**Fig. 11**

Determine the bending strain energy in region $AB$ of the beam shown in Fig. 11$a$. $EI$ is constant.

## SOLUTION

A free-body diagram of the beam is shown in Fig. 11$b$. To obtain the answer we can express the internal moment in terms of any one of the indicated three "$x$" coordinates and then apply Eq. 17. Each of these solutions will now be considered.

$0 \leq x_1 \leq L$. From the free-body diagram of the section in Fig. 11$c$, we have

$$\zeta + \Sigma M_{NA} = 0; \qquad M_1 + Px_1 = 0$$

$$M_1 = -Px_1$$

$$U_i = \int \frac{M^2 \, dx}{2EI} = \int_0^L \frac{(-Px_1)^2 \, dx_1}{2EI} = \frac{P^2 L^3}{6EI} \qquad Ans.$$

$0 \leq x_2 \leq L$. Using the free-body diagram of the section in Fig. 11$d$ gives

$$\zeta + \Sigma M_{NA} = 0; \qquad -M_2 + 2P(x_2) - P(x_2 + L) = 0$$

$$M_2 = P(x_2 - L)$$

$$U_i = \int \frac{M^2 \, dx}{2EI} = \int_0^L \frac{[P(x_2 - L)]^2 \, dx_2}{2EI} = \frac{P^2 L^3}{6EI} \qquad Ans.$$

$L \leq x_3 \leq 2L$. From the free-body diagram in Fig. 11$e$, we have

$$\zeta + \Sigma M_{NA} = 0; \qquad -M_3 + 2P(x_3 - L) - P(x_3) = 0$$

$$M_3 = P(x_3 - 2L)$$

$$U_i = \int \frac{M^2 \, dx}{2EI} = \int_L^{2L} \frac{[P(x_3 - 2L)]^2 \, dx_3}{2EI} = \frac{P^2 L^3}{6EI} \qquad Ans.$$

**NOTE:** This and the previous example indicate that the strain energy for the beam can be found using *any* suitable $x$ coordinate. It is only necessary to integrate over the range of the coordinate where the internal energy is to be determined. Here the choice of $x_1$ provides the simplest solution.

**Transverse Shear.** The strain energy due to shear stress in a beam element can be determined by applying Eq. 11. Here we will consider the beam to be prismatic and to have an axis of symmetry about the $y$ axis as shown in Fig. 12. If the internal shear at the section $x$ is $V$, then the shear stress acting on the volume element of material, having an area $dA$ and length $dx$, is $\tau = VQ/It$. Substituting into Eq. 11, the strain energy for shear becomes

$$U_i = \int_V \frac{\tau^2}{2G} dV = \int_V \frac{1}{2G}\left(\frac{VQ}{It}\right)^2 dA\ dx$$

$$U_i = \int_0^L \frac{V^2}{2GI^2}\left(\int_A \frac{Q^2}{t^2} dA\right) dx$$

**Fig. 12**

The integral in parentheses can be simplified if we define the *form factor* for shear as

$$f_s = \frac{A}{I^2}\int_A \frac{Q^2}{t^2} dA \qquad (18)$$

Substituting into the above equation, we get

$$\boxed{U_i = \int_0^L \frac{f_s V^2\ dx}{2GA}} \qquad (19)$$

The form factor defined by Eq. 18 is a dimensionless number that is unique for each specific cross-sectional area. For example, if the beam has a rectangular cross section of width $b$ and height $h$, Fig. 13, then

$$t = b$$

$$dA = b\,dy$$

$$I = \frac{1}{12}bh^3$$

$$Q = \bar{y}'A' = \left(y + \frac{(h/2) - y}{2}\right)b\left(\frac{h}{2} - y\right) = \frac{b}{2}\left(\frac{h^2}{4} - y^2\right)$$

Substituting these terms into Eq. 18, we get

$$f_s = \frac{bh}{\left(\frac{1}{12}bh^3\right)^2}\int_{-h/2}^{h/2} \frac{b^2}{4b^2}\left(\frac{h^2}{4} - y^2\right)^2 b\,dy = \frac{6}{5} \qquad (20)$$

The form factor for other sections can be determined in a similar manner. Once obtained, this factor is substituted into Eq. 19 and the strain energy for transverse shear can then be evaluated.

**Fig. 13**

## EXAMPLE | 4

Determine the strain energy in the cantilevered beam due to shear if the beam has a square cross section and is subjected to a uniform distributed load $w$, Fig. 14a. $EI$ and $G$ are constant.

(a)                                              (b)

**Fig. 14**

### SOLUTION

From the free-body diagram of an arbitrary section, Fig. 14b, we have

$$+\uparrow \Sigma F_y = 0; \qquad\qquad -V - wx = 0$$

$$V = -wx$$

Since the cross section is square, the form factor $f_s = \frac{6}{5}$ (Eq. 20) and therefore Eq. 19 becomes

$$(U_i)_s = \int_0^L \frac{\frac{6}{5}(-wx)^2 \, dx}{2GA} = \frac{3w^2}{5GA} \int_0^L x^2 \, dx$$

or

$$(U_i)_s = \frac{w^2 L^3}{5GA} \qquad\qquad\qquad Ans.$$

**NOTE:** Using the results of Example 2, with $A = a^2, I = \frac{1}{12}a^4$, the ratio of shear to bending strain energy is

$$\frac{(U_i)_s}{(U_i)_b} = \frac{w^2 L^3 / 5Ga^2}{w^2 L^5 / 40E\left(\frac{1}{12}a^4\right)} = \frac{2}{3}\left(\frac{a}{L}\right)^2 \frac{E}{G}$$

Since $G = E/2(1 + v)$ and $v \le \frac{1}{2}$, then as an *upper* bound, $E = 3G$, so that

$$\frac{(U_i)_s}{(U_i)_b} = 2\left(\frac{a}{L}\right)^2$$

It can be seen that this ratio will increase as $L$ decreases. However, even for very short beams, where, say, $L = 5a$, the contribution due to shear strain energy is only 8% of the bending strain energy. For this reason, the shear strain energy stored in beams is usually neglected in engineering analysis.

## Torsional Moment.

To determine the internal strain energy in a circular shaft or tube due to an applied torsional moment, we must apply Eq. 11. Consider the slightly tapered shaft in Fig. 15. A section of the shaft taken a distance $x$ from one end is subjected to an internal torque $T$. The shear stress distribution that causes this torque varies linearly from the center of the shaft. On the arbitrary element of area $dA$ and length $dx$, the stress is $\tau = T\rho/J$. The strain energy stored in the shaft is thus

$$U_i = \int_V \frac{\tau^2}{2G} dV = \int_V \frac{1}{2G}\left(\frac{T\rho}{J}\right)^2 dA\ dx = \int_0^L \frac{T^2}{2GJ^2}\left(\int_A \rho^2\ dA\right) dx$$

Since the area integral represents the polar moment of inertia $J$ for the shaft at the section, the final result can be written as

$$U_i = \int_0^L \frac{T^2}{2GJ} dx \qquad (21)$$

**Fig. 15**

The most common case occurs when the shaft (or tube) has a constant cross-sectional area and the applied torque is constant, Fig. 16. Integration of Eq. 21 then gives

$$U_i = \frac{T^2L}{2GJ} \qquad (22)$$

From this equation we may conclude that, like an axially loaded member, the energy-absorbing capacity of a torsionally loaded shaft is *decreased* by increasing the diameter of the shaft, since this increases $J$.

**Fig. 16**

---

## Important Points

- A *force* does work when it moves through a *displacement*. When a force is applied to a body and its magnitude is increased gradually from zero to $F$, the work is $U = (F/2)\Delta$, whereas if the force is constant when the displacement occurs then $U = F\Delta$.

- A *couple moment* does work when it displaces through a *rotation*.

- *Strain energy* is caused by the internal work of the normal and shear stresses. It is always a *positive* quantity.

- The strain energy can be related to the resultant internal loadings $N, V, M,$ and $T$.

- As the beam becomes longer, the strain energy due to bending becomes much larger than the strain energy due to shear. For this reason, the *shear strain energy* in beams can generally be *neglected*.

---

The following example illustrates how to determine the strain energy in a circular shaft due to a torsional loading.

EXAMPLE 5

The tubular shaft in Fig. 17a is fixed at the wall and subjected to two torques as shown. Determine the strain energy stored in the shaft due to this loading. $G = 75$ GPa.

(a)

(b)

**Fig. 17**

## SOLUTION

Using the method of sections, the internal torque is first determined within the two regions of the shaft where it is constant, Fig. 17b. Although these torques (40 N · m and 15 N · m) are in opposite directions, this will be of no consequence in determining the strain energy, since the torque is squared in Eq. 22. In other words, the strain energy is always positive. The polar moment of inertia for the shaft is

$$J = \frac{\pi}{2}[(0.08 \text{ m})^4 - (0.065 \text{ m})^4] = 36.30(10^{-6}) \text{ m}^4$$

Applying Eq. 22, we have

$$U_i = \sum \frac{T^2 L}{2GJ}$$

$$= \frac{(40 \text{ N} \cdot \text{m})^2(0.750 \text{ m})}{2[75(10^9) \text{ N/m}^2]36.30(10^{-6}) \text{ m}^4} + \frac{(15 \text{ N} \cdot \text{m})^2(0.300 \text{ m})}{2[75(10^9) \text{ N/m}^2]36.30(10^{-6}) \text{ m}^4}$$

$$= 233 \ \mu\text{J} \qquad\qquad Ans.$$

## PROBLEMS

**1.** A material is subjected to a general state of plane stress. Express the strain energy density in terms of the elastic constants $E$, $G$, and $\nu$ and the stress components $\sigma_x$, $\sigma_y$, and $\tau_{xy}$.

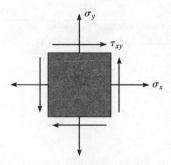

**Prob. 1**

**2.** The strain-energy density must be the same whether the state of stress is represented by $\sigma_x$, $\sigma_y$, and $\tau_{xy}$, or by the principal stresses $\sigma_1$ and $\sigma_2$. This being the case, equate the strain–energy expressions for each of these two cases and show that $G = E/[2(1 + \nu)]$.

**3.** Determine the strain energy in the stepped rod assembly. Portion $AB$ is steel and $BC$ is brass. $E_{br} = 101$ GPa, $E_{st} = 200$ GPa, $(\sigma_Y)_{br} = 410$ MPa, $(\sigma_Y)_{st} = 250$ MPa.

**Prob. 3**

**\*4.** Determine the torsional strain energy in the A-36 steel shaft. The shaft has a radius of 30 mm.

**Prob. 4**

**5.** Using bolts of the same material and cross-sectional area, two possible attachments for a cylinder head are shown. Compare the strain energy developed in each case, and then explain which design is better for resisting an axial shock or impact load.

(a)

(b)

**Prob. 5**

**6.** If $P = 60$ kN, determine the total strain energy stored in the truss. Each member has a cross-sectional area of $2.5(10^3)$ mm$^2$ and is made of A-36 steel.

**7.** Determine the maximum force $\mathbf{P}$ and the corresponding maximum total strain energy stored in the truss without causing any of the members to have permanent deformation. Each member has the cross-sectional area of $2.5(10^3)$ mm$^2$ and is made of A-36 steel.

**Probs. 6/7**

811

**\*8.** Determine the torsional strain energy in the A-36 steel shaft. The shaft has a diameter of 40 mm.

**Prob. 8**

**9.** Determine the torsional strain energy in the A-36 steel shaft. The shaft has a radius of 40 mm.

**Prob. 9**

**10.** The shaft assembly is fixed at $C$. The hollow segment $BC$ has an inner radius of 20 mm and outer radius of 40 mm, while the solid segment $AB$ has a radius of 20 mm. Determine the torsional strain energy stored in the shaft. The shaft is made of 2014-T6 aluminum alloy. The coupling at $B$ is rigid.

**Prob. 10**

**11.** Determine the bending strain energy in the A-36 structural steel W10 × 12 beam. Obtain the answer using the coordinates (a) $x_1$ and $x_4$, and (b) $x_2$ and $x_3$.

**Prob. 11**

**\*12.** If $P = 10$ kip, determine the total strain energy stored in the truss. Each member has a diameter of 2 in. and is made of A992 steel.

**13.** Determine the maximum force **P** and the corresponding maximum total strain energy that can be stored in the truss without causing any of the members to have permanent deformation. Each member of the truss has a diameter of 2 in. and is made of A-36 steel.

**Probs. 12/13**

**14.** This problem has been intentionally excluded from this edition.

**15.** Determine the bending strain energy stored in the simply supported beam subjected to the uniform distributed load. *EI* is constant.

Prob. 15

**\*16.** Determine the bending strain energy in the A992 steel beam due to the loading shown. Obtain the answer using the coordinates (a) $x_1$ and $x_4$, and (b) $x_2$ and $x_3$. $I = 53.4$ in$^4$.

8 kip/ft

$x_1$   $x_2$   $x_3$   $x_4$

10 ft    5 ft

Prob. 16

**17.** Determine the bending strain energy stored in the simply supported beam subjected to the triangular distributed load. *EI* is constant.

$w_0$

$\dfrac{L}{2}$    $\dfrac{L}{2}$

Prob. 17

**18.** Determine the bending strain energy stored in the simply supported beam subjected to the triangular distributed load. *EI* is constant.

$w_0$

$L$

Prob. 18

**19.** Determine the strain energy in the *horizontal* curved bar due to torsion. There is a *vertical* force **P** acting at its end. *JG* is constant.

$r$

90°

**P**

Prob. 19

**\*20.** The concrete column contains six 1-in.-diameter steel reinforcing rods. If the column supports a load of 300 kip, determine the strain energy in the column. $E_{st} = 29(10^3)$ ksi, $E_c = 3.6(10^3)$ ksi.

300 kip

12 in.

5 ft

Prob. 20

**21.** A load of 5 kN is applied to the center of the A992 steel beam, for which $I = 4.5(10^6)$ mm$^4$. If the beam is supported on two springs, each having a stiffness of $k = 8$ MN/m, determine the strain energy in each of the springs and the bending strain energy in the beam.

**23.** Determine the bending strain energy in the cantilevered beam due to a uniform load $w$. Solve the problem two ways. (a) Apply Eq. 17. (b) The load $w\,dx$ acting on a segment $dx$ of the beam is displaced a distance $y$, where $y = w(-x^4 + 4L^3 x - 3L^4)/(24EI)$, the equation of the elastic curve. Hence the internal strain energy in the differential segment $dx$ of the beam is equal to the external work, i.e., $dU_i = \frac{1}{2}(w\,dx)(-y)$. Integrate this equation to obtain the total strain energy in the beam. $EI$ is constant.

**Prob. 21**

**Prob. 23**

**22.** Determine the bending strain energy in the beam and the axial strain energy in each of the two posts. All members are made of aluminum and have a square cross section 50 mm by 50 mm. Assume the posts only support an axial load. $E_{al} = 70$ GPa.

**\*24.** Determine the bending strain energy in the simply supported beam due to a uniform load $w$. Solve the problem two ways. (a) Apply Eq. 17. (b) The load $w\,dx$ acting on the segment $dx$ of the beam is displaced a distance $y$, where $y = w(-x^4 + 2Lx^3 - L^3x)/(24EI)$, the equation of the elastic curve. Hence the internal strain energy in the differential segment $dx$ of the beam is equal to the external work, i.e., $dU_i = \frac{1}{2}(w\,dx)(-y)$. Integrate this equation to obtain the total strain energy in the beam. $EI$ is constant.

**Prob. 22**

**Prob. 24**

# 3 Conservation of Energy

All energy methods used in mechanics are based on a balance of energy, often referred to as the conservation of energy. In this chapter, only mechanical energy will be considered in the energy balance; that is, the energy developed by heat, chemical reactions, and electromagnetic effects will be neglected. As a result, if a loading is applied *slowly* to a body, then physically the external loads tend to deform the body so that the loads do *external work* $U_e$ as they are displaced. This external work on the body is transformed into *internal work* or strain energy $U_i$, which is stored in the body. Furthermore, when the loads are removed, the strain energy restores the body back to its original undeformed position, provided the material's elastic limit is not exceeded. The conservation of energy for the body can therefore be stated mathematically as

$$U_e = U_i \qquad (23)$$

We will now show three examples of how this equation can be applied to determine the displacement of a point on a deformable member or structure. As the first example, consider the truss in Fig. 18 subjected to the load **P**. Provided **P** is applied gradually, the external work done by **P** is determined from Eq. 2, that is, $U_e = \frac{1}{2}P\Delta$, where $\Delta$ is the vertical displacement of the truss at the joint where **P** is applied. Assuming that **P** develops an axial force **N** in a particular member, the strain energy stored in this member is determined from Eq. 16, that is, $U_i = N^2L/2AE$. Summing the strain energies for all the members of the truss, we can write Eq. 23 as

$$\frac{1}{2}P\Delta = \sum \frac{N^2L}{2AE} \qquad (24)$$

Once the internal forces ($N$) in all the members of the truss are determined and the terms on the right calculated, it is then possible to determine the unknown displacement $\Delta$.

**Fig. 18**

As a second example, consider finding the vertical displacement $\Delta$ under the load **P** acting on the beam in Fig. 19. Again, the external work is $U_e = \frac{1}{2}P\Delta$. In this case the strain energy is the result of internal shear and moment loadings caused by **P**. In particular, the contribution of strain energy due to shear is generally *neglected* in most beam deflection problems unless the beam is short and supports a very large load. (See Example 4.) Consequently, the beam's strain energy will be determined only by the internal bending moment $M$, and therefore, using Eq. 17, Eq. 23 can be written symbolically as

**Fig. 19**

$$\frac{1}{2}P\Delta = \int_0^L \frac{M^2}{2EI}dx \qquad (25)$$

Once $M$ is expressed as a function of position $x$ and the integral is evaluated, $\Delta$ can then be determined.

As a last example, we will consider a beam loaded by a couple moment **M**$_0$ as shown in Fig. 20. This moment causes the rotational displacement $\theta$ at the point of application of the couple moment. Since the couple moment only does work when it *rotates*, using Eq. 5, the external work is $U_e = \frac{1}{2}M_0\,\theta$. Therefore Eq. 23 becomes

**Fig. 20**

$$\frac{1}{2}M_0\,\theta = \int_0^L \frac{M^2}{2EI}dx \qquad (26)$$

Here the strain energy is the result of the internal bending moment $M$ caused by application of the couple moment **M**$_0$. Once $M$ has been expressed as a function of $x$ and the strain energy evaluated, then $\theta$ which measures the slope of the elastic curve can be determined.

In each of the above examples, it should be noted that application of Eq. 23 is *quite limited*, because only a *single* external force or couple moment must act on the member or structure. Also, the displacement can *only* be calculated at the point and in the direction of the external force or couple moment. If more than one external force or couple moment were applied, then the external work of each loading would involve its associated unknown displacement. As a result, *all* these unknown displacements could not be determined, since only the single Eq. 23 is available for the solution. Although application of the conservation of energy as described here has these restrictions, it does serve as an introduction to more general energy methods, which we will consider throughout the rest of this chapter.

EXAMPLE 6

The three-bar truss in Fig. 21a is subjected to a horizontal force of 5 kip. If the cross-sectional area of each member is 0.20 in², determine the horizontal displacement at point $B$. $E = 29(10^3)$ ksi.

(a)                                    (b)

**Fig. 21**

SOLUTION

We can apply the conservation of energy to solve this problem because only a *single* external force acts on the truss and the required displacement happens to be in the *same direction* as the force. Furthermore, the reactive forces on the truss do no work since they are not displaced.

Using the method of joints, the force in each member is determined as shown on the free-body diagrams of the pins at $B$ and $C$, Fig. 21b.

Applying Eq. 24, we have

$$\frac{1}{2}P\Delta = \sum \frac{N^2 L}{2AE}$$

$$\frac{1}{2}(5 \text{ kip})(\Delta_B)_h = \frac{(2.89 \text{ kip})^2(2 \text{ ft})}{2AE} + \frac{(-5.77 \text{ kip})^2(4 \text{ ft})}{2AE}$$

$$+ \frac{(5 \text{ kip})^2(3.46 \text{ ft})}{2AE}$$

$$(\Delta_B)_h = \frac{47.32 \text{ kip} \cdot \text{ft}}{AE}$$

Notice that since $N$ is squared, it does not matter if a particular member is in tension or compression. Substituting in the numerical data for $A$ and $E$ and solving, we get

$$(\Delta_B)_h = \frac{47.32 \text{ kip} \cdot \text{ft}(12 \text{ in./ft})}{(0.2 \text{ in}^2)[29(10^3) \text{ kip/in}^2]}$$

$$= 0.0979 \text{ in.} \rightarrow \qquad\qquad Ans.$$

# EXAMPLE | 7

P

$\square h$
$b$

L

(a)

P

$x$

$M = -Px$
$V = -P$

(b)

**Fig. 22**

The cantilevered beam in Fig. 22a has a rectangular cross section and is subjected to a load **P** at its end. Determine the displacement of the load. $EI$ is constant.

## SOLUTION

The internal shear and moment in the beam as a function of $x$ are determined using the method of sections, Fig. 22b.

When applying Eq. 23 we will consider the strain energy due to both shear and bending. Using Eqs. 19 and 17, we have

$$\frac{1}{2}P\Delta = \int_0^L \frac{f_s V^2 \, dx}{2GA} + \int_0^L \frac{M^2 \, dx}{2EI}$$

$$= \int_0^L \frac{\left(\frac{6}{5}\right)(-P)^2 dx}{2GA} + \int_0^L \frac{(-Px)^2 dx}{2EI} = \frac{3P^2L}{5GA} + \frac{P^2L^3}{6EI} \quad (1)$$

The first term on the right side of this equation represents the strain energy due to shear, while the second is the strain energy due to bending. As stated in Example 4, for most beams the shear strain energy is much smaller than the bending strain energy. To show when this is the case for the beam in Fig. 22a, we require

$$\frac{3}{5}\frac{P^2L}{GA} \ll \frac{P^2L^3}{6EI}$$

$$\frac{3}{5}\frac{P^2L}{G(bh)} \ll \frac{P^2L^3}{6E\left[\frac{1}{12}(bh^3)\right]}$$

$$\frac{3}{5G} \ll \frac{2L^2}{Eh^2}$$

Since $E \le 3G$ (see Example 4), then

$$0.9 \ll \left(\frac{L}{h}\right)^2$$

Hence if $L$ is relatively long compared with $h$, the beam becomes slender and the shear strain energy can be neglected. In other words, the *shear strain energy* becomes important *only* for *short, deep beams*. For example, beams for which $L = 5h$ have approximately 28 times more bending strain energy than shear strain energy, so neglecting the shear strain energy represents an error of about 3.6%. With this in mind, Eq. 1 can be simplified to

$$\frac{1}{2}P\Delta = \frac{P^2L^3}{6EI}$$

so that

$$\Delta = \frac{PL^3}{3EI} \qquad\qquad Ans.$$

## PROBLEMS

**25.** Determine the horizontal displacement of joint $B$. The members of the truss are A992 steel bars, each with a cross-sectional area of 2500 mm$^2$.

**27.** Determine the horizontal displacement of joint $A$. The members of the truss are A992 steel rods, each having a diameter of 2 in.

**Prob. 25**

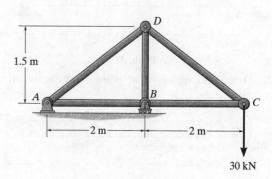

**Prob. 27**

**26.** Determine the vertical displacement of joint $C$. $AE$ is constant.

**\*28.** Determine the vertical displacement of joint $C$. The members of the truss are 2014-T6 aluminum, 40 mm diameter rods.

**Prob. 26**

**Prob. 28**

**29.** Determine the displacement of point $B$ on the A992 steel beam. $I = 250$ in⁴.

Prob. 29

**30.** Determine the vertical displacement of end $B$ of the cantilevered 6061-T6 aluminum alloy rectangular beam. Consider both shearing and bending strain energy.

Prob. 30

**31.** Determine the displacement of point $B$ on the A992 steel beam. $I = 80(10^6)$ mm⁴.

Prob. 31

**\*32.** Determine the slope at point $A$ of the beam. $EI$ is constant.

Prob. 32

**33.** The A992 steel bars are pin connected at $C$ and $D$. If they each have the same rectangular cross section, with a height of 200 mm and a width of 100 mm, determine the vertical displacement at $B$. Neglect the axial load in the bars.

Prob. 33

**34.** The A992 steel bars are pin connected at $C$. If they each have a diameter 2 in., determine the displacement at $E$.

Prob. 34

**35.** Determine the slope of the beam at the pin support $A$. Consider only bending strain energy. $EI$ is constant.

Prob. 35

**\*36.** The curved rod has a diameter $d$. Determine the vertical displacement of end $B$ of the rod. The rod is made of material having a modulus of elasticity of $E$. Consider only bending strain energy.

Prob. 36

**37.** The load **P** causes the open coils of the spring to make an angle $\theta$ with the horizontal when the spring is stretched. Show that for this position this causes a torque $T = PR\cos\theta$ and a bending moment $M = PR\sin\theta$ at the cross section. Use these results to determine the maximum normal stress in the material.

**38.** The coiled spring has $n$ coils and is made from a material having a shear modulus $G$. Determine the stretch of the spring when it is subjected to the load **P**. Assume that the coils are close to each other so that $\theta \approx 0°$ and the deflection is caused entirely by the torsional stress in the coil.

**Probs. 37/38**

**39.** The pipe assembly is fixed at $A$. Determine the vertical displacement of end $C$ of the assembly. The pipe has an inner diameter of 40 mm and outer diameter of 60 mm and is made of A-36 steel. Neglect the shearing strain energy.

**Prob. 39**

**\*40.** The rod has a circular cross section with a moment of inertia $I$. If a vertical force **P** is applied at $A$, determine the vertical displacement at this point. Only consider the strain energy due to bending. The modulus of elasticity is $E$.

**Prob. 40**

**41.** Determine the vertical displacement of end $B$ of the frame. Consider only bending strain energy. The frame is made using two A-36 steel W460 × 68 wide-flange sections.

**Prob. 41**

821

# 4 Impact Loading

Fig. 23

Throughout this text we have considered all loadings to be applied to a body in a gradual manner, such that when they reach a maximum value the body remains static. Some loadings, however, are dynamic; that is, they vary with time. A typical example would be caused by the collision of objects. This is called an impact loading. Specifically, ***impact*** occurs when one object strikes another, such that large forces are developed between the objects during a very short period of time.

If we assume no energy is lost during impact, due to heat, sound or localized plastic deformations, then we can study the mechanics of impact using the conservation of energy. To show how this is done, we will first analyze the motion of a simple block-and-spring system as shown in Fig. 23. When the block is released from rest, it falls a distance $h$, striking the spring and compressing it a distance $\Delta_{max}$ before momentarily coming to rest. If we neglect the mass of the spring and assume that the spring responds *elastically*, then the conservation of energy requires that the energy of the falling block be transformed into stored (strain) energy in the spring; or in other words, the work done by the block's weight, falling $h + \Delta_{max}$, is equal to the work needed to displace the end of the spring by an amount $\Delta_{max}$. Since the force in a spring is related to $\Delta_{max}$ by the equation $F = k\Delta_{max}$, where $k$ is the spring stiffness, then applying the conservation of energy and Eq. 2, we have

$$U_e = U_i$$

$$W(h + \Delta_{max}) = \frac{1}{2}(k\Delta_{max})\,\Delta_{max}$$

$$W(h + \Delta_{max}) = \frac{1}{2}k\Delta_{max}^2 \qquad (27)$$

$$\Delta_{max}^2 - \frac{2W}{k}\Delta_{max} - 2\left(\frac{W}{k}\right)h = 0$$

This quadratic equation may be solved for $\Delta_{max}$. The maximum root is

$$\Delta_{max} = \frac{W}{k} + \sqrt{\left(\frac{W}{k}\right)^2 + 2\left(\frac{W}{k}\right)h}$$

If the weight $W$ is supported statically by the spring, then the top displacement of the spring is $\Delta_{st} = W/k$. Using this simplification, the above equation becomes

$$\Delta_{max} = \Delta_{st} + \sqrt{(\Delta_{st})^2 + 2\Delta_{st}h}$$

or

$$\Delta_{max} = \Delta_{st}\left[1 + \sqrt{1 + 2\left(\frac{h}{\Delta_{st}}\right)}\right] \qquad (28)$$

This crash barrier is designed to absorb the impact energy of moving vehicles.

Once $\Delta_{\max}$ is calculated, the maximum force applied to the spring can be determined from

$$F_{\max} = k\Delta_{\max} \tag{29}$$

It should be realized, however, that this force and associated displacement occur only at an *instant*. Provided the block does not rebound off the spring, it will continue to vibrate until the motion dampens out and the block assumes the static position, $\Delta_{st}$. Note also that if the block is held just above the spring, $h = 0$, and released, then, from Eq. 28, the maximum displacement of the block is

$$\Delta_{\max} = 2\Delta_{st}$$

In other words, when the block is released from the top of the spring (a dynamic load), the displacement is *twice* what it would be if it were set on the spring (a static load).

Using a similar analysis, it is also possible to determine the maximum displacement of the end of the spring if the block is sliding on a smooth horizontal surface with a known velocity **v** just before it collides with the spring, Fig. 24. Here the block's kinetic energy,* $\frac{1}{2}(W/g)v^2$, will be transformed into stored energy in the spring. Hence,

$$U_e = U_i$$

$$\frac{1}{2}\left(\frac{W}{g}\right)v^2 = \frac{1}{2}k\Delta_{\max}^2$$

$$\Delta_{\max} = \sqrt{\frac{Wv^2}{gk}} \tag{30}$$

**Fig. 24**

Since the static displacement at the top of the spring caused by the weight $W$ resting on it is $\Delta_{st} = W/k$, then

$$\Delta_{\max} = \sqrt{\frac{\Delta_{st}v^2}{g}} \tag{31}$$

The results of this simplified analysis can be used to determine both the approximate deflection and the stress developed in a deformable member when it is subjected to impact. To do this we must make the necessary assumptions regarding the collision, so that the behavior of the colliding bodies is similar to the response of the block-and-spring models discussed above. Hence we will consider the moving body to be *rigid* like the block and the stationary body to be deformable like the spring. Also, it is assumed that the material behaves in a linear-elastic manner. When collision occurs, the bodies remain in contact until the elastic body reaches its maximum deformation, and during the motion the inertia or mass of the elastic body is neglected. Realize that each of these assumptions will lead to a *conservative* estimate of both the maximum stress and deflection of the elastic body. In other words, their values will be larger than those that actually occur.

---

*Recall from physics that kinetic energy is "energy of motion." For the translation of a body it is determined from $\frac{1}{2}mv^2$, where $m$ is the body's mass, $m = W/g$.

**Fig. 25**

A few examples of when this theory can be applied are shown in Fig. 25. Here a block of known weight is dropped onto a post and a beam, causing them to deform a maximum amount $\Delta_{max}$. The energy of the falling block is transformed momentarily into axial strain energy in the post and bending strain energy in the beam.* In order to determine the deformation $\Delta_{max}$, we could use the same approach as for the block–spring system, and that is to write the conservation-of-energy equation for the block and post or block and beam, and then solve for $\Delta_{max}$. However, we can also solve these problems in a more direct manner by modeling the post and beam by an *equivalent spring*. For example, if a force **P** displaces the top of the post $\Delta = PL/AE$, then a spring having a stiffness $k = AE/L$ would be displaced the same amount by **P**, that is, $\Delta = P/k$. In a similar manner, a force **P** applied to the center of a simply supported beam displaces the center $\Delta = PL^3/48EI$, and therefore an equivalent spring would have a stiffness of $k = 48EI/L^3$. It is not necessary, however, to actually find the equivalent spring stiffness to apply Eq. 28 or 30. All that is needed to determine the dynamic displacement, $\Delta_{max}$, is to calculate the *static displacement*, $\Delta_{st}$, due to the weight $P_{st} = W$ of the block resting on the member.

Once $\Delta_{max}$ is determined, the maximum dynamic force can then be calculated from $P_{max} = k\Delta_{max}$. If we consider $P_{max}$ to be an *equivalent static load* then the maximum stress in the member can be determined using statics and the theory of mechanics of materials. Recall that this stress acts only for an *instant*. In reality, vibrational waves pass through the material, and the stress in the post or the beam, for example, does not remain constant.

The ratio of the equivalent static load $P_{max}$ to the static load $P_{st} = W$ is called the *impact factor*, $n$. Since $P_{max} = k\Delta_{max}$ and $P_{st} = k\Delta_{st}$, then from Eq. 28, we can express it as

$$n = 1 + \sqrt{1 + 2\left(\frac{h}{\Delta_{st}}\right)} \qquad (32)$$

This factor represents the magnification of a statically applied load so that it can be treated dynamically. Using Eq. 32, $n$ can be calculated for any member that has a linear relationship between load and deflection. For a complicated system of connected members, however, impact factors are determined from experience and experimental testing. Once $n$ is determined, the dynamic stress and deflection at the point of impact are easily found from the static stress $\sigma_{st}$ and static deflection $\Delta_{st}$ caused by the load $W$, that is, $\sigma_{max} = n\sigma_{st}$ and $\Delta_{max} = n\Delta_{st}$.

The members of this crash guard must be designed to resist a prescribed impact loading in order to arrest the motion of a rail car.

---

*Strain energy due to shear is neglected for reasons discussed in Example 4.

824

## Important Points

- *Impact* occurs when a large force is developed between two objects which strike one another during a short period of time.

- We can analyze the effects of impact by assuming the moving body is rigid, the material of the stationary body is linear elastic, no energy is lost during collision, the bodies remain in contact during collision, and the inertia of the elastic body is neglected.

- The dynamic load on a body can be determined by multiplying the static load by an *impact factor*.

## EXAMPLE | 8

The aluminum pipe shown in Fig. 26 is used to support a load of 150 kip. Determine the maximum displacement at the top of the pipe if the load is (a) applied gradually, and (b) applied by suddenly releasing it from the top of the pipe when $h = 0$. Take $E_{al} = 10(10^3)$ ksi and assume that the aluminum behaves elastically.

**Fig. 26**

### SOLUTION

**Part (a).** When the load is applied gradually, the work done by the weight is transformed into elastic strain energy in the pipe. Applying the conservation of energy, we have

$$U_e = U_i$$

$$\frac{1}{2}W\Delta_{st} = \frac{W^2 L}{2AE}$$

$$\Delta_{st} = \frac{WL}{AE} = \frac{150 \text{ kip}(12 \text{ in.})}{\pi[(3 \text{ in.})^2 - (2.5 \text{ in.})^2]\, 10\,(10^3)\,\text{kip/in}^2}$$

$$= 0.02083 \text{ in.} = 0.0208 \text{ in.} \qquad Ans.$$

**Part (b).** Here Eq. 28 can be applied, with $h = 0$. Hence,

$$\Delta_{max} = \Delta_{st}\left[1 + \sqrt{1 + 2\left(\frac{h}{\Delta_{st}}\right)}\right]$$

$$= 2\Delta_{st} = 2(0.02083 \text{ in.})$$

$$= 0.0417 \text{ in.} \qquad Ans.$$

Hence, the displacement of the weight when applied dynamically is twice as great as when the load is applied statically. In other words, the impact factor is $n = 2$, Eq. 32.

## EXAMPLE 9

(a)

**Fig. 27**

The A992 steel beam shown in Fig. 27a is a W10 × 39. Determine the maximum bending stress in the beam and the beam's maximum deflection if the weight $W = 1.50$ kip is dropped from a height $h = 2$ in. onto the beam. $E_{st} = 29(10^3)$ ksi.

### SOLUTION I

We will apply Eq. 28. First, however, we must calculate $\Delta_{st}$. Using the properties of a W10 × 39, we have

$$\Delta_{st} = \frac{WL^3}{48EI} = \frac{(1.50 \text{ kip})(16 \text{ ft})^3(12 \text{ in./ft})^3}{48[29(10^3) \text{ ksi}](209 \text{ in}^4)} = 0.03649 \text{ in.}$$

$$\Delta_{max} = \Delta_{st}\left[1 + \sqrt{1 + 2\left(\frac{h}{\Delta_{st}}\right)}\right]$$

$$= 0.03649 \text{ in.}\left[1 + \sqrt{1 + 2\left(\frac{2 \text{ in.}}{0.03649 \text{ in.}}\right)}\right] = 0.420 \text{ in.} \quad Ans.$$

The equivalent static load that causes this displacement is therefore

$$P_{max} = \frac{48EI}{L^3}\Delta_{max} = \frac{48(29(10^3) \text{ ksi})(209 \text{ in}^4)}{(16 \text{ ft})^3(12 \text{ in./ft})^3}(0.420 \text{ in.}) = 17.3 \text{ kip}$$

The internal moment caused by this load is maximum at the center of the beam, such that by the method of sections, Fig. 27b, $M_{max} = P_{max}L/4$. Applying the flexure formula to determine the bending stress, we have

$$\sigma_{max} = \frac{M_{max}\,c}{I} = \frac{P_{max}Lc}{4I} = \frac{12E\,\Delta_{max}\,c}{L^2}$$

$$= \frac{12[29(10^3) \text{ kip/in}^2](0.420 \text{ in.})\,(9.92 \text{ in.}/2)}{(16 \text{ ft})^2(12 \text{ in./ft})^2} = 19.7 \text{ ksi} \quad Ans.$$

### SOLUTION II

It is also possible to obtain the dynamic or maximum deflection $\Delta_{max}$ from first principles. The external work of the falling weight $W$ is $U_e = W(h + \Delta_{max})$. Since the beam deflects $\Delta_{max}$, and $P_{max} = 48EI\Delta_{max}/L^3$, then

$$U_e = U_i$$

$$W(h + \Delta_{max}) = \frac{1}{2}\left(\frac{48EI\Delta_{max}}{L^3}\right)\Delta_{max}$$

$$(1.50 \text{ kip})(2 \text{ in.} + \Delta_{max}) = \frac{1}{2}\left[\frac{48[29(10^3)\text{kip/in}^2]209 \text{ in}^4}{(16 \text{ ft})^3(12 \text{ in./ft})^3}\right]\Delta_{max}^2$$

$$20.55\Delta_{max}^2 - 1.50\Delta_{max} - 3.00 = 0$$

Solving and choosing the positive root yields

$$\Delta_{max} = 0.420 \text{ in.} \qquad Ans.$$

## EXAMPLE | 10

A railroad car that is assumed to be rigid and has a mass of 80 Mg is moving forward at a speed of $v = 0.2$ m/s when it strikes a steel 200-mm by 200-mm post at $A$, Fig. 28$a$. If the post is fixed to the ground at $C$, determine the maximum horizontal displacement of its top $B$ due to the impact. Take $E_{st} = 200$ GPa.

(a)

### SOLUTION

Here the kinetic energy of the railroad car is transformed into internal bending strain energy only for region $AC$ of the post. (Region $BA$ is not subjected to an internal loading.) Assuming that point $A$ is displaced $(\Delta_A)_{max}$, then the force $P_{max}$ that causes this displacement can be determined. We have

$$P_{max} = \frac{3EI(\Delta_A)_{max}}{L_{AC}^3} \qquad (1)$$

$$U_e = U_i; \qquad \frac{1}{2}mv^2 = \frac{1}{2}P_{max}(\Delta_A)_{max}$$

$$\frac{1}{2}mv^2 = \frac{1}{2}\frac{3EI}{L_{AC}^3}(\Delta_A)_{max}^2; \qquad (\Delta_A)_{max} = \sqrt{\frac{mv^2 L_{AC}^3}{3EI}}$$

Substituting in the numerical data yields

$$(\Delta_A)_{max} = \sqrt{\frac{80(10^3)\ \text{kg}(0.2\ \text{m/s})^2(1.5\ \text{m})^3}{3[200(10^9)\ \text{N/m}^2][\frac{1}{12}(0.2\ \text{m})^4]}} = 0.01162\ \text{m} = 11.62\ \text{mm}$$

Using Eq. 1, the force $P_{max}$ is therefore

$$P_{max} = \frac{3[200(10^9)\ \text{N/m}^2][\frac{1}{12}(0.2\ \text{m})^4](0.01162\ \text{m})}{(1.5\ \text{m})^3} = 275.4\ \text{kN}$$

(b)

**Fig. 28**

With reference to Fig. 28$b$, segment $AB$ of the post remains straight. To determine the maximum displacement at $B$, we must first determine the slope at $A$. Using the appropriate formula to determine $\theta_A$, we have

$$\theta_A = \frac{P_{max}L_{AC}^2}{2EI} = \frac{275.4(10^3)\ \text{N}\ (1.5\ \text{m})^2}{2[200(10^9)\ \text{N/m}^2][\frac{1}{2}(0.2\ \text{m})]^4} = 0.01162\ \text{rad}$$

The maximum displacement at $B$ is thus

$$(\Delta_B)_{max} = (\Delta_A)_{max} + \theta_A L_{AB}$$

$$= 11.62\ \text{mm} + (0.01162\ \text{rad})\ 1(10^3)\ \text{mm} = 23.2\ \text{mm} \quad Ans.$$

## PROBLEMS

**42.** A bar is 4 m long and has a diameter of 30 mm. If it is to be used to absorb energy in tension from an impact loading, determine the total amount of elastic energy that it can absorb if (a) it is made of steel for which $E_{st} = 200$ GPa, $\sigma_Y = 800$ MPa, and (b) it is made from an aluminum alloy for which $E_{al} = 70$ GPa, $\sigma_Y = 405$ MPa.

**43.** Determine the diameter of a red brass C83400 bar that is 8 ft long if it is to be used to absorb 800 ft · lb of energy in tension from an impact loading. No yielding occurs.

**\*44.** Determine the speed $v$ of the 50-Mg mass when it is just over the top of the steel post, if after impact, the maximun stress developed in the post is 550 MPa. The post has a length of $L = 1$ m and a cross-sectional area of 0.01 m². $E_{st} = 200$ GPa, $\sigma_Y = 600$ MPa.

**Prob. 44**

**45.** The collar has a weight of 50 lb and falls down the titanium bar. If the bar has a diameter of 0.5 in., determine the maximum stress developed in the bar if the weight is (a) dropped from a height of $h = 1$ ft, (b) released from a height $h \approx 0$, and (c) placed slowly on the flange at $A$. $E_{ti} = 16(10^3)$ ksi, $\sigma_Y = 60$ ksi.

**Prob. 45**

**46.** The collar has a weight of 50 lb and falls down the titanium bar. If the bar has a diameter of 0.5 in., determine the largest height $h$ at which the weight can be released and not permanently damage the bar after striking the flange at $A$. $E_{ti} = 16(10^3)$ ksi, $\sigma_Y = 60$ ksi.

**Prob. 46**

**47.** A steel cable having a diameter of 0.4 in. wraps over a drum and is used to lower an elevator having a weight of 800 lb. The elevator is 150 ft below the drum and is descending at the constant rate of 2 ft/s when the drum suddenly stops. Determine the maximum stress developed in the cable when this occurs. $E_{st} = 29(10^3)$ ksi, $\sigma_Y = 50$ ksi.

**Prob. 47**

**\*48.** A steel cable having a diameter of 0.4 in. wraps over a drum and is used to lower an elevator having a weight of 800 lb. The elevator is 150 ft below the drum and is descending at the constant rate of 3 ft/s. when the drum suddenly stops. Determine the maximum stress developed in the cable when this occurs. $E_{st} = 29(10^3)$ ksi, $\sigma_Y = 50$ ksi.

**Prob. 48**

**49.** The steel beam $AB$ acts to stop the oncoming railroad car, which has a mass of 10 Mg and is coasting towards it at $v = 0.5$ m/s. Determine the maximum stress developed in the beam if it is struck at its center by the car. The beam is simply supported and only horizontal forces occur at $A$ and $B$. Assume that the railroad car and the supporting framework for the beam remain rigid. Also, compute the maximum deflection of the beam. $E_{st} = 200$ GPa, $\sigma_Y = 250$ MPa.

**Prob. 49**

**50.** The aluminum bar assembly is made from two segments having diameters of 40 mm and 20 mm. Determine the maximum axial stress developed in the bar if the 10-kg collar is dropped from a height of $h = 150$ mm. Take $E_{al} = 70$ GPa, $\sigma_Y = 410$ MPa.

**Probs. 50**

**51.** Rods $AB$ and $AC$ have a diameter of 20 mm and are made of 6061-T6 aluminum alloy. They are connected to the rigid collar $A$ which slides freely along the vertical guide rod. If the 50-kg block $D$ is dropped from height $h = 200$ mm above the collar, determine the maximum normal stress developed in the rods.

**\*52.** Rods $AB$ and $AC$ have a diameter of 20 mm and are made of 6061-T6 aluminum alloy. They are connected to the rigid collar which slides freely along the vertical guide rod. Determine the maximum height $h$ from which the 50-kg block $D$ can be dropped without causing yielding in the rods when the block strikes the collar.

**Probs. 51/52**

**53.** The composite aluminum 2014-T6 bar is made from two segments having diameters of 7.5 mm and 15 mm. Determine the maximum axial stress developed in the bar if the 10-kg collar is dropped from a height of $h = 100$ mm.

**55.** When the 100-lb block is at $h = 3$ ft above the cylindrical post and spring assembly, it has a speed of $v = 20$ ft/s. If the post is made of 2014-T6 aluminum and the spring has the stiffness of $k = 250$ kip/in., determine the required minimum diameter $d$ of the post to the nearest $\frac{1}{8}$ in. so that it will not yield when it is struck by the block.

7.5 mm — 300 mm

200 mm

15 mm

$h$

**Prob. 53**

$A$  $v$

$d$

$h$

$k$  1.5 ft

**Prob. 55**

**54.** The composite aluminum 2014-T6 bar is made from two segments having diameters of 7.5 mm and 15 mm. Determine the maximum height $h$ from which the 10-kg collar should be dropped so that it produces a maximum axial sterss in the bar of $\sigma_{max} = 300$ MPa.

**\*56.** When the 100-lb block is at $h = 3$ ft above the cylindrical post and spring assembly, it has a speed of $v = 20$ ft/s. If the post is made of 2014-T6 aluminum and has a diameter of $d = 2$ in., determine the required minimum stiffness $k$ of the spring so that the post will not yield when it is struck by the block.

**57.** When the 100-lb block is at $h = 3$ ft above the post and spring assembly, it has a speed of $v = 20$ ft/s. If the post has a diameter of $d = 2$ in., and is made of 2014-T6 aluminum, and the spring has a stiffness of $k = 500$ kip/in., determine the maximum normal stress developed in the post.

7.5 mm — 300 mm

200 mm

15 mm

$h$

**Prob. 54**

$A$  $v$

$d$

$h$

$k$  1.5 ft

**Probs. 56/57**

**58.** The tugboat has a weight of 120 000 lb and is traveling forward at 2 ft/s when it strikes the 12-in.-diameter fender post *AB* used to protect a bridge pier. If the post is made from treated white spruce and is assumed fixed at the river bed, determine the maximum horizontal distance the top of the post will move due to the impact. Assume the tugboat is rigid and neglect the effect of the water.

**Prob. 58**

**59.** The wide-flange beam has a length of $2L$, a depth $2c$, and a constant $EI$. Determine the maximum height $h$ at which a weight $W$ can be dropped on its end without exceeding a maximum elastic stress $\sigma_{max}$ in the beam.

**Prob. 59**

**\*60.** The weight of 175 lb is dropped from a height of 4 ft from the top of the A992 steel beam. Determine the maximum deflection and maximum stress in the beam if the supporting springs at *A* and *B* each have a stiffness of $k = 500$ lb/in. The beam is 3 in. thick and 4 in. wide.

**61.** The weight of 175 lb, is dropped from a height of 4 ft from the top of the A992 steel beam. Determine the load factor $n$ if the supporting springs at *A* and *B* each have a stiffness of $k = 500$ lb/in. The beam is 3 in. thick and 4 in. wide.

**Probs. 60/61**

**62.** The 200-lb block has a downward velocity of 4 ft/s when it is 3 ft from the top of the wooden beam. Determine the maximum stress in the beam due to the impact and compute the maximum deflection of its end $C. E_w = 1.9(10^3)$ ksi, $\sigma_Y = 6$ ksi.

**63.** The 100-lb block has a downward velocity of 4 ft/s when it is 3 ft from the top of the wooden beam. Determine the maximum stress in the beam due to the impact and compute the maximum deflection of point $B. E_w = 1.9(10^3)$ ksi, $\sigma_Y = 8$ ksi.

**Probs. 62/63**

**\*64.** The 50 kg block is dropped from $h = 0.9$ m onto the cantilever beam. If the beam is made from A992 steel and is a W200 × 46 wide-flange section, determine the maximum bending stress developed in the beam.

**65.** Determine the maximum height $h$ from which the 50-kg block can be dropped without causing yielding in the cantilever beam. The beam is made from A992 steel and is a W200 × 46 wide-flange section.

**Probs. 64/65**

**66.** The overhang beam is made of 2014-T6 aluminum. If the 75-kg block has a speed of $v = 3$ m/s at $h = 0.75$ m, determine the maximum bending stress developed in the beam.

**67.** The overhang beam is made of 2014-T6 aluminum. Determine the maximum height $h$ from which the 100-kg block can be dropped from rest ($v = 0$), without causing the beam to yield.

**Probs. 66/67**

**\*68.** A 40-lb weight is dropped from a height of $h = 2$ ft onto the center of the cantilevered A992 steel beam. If the beam is a W10 × 15, determine the maximum bending stress developed in the beam.

**69.** If the maximum allowable bending stress for the W10 × 15 structural A992 steel beam is $\sigma_{allow} = 20$ ksi, determine the maximum height $h$ from which a 50-lb weight can be released from rest and strike the center of the beam.

**70.** A 40-lb weight is dropped from a height of $h = 2$ ft onto the center of the cantilevered A992 steel beam. If the beam is a W10 × 15, determine the vertical displacement of its end $B$ due to the impact.

**Probs. 68/69/70**

**71.** The car bumper is made of polycarbonate-polybutylene terephthalate. If $E = 2.0$ GPa, determine the maximum deflection and maximum stress in the bumper if it strikes the rigid post when the car is coasting at $v = 0.75$ m/s. The car has a mass of 1.80 Mg, and the bumper can be considered simply supported on two spring supports connected to the rigid frame of the car. For the bumper take $I = 300(10^6)$ mm$^4$, $c = 75$ mm, $\sigma_Y = 30$ MPa and $k = 1.5$ MN/m.

**Prob. 71**

# 5 Principle of Virtual Work

The principle of virtual work was developed by John Bernoulli in 1717, and like other energy methods of analysis, it is based on the conservation of energy. Although the principle of virtual work has many applications in mechanics, in this text we will use it to obtain the displacement and slope at a point on a deformable body.

To do this, we will consider the body to be of arbitrary shape as shown in Fig. 29b, and to be subjected to the "real loads" $P_1$, $P_2$, and $P_3$. It is assumed that these loads cause no movement of the supports; however, in general they can strain the material *beyond* the elastic limit. Suppose that it is necessary to determine the displacement $\Delta$ of point $A$ on the body. Since there is no force acting at $A$, then $\Delta$ will *not* be included as an external "work term" in the equation when the conservation of energy principle is applied to the body. In order to get around this limitation, we will place an *imaginary* or "virtual" force $P'$ on the body at point $A$, such that $P'$ acts in the *same direction* as $\Delta$. Furthermore, this load is applied to the body *before* the real loads are applied, Fig. 29a. For convenience, which will be made clear later, we will choose $P'$ to have a "unit" magnitude; that is, $P' = 1$. It is to be emphasized that the term "*virtual*" is used to describe this load because it is *imaginary* and does not actually exist as part of the real loading.

This external virtual load, however, does create an internal virtual load $u$ in a representative element or fiber of the body, as shown in Fig. 29a. As expected, $P'$ and $u$ can be related by the equations of equilibrium. Also, because of $P'$ and $u$, the body and the element will each undergo a virtual (imaginary) displacement, although we will *not* be

Application of virtual unit load
(a)

Application of real loads
(b)

**Fig. 29**

concerned with their magnitudes. Once the virtual load is applied and *then* the body is subjected to the *real loads* $\mathbf{P}_1$, $\mathbf{P}_2$, and $\mathbf{P}_3$, point *A* will be displaced a real amount $\Delta$, which causes the element to be displaced $dL$, Fig. 29*b*. As a result, the external virtual force $\mathbf{P}'$ and internal virtual load **u** "ride along" or are displaced by $\Delta$ and $dL$, respectively. Consequently these loads perform *external virtual work* $1 : \Delta$ on the body and *internal virtual work* $u \cdot dL$ on the element. Considering *only* the conservation of *virtual* energy, the external virtual work is then equal to the internal virtual work done on all the elements of the body. Therefore, we can write the virtual-work equation as

$$\overbrace{1 \cdot \Delta}^{\text{virtual loadings}} = \underbrace{\Sigma u \cdot dL}_{\text{real displacements}} \qquad (33)$$

Here

$P' = 1 =$ external virtual unit load acting in the direction of $\Delta$

$u =$ internal virtual load acting on the element

$\Delta =$ external displacement caused by the real loads

$dL =$ external displacement of the element in the direction of **u**, caused by the real loads

By choosing $P' = 1$, it can be seen that the solution for $\Delta$ follows directly, since $\Delta = \Sigma u \, dL$.

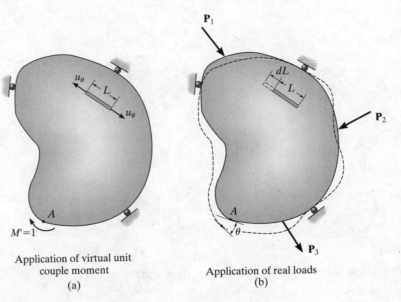

Application of virtual unit couple moment
(a)

Application of real loads
(b)

**Fig. 30**

In a similar manner, if the angular displacement or slope of the tangent at a point on the body is to be determined at $A$, Fig. 30$b$, then a virtual *couple moment* $\mathbf{M'}$, having a"unit" magnitude, is applied at the point, Fig. 30$a$. As a result, this couple moment causes a virtual load $u_\theta$ in one of the elements of the body. Assuming the real loads $\mathbf{P_1}$, $\mathbf{P_2}$, $\mathbf{P_3}$ deform the element an amount $dL$, the angular displacement $\theta$ can be found from the virtual-work equation

$$\overset{\text{virtual loadings}}{\underset{\text{real displacements}}{1 \cdot \theta = \Sigma u_\theta \, dL}} \tag{34}$$

Here

$M' = 1 =$ external virtual unit couple moment acting in the direction of $\theta$

$u_\theta =$ internal virtual load acting on an element

$\theta =$ external angular displacement in radians caused by the real loads

$dL =$ internal displacement of the element in the direction of $u_\theta$, caused by the real loads

This method for applying the principle of virtual work is often referred to as the *method of virtual forces*, since a *virtual force* is applied, resulting in a determination of an external *real displacement*. The equation of virtual work in this case represents a statement of *compatibility requirements* for the body. Although it is not important here, realize that we can also apply the principle of virtual work as a *method of virtual displacements*. In this case, *virtual displacements* are imposed on the body when the body is subjected to *real loadings*. This method can be used to determine the external reactive force on the body or an unknown internal loading. When it is used in this manner, the equation of virtual work is a statement of the *equilibrium requirements* for the body.*

## Internal Virtual Work.

The terms on the right side of Eqs. 34 and 35 represent the internal virtual work developed in the body. The real internal displacements $dL$ in these terms can be produced in several different ways. For example, these displacements may result from geometric fabrication errors, from a change in temperature, or more commonly from stress. In particular, no restriction has been placed on the magnitude of the external loading, so the stress may be large enough to cause yielding or even strain hardening of the material.

*See *Engineering Mechanics: Statics*, 13th edition, R.C. Hibbeler, Prentice Hall, Inc., 2012.

| TABLE 1 | | |
|---|---|---|
| **Deformation caused by** | **Strain energy** | **Internal virtual work** |
| Axial load $N$ | $\int_0^L \dfrac{N^2}{2EA}\,dx$ | $\int_0^L \dfrac{nN}{EA}\,dx$ |
| Shear $V$ | $\int_0^L \dfrac{f_s V^2}{2GA}\,dx$ | $\int_0^L \dfrac{f_s vV}{GA}\,dx$ |
| Bending moment $M$ | $\int_0^L \dfrac{M^2}{2EI}\,dx$ | $\int_0^L \dfrac{mM}{EI}\,dx$ |
| Torsional moment $T$ | $\int_0^L \dfrac{T^2}{2GJ}\,dx$ | $\int_0^L \dfrac{tT}{GJ}\,dx$ |

If we assume that the material behavior is linear elastic and the stress does not exceed the proportional limit, we can then formulate the expressions for internal virtual work caused by stress using the equations of elastic strain energy developed in Sec. 2. They are listed in the center column of Table 1. Recall that each of these expressions assumes that the internal loading $N$, $V$, $M$, or $T$ was applied gradually from zero to its full value. As a result, the work done by these resultants is shown in these expressions as *one-half* the product of the internal loading and its displacement. In the case of the virtual-force method, however, the "full" virtual internal loading is applied *before* the real loads cause displacements, and therefore the work of the virtual loading is simply the product of the virtual load and its real displacement. Referring to these internal virtual loadings ($u$) by the corresponding lowercase symbols $n$, $v$, $m$, and $t$, the virtual work due to axial load, shear, bending moment, and torsional moment is listed in the right-hand column of Table 1. Using these results, the virtual-work equation for a body subjected to a general loading can therefore be written as

$$1 \cdot \Delta = \int \frac{nN}{AE}\,dx + \int \frac{mM}{EI}\,dx + \int \frac{f_s vV}{GA}\,dx + \int \frac{tT}{GJ}\,dx \tag{35}$$

In the following sections we will apply the above equation to problems involving the displacement of joints on trusses, and points on beams and mechanical elements. We will also include a discussion of how to handle the effects of fabrication errors and differential temperature. For application it is important that a consistent set of units be used for all the terms. For example, if the real loads are expressed in kilonewtons and the body's dimensions are in meters, a 1-kN virtual force or 1-kN · m virtual couple should be applied to the body. By doing so a calculated displacement $\Delta$ will be in meters, and a calculated slope will be in radians.

# 6 Method of Virtual Forces Applied to Trusses

In this section, we will apply the method of virtual forces to determine the displacement of a truss joint. To illustrate the principles, the vertical displacement of joint $A$ of the truss shown in Fig. 31$b$ will be determined. To do this, we must place a virtual unit force at this joint, Fig. 31$a$, so that when the real loads $\mathbf{P}_1$ and $\mathbf{P}_2$ are applied to the truss, they cause the external virtual work $1 \cdot \Delta$. The internal virtual work in each member is $n\Delta L$. Since each member has a constant cross-sectional area $A$, and $n$ and $N$ are constant throughout the member's length, then from Table 1, the internal virtual work for each member is

$$\int_0^L \frac{nN}{AE}dx = \frac{nNL}{AE} \tag{36}$$

Therefore, the virtual-work equation for the entire truss is

$$1 \cdot \Delta = \sum \frac{nNL}{AE} \tag{37}$$

Here

$1 =$ external virtual unit load acting on the truss joint in the direction of $\Delta$

$\Delta =$ joint displacement caused by the real loads on the truss

$n =$ internal virtual force in a truss member caused by the external virtual unit load

$N =$ internal force in a truss member caused by the real loads

$L =$ length of a member

$A =$ cross-sectional area of a member

$E =$ modulus of elasticity of a member

Application of virtual unit load

(a)

Application of real loads

(b)

**Fig. 31**

**Temperature Change.**   Truss members can change their length due to a change in temperature. If $\alpha$ is the coefficient of thermal expansion for a member and $\Delta T$ is the change in temperature, the change in length of a member is $\Delta L = \alpha \, \Delta TL$. Hence, we can determine the displacement of a selected truss joint due to this temperature change from Eq. 34, written as

$$1 \cdot \Delta \;=\; \Sigma n\alpha \, \Delta TL \tag{38}$$

Here

  1 = external virtual unit load acting on the truss joint in the direction of $\Delta$

  $\Delta$ = joint displacement caused by the temperature change

  $n$ = internal virtual force in a truss member caused by the external virtual unit load

  $\alpha$ = coefficient of thermal expansion of material

  $\Delta T$ = change in temperature of member

  $L$ = length of member

**Fabrication Errors.**   Occasionally errors in fabricating the lengths of the members of a truss may occur. If this happens, the displacement $\Delta$ in a particular direction of a truss joint from its expected position can be determined from direct application of Eq. 34 written as

$$1 \cdot \Delta \;=\; \Sigma n \, \Delta L \tag{39}$$

Here

  1 = external virtual unit load acting on the truss joint in the direction of $\Delta$

  $\Delta$ = joint displacement caused by the fabrication errors

  $n$ = internal virtual force in a truss member caused by the external virtual unit load

  $\Delta L$ = difference in length of the member from its intended length caused by a fabrication error

A combination of the right-hand sides of Eqs. 37 through 39 will be necessary if external loads act on the truss and some of the members undergo a temperature change or have been fabricated with the wrong dimensions.

## Procedure for Analysis

The following procedure provides a method that may be used to determine the displacement of any joint on a truss using the method of virtual forces.

### Virtual Forces n.

- Place the virtual unit load on the truss at the joint where the displacement is to be determined. The load should be directed along the line of action of the displacement.
- With the unit load so placed and all the real loads *removed* from the truss, calculate the internal $n$ force in each truss member. Assume that tensile forces are positive and compressive forces are negative.

### Real Forces N.

- Determine the $N$ forces in each member. These forces are caused only by the real loads acting on the truss. Again, assume that tensile forces are positive and compressive forces are negative.

### Virtual-Work Equation.

- Apply the equation of virtual work to determine the desired displacement. It is important to retain the algebraic sign for each of the corresponding $n$ and $N$ forces when substituting these terms into the equation.
- If the resultant sum $\Sigma nNL/AE$ is positive, the displacement $\Delta$ is in the same direction as the virtual unit load. If a negative value results, $\Delta$ is opposite to the virtual unit load.
- When applying $1 \cdot \Delta = \Sigma n\alpha \, \Delta TL$, an *increase* in temperature, $\Delta T$, will be *positive*; whereas a *decrease* in temperature will be *negative*.
- For $1 \cdot \Delta = \Sigma n \, \Delta L$, when a fabrication error causes an increase in the length of a member, $\Delta L$ is *positive*, whereas a *decrease* in length is *negative*.
- When applying this method, attention should be paid to the units of each numerical quantity. Notice, however, that the virtual unit load can be assigned any arbitrary unit: pounds, kips, newtons, etc., since the $n$ forces will have these *same* units, and as a result, the units for both the virtual unit load and the $n$ forces will cancel from both sides of the equation.

# EXAMPLE | 11

Determine the vertical displacement of joint $C$ of the steel truss shown in Fig. 32a. The cross-sectional area of each member is $A = 400$ mm$^2$ and $E_{st} = 200$ GPa.

(a)

Virtual forces

(b)

## SOLUTION

**Virtual Forces n.** Since the vertical displacement at joint $C$ is to be determined, *only* a vertical 1-kN virtual load is placed at joint $C$; and the force in each member is calculated using the method of joints. The results of this analysis are shown in Fig. 32b. Using our sign convention, positive numbers indicate tensile forces and negative numbers indicate compressive forces.

**Real Forces N.** The applied load of 100 kN causes forces in the members that are also calculated using the method of joints. The results of this analysis are shown in Fig. 32c.

Real forces

(c)

**Fig. 32**

**Virtual-Work Equation.** Arranging the data in tabular form, we have

| Member | $n$ | $N$ | $L$ | $nNL$ |
|--------|-----|-----|-----|-------|
| $AB$ | 0 | −100 | 4 | 0 |
| $BC$ | 0 | 141.4 | 2.828 | 0 |
| $AC$ | −1.414 | −141.4 | 2.828 | 565.7 |
| $CD$ | 1 | 200 | 2 | 400 |
|  |  |  |  | $\Sigma$ 965.7 kN$^2$ · m |

Thus,

$$1 \text{ kN} \cdot \Delta_{C_v} = \sum \frac{nNL}{AE} = \frac{965.7 \text{ kN}^2 \cdot \text{m}}{AE}$$

Substituting the numerical values for $A$ and $E$, we have

$$1 \text{ kN} \cdot \Delta_{Cv} = \frac{965.7 \text{ kN}^2 \cdot \text{m}}{[400(10^{-6}) \text{ m}^2][200(10^6) \text{ kN/m}^2]}$$

$$\Delta_{Cv} = 0.01207 \text{ m} = 12.1 \text{ mm} \qquad \textit{Ans.}$$

## EXAMPLE | 12

Determine the horizontal displacement of the roller at $B$ of the truss shown in Fig. 33a. Due to radiant heating, member $AB$ is subjected to an *increase* in temperature of $\Delta T = +60°C$, and this member has been fabricated 3 mm too short. The members are made of steel, for which $\alpha_{st} = 12(10^{-6})/°C$ and $E_{st} = 200$ GPa. The cross-sectional area of each member is 250 mm².

(a)

Virtual forces

(b)

### SOLUTION

**Virtual Forces n.** A horizontal 1-kN virtual load is applied to the truss at joint $B$, and the forces in each member are calculated, Fig. 33b.

**Real Forces N.** Since the $n$ forces in members $AC$ and $BC$ are *zero*, the $N$ forces in these members do *not* have to be determined. Why? For completeness, though, the entire "real" force analysis is shown in Fig. 33c.

**Virtual-Work Equation.** The loads, temperature, and the fabrication error all affect the displacement of point $B$; therefore, Eqs. 37, 38, and 39 must be combined, which gives

$$1 \text{ kN} \cdot \Delta_{B_h} = \sum \frac{nNL}{AE} + \Sigma n\alpha \, \Delta TL + \Sigma n\Delta L$$

$$= 0 + 0 + \frac{(-1.155 \text{ kN})(-12 \text{ kN})(4 \text{ m})}{[250(10^{-6}) \text{ m}^2][200(10^6) \text{ kN/m}^2]}$$

$$+ 0 + 0 + (-1.155 \text{ kN})[12(10^{-6})/°C](60°C)(4 \text{ m})$$

$$+ (-1.155 \text{ kN})(-0.003 \text{ m})$$

$$\Delta_{B_h} = 0.00125 \text{ m}$$

$$= 1.25 \text{ mm} \leftarrow \qquad Ans.$$

Real forces

(c)

**Fig. 33**

# PROBLEMS

*72. Determine the vertical displacement of joint A. Each A992 steel member has a cross-sectional area of 400 mm². 

75. Determine the vertical displacement of joint B. For each A992 steel member $A = 1.5$ in². 

*76. Determine the vertical displacement of joint E. For each A992 steel member $A = 1.5$ in².

**Prob. 72**

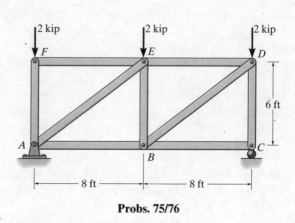

**Probs. 75/76**

73. Determine the horizontal displacement of joint B. Each A992 steel member has a cross-sectional area of 2 in². 

74. Determine the vertical displacement of joint B. Each A992 steel member has a cross-sectional area of 2 in².

77. Determine the vertical displacement of point B. Each A992 steel member has a cross-sectional area of 4.5 in². 

78. Determine the vertical displacement of point E. Each A992 steel member has a cross-sectional area of 4.5 in².

**Probs. 73/74**

**Probs. 77/78**

**79.** Determine the horizontal displacement of joint *B* of the truss. Each A992 steel member has a cross-sectional area of 400 mm².

**\*80.** Determine the vertical displacement of joint *C* of the truss. Each A992 steel member has a cross-sectional area of 400 mm².

**83.** Determine the vertical displacement of joint *A*. The truss is made from A992 steel rods having a diameter of 30 mm.

**\*84.** Determine the vertical displacement of joint *D*. The truss is made from A992 steel rods having a diameter of 30 mm.

**Probs. 79/80**

**Probs. 83/84**

**81.** Determine the horizontal displacement of joint *C* on the truss. Each A992 steel member has a cross-sectional area of 3 in².

**82.** Determine the horizontal displacement of joint *B* on the truss. Each A992 steel member has a cross-sectional area of 3 in².

**85.** Determine the vertical displacement of joint *C* on the truss. Each A992 steel member has a cross-sectional area of $A = 300$ mm².

**86.** Determine the vertical displacement of joint *D* on the truss. Each A992 steel member has a cross-sectional area of $A = 300$ mm².

**Probs. 81/82**

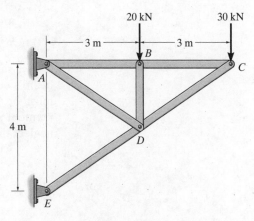

**Probs. 85/86**

# 7 Method of Virtual Forces Applied to Beams

In this section we will apply the method of virtual forces to determine the displacement and slope at a point on a beam. To illustrate the principles, the vertical displacement $\Delta$ of point $A$ on the beam shown in Fig. 34$b$ will be determined. To do this we must place a vertical unit load at this point, Fig. 34$a$, so that when the "real" distributed load $w$ is applied to the beam it will cause the internal virtual work $1 \cdot \Delta$. Because the load causes both a shear $V$ and moment $M$ within the beam, we must actually consider the internal virtual work due to both of these loadings. In Example 7, however, it was shown that beam deflections due to shear are negligible compared with those caused by bending, particularly if the beam is long and slender. Since this type of beam is most often used in practice, we will only consider the virtual strain energy due to bending, Table 1. Hence, the real load causes the element $dx$ to deform so its sides rotate by an angle $d\theta = (M/EI)dx$, which causes internal virtual work $m \, d\theta$. Applying Eq. 34, the virtual-work equation for the entire beam, we have

$$1 \cdot \Delta = \int_0^L \frac{mM}{EI} dx \tag{40}$$

Here

$1 = $ external virtual unit load acting on the beam in the direction of $\Delta$

$\Delta = $ displacement caused by the real loads acting on the beam

$m = $ internal virtual moment in the beam, expressed as a function of $x$ and caused by the external virtual unit load

$M = $ internal moment in the beam, expressed as a function of $x$ and caused by the real loads

$E = $ modulus of elasticity of the material

$I = $ moment of inertia of the cross-sectional area about the neutral axis

In a similar manner, if the slope $\theta$ of the tangent at a point on the beam's elastic curve is to be determined, a virtual unit couple moment must be applied at the point, and the corresponding internal virtual moment $m_\theta$ has to be determined. If we apply Eq. 35 for this case and neglect the effect of shear deformations, we have

$$1 \cdot \theta = \int_0^L \frac{m_\theta M}{EI} dx \tag{41}$$

Virtual loads
(a)

Real loads
(b)

**Fig. 34**

When applying these equations, keep in mind that the integrals on the right side represent the amount of virtual bending strain energy that is *stored* in the beam. If concentrated forces or couple moments act on the beam or the distributed load is discontinuous, a single integration *cannot* be performed across the beam's entire length. Instead, separate $x$ coordinates must be chosen within regions that have no discontinuity of loading. Also, it is not necessary that each $x$ have the same origin; however, the $x$ selected for determining the real moment $M$ in a particular region must be the *same x* as that selected for determining the virtual moment $m$ or $m_\theta$ within the same region. For example, consider the beam shown in Fig. 35. In order to determine the displacement at $D$, we can use $x_1$ to determine the strain energy in region $AB$, $x_2$ for region $BC$, $x_3$ for region $DE$, and $x_4$ for region $DC$. In any case, each $x$ coordinate should be selected so that both $M$ and $m$ (or $m_\theta$) can easily be formulated.

Unlike beams, as discussed here, some members may also be subjected to significant virtual strain energy caused by axial load, shear, and torsional moment. When this is the case, we must include in the above equations the energy terms for these loadings as formulated in Eq. 36.

Virtual load
(a)

Real loads
(b)

**Fig. 35**

845

## Procedure for Analysis

The following procedure provides a method that may be used to determine the displacement and slope at a point on the elastic curve of a beam using the method of virtual forces.

### Virtual Moments $m$ or $m_\theta$.

- Place a *virtual unit load* on the beam at the point and directed along the line of action of the desired displacement.
- If the slope is to be determined, place a *virtual unit couple moment* at the point.
- Establish appropriate $x$ coordinates that are valid within regions of the beam where there is no discontinuity of both real and virtual load.
- With the virtual load in place, and all the real loads *removed* from the beam, calculate the internal moment $m$ or $m_\theta$ as a function of each $x$ coordinate.
- Assume that $m$ or $m_\theta$ acts in the positive direction according to the established beam sign convention for positive moment.

### Real Moments.

- Using the *same $x$* coordinates as those established for $m$ or $m_\theta$, determine the internal moments $M$ caused by the real loads.
- Since positive $m$ or $m_\theta$ was assumed to act in the conventional "positive direction," it is important that positive $M$ acts in this *same direction*. This is necessary since positive or negative internal virtual work depends on the directional sense of *both* the virtual load, defined by $\pm m$ or $\pm m_\theta$, and displacement, caused by $\pm M$.

### Virtual-Work Equation.

- Apply the equation of virtual work to determine the desired displacement $\Delta$ or slope $\theta$. It is important to retain the algebraic sign of each integral calculated within its specified region.
- If the algebraic sum of all the integrals for the entire beam is positive, $\Delta$ or $\theta$ is in the same direction as the virtual unit load or virtual unit couple moment. If a negative value results, $\Delta$ or $\theta$ is opposite to the virtual unit load or couple moment.

EXAMPLE | **13**

Determine the displacement of point $B$ on the beam shown in Fig. 36a. $EI$ is constant.

(a)

Virtual loads
(b)

Real loads
(c)

**Fig. 36**

## SOLUTION

**Virtual Moment m.** The vertical displacement of point $B$ is obtained by placing a virtual unit load at $B$, Fig. 36b. By inspection, there are no discontinuities of loading on the beam for *both* the real and virtual loads. Thus, a *single x* coordinate can be used to determine the virtual strain energy. This coordinate will be selected with its origin at $B$, so that the reactions at $A$ do not have to be determined in order to find the internal moments $m$ and $M$. Using the method of sections, the internal moment $m$ is shown in Fig. 36b.

**Real Moment M.** Using the *same x* coordinate, the internal moment $M$ is shown in Fig. 36c.

**Virtual-Work Equation.** The vertical displacement at $B$ is thus

$$1 \cdot \Delta_B = \int \frac{mM}{EI} dx = \int_0^L \frac{(-1x)(-wx^2/2)\, dx}{EI}$$

$$\Delta_B = \frac{wL^4}{8EI} \qquad\qquad Ans.$$

## EXAMPLE | 14

Determine the slope at point $B$ of the beam shown in Fig. 37a. $EI$ is constant.

Fig. 37

### SOLUTION

**Virtual Moments $m_\theta$.** The slope at $B$ is determined by placing a virtual unit couple moment at $B$, Fig. 37b. Two $x$ coordinates must be selected in order to determine the total virtual strain energy in the beam. Coordinate $x_1$ accounts for the strain energy within segment $AB$, and coordinate $x_2$ accounts for the strain energy in segment $BC$. Using the method of sections the internal moments $m_\theta$ within each of these segments are shown in Fig. 37b.

**Real Moments M.** Using the *same coordinates* $x_1$ and $x_2$ (Why?), the internal moments $M$ are shown in Fig. 37c.

**Virtual-Work Equation.** The slope at $B$ is thus

$$1 \cdot \theta_B = \int \frac{m_\theta M}{EI} \, dx$$

$$= \int_0^{L/2} \frac{0(-Px_1) \, dx_1}{EI} + \int_0^{L/2} \frac{1\{-P[(L/2) + x_2]\} \, dx_2}{EI}$$

$$\theta_B = -\frac{3PL^2}{8EI} \qquad\qquad Ans.$$

The *negative sign* indicates that $\theta_B$ is *opposite* to the direction of the virtual couple moment shown in Fig. 37b.

## PROBLEMS

**87.** Determine the displacement at point $C$. $EI$ is constant.

**Prob. 87**

**\*88.** The beam is made of southern pine for which $E_p = 13$ GPa. Determine the displacement at $A$.

**Prob. 88**

**89.** Determine the displacement at point $C$. $EI$ is constant.

**90.** Determine the slope at point $C$. $EI$ is constant.

**91.** Determine the slope at point $A$. $EI$ is constant.

**Probs. 89/90/91**

**\*92.** Determine the displacement of point $C$ of the beam made from A992 steel and having a moment of inertia of $I = 53.8$ in$^4$.

**93.** Determine the slope at $B$ of the beam made from A992 steel and having a moment of inertia of $I = 53.8$ in$^4$.

**Probs. 92/93**

**94.** The beam is made of Douglas fir. Determine the slope at $C$.

**Prob. 94**

**95.** Determine the displacement at pulley $B$. The A992 steel shaft has a diameter of 30 mm.

**Prob. 95**

**\*96.** The A992 steel beam has a moment of inertia of $I = 125(10^6)$ mm$^4$. Determine the displacement at $D$.

**97.** The A992 steel beam has a moment of inertia of $I = 125(10^6)$ mm$^4$. Determine the slope at $A$.

**98.** The A992 structural steel beam has a moment of inertia of $I = 125(10^6)$ mm$^4$. Determine the slope of the beam at $B$.

**Probs. 96/97/98**

**99.** Determine the displacement at $C$ of the shaft. $EI$ is constant.

**\*100.** Determine the slope at $A$ of the shaft. $EI$ is constant.

**Probs. 99/100**

**101.** Determine the slope of end $C$ of the overhang beam. $EI$ is constant.

**102.** Determine the displacement of point $D$ of the overhang beam. $EI$ is constant.

**Probs. 101/102**

**103.** Determine the slope at $A$ of the 2014-T6 aluminum shaft having a diameter of 100 mm.

**\*104.** Determine the displacement at $C$ of the 2014-T6 aluminum shaft having a diameter of 100 mm.

**Probs. 103/104**

**105.** Determine the displacement of point $B$. The moment of inertia of the center portion $DG$ of the shaft is $2I$, whereas the end segments $AD$ and $GC$ have a moment of inertia $I$. The modulus of elasticity for the material is $E$.

**Prob. 105**

**106.** Determine the displacement of point $C$ of the W14 × 26 beam made from A992 steel.

**107.** Determine the slope at $A$ of the W14 × 26 beam made from A992 steel.

**Probs. 106/107**

**\*108.** Determine the slope at *A*. *EI* is constant.

**Prob. 108**

**109.** Determine the slope at end *C* of the overhang white spruce beam.

**110.** Determine the displacement at point *D* of the overhang white spruce beam.

**Probs. 109/110**

**111.** The simply supported beam having a square cross section is subjected to a uniform load *w*. Determine the maximum deflection of the beam caused only by bending, and caused by bending and shear. Take $E = 3G$.

**Prob. 111**

**\*112.** Determine the displacement of the shaft *C*. *EI* is constant.

**Prob. 112**

**113.** Determine the slope of the shaft at the bearing support *A*. *EI* is constant.

**Prob. 113**

**114.** Determine the vertical displacement of point *A* on the angle bracket due to the concentrated force **P**. The bracket is fixed connected to its support. *EI* is constant. Consider only the effect of bending.

**Prob. 114**

**115.** Beam *AB* has a square cross section of 100 mm by 100 mm. Bar *CD* has a diameter of 10 mm. If both members are made of A992 steel, determine the vertical displacement of point *B* due to the loading of 10 kN.

**\*116.** Beam *AB* has a square cross section of 100 mm by 100 mm. Bar *CD* has a diameter of 10 mm. If both members are made of A992 steel, determine the slope at *A* due to the loading of 10 kN.

**Probs. 115/116**

**117.** Bar *ABC* has a rectangular cross section of 300 mm by 100 mm. Attached rod *DB* has a diameter of 20 mm. If both members are made of A-36 steel, determine the vertical displacement of point *C* due to the loading. Consider only the effect of bending in *ABC* and axial force in *DB*.

**118.** Bar *ABC* has a rectangular cross section of 300 mm by 100 mm. Attached rod *DB* has a diameter of 20 mm. If both members are made of A-36 steel, determine the slope at *A* due to the loading. Consider only the effect of bending in *ABC* and axial force in *DB*.

**Probs. 117/118**

**119.** The L-shaped frame is made from two segments, each of length *L* and flexural stiffness *EI*. If it is subjected to the uniform distributed load, determine the horizontal displacement of the end *C*.

**\*120.** The L-shaped frame is made from two segments, each of length *L* and flexural stiffness *EI*. If it is subjected to the uniform distributed load, determine the vertical displacement of point *B*.

**Probs. 119/120**

**121.** Determine the displacement at *C*. *EI* is constant.

**Prob. 121**

**122.** Determine the slope at *B*. *EI* is constant.

**Prob. 122**

# 8 Castigliano's Theorem

In 1879, Alberto Castigliano, an Italian railroad engineer, published a book in which he outlined a method for determining the displacement and slope at a point in a body. This method, which is referred to as Castigliano's second theorem, applies only to bodies that have constant temperature and material with linear-elastic behavior. If the displacement at a point is to be determined, the theorem states that the displacement is equal to the first partial derivative of the strain energy in the body with respect to a force acting at the point and in the direction of displacement. In a similar manner, the slope of the tangent at a point in a body is equal to the first partial derivative of the strain energy in the body with respect to a couple moment acting at the point and in the direction of the slope angle.

To derive Castigliano's second theorem, consider a body of any arbitrary shape, which is subjected to a series of $n$ forces $\mathbf{P}_1, \mathbf{P}_2, \ldots, \mathbf{P}_n$, Fig. 38. According to the conservation of energy, the external work done by these forces is equal to the internal strain energy stored in the body. However, the external work is a function of the external loads, $U_e = \Sigma \int P \, dx$, Eq. 1, so the internal work is also a function of the external loads. Thus,

$$U_i = U_e = f(P_1, P_2, \ldots, P_n) \tag{42}$$

Now, if any one of the external forces, say $P_j$, is increased by a differential amount $dP_j$, the internal work will also be increased, such that the strain energy becomes

$$U_i + dU_i = U_i + \frac{\partial U_i}{\partial P_j} dP_j \tag{43}$$

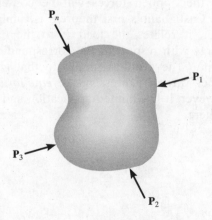

**Fig. 38**

853

This value, however, will not depend on the sequence in which the $n$ forces are applied to the body. For example, we could apply $d\mathbf{P}_j$ to the body *first*, then apply the loads $\mathbf{P}_1, \mathbf{P}_2, \ldots, \mathbf{P}_n$. In this case, $d\mathbf{P}_j$ would cause the body to displace a differential amount $d\Delta_j$ in the direction of $d\mathbf{P}_j$. By Eq. 2 ($U_e = \frac{1}{2}P_j\,\Delta_j$), the increment of strain energy would be $\frac{1}{2}dP_j\,d\Delta_j$. This quantity, however, is a second-order differential and may be neglected. Further application of the loads $\mathbf{P}_1, \mathbf{P}_2, \ldots, \mathbf{P}_n$ causes $d\mathbf{P}_j$ to move through the displacement $\Delta_j$ so that now the strain energy becomes

$$U_i + dU_i = U_i + dP_j\,\Delta_j \tag{44}$$

Here, as above, $U_i$ is the internal strain energy in the body, caused by the loads $\mathbf{P}_1, \mathbf{P}_2, \ldots, \mathbf{P}_n$, and $dP_j\,\Delta_j$ is the *additional* strain energy caused by $d\mathbf{P}_j$.

In summary, Eq. 43 represents the strain energy in the body determined by first applying the loads $\mathbf{P}_1, \mathbf{P}_2, \ldots, \mathbf{P}_n$, then $d\mathbf{P}_j$; Eq. 44 represents the strain energy determined by first applying $d\mathbf{P}_j$ and then the loads $\mathbf{P}_1, \mathbf{P}_2, \ldots, \mathbf{P}_n$. Since these two equations must be equal, we require

$$\Delta_j = \frac{\partial U_i}{\partial P_j} \tag{45}$$

which proves the theorem; i.e., the displacement $\Delta_j$ in the direction of $\mathbf{P}_j$ is equal to the first partial derivative of the strain energy with respect to $\mathbf{P}_j$.

Castigliano's second theorem, Eq. 45, is a statement regarding the body's *compatibility requirements*, since it is a condition related to displacement. Also, the above derivation requires that *only conservative forces* be considered for the analysis. These forces can be applied in any order, and furthermore, they do work that is independent of the path and therefore create no energy loss. As long as the material has linear-elastic behavior, the applied forces will be conservative and the theorem is valid. Castigliano's first theorem is similar to his second theorem; however, it relates the load $P_j$ to the partial derivative of the strain energy with respect to the corresponding displacement, that is, $P_j = \partial U_i/\partial \Delta_j$. The proof is similar to that given above. This theorem is another way of expressing the *equilibrium requirements* for the body; however, it has limited application and therefore it will not be discussed here.

# 9 Castigliano's Theorem Applied to Trusses

Since a truss member is only subjected to an axial load, the strain energy for the member is given by Eq. 16, $U_i = N^2 L/2AE$. Substituting this equation into Eq. 45 and omitting the subscript $i$, we have

$$\Delta = \frac{\partial}{\partial P} \sum \frac{N^2 L}{2AE}$$

It is generally easier to perform the differentiation prior to summation. Also, $L$, $A$, and $E$ are constant for a given member, and therefore we can write

$$\boxed{\Delta = \sum N \left( \frac{\partial N}{\partial P} \right) \frac{L}{AE}} \qquad (46)$$

Here

$\Delta$ = displacement of the truss joint

$P$ = an external force of *variable magnitude* applied to the truss joint in the direction of $\Delta$

$N$ = internal axial force in a member caused by *both* force **P** and the actual loads on the truss

$L$ = length of a member

$A$ = cross-sectional area of a member

$E$ = modulus of elasticity of the material

By comparison, Eq. 46 is similar to that used for the method of virtual forces, Eq. 37 ($1 \cdot \Delta = \Sigma nNL/AE$), except that $n$ is replaced by $\partial N/\partial P$. These terms, $n$ and $\partial N/\partial P$, are the *same*, since they represent the change of the member's axial force with respect to the load $P$ or, in other words, the axial force per unit load.

## Procedure for Analysis

The following procedure provides a method that may be used to determine the displacement of any joint on a truss using Castigliano's second theorem.

### External Force *P*.

- Place a force **P** on the truss at the joint where the displacement is to be determined. This force is assumed to have a *variable magnitude* and should be directed along the line of action of the displacement.

### Internal Forces *N*.

- Determine the force $N$ in each member in terms of both the actual (numerical) loads and the (variable) force $P$. Assume that tensile forces are positive and compressive forces are negative.

- Find the respective partial derivative $\partial N/\partial P$ for each member.

- *After* $N$ and $\partial N/\partial P$ have been determined, assign $P$ its numerical value if it has actually replaced a real force on the truss. Otherwise, set $P$ equal to zero.

### Castigliano's Second Theorem.

- Apply Castigliano's second theorem to determine the desired displacement $\Delta$. It is important to retain the algebraic signs for corresponding values of $N$ and $\partial N/\partial P$ when substituting these terms into the equation.

- If the resultant sum $\Sigma N(\partial N/\partial P)L/AE$ is positive, $\Delta$ is in the same direction as **P**. If a negative value results, $\Delta$ is opposite to **P**.

## EXAMPLE | 15

(a)

**Fig. 39**

Determine the vertical displacement of joint $C$ of the steel truss shown in Fig. 39a. The cross-sectional area of each member is $A = 400 \text{ mm}^2$, and $E_{st} = 200$ GPa.

### SOLUTION

**External Force P.**  A vertical force **P** is applied to the truss at joint $C$, since this is where the vertical displacement is to be determined, Fig. 39b.

(b)

(c)

Fig. 39 (cont.)

**Internal Forces N.** The reactions at the truss supports $A$ and $D$ are calculated and the results are shown in Fig. 39b. Using the method of joints, the $N$ forces in each member are determined, Fig. 39c.* For convenience, these results along with their partial derivatives $\partial N/\partial P$ are listed in tabular form. Note that since **P** does not actually exist as a real load on the truss, we require $P = 0$.

| Member | $N$ | $\dfrac{\partial N}{\partial P}$ | $N(P=0)$ | $L$ | $N\left(\dfrac{\partial N}{\partial P}\right)L$ |
|---|---|---|---|---|---|
| $AB$ | $-100$ | $0$ | $-100$ | $4$ | $0$ |
| $BC$ | $141.4$ | $0$ | $141.4$ | $2.828$ | $0$ |
| $AC$ | $-(141.4 + 1.414P)$ | $-1.414$ | $-141.4$ | $2.828$ | $565.7$ |
| $CD$ | $200 + P$ | $1$ | $200$ | $2$ | $400$ |
| | | | | | $\Sigma\ 965.7\ \text{kN} \cdot \text{m}$ |

**Castigliano's Second Theorem.** Applying Eq. 46, we have

$$\Delta_{C_v} = \Sigma N\left(\frac{\partial N}{\partial P}\right)\frac{L}{AE} = \frac{965.7\ \text{kN} \cdot \text{m}}{AE}$$

Substituting the numerical values for $A'$ and $E$, we get

$$\Delta_{C_v} = \frac{965.7\ \text{kN} \cdot \text{m}}{[400(10^{-6})\ \text{m}^2]\,200(10^6)\ \text{kN/m}^2}$$

$$= 0.01207\ \text{m} = 12.1\ \text{mm} \qquad Ans.$$

This solution should be compared with that of Example 11, using the virtual-work method.

*It may be more convenient to analyze the truss with just the 100-kN load on it, then analyze the truss with the **P** load on it. The results can then be summed algebraically to give the $N$ forces.

## PROBLEMS

**123.** Solve Prob. 73 using Castigliano's theorem.

**\*124.** Solve Prob. 74 using Castigliano's theorem.

**125.** Solve Prob. 75 using Castigliano's theorem.

**126.** Solve Prob. 76 using Castigliano's theorem.

**127.** Solve Prob. 77 using Castigliano's theorem.

**\*128.** Solve Prob. 78 using Castigliano's theorem.

**129.** Solve Prob. 81 using Castigliano's theorem.

**130.** Solve Prob. 82 using Castigliano's theorem.

**131.** Solve Prob. 85 using Castigliano's theorem.

**\*132.** Solve Prob. 86 using Castigliano's theorem.

## 10 Castigliano's Theorem Applied to Beams

The internal strain energy for a beam is caused by both bending and shear. However, as pointed out in Example 7, if the beam is long and slender, the strain energy due to shear can be neglected compared with that of bending. Assuming this to be the case, the internal strain energy for a beam is given by $U_i = \int M^2\, dx / 2EI$, Eq. 17. Omitting the subscript $i$, Castigliano's second theorem, $\Delta_i = \partial U_i / \partial P_i$, becomes

$$\Delta = \frac{\partial}{\partial P} \int_0^L \frac{M^2\, dx}{2EI}$$

Rather than squaring the expression for internal moment, integrating, and then taking the partial derivative, it is generally easier to differentiate prior to integration. Then we have

$$\Delta = \int_0^L M \left( \frac{\partial M}{\partial P} \right) \frac{dx}{EI} \tag{47}$$

Here

$\Delta$ = displacement of the point caused by the real loads acting on the beam

$P$ = an external force of *variable magnitude* applied to the beam at the point and in the direction of $\Delta$

$M$ = internal moment in the beam, expressed as a function of $x$ and caused by both the force $P$ and the actual loads on the beam

$E$ = modulus of elasticity of the material

$I$ = moment of inertia of cross-sectional area about the neutral axis

If the slope of the tangent $\theta$ at a point on the elastic curve is to be determined, the partial derivative of the internal moment $M$ with respect to an *external couple moment M'* acting at the point must be found. For this case,

$$\theta = \int_0^L M\left(\frac{\partial M}{\partial M'}\right)\frac{dx}{EI} \tag{48}$$

The above equations are similar to those used for the method of virtual forces, Eqs. 40 and 41, except $m$ and $m_\theta$ replace $\partial M/\partial P$ and $\partial M/\partial M'$, respectively.

In addition, if axial load, shear, and torsion cause significant strain energy within the member, then the effects of all these loadings should be included when applying Castigliano's theorem. To do this we must use the strain-energy functions developed in Sec. 2, along with their associated partial derivatives. The result is

$$\Delta = \Sigma N\left(\frac{\partial N}{\partial P}\right)\frac{L}{AE} + \int_0^L f_s V\left(\frac{\partial V}{\partial P}\right)\frac{dx}{GA} + \int_0^L M\left(\frac{\partial M}{\partial P}\right)\frac{dx}{EI} + \int_0^L T\left(\frac{\partial T}{\partial P}\right)\frac{dx}{GJ} \tag{49}$$

The method of applying this general formulation is similar to that used to apply Eqs. 47 and 48.

## Procedure for Analysis

The following procedure provides a method that may be used to apply Castigliano's second theorem.

### External Force P or Couple Moment M'.

- Place a force **P** on the beam at the point and directed along the line of action of the desired displacement.
- If the slope of the tangent is to be determined at the point, place a couple moment **M'** at the point.
- Assume that both **P** and **M'** have a variable magnitude.

### Internal Moments M.

- Establish appropriate $x$ coordinates that are valid within regions of the beam where there is no discontinuity of force, distributed load, or couple moment.
- Determine the internal moments $M$ as a function of $x$, the actual (numerical) loads, and $P$ or $M'$, and then find the partial derivatives $\partial M/\partial P$ or $\partial M/\partial M'$ for each coordinate $x$.
- *After* $M$ and $\partial M/\partial P$ or $\partial M/\partial M'$ have been determined, assign $P$ or $M'$ its numerical value if it has actually replaced a real force or couple moment. Otherwise, set $P$ or $M'$ equal to zero.

### Castigliano's Second Theorem.

- Apply Eq. 47 or 48 to determine the desired displacement $\Delta$ or $\theta$. It is important to retain the algebraic signs for corresponding values of $M$ and $\partial M/\partial P$ or $\partial M/\partial M'$.
- If the resultant sum of all the definite integrals is positive, $\Delta$ or $\theta$ is in the same direction as **P** or **M'**. If a negative value results, $\Delta$ or $\theta$ is opposite to **P** or **M'**.

## EXAMPLE | 16

Determine the displacement of point $B$ on the beam shown in Fig. 40a. $EI$ is constant.

(a)

(b)

**Fig. 40**

(c)

## SOLUTION

**External Force P.**  A vertical force **P** is placed on the beam at $B$ as shown in Fig. 40b.

**Internal Moments M.**  A single $x$ coordinate is needed for the solution, since there are no discontinuities of loading between $A$ and $B$. Using the method of sections, Fig. 40c, the internal moment and its partial derivative are determined as follows:

$$\zeta +\Sigma M_{NA} = 0; \quad M + wx\left(\frac{x}{2}\right) + P(x) = 0$$

$$M = -\frac{wx^2}{2} - Px$$

$$\frac{\partial M}{\partial P} = -x$$

Setting $P = 0$ gives

$$M = \frac{-wx^2}{2} \quad \text{and} \quad \frac{\partial M}{\partial P} = -x$$

**Castigliano's Second Theorem.**  Applying Eq. 47, we have

$$\Delta_B = \int_0^L M\left(\frac{\partial M}{\partial P}\right)\frac{dx}{EI} = \int_0^L \frac{(-wx^2/2)(-x)\,dx}{EI}$$

$$= \frac{wL^4}{8EI} \qquad\qquad Ans.$$

The similarity between this solution and that of the virtual-work method, Example 13, should be noted.

## EXAMPLE | 17

**Fig. 41**

Determine the slope at point $B$ of the beam shown in Fig. 41a. $EI$ is constant.

### SOLUTION

**External Couple Moment M′.** Since the slope at point $B$ is to be determined, an external couple moment $\mathbf{M}'$ is placed on the beam at this point, Fig. 41b.

**Internal Moments M.** Two coordinates, $x_1$ and $x_2$, must be used to completely describe the internal moments within the beam since there is a discontinuity, $M'$, at $B$. As shown in Fig. 41b, $x_1$ ranges from $A$ to $B$ and $x_2$ ranges from $B$ to $C$. Using the method of sections, Fig. 41c, the internal moments and the partial derivatives for $x_1$ and $x_2$ are determined as follows:

$$\zeta + \Sigma M_{NA} = 0; \qquad M_1 = -Px_1, \quad \frac{\partial M_1}{\partial M'} = 0$$

$$\zeta + \Sigma M_{NA} = 0; \qquad M_2 = M' - P\left(\frac{L}{2} + x_2\right), \quad \frac{\partial M_2}{\partial M'} = 1$$

**Castigliano's Second Theorem.** Setting $M' = 0$ and applying Eq. 48, we have

$$\theta_B = \int_0^L M\left(\frac{\partial M}{\partial M'}\right)\frac{dx}{EI} = \int_0^{L/2}\frac{(-Px_1)(0)\,dx_1}{EI} + \int_0^{L/2}\frac{-P[(L/2) + x_2](1)\,dx_2}{EI} = -\frac{3PL^2}{8EI} \quad Ans.$$

Note the similarity between this solution and that of Example 14.

## PROBLEMS

**133.** Solve Prob. 90 using Castigliano's theorem.

**134.** Solve Prob. 91 using Castigliano's theorem.

**135.** Solve Prob. 92 using Castigliano's theorem.

**\*136.** Solve Prob. 93 using Castigliano's theorem.

**137.** Solve Prob. 95 using Castigliano's theorem.

**138.** Solve Prob. 96 using Castigliano's theorem.

**139.** Solve Prob. 97 using Castigliano's theorem.

**\*140.** Solve Prob. 98 using Castigliano's theorem.

**141.** Solve Prob. 108 using Castigliano's theorem.

**142.** Solve Prob. 119 using Castigliano's theorem.

**143.** Solve Prob. 120 using Castigliano's theorem.

**\*144.** Solve Prob. 121 using Castigliano's theorem.

**145.** Solve Prob. 122 using Castigliano's theorem.

# CHAPTER REVIEW

| | |
|---|---|
| When a force (couple moment) acts on a deformable body it will do external work when it displaces (rotates). The internal stresses produced in the body also undergo displacement, thereby creating elastic strain energy that is stored in the material. The conservation of energy states that the external work done by the loading is equal to the internal elastic strain energy produced by the stresses in the body. | $$U_e = U_i$$ |
| The conservation of energy can be used to solve problems involving elastic impact, which assumes the moving body is rigid and all the strain energy is stored in the stationary body. This leads to use of an impact factor $n$, which is a ratio of the dynamic load to the static load. It is used to determine the maximum stress and displacement of the body at the point of impact. | $$n = 1 + \sqrt{1 + 2\left(\frac{h}{\Delta_{st}}\right)}$$ $$\sigma_{max} = n\sigma_{st}$$ $$\Delta_{max} = n\Delta_{st}$$ |
| The principle of virtual work can be used to determine the displacement of a joint on a truss or the slope and the displacement of points on a beam. It requires placing an external virtual unit force (virtual unit couple moment) at the point where the displacement (rotation) is to be determined. The external virtual work that is produced by the external loading is then equated to the internal virtual strain energy in the structure. | $$1 \cdot \Delta = \sum \frac{nNL}{AE}$$ $$1 \cdot \Delta = \int_0^L \frac{mM}{EI}dx$$ $$1 \cdot \theta = \int_0^L \frac{m_\theta M}{EI}dx$$ |
| Castigliano's second theorem can also be used to determine the displacement of a joint on a truss or the slope and the displacement at a point on a beam. Here a variable force $P$ (couple moment $M'$) is placed at the point where the displacement (slope) is to be determined. The internal loading is then determined as a function of $P$ ($M'$) and its partial derivative with respect to $P$ ($M'$) is determined. Castigliano's second theorem is then applied to obtain the desired displacement (rotation). | $$\Delta = \sum N\left(\frac{\partial N}{\partial P}\right)\frac{L}{AE}$$ $$\Delta = \int_0^L M\left(\frac{\partial M}{\partial P}\right)\frac{dx}{EI}$$ $$\theta = \int_0^L M\left(\frac{\partial M}{\partial M'}\right)\frac{dx}{EI}$$ |

# REVIEW PROBLEMS

**146.** Determine the total axial and bending strain energy in the A992 steel beam. $A = 2300$ mm², $I = 9.5(10^6)$ mm⁴.

**Prob. 146**

**147.** The 200-kg block $D$ is dropped from a height $h = 1$ m onto end $C$ of the A992 steel W200 × 36 overhang beam. If the spring at $B$ has a stiffness $k = 200$ kN/m, determine the maximum bending stress developed in the beam.

**\*148.** Determine the maximum height $h$ from which the 200-kg block $D$ can be dropped without causing the A992 steel W200 × 36 overhang beam to yield. The spring at $B$ has a stiffness $k = 200$ kN/m.

**Probs. 147/148**

**149.** The A992 steel bars are pin connected at $B$ and $C$. If they each have a diameter of 30 mm, determine the slope at $E$.

**Prob. 149**

**150.** The steel chisel has a diameter of 0.5 in. and a length of 10 in. It is struck by a hammer that weighs 3 lb, and at the instant of impact it is moving at 12 ft/s. Determine the maximum compressive stress in the chisel, assuming that 80% of the impacting energy goes into the chisel. $E_{st} = 29(10^3)$ ksi, $\sigma_Y = 100$ ksi.

**Prob. 150**

**151.** Determine the total axial and bending strain energy in the A992 structural steel W8 × 58 beam.

**154.** The cantilevered beam is subjected to a couple moment $M_0$ applied at its end. Determine the slope of the beam at $B$. $EI$ is constant. Use the method of virtual work.

**155.** Solve Prob. 154 using Castigliano's theorem.

**Prob. 151**

**Probs. 154/155**

*156.** Determine the slope and displacement at point $C$. $EI$ is constant.

*152.** Determine the vertical displacement of joint $C$. The truss is made from A992 steel rods each having a diameter of 1 in.

**153.** Determine the horizontal displacement of joint $B$. The truss is made from A992 steel rods each having a diameter of 1 in.

**Prob. 156**

**157.** Determine the displacement at $B$. $EI$ is constant.

**Probs. 152/153**

**Prob. 157**

# Selected Answers

1. $\dfrac{U_i}{V} = \dfrac{1}{2E}(\sigma_x^2 + \sigma_y^2 - 2\nu\sigma_x\sigma_y) + \dfrac{\tau_{xy}^2}{2G}$

3. $U_i = 3.28$ J

5. $U_A = \dfrac{N^2 L_1}{2AE}, \; U_B = \dfrac{N^2 L_2}{2AE}$

   Since $U_B > U_A$, i.e., $L_2 > L_1$, the design for case (b) is better able to absorb energy.

6. $U_i = 43.2$ J

7. $P = 375$ kN, $U_i = 1.69$ kJ

9. $U_i = 149$ J

10. $U_i = 0.0638$ J

11. $(U_b)_i = 4.31$ in. $\cdot$ kip

13. $P = 113$ kip, $U_i = 7.37$ in $\cdot$ kip

15. $(U_b)_i = \dfrac{17 w^2 L^5}{15360 EI}$

17. $(U_b)_i = \dfrac{17 w_0^2 L^5}{10080 EI}$

18. $(U_b)_i = \dfrac{w_0^2 L^5}{945 EI}$

19. $(U_t)_i = \dfrac{P^2 r^3}{JG}\left(\dfrac{3\pi}{8} - 1\right)$

21. $(U_b)_i = 62.5$ J, $(U_i)_{sp} = 0.391$ J

22. $(U_b)_i = 1.78$ kJ, $(U_a)_i = 0.617$ J

23. $(U_b)_i = \dfrac{w^2 L^5}{40 EI}$

25. $(\Delta_B)_h = 0.2025$ mm

26. $(\Delta_C)_v = \dfrac{2PL}{AE}$

27. $(\Delta_h)_A = 0.0830$ in.

29. $\Delta_B = 2.15$ in.

30. $\Delta_B = 3.46$ mm

31. $\Delta_B = 11.7$ mm

33. $\Delta_B = 0.100$ mm

34. $\Delta_g = 5.46$ in.

35. $\theta_A = -\dfrac{M_0 L}{3EI}$

37. $\sigma_{max} = \dfrac{16 PR}{\pi d^3}(\sin\theta + 1)$

38. $\Delta = \dfrac{64 n P R^3}{d^4 G}$

39. $(\Delta_C)_v = 2.13$ mm

41. $(\Delta_B)_v = 15.2$ mm

42. (a) $U_i = 4.52$ kJ

    (b) $U_i = 3.31$ kJ

43. $d = 5.35$ in.

45. (a) $\sigma_{max} = 45.4$ ksi

    (b) $\sigma_{max} = 509$ psi

    (c) $\sigma_{max} = 254$ psi

46. $h = 1.75$ ft

47. $\sigma_{max} = 20.3$ ksi

49. $\Delta_{max} = 3.95$ mm, $\sigma_{max} = 237$ MPa

50. $\sigma_{max} = 85.7$ MPa

51. $(\sigma_{max})_{AB} = (\sigma_{max})_{AC} = 233$ MPa

53. $\sigma_{max} = 414$ MPa

54. $h = 95.6$ mm

55. Use $d = 2\dfrac{1}{8}$ in.

57. $\sigma_{max} = 57.1$ ksi

58. $(\Delta_A)_{max} = 15.4$ in.

59. $h = \dfrac{\sigma_{max} L^2}{3Ec}\left[\dfrac{\sigma_{max} I}{WLc} - 2\right]$

61. $n = 16.7$

62. $\sigma_{max} = 4.55$ ksi, $\Delta_C = 0.799$ in.

63. $\Delta_B = 0.226$ in., $\sigma_{max} = 3.22$ ksi

65. $h = 1.37$ m

66. $\sigma_{max} = 137$ MPa

67. $h = 8.66$ m

69. $h = 7.45$ in.

70. $(\Delta_B)_{max} = 0.661$ in.

71. $\Delta_{max} = 23.3$ mm, $\sigma_{max} = 4.89$ MPa

73. $(\Delta_B)_h = 0.223(10^{-3})$ in. $\leftarrow$

74. $(\Delta_B)_v = 0.00112$ in. $\downarrow$

75. $(\Delta_B)_v = 0.0132$ in. $\downarrow$

77. $(\Delta_B)_v = 0.0124$ in. $\downarrow$

78. $(\Delta_E)_v = 0.00966$ in. $\downarrow$

79. $(\Delta_B)_h = 0.367$ mm

81. $(\Delta_C)_h = 0.0482$ in.

82. $(\Delta_B)_h = 0.0420$ in.

83. $(\Delta_A)_v = 3.18$ mm

85. $(\Delta_C)_v = 20.4$ mm

**86.** $(\Delta_D)_v = 4.88$ mm

**87.** $\Delta_C = \dfrac{23Pa^3}{24EI}$

**89.** $\Delta_C = \dfrac{2Pa^3}{3EI}$

**90.** $\theta_C = -\dfrac{5Pa^2}{6EI}$

**91.** $\theta_A = \dfrac{Pa^2}{6EI}$

**93.** $\theta_B = -0.353°$

**94.** $\theta_C = 5.89(10^{-3})$ rad

**95.** $\Delta_B = 47.8$ mm

**97.** $\theta_A = 0.289°$

**98.** $\theta_B = 0.124°$

**99.** $\Delta_C = \dfrac{PL^3}{8EI}$

**101.** $\theta_C = -\dfrac{13wL^3}{576EI}$

**102.** $\Delta_D = \dfrac{wL^4}{96EI}\downarrow$

**103.** $\theta_A = -0.0223$ rad

**105.** $\Delta_B = \dfrac{65wa^4}{48EI}$

**106.** $\Delta_C = 0.122$ in.

**107.** $\theta_A = 4.05(10^{-3})$ rad

**109.** $\theta_C = -0.0198$ rad

**110.** $\Delta_D = 0.219$ in.

**111.** $\Delta_{\text{tot}} = \left(\dfrac{w}{G}\right)\left(\dfrac{L}{a}\right)^2\left[\left(\dfrac{5}{96}\right)\left(\dfrac{L}{a}\right)^2 + \dfrac{3}{20}\right]$,

$\quad\quad \Delta_b = \dfrac{5w}{96G}\left(\dfrac{L}{a}\right)^4$

**113.** $\theta_A = -\dfrac{5w_0L^3}{192EI}$

**114.** $(\Delta_A)_v = \dfrac{4PL^3}{3EI}$

**115.** $\Delta_B = 43.5$ mm

**117.** $\Delta_C = 17.9$ mm

**118.** $\theta_A = 0.991(10^{-3})$ rad

**119.** $\Delta_C = \dfrac{5wL^4}{8EI}$

**121.** $\Delta_C = \dfrac{wL^4}{4EI}$

**122.** $\theta_B = \dfrac{wL^3}{8EI}$

**123.** $(\Delta_B)_h = 0.223(10^{-3})$ in. $\leftarrow$

**125.** $(\Delta_B)_v = 0.0132$ in. $\downarrow$

**126.** $(\Delta_E)_v = 0.0149$ in.

**127.** $(\Delta_B)_v = 0.0124$ in. $\downarrow$

**129.** $(\Delta_C)_v = 0.0482$ in.

**130.** $(\Delta_B)_h = 0.0420$ in.

**131.** $(\Delta_C)_v = 20.4$ mm

**133.** $\theta_C = -\dfrac{5Pa^2}{6EI}$

**134.** $\theta_A = \dfrac{Pa^2}{6EI}$

**135.** $\Delta_C = 0.369$ in.

**137.** $\Delta_B = 47.8$ mm

**138.** $\Delta_D = 3.24$ mm

**139.** $\theta_A = 0.289°$

**141.** $\theta_A = \dfrac{wL^3}{24EI}$

**142.** $\Delta_C = \dfrac{5wL^4}{8EI}$

**143.** $\Delta_B = \dfrac{wL^4}{4EI}$

**145.** $\theta_B = \dfrac{wL^3}{8EI}$

**146.** $U_i = 496$ J

**147.** $\sigma_{\max} = 116$ MPa

**149.** $\theta_E = -3.15°$

**150.** $\sigma_{\max} = 43.6$ ksi

**151.** $U_i = 45.5$ ft·lb

**153.** $(\Delta_B)_h = 0.0876$ in. $\leftarrow$

**154.** $\theta_B = \dfrac{M_0L}{EI}$

**155.** $\theta_B = \dfrac{M_0L}{EI}$

**157.** $\Delta_B = \dfrac{wL^4}{128EI}$

# Index

Page references followed by "f" indicate illustrated figures or photographs; followed by "t" indicates a table.